S0-AWP-983

教會聖詩

Hymns for God's People

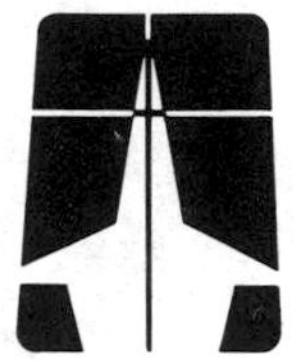

522 W. BROADWAY
GLENDALE, CALIFORNIA 91204
Tel:(818) 240-5633

感　謝　的　話

當這本「教會聖詩」呈現在您面前時，我們的內心真是充滿了無數的感謝！

首先，我們應當感謝全能的父神，因祂的感動、引領、保守與成全，使此歷經許多艱難的聖詩出版工作，得告完成。

其次，我們要向許多對於這本聖詩表示支持、給予鼓勵以及採用的教會、教牧、長執、同工以及弟兄姐妹們表示由衷的感謝。

最後，要感謝的是，許多參與這本聖詩出版事工的同工與弟兄姐妹們。深信您們一切在主裡面的勞苦，一定不會徒然的。

我們願將這本聖詩以及一切的感謝獻給慈愛的父神，因為萬有都是本於祂，倚靠祂，歸於祂。願榮耀歸給祂，直到永遠。阿們。

"教會聖詩" 編輯委員會
一九八四年七月

A WORD OF THANKSGIVING

With the completion of "Hymns for God's People", our hearts are filled with thanksgiving.

First of all, we are especially thankful to our Almighty God and Father. He has enabled us to accomplish the difficult task of publishing this hymnal through His actions, guidance, protection and providence.

Secondly, we wish to express our sincere gratitude to you, the various churches, pastors, church leaders, and brothers and sisters in Christ. You have shown your support and encouragement by using this hymnal.

Finally, we are appreciative to those brothers and sisters who have labored together for the publication of this hymnal. We are confident that their hard work in Christ will glorify our Lord's name and be useful in His work.

We dedicate this hymnal and all our thanksgiving to our Father in Heaven. "For from Him and through Him and to Him are all things. To Him be the glory forever! Amen." (Romans 11:36).

Publication Committee of "Hymns for God's People"
July 1984.

簡　　介

這本「教會聖詩」是為了配合中國教會的增長與事工發展的需要而產生。

我們非常樂意將這本「教會聖詩」的幾個特色介紹如下：

一、全部聖詩495首。其中多數係選自當今美國各大教會所喜愛的詩本「Hymns for The Family of God」，此外尚包括大衆所愛好的各類新、舊詩歌。內容廣泛，可適合教會崇拜、各種聚會以及大、小團契，甚至家庭與個人等的不同需要。

二、全部歌詞，包括中國人的作品，都有中英文對照。歌詞翻譯方面，盡量保留原有的譯詞。但在新詩的譯詞中，我們力求詞句通順、易懂、忠於原意以及符合節拍與韻律。

三、在聖詩中附有許多詩篇經句，聖經章節，以及意義深長的精美短文配合詩歌內容與主題，適合於靈修或會衆啓應文之需要。

四、為了保持美觀耐久、盡善盡美起見，全部在美印製。成本雖然較高，但這是　神的工作，是值得我們投上的。

雖然這本聖詩從選詩、翻譯、修正、製譜、校對、編排、以至出版的每一過程中，我們都採取極其審慎的態度，務求達到完美的地步，但相信仍然難免會有許多未經發覺的缺點。我們竭誠地期待着您對這本詩歌的寶貴意見、批評與指教。希望能在再版時予以訂正與補充。非常感謝。

INTRODUCTION

"Hymns for God's People" was created to serve the needs of the Chinese Church - for Her growth and the furtherance of God's ministry.

Some of the special features of this hymnal are: ·

1. The hymnal contains 495 hymns. Most of the hymns are selected from the "HYMNS FOR THE FAMILY OF GOD", a widely used hymnal used today by churches in North America. Others are gathered from good existing translations. These hymns include some of the more familiar and traditional hymns as well as some comtemporary hymns for use in formal worship services and other informal church activities as well as personal use.
2. Each hymn is printed in both English and Chinese. Special efforts were made to preserve the original meaning in the translation.
3. Throughout the hymnal are verses from the Psalms and other verses from the Bible. Short poems and prose are also included.
4. The hymnal is printed attractively by a reputable company in the U.S.which specializes in printing and binding hymnals.

Although we have exercised the utmost care in the preparation of this hymnal (in the selection of music, translation, the arrangement of music, proof reading, design and layout to the actual publication), we earnestly await your valuable suggestions and constructive criticisms which will be incorporated in future editions. Your help is greatly appreciated.

目　　錄

Table of Contents

齊來稱頌偉大之神
Great God, We Sing Your Mighty Hand

Even there shall Thy hand lead me, and Thy right hand shall hold me. — Psalm 139:10

GERMANY
William Gardiner's *Sacred Melodies*

Philip Doddridge, alt.

1. 齊 來 稱 頌 偉 大 之 神 ， 大 能 之 手 扶
2. 不 論 日 夜 或 出 或 入 ， 恩 主 時 常 保
3. 時 有 痛 苦 時 有 歡 暢 ， 但 在 主 裡 喜
4. 雖 有 一 日 面 臨 死 亡 ， 暫 時 停 止 口
1 Great God, we sing Your might - y hand By which sup - port - ed
2 By day, by night, at home, a - broad, Still are we guard - ed
3 In scenes ex - alt - ed or de - pressed, You are our joy, and
4 When death shall in - ter - rupt our songs And seal in si - lence
1. 持 我 們 ； 歲 首 年 終 慈 愛 不 變 ，
2. 守 看 顧 ； 恩 典 無 窮 供 我 需 用 ，
3. 樂 安 祥 ； 慈 善 救 主 賜 我 盼 望 ，
4. 舌 歌 唱 ； 但 在 榮 耀 天 家 美 境 ，
1 still we stand; The o - pening year Your mer - cy shows,
2 by our God, By His in - ces - sant boun - ty fed,
3 You our rest; Your good - ness all our hopes shall raise,
4 mor - tal tongues, In fair - er realms, O God, shall we
1. 恩 典 為 我 年 歲 冠 冕 。
2. 諄 諄 指 教 恩 師 情 重 。
3. 我 願 一 生 稱 頌 讚 揚 。
4. 稱 頌 讚 美 永 無 止 盡 。 阿 門 。
1 That mer - cy crowns it 'til its close.
2 By His un - err - ing coun - sel led.
3 A - dored through all our chang - ing days.
4 Your prais - es sing e - ter - nal - ly. A - men.

2

祢真偉大

How Great Thou Art

Great is the Lord and greatly to be praised. — Psalm 48:1

Stuart K. Hine

O STORE GUD
Stuart K. Hine

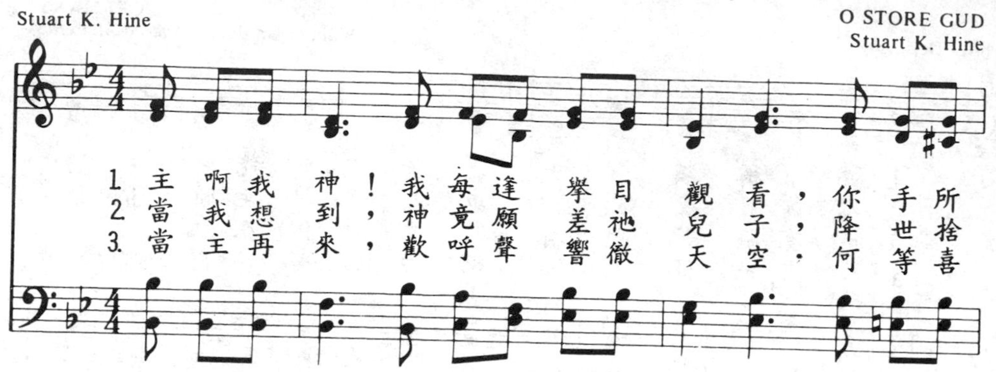
1. 主 啊 我 神 ！ 我 每 逢 舉 目 觀 看 ， 你 手 所
2. 當 我 想 到 ， 神 竟 願 差 祂 兒 子 ， 降 世 捨
3. 當 主 再 來 ， 歡 呼 聲 響 徹 天 空 ， 何 等 喜
1. O Lord my God! when I in awe-some won-der Con-sid-er
2. And when I think that God, His Son not spar-ing, Sent Him to
3. When Christ shall come with shout of ac-cla-ma-tion And take me

1. 造 一 切 奇 妙 大 工 ； 看 見 星 宿 ， 又
2. 命 我 幾 乎 不 領 會 ； 主 在 十 架 ， 甘
3. 樂 主 接 我 回 天 家 ； 我 要 跪 下 ， 謙
1 all the worlds Thy hands have made, I see the stars, I
2. die, I scarce can take it in; That on the cross, my
3. home, what joy shall fill my heart! Then I shall bow in

1. 聽 到 隆 隆 雷 聲 ， 祢 的 大 工 遍 滿 了 宇 宙
2. 願 背 我 的 重 擔 ， 流 血 捨 身 為 要 赦 免 我
3. 恭 的 崇 拜 敬 奉 ， 並 要 頌 揚 神 啊 祢 真 偉
1 hear the roll-ing thun-der, Thy power through-out the u-ni-verse dis-
2. bur-den glad-ly bear-ing, He bled and died to take a-way my
3. hum-ble ad-o-ra-tion, And there pro-claim, my God, how great Thou

1. 中。 我靈歌 唱，讚美救 主我 神；
2. 罪。 Then sings my soul, my Sav-ior God, to Thee:
3. 大！
1 played:
2 sin:
3 art!
祢真偉 大， 何 等偉 大！ 我靈歌唱，讚
How great Thou art, how great Thou art! Then sings my soul, my
美救 主我 神；祢真偉 大，何等偉 大！
Sav-ior God, to Thee: How great Thou art, how great Thou art!

3

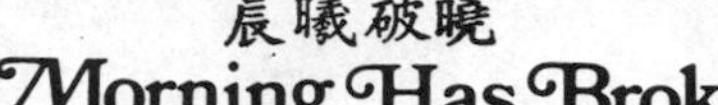
晨曦破曉

Morning Has Broken

Eleanor Farjeon

This is the day that the Lord hath made; we shall rejoice . . .
Psalm 118: 24

BUNESSAN
Traditional Gaelic Melody
Arranged by David Evans

Unison

1. 破曉的晨曦，充滿了希望，
2. 新雨淋大地，彩虹飛天上，
3. 我擁有晨曦，我擁有朝陽，

1 Morn-ing has bro - ken Like the first morn - ing,
2 *Sweet the rain's new fall Sun - lit from heav - en,*
3 Mine is the sun - light! Mine is the morn - ing

1. 小鳥兒清歌，一曲高唱。
2. 青草兒得着，滋養生長。
3. 運行在伊甸，太初之光！

1 Black-bird has spo - ken Like the first bird.
2 *Like the first dew - fall On the first grass.*
3 Born of the one light E - den saw play!

1. 每日要歡欣，每日要頌揚，
2. 每日要歡欣，每日要頌揚，
3. 每日要歡欣，每日要頌揚，

1 Praise for the sing - ing! Praise for the morn - ing!
2 *Praise for the sweet - ness Of the wet gar - den,*
3 Praise with e - la - tion, Praise ev - ery morn - ing,

1. 每日的豐富，主恩無量！
2. 天父的大愛，有熱有光。
3. 生命與能力，越久越長。 阿們。

1 Praise for them, spring - ing Fresh from the Word!
2 *Sprung in com-plete - ness Where His feet pass.*
3 God's re - cre - a - tion Of the new day! A - men.

大地風光
For the Beauty of the Earth

He hath made all things beautiful. — Ecclesiastes 3:11

DIX

Folliott S. Pierpoint, alt.

Adapted by Conrad Kocher

1. 環觀大地好風光，仰視美麗好穹蒼，
2. 靜觀晝夜每時分，形形色色美麗中，
3. 神賜人間父母愛，兄弟姐妹手足親，
4. 因主聖手常施恩，教會事工得興盛，
5. 神聖之主恩無量，奇妙大愛無窮盡；

1 For the beau - ty of the earth, For the glo - ry of the skies,
2 *For the won - der of each hour Of the day and of the night,*
3 For the joy of hu - man love, Broth - er, sis - ter, par - ent, child;
4 *For Thy Church that ev - er - more Lift - eth ho - ly hands a - bove,*
5 For Thy - self, best gift di - vine, To our race so free - ly given;

1. 想起出生到如今，主愛時常繞我旁。
2. 綠水青山描寫巧，日月星辰點綴工。
3. 人間天上友朋多，長享主愛與深情。
4. 為愛世上眾罪人，恩主甘心獻己身。
5. 白白賜給世上人，從此天人享安寧。

1 For the love which from our birth O - ver and a - round us lies:
2 *Hill and vale and tree and flower, Sun and moon and stars of light:*
3 Friends on earth and friends a - bove; For all gen - tle thoughts and mild:
4 *Off - ering up on ev - ery shore Her pure sac - ri - fice of love:*
5 For that great, great love of Thine, Peace on earth and joy in heaven:

敬向全能萬有神，獻上頌揚與感恩。阿門。
Lord of all, to Thee we raise This our hymn of grate - ful praise. A-men.

5

這是天父世界
This Is My Father's World

The earth is the Lord's and the fullness thereof. . . . — Psalm 24:1

Maltbie D. Babcock

TERRA BEATA
English Melody
Adapted by Franklin L. Sheppard

1. 這是天父世界，孩童側耳要聽，
2. 這是天父世界；小鳥長翅飛鳴，
3. 這是天父世界，求主叫我不忘，
1 This is my Fa-ther's world, And to my lis-tening ears
2 This is my Fa-ther's world, The birds their car-ols raise,
3 This is my Fa-ther's world, O let me ne'er for-get
1. 宇宙歌唱四圍響應；星辰作樂同聲。
2. 清晨明亮好花美麗，證明天理精深。
3. 罪惡雖然好像得勝，天父却仍掌管。
1 All na-ture sings, and 'round me rings The mu-sic of the spheres.
2 The morn-ing light, the lil-y white, De-clare their Mak-er's praise.
3 That though the wrong seems oft so strong, God is the rul-er yet.
1. 這是天父世界，我心滿有安寧，樹
2. 這是天父世界，祂愛普及萬千，風
3. 這是天父世界，我心不必憂傷，父
1 This is my Fa-ther's world: I rest me in the thought Of
2 This is my Fa-ther's world: He shines in all that's fair; In the
3 This is my Fa-ther's world: The bat-tle is not done; Je-
1. 木花草，蒼天碧海，述說天父全能。
2. 吹之草，將祂表現，天父充滿世間。
3. 神是王，天地同唱，歌聲充滿萬方。
1 rocks and trees, of skies and seas— His hand the won-ders wrought.
2 rus-tling grass I hear Him pass, He speaks to me ev-ery-where.
3 sus who died shall be sat-is-fied, And earth and heaven be one.

何等的大奇妙
The Wonder of It All

For we are His workmanship created in Christ Jesus unto good works.
Ephesians 2:10

WONDER OF IT ALL

George Beverly Shea — George Beverly Shea

1. 日落西沉的景色真奇妙，日旭東升也真奇妙；但我心中最希奇的大奇妙，就是奇妙的神愛我。
2. 春風秋雨四季真是奇妙，日月星辰造物奇妙；但我心中最希奇的大奇妙，就是奇妙的神先愛我。
1 There's the won-der of sun-set at eve-ning, The won-der as sun-rise I see; But the won-der of won-ders that thrills my soul Is the won-der that God loves me.
2 There's the won-der of spring-time and har-vest, The sky, the stars, the sun; But the won-der of won-ders that thrills my soul Is a won-der that's on-ly be-gun.
哦，何等的大奇妙！何等的大奇妙！每當想起神愛我。哦，何等的大奇妙！何等的大奇妙！每當想起神愛我。
O, the won-der of it all! The won-der of it all! Just to think that God loves me. O the won-der of it all! The won-der of it all! Just to think that God loves me.

7

祢的信實廣大
Great Is Thy Faithfulness

. . . For He is faithful that promised. — Hebrews 10:23

Based on Lamentations 3:22, 23
Thomas O. Chisholm

FAITHFULNESS
William M. Runyan

1. 祢 的 信 實 廣 大，我 神 我 天 父，全 無 轉
2. 春 夏 秋 冬 四 季，有 栽 種 收 成，日 月 星
3. 祢 赦 免 我 罪 愆，賜 我 永 平 安，祢 的 容
1 Great is Thy faith - ful-ness, O God my Fa - ther! There is no
2 *Sum - mer and win - ter, and spring-time and har - vest, Sun, moon, and*
3 Par - don for sin and a peace that en - dur - eth, Thine own dear

1. 動 影 兒，藏 在 祢 心；祢 不 改 變，祢 慈
2. 辰 時 刻，循 轉 不 止；宇 宙 萬 物，都 為
3. 光 親 自，安 慰 導 引；日 日 加 力，更 賜
1 shad - ow of turn - ing with Thee; Thou chang - est not, Thy com -
2 *stars in their cours - es a - bove, Join with all na - ture in*
3 pres - ence to cheer and to guide, Strength for to - day and bright

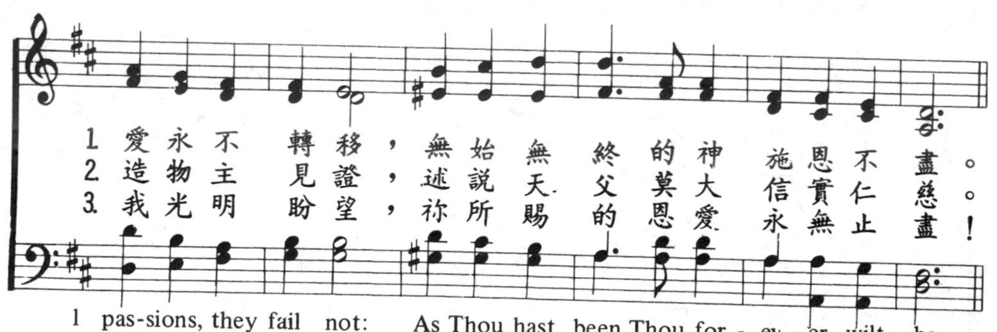

1. 愛 永 不 轉 移，無 始 無 終 的 神 施 恩 不 盡。
2. 造 物 主 見 證，述 説 天 父 莫 大 信 實 仁 慈。
3. 我 光 明 盼 望，祢 所 賜 的 恩 愛 永 無 止 盡！
1 pas-sions, they fail not: As Thou hast been Thou for - ev - er wilt be.
2 *man - i - fold wit - ness To Thy great faith - ful-ness, mer - cy, and love.*
3 hope for to - mor - row— Bless-ings all mine, with ten thou-sand be - side!

祢的信實廣大，祢的信實廣大，每早晨
Great is Thy faith-ful-ness, Great is Thy faith-ful-ness, Morn - ing by
賜下新豐富恩惠，我一切需要祢
morn - ing new mer- cies I see; All I have need - ed Thy
手豐富預備，祢的信實廣大，顯在我身！阿門。
hand hath pro- vid - ed—Great is Thy faith - ful-ness, Lord, un-to me! A - men.

我們不至消滅，是出於耶和華諸般的慈愛，是因祂的憐憫，不至斷絕。
每早晨這都是新的，祢的誠實，極其廣大。
我心裡說，耶和華是我的分，因此，我要仰望祂。

耶利米哀歌三章
22 — 24

Because of the Lord's great love we are not consumed,
for his compassions never fail.
They are new every morning;
great is your faithfulness.
I say to myself, "The Lord is my portion;
therefore I will wait for him."

— Lamentations 3:22-24. NIV

8

歡樂平安的聖日
O Day of Rest and Gladness

Upon the first day of the week . . . the disciples came together. — Acts 20:7

Christopher Wordsworth

MENDEBRAS
Traditional German Melody
Arranged by Lowell Mason

1. 歡樂平安的聖日，充滿無限歡欣，
2. 這是真神創造日，光明應命而生，
3. 今日世人之所需，主以嗎哪供應，
4. 歡樂平安的聖日，主賜豐富恩典，
1 O day of rest and gladness, O day of joy and light,
2 On thee, at the cre - a - tion, The light first had its birth;
3 To - day on wea-ry na - tions The heaven-ly man-na falls;
4 New grac - es ev - er gain - ing From this our day of rest,
1. 勞苦憂愁得安慰，何等美麗光明；
2. 這是救主復活日，救贖大功完成；
3. 銀號筒吹響之時，召集屬主子民；
4. 我靈在此得安息，我蒙福到永遠；
1 O balm of care and sad - ness, Most beau - ti - ful, most bright:
2 On thee, for our sal - va - tion, Christ rose from depths of earth;
3 To ho - ly con - vo - ca - tions The sil - ver trump - et calls,
4 We reach the rest re - main - ing To spir - its of the blest;
1. 在主的寶座台前，萬民齊聲響應，唱
2. 這是救主得勝日，聖靈由天降臨，這
3. 福音之真光普照，燦爛純潔如銀，活
4. 齊來向聖父讚美，讚美聖子聖靈，敎
1 On thee the high and low - ly, Through a - ges joined in tune, Sing
2 On thee our Lord vic - to - rious The Spir - it sent from heaven; And
3 Where gos - pel light is glow - ing With pure and ra - diant beams, And
4 To Ho - ly Ghost be prais - es, To Fa - ther and to Son; The

1. "聖哉，聖哉，聖哉，" 讚美三一真神。
2. 是救主榮耀日 我們一同歡慶。
3. 水之泉源湧流 能甦醒人心靈。
4. 會信徒同聲唱 讚美三一真神。阿門。
1 "Ho - ly, ho - ly, ho - ly," To the great God Tri - une.
2 thus on thee most glo - rious A tri - ple light was given.
3 liv - ing wa - ter flow - ing With soul - re - fresh - ing streams.
4 Church her voice up - rais - es To Thee, blest Three in One. A - men.

上主在祂的聖殿中 9

The Lord Is In His Holy Temple

Choose you this day whom ye will serve. — Joshua 24:15

(Habakkuk 2:20)

William J. Kirkpatrick

上主在祂的聖殿中，普天下的人，都應當肅靜；當肅靜，當肅靜，在主前當肅靜。

The Lord is in His holy temple Let all the earth keep silence before Him. Keep silence, keep silence, keep silence before Him.

清晨歌
Morning Hymn

Mine eyes have seen the King, the Lord of hosts

– Isaiah 6:5

Le P'ing
Eng. Tr. by Marshall Huang

Hu Te-ngai
Chao Tzu-Chen

1. 清 早 起 來 看， 紅 日 出 東 方，
2. 懇 求 聖 天 父， 將 我 妥 保 存，
3. 但 願 今 天 好， 時 刻 靠 耶 穌，
1. Ear - ly morn - ing sun - -, Light's the east - ern sky;
2. Heavn - ly Fa-ther, God - -, Keep me safe this day;
3. Give me strength to - day - - -, My fee- ble faith aug - ment;

1. 雄 壯 像 勇 士， 美 好 像 新 郎；
2. 行 為 能 良 善， 顔 色 會 和 溫；
3. 頭 上 青 天 在， 心 中 惡 念 無；
1. Fresh the morn - ing dew - -, Hea - ven's peace is nigh.
2. With all hu - mi - li - ty - - -, Teach lit - tle ones Thy way;
3. Keep me in Thy way - - -, All e - vil thoughts pre - vent.

1. 天 高 飛 鳥 過， 地 闊 野 花 香，
2. 虛 心 敎 小 輩， 克 己 敬 年 尊，
3. 樂 得 布 衣 暖， 不 嫌 麥 飯 粗，
1 Flow'rs a - wake from slum - ber, Birds be - gin to fly;
Self con - trol, res - pect - - -, God's dear laws to o - bey;
Food and clothes that Thou pro - vide, let me be con - tent;

1. 照我勤工作，天父有恩光。
2. 常常勤服務，表明天父恩。
3. 千千萬萬事，樣樣主幫扶。
1. May my work this day — — —, Lord, Thee glo - ri - fy.
2. In my ac - tions gen-tle-ness Thy grace to dis - play.
3. Glo-ry, ho - nor be to Thee, Lord God om - ni - po - tent.

完全的心
A Perfect Heart

10-1

I will give you a new heart and put a new spirit in you. Ezek. 36:26

Dony McGuire

Reba Rambo

稱頌主（稱頌主）美好都屬祂；稱頌主（稱頌主）
Bless the Lord (bless the Lord) who reigns in beau-ty; Bless the Lord (bless the Lord)

智慧能力權柄屬祂。稱頌主（稱頌主）
who reigns in wis - dom and with pow'r. Bless the Lord (bless the Lord)

我也屬祂，因祂愛我，祂賜我完全的心。
who reigns my life with so much love, He can make a per-fect heart.

11

萬國啊！

All Ye Nations

Behold, the Kingdom of God is within you.

— Luke 17:21

Based on Psalm 117
Eng. Tr. by Marshall Huang
Chinese Traditional Melody
萬 國 啊，你們都當 讚美耶和華，萬 民
Praise the Lord, All ye na-tions, All ye peo-ple, praise, Praise the
哪，你們都當 頌 讚 祂。因 為 祂 向
Lord, All ye peo-ple, Bless His Ho-ly name. For His mer-cy
我 們 大 施 慈 愛，耶 和 華 的 誠
is so great to-ward us, All the truth of the
實，存 到 永 遠，你 們 要 讚 美 耶和華。
Lord, lasts for ev - er, Let us praise the name of the Lord.

父恩廣大

Great Are Thy Mercies, Heavenly Father

Blessed be His glorious name forever; let the whole earth be filled with His glory.
— Psalm 72:19

Chao Tzu-Chen
Eng. Tr. by Marshall Huang

Chinese Traditional Melody
Song of The Hoe

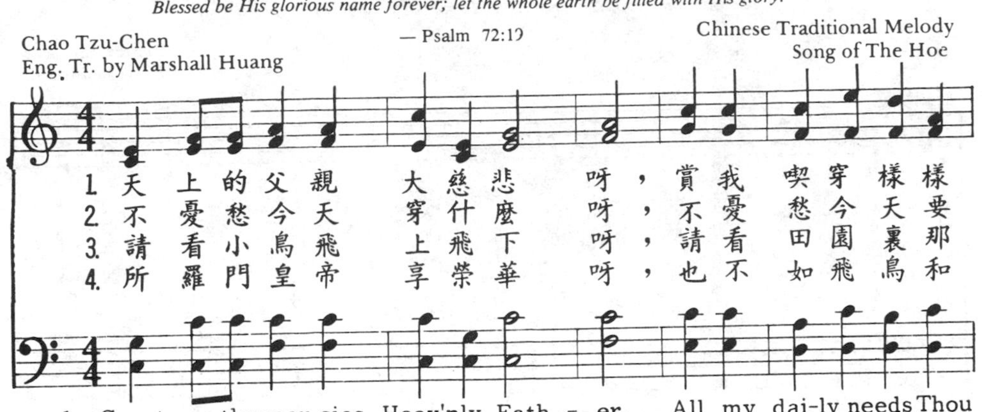
1. 天上的父親大慈悲呀，賞我喫穿樣樣
2. 不憂愁今天穿什麼呀，不憂愁今天要
3. 請看小鳥飛上飛下呀，請看田園裏那
4. 所羅門皇帝享榮華呀，也不如飛鳥和

1. Great are thy mer-cies, Heav'nly Fath - er, All my dai-ly needs Thou
2. *Take no more thought o'er what you must wear, Nei-ther wor-ry o'er your*
3. Be-hold the birds up in the blue sky, And the li-lies grow-ing
4. *King So-lo-mon in all his glo - ry, Yet was not ar-rayed like*

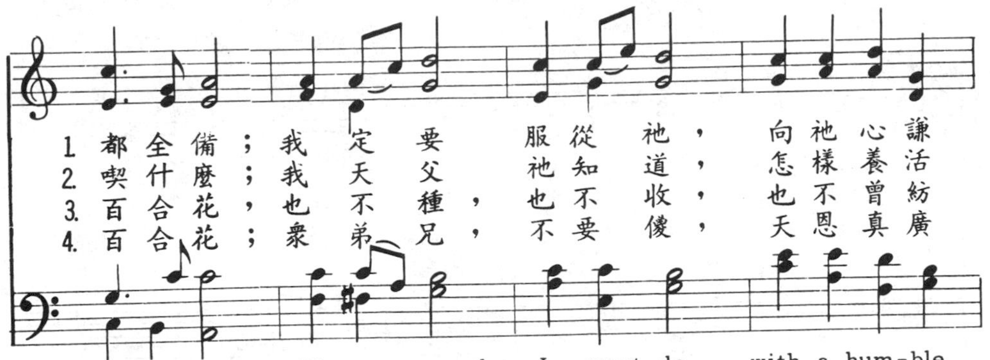
1. 都全備；我定要服從祂，向祂心謙
2. 喫什麼；我天父祂知道，怎樣養活
3. 百合花，也不種，也不收，也不曾紡
4. 百合花；衆弟兄，不要傻，天恩真廣

1. hast sup-plied; Thy com-mands, I must do, with a hum-ble
2. *dai-ly bread; My heavn'ly Lord, Knows my needs, And He will sup -*
3. in the field, They toil not, nor do they spin, Nei-ther do they
4. *one of these, O my friends, be not fools, God's grace is im -*

1. 卑；祂是春風我是草，讓祂吹。
2. 我；祇要為祂勤做工，心穩妥。
3. 紗；天父尚且養活它，何況咱！
4. 大；天父恩典夠你用，夠我用。

1. heart; Thou the Spring Wind, I am grass, Blow o'er me.
2. *ply; I need on-ly do my best, In Thee rest.*
3. reap; Yet my Fa-ther fee-deth them, Why not me?
4. *mense, It suf - fi-ces for your needs, And for mine.*

13

慈愛天父，我心真感激祢

Heavenly Father, I Appreciate You

Rejoice in the Lord, O Ye righteous, for praise is comely for the upright.

— Psalm 33:1

Unknown

Traditional
Arr. Don Marsh

1. 慈愛天父，我心真感激祢，慈愛
2. 聖子耶穌，我願尊祢為大，聖子
3. 至善聖靈，祢常安慰我心，至善
4. 三一真神，我願尊祢為大，三一
1. Heav'n-ly Fa - ther, I ap - pre - ci - ate You. Heav'n-ly
2. Son of God I mag - ni - fy You. Son of
3. Ho - ly Spir - it, You're a com - fort to me. Ho - ly
4. Tri - une God, I mag - ni - fy You. Tri - une
1. 天父，我心真感激祢。我
2. 耶穌，我願尊祢為大。我
3. 聖靈，祢常安慰我心。我
4. 真神，我願尊祢為大。我
1. Fa - ther, I ap - pre - ci - ate You. I
2. God I mag - ni - fy You. I
3. Spir - it, You're a com - fort to me. I
4. God, I mag - ni - fy You. I
1. 愛祢，敬佩祢，我屈膝敬
2. 愛祢，敬佩祢，我屈膝敬
3. 愛祢，敬佩祢，我屈膝敬
4. 愛祢，敬佩祢，我屈膝敬
1. love You, a - dore You, I bow down be -
2. love You, a - dore You, I bow down be -
3. love You, a - dore You, I bow down be -
4. love You, a - dore You, I bow down be -

1. 拜 祢，慈 愛 天 父，我 心 真 感 激 祢。
2. 拜 祢，聖 子 耶 穌，我 願 尊 祢 為 大。
3. 拜 祢，至 善 聖 靈，祢 常 安 慰 我 心。
4. 拜 祢，三 一 真 神，我 願 尊 祢 為 大。
1. fore You, Heav'n-ly Fa - ther, I ap - pre - ci - ate You.
2. fore You, Son of God, I mag - ni - fy You.
3. fore You, Ho - ly Spir - it You're a com - fort to me.
4. fore You, Tri - une God, I mag - ni - fy You.

耶穌，我愛你 （哈利路亞） **13-1**

Jesus, I Love You

Christ . . . is God over all, forever praised! Rom. 9:5

Jude Del Hierrs — Jude Del Hierrs

Unison

耶 穌，我 愛 祢，我 屈 膝 敬 拜 祢， 讚 美 與

Je - sus, I love you, I bow down be - fore you. Praise-es and

尊 崇 歸 我 王， 哈 利 路 亞，

wor - ship to our king. Al - le - lu - ia,

哈 利 路 亞，哈 利 路 亞，哈 利 路。

Al - le - lu - ia, Al - le - lu - ia, Al - le - lu.

14

真神之愛
The Love of God

Who shall separate us from the love of Christ? — Romans 8:35

F. M. Lehman

F. M. Lehman
Arranged by Claudia Lehman Mays

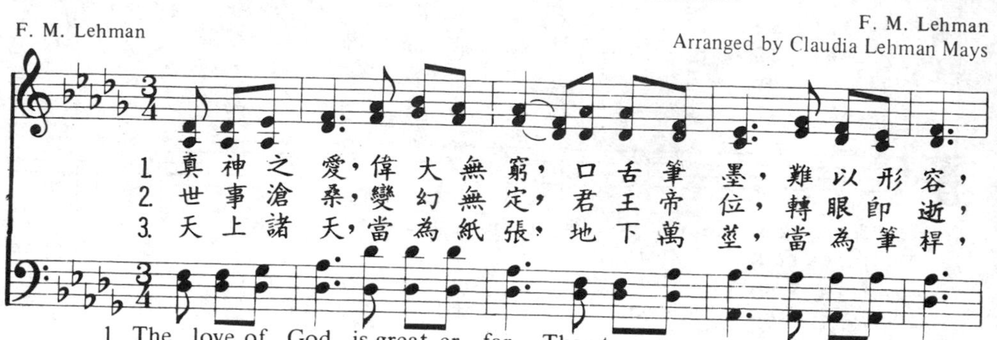
1 真神之愛，偉大無窮，口舌筆墨，難以形容，
2 世事滄桑，變幻無定，君王帝位，轉眼即逝，
3 天上諸天，當為紙張，地下萬莖，當為筆桿，
1 The love of God is great-er far Than tongue or pen can ev-er tell;
2 When years of time shall pass a - way, And earth-ly thrones and kingdoms fall,
3 Could we with ink the o-cean fill, And were the skies of parchment made,

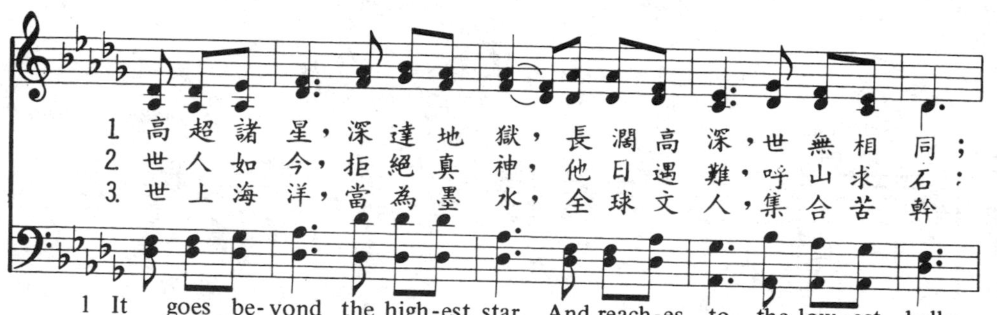
1 高超諸星，深達地獄，長闊高深，世無相同；
2 世人如今，拒絕真神，他日遇難，呼山求石；
3 世上海洋，當為墨水，全球文人，集合苦幹
1 It goes be-yond the high-est star, And reach-es to the low-est hell;
2 When men, who here re-fuse to pray, On rocks and hills and mountains call,
3 Were ev-ery stalk on earth a quill, And ev-ery man a scribe by trade,

1 始祖犯罪，墮入引誘，神遣愛子拯救，
2 但神慈愛，永存不變，偉大無限無量，
3 耗盡智力，描寫神愛，海洋墨水會乾，
1 The guilt-y pair, bowed down with care, God gave His Son to win;
2 God's love so sure, shall still en-dure, All mea-sure-less and strong;
3 To write the love of God a-bove Would drain the o - cean dry.

1. 使我罪人，與神和好，赦免一切罪尤。
2. 向人所顯，救贖恩典，聖徒天使頌揚。
3. 案卷雖長，如天連天，仍難表達透暢。
1 His err-ing child He rec-on-ciled, And par-doned from his sin.
2 Re-deem-ing grace to A-dam's race–The saints' and an-gels' song.
3 Nor could the scroll con-tain the whole, Though stretched from sky to sky.

啊！神之愛，何等豐富，偉大無限無量。
O love of God, how rich and pure! How mea-sure-less and strong!

永遠堅定，永遠不變，天使聖徒頌揚。
It shall for ev-er-more en-dure The saints' and an-gels' song.

你看父賜給我們是何等的慈愛，使我們得稱為神的兒女，我們也真是祂的兒女。

約翰壹書三章1節

How great is the love the Father has lavished on us, that we should be called children of God!
And that is what we are!

— I John 3:1

15

神愛世人

God So Loved the World

. . . He gave His only begotten Son . . . . — John 3:16

John 3:16, 17

STAINER
John Stainer

神 極愛 世 人， 神 極愛 世 人，
God so loved the world, God so loved the world,

甚至将 獨 生子賜 給他 們，凡 信靠祂
that He gave His on - ly be - got - ten Son, that who - so be -

的 人，信 靠祂 的 人， 不 至 滅亡，不 至
liev - eth, be - liev - eth in Him should not per - ish, should not

滅亡，反 得着 永 遠 生 命。 因神 差祂愛
per - ish but have ev - er - last - ing life. For God sent not His

1

子降世不是定世人的罪，神差祂愛子降世不
Son in-to the world to con-demn the world, God sent not His Son in-to the
是定世人的罪，乃是叫世人因祂得
world to con-demn the world, but that the world through Him might be
D.C.
2
拯救。命，得永遠生命，永遠生命，
sav - ed. life, ev-er-last-ing life, ev-er-last-ing,
得永遠生命。神極愛世人，
ev-er-last-ing life. God so loved the world,
神極愛世人，神極愛世人。
God so loved the world, God so loved the world.

16

神聖妙愛
Love Divine, All Loves Excelling

For the law of the Spirit of Life, . . . hath made us free from the law of sin and death.
— Romans 8:2 (Read Romans 7:24, 25; 8:1-5)

Charles Wesley

BEECHER
John Zundel

1. 神聖妙愛超乎一切，天上喜樂降人間，
2. 福雨降下聖靈充滿，慰我心懷驅艱難，
3. 全能恩主施行拯救，願祢進入我心中，
4. 求主完成再造深恩，使我清潔無瑕疵，

1 Love di-vine, all loves ex-cel-ling, Joy of heaven to earth come down,
2 *Breathe, O breathe Thy lov-ing Spir-it In - to ev-ery trou-bled breast;*
3 Come, Al-might-y to de-liv-er, Let us all Thy life re-ceive;
4 *Fin - ish then Thy new cre-a-tion, Pure and spot-less let us be;*

1. 加我信心學主謙卑，仁義聖潔将主現；
2. 我與救主同得基業，永為主伴享平安；
3. 使我愛祢與祢聯合，容我常住祢殿中；
4. 使我見祢偉大救恩，重造完全的心志；

1 Fix in us Thy hum-ble dwell-ing, All Thy faith-ful mer-cies crown.
2 *Let us all in Thee in-her-it, Let us find Thy prom-ised rest.*
3 Sud-den-ly re-turn, and nev-er, Nev-er-more Thy tem-ples leave.
4 *Let us see Thy great sal-va-tion Per-fect-ly re-stored in Thee.*

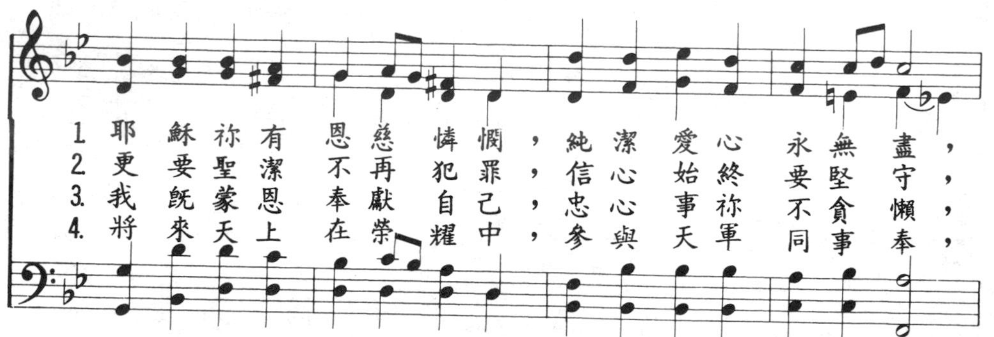

1. 耶穌祢有恩慈憐憫，純潔愛心永無盡，
2. 更要聖潔不再犯罪，信心始終要堅守，
3. 我既蒙恩奉獻自己，忠心事祢不貪懶，
4. 将來天上在榮耀中，參與天軍同事奉，

1 Je - sus, Thou art all com-pas-sion, Pure, un-bound-ed love Thou art;
2 *Take a-way our bent to sin-ning, Al - pha and O - me-ga be;*
3 Thee we would be al-ways bless-ing, Serve Thee as Thy hosts a-bove,
4 *Changed from glo-ry in-to glo-ry, 'Til in heaven we take our place,*

1. 祢 以 浩 大 完 備 救 恩，充 滿 我 的 戰 兢 心。
2. 祢 是 忠 信 誠 實 恩 主，使 我 釋 放 得 自 由。
3. 獻 上 祭 物 不 住 禱 告，衷 心 愛 祢 到 永 遠。
4. 虔 誠 跪 拜 以 主 為 榮，在 主 面 前 齊 歌 頌。阿 門。

1 Vis - it us with Thy sal - va-tion, En - ter ev - ery trem-bling heart.
2 *End of faith, as its be - gin-ning, Set our hearts at lib - er - ty.*
3 Pray, and praise Thee with-out ceas-ing, Glo - ry in Thy per-fect love.
4 *'Til we cast our crowns be-fore Thee, Lost in won-der, love, and praise.* A-men.

17

耶穌喜愛小孩

Jesus Loves the Little Children

"Suffer little children . . . to come unto Me." — Matthew 19:14

CHILDREN
George F. Root

Unknown

耶 穌 喜 愛 世 上 小 孩， 世 上 所 有 的 小
Je - sus loves the lit - tle chil - dren, All the chil-dren of the

孩。 無 論 紅 黄 黑 白 種，都 是 耶 穌 心 寶 貝，
world. Red and yel-low, black and white, They are pre-cious in His sight —

耶 穌 喜 愛 世 上 所 有 的 小 孩。
Je - sus loves the lit - tle chil - dren of the world.

18

古老福音

Tell Me the Old, Old Story

Of which salvation the prophets have enquired . . . who prophesied of the grace that should come . . . . — I Peter 1:10

Katherine Hankey

EVANGEL
William H. Doane

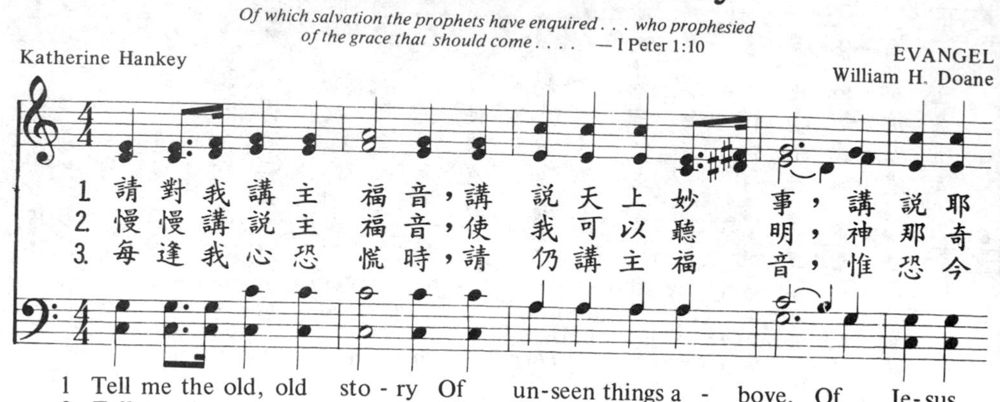

1. 請對我講主福音，講說天上妙事，講說耶
2. 慢慢講說主福音，使我可以聽明，神那奇
3. 每逢我心恐慌時，請仍講主福音，惟恐今
1 Tell me the old, old sto - ry Of un-seen things a - bove, Of Je-sus
2 Tell me the sto - ry slow - ly, That I may take it in— That won-der-
3 Tell me the same old sto - ry When you have cause to fear, That this world's

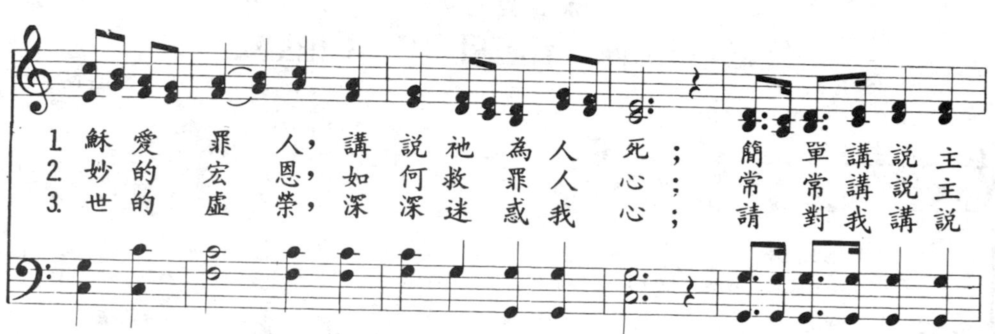

1. 穌愛罪人，講說祂為人死；簡單講說主
2. 妙的宏恩，如何救罪人心；常常講說主
3. 世的虛榮，深深迷惑我心；請對我講說
1 and His glo - ry, Of Je - sus and His love. Tell me the sto - ry
2 ful re - demp - tion, God's rem-e - dy for sin. Tell me the sto - ry
3 emp - ty glo - ry Is cost-ing me too dear. Yes, and when that world's

1. 福音，像對兒童講說，因我軟弱又愚笨，
2. 福音，因我容易忘記，像清晨草上甘露，
3. 福音，講說老舊福音，請仍講主福音說：
1 sim - ply, As to a lit - tle child; For I am weak and wea - ry,
2 of - ten, For I for - get so soon; The ear - ly dew of morn - ing
3 glo - ry Is dawn-ing on my soul, Tell me the old, old sto - ry:

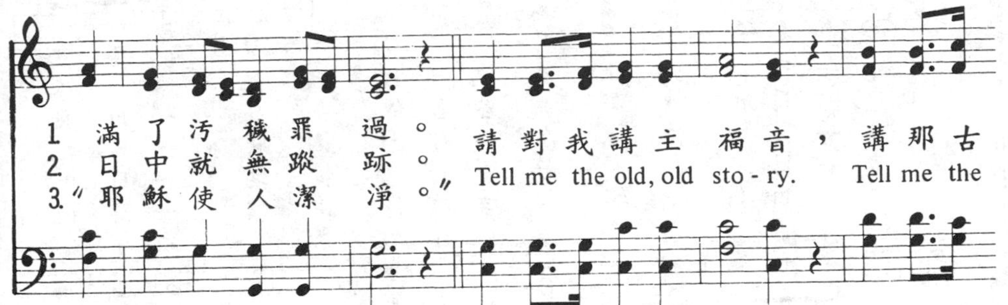
1. 滿 了 汚 穢 罪 過 。
2. 日 中 就 無 蹤 跡 。
3. "耶 穌 使 人 潔 淨 。"
請 對 我 講 主 福 音 ， 講 那 古
Tell me the old, old sto - ry. Tell me the

1 And help - less and de - filed.
2 *Has passed a - way at noon.*
3 "Christ Je - sus makes thee whole."

老 的 福 音 。講 説 耶 穌 愛 罪 人，講 説 耶 穌 救 恩 。
old, old sto - ry. Tell me the old, old sto-ry, Of Je-sus and His love.

信道是從聽道來的，聽道是從基督的話來的。

羅馬人書十章
17 節

So faith comes from what is heard, and what is heard comes by the preaching of Christ.

— Romans 10:17, RSV

19

一日
One Day

When the fullness of time was come, God sent forth His son . . . . — Galatians 4:4
J. Wilbur Chapman
ONE DAY
Charles H. Marsh
1. 一日高天上，充滿頌讚歌聲，一日人
2. 一日祂被帶到各各他山巔，一日祂
3. 一日祂被撇在曠野山園間，一日祂
4. 一日死威權無力將祂拘禁，一日大
5. 一日角聲響，報告祂將復臨，一日祂
1 One day when heav - en was filled with His prais - es, One day when
2 One day they led Him up Cal - va - ry's moun-tain, One day they
3 One day they left Him a - lone in the gar - den, One day He
4 One day the grave could con - ceal Him no long - er, One day the
5 One day the trum - pet will sound for His com - ing, One day the
1. 罪惡使全世幽暗；耶穌來塵世，藉
2. 被掛在十字架上；備嚐諸痛苦，受
3. 安息遠離諸艱苦；天使從天降，晝
4. 磐石離穴而傾倒；救主自墓出，戰
5. 榮光在全世普照；奇妙之大日，親
1 sin was as black as could be, Je - sus came forth to be
2 nailed Him to die on the tree; Suf - fer - ing an - guish, de -
3 rest - ed, from suf - fer - ing free; An - gels came down o'er His
4 stone rolled a - way from the door; Then He a - rose, o - ver
5 skies with His glo - ry will shine; Won - der - ful day, my be -
1. 童女身降生，居住在人間，發光輝燦爛。
2. 藐視遺厭棄，擔負我罪愆，祂慈愛無量。
3. 夜守護墓門，絕望仍有望，祂是我救主！
4. 勝死亡權勢，升到高天上，永作我中保。
5. 愛聖徒復起，被接至父家，永享主榮耀。
1 born of a vir - gin, Dwelt a - mong men—my ex - am - ple is He!
2 spised and re - ject - ed, Bear - ing our sins, my Re - deem - er is He!
3 tomb to keep vig - il— Hope of the hope - less, my Sav - ior is He!
4 death He had con - quered, Now is as - cend - ed, my Lord ev - er - more!
5 lov - ed ones bring - ing! Glo - ri - ous Sav - ior, this Je - sus is mine!

降世，祂愛我，釘死，祂救我，埋葬，祂
Liv-ing, He loved me! dy-ing, He saved me! Bur-ied, He
帶去我一切罪愆；復活，使我稱義，
car-ried my sins far a-way! Ris-ing, He jus-ti-fied
永脫罪權勢，一日祂再來，我得福無邊。
free-ly, for-ev-er! One day He's com-ing– O glo-ri-ous day!

20

請對我說耶穌的故事

Tell Me the Stories of Jesus

. . I count all things but loss for the excellency of the knowledge of Christ Jesus . .
William H. Parker
STORIES OF JESUS
Frederic A. Challinor
Unison or duet
1. 我愛聽耶穌的故事，請對我說，
2. 耶穌愛衆孩童故事，請對我說，
3. 當年耶穌進入城中，孩童跟隨，
1 Tell me the sto - ries of Je - sus I love to hear;
2 First let me hear how the chil - dren Stood 'round His knee,
3 In - to the cit - y I'd fol - low The chil - dren's band,
1. 祂若在此我必求問祂回答我；
2. 我渴慕也能蒙恩福因祂愛我；
3. 手拿棕樹枝齊揮搖同聲讚美；
1 Things I would ask Him to tell me If He were here:
2 I shall im - ag - ine His bless - ing Rest - ing on me;
3 Wav - ing a branch of the palm - tree High in my hand;
1. 當年在路旁，海邊行走，
2. 祂滿有恩典，言語謙和，
3. 歡樂的歌聲，我願同唱，
1 Scenes by the way - side, Tales of the sea,
2 Words full of kind - ness, Deeds full of grace,
3 One of His her - alds, Yes, I would sing
1. 祂一生事蹟，請告訴我。
2. 光潔的容面，慈愛溫柔。
3. 高呼"和散拿，耶穌是王！"
1 Sto - ries of Je - sus, Tell them to me.
2 All in the bright - ness Of Je - sus' face.
3 Loud - est ho - san - nas, "Je - sus is King!"

祂為何要愛我

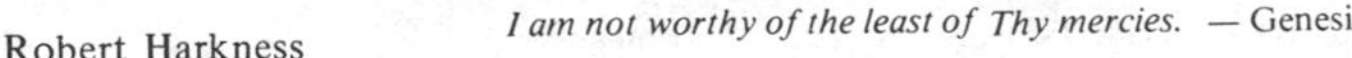
Why Should He Love Me So?

I am not worthy of the least of Thy mercies. — Genesis 32:10

Robert Harkness

LOVE ME
Robert Harkness

1. 神遣愛子救主為我捨命—祂為何要愛我？
2. 為我罪，主手足被釘十架—祂為何要愛我？
3. 何等痛苦主替我罪受刑—祂為何要愛我？

1 Love sent my Sav-ior to die in my stead — Why should He love me so?
2 *Nails pierced His hands and His feet for my sin — Why should He love me so?*
3 O how He ag-o-nized there in my place — Why should He love me so?

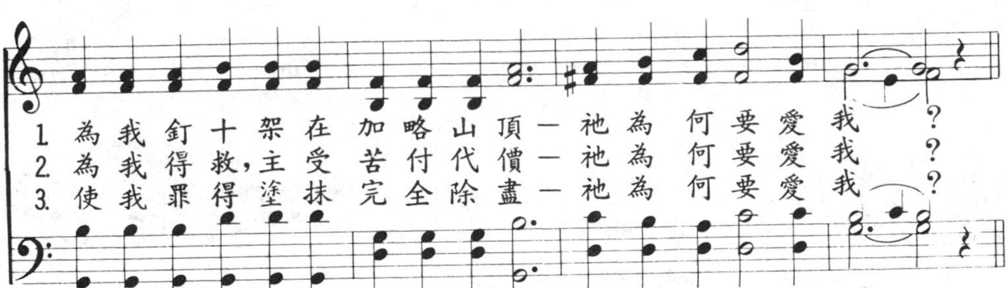
1. 為我釘十架在加略山頂—祂為何要愛我？
2. 為我得救，主受苦付代價—祂為何要愛我？
3. 使我罪得塗抹完全除盡—祂為何要愛我？

1 Meek-ly to Cal-va-ry's cross He was led — Why should He love me so?
2 *He suf-fered sore my sal-va-tion to win — Why should He love me so?*
3 Noth-ing with-hold-ing my sin to ef-face — Why should He love me so?

祂為何要愛我？祂為何要愛我？
Why should He love me so? Why should He love me so?
為何救主在加略山受苦？祂為何要愛我？
Why should my Sav-ior to Cal-va-ry go? Why should He love me so?

22

耶穌大愛深不可測

O the Deep, Deep Love of Jesus

Who shall separate us from the love of Jesus? Romans 8:35

Samuel Trevor Francis

EBENEZER
Thomas J. Williams

Unison
1. 耶 穌 大 愛 深 不 可 測，廣 不 可 量
2. 耶 穌 大 愛 深 不 可 測，走 遍 四 方
3. 耶 穌 大 愛 深 不 可 測，愛 中 之 愛
1 O the deep, deep love of Je-sus, Vast, un-mea-sured
2 O the deep, deep love of Je-sus– Spread His praise from
3 O the deep, deep love of Je-sus, Love of ev-ery
1. 寬 無 邊！滾 滾 尤 如 遼 濶 海 洋，如 衆
2. 去 傳 揚！他 有 慈 愛 長 久 的 愛，永 不
3. 愛 無 量！賜 福 衆 多 大 過 海 洋，是 避
1 bound-less, free! Roll-ing as a might-y o-cean In its
2 shore to shore! How He lov-eth, ev-er lov-eth, Chang-eth
3 love the best! 'Tis an o-cean full of bless-ing, 'Tis a
1. 水 將 我 身 淹！在 上 遮 蓋，四 圍 環 繞，
2. 改 變 亙 古 長！主 眼 看 顧 祂 的 兒 女，
3. 難 所 有 安 祥！耶 穌 大 愛 深 不 可 測，
1 full-ness o-ver me! Un-der-neath me, all a-round me,
2 nev-er, nev-er-more! How He watch-es o'er His loved ones,
3 ha-ven giv-ing rest! O the deep, deep love of Je-sus–

1. 在 主 愛 中 得 安 祥； 引 導 前 行，
2. 捨 身 向 他 們 呼 召； 親 自 代 禱，
3. 遠 超 太 空 天 上 天； 將 我 高 舉，
1 Is the cur - rent of Thy love– Lead - ing on - ward,
2 Died to call them all His own; How for them He
3 'Tis a heaven of heavens to me; And it lifts me
1. 走 向 天 家，安 息 在 榮 耀 天 上！
2. 時 常 關 照，從 寶 座 上 顯 榮 耀！
3. 在 榮 耀 中，歌 頌 讚 美 到 永 遠！ 阿 們。
1 lead - ing home - ward, To Thy glo - rious rest a - bove!
2 in - ter - ced - eth, Watch - eth o'er them from the throne!
3 up to glo - ry, For it lifts me up to Thee! A-men.

我們若說是與神相交，却在黑暗裡行，就是說謊話，不行真理了。

我們若在光明中行，如同神在光明中，就彼此相交。

祂兒子耶穌的血，也洗淨我們一切的罪。

我們若說自己無罪，便是自欺，真理不在我們心裡了。

我們若認自己的罪，神是信實的、是公義的，

必要赦免我們的罪，洗淨我們一切的不義。

約翰壹書一章
6 — 9 節

23

我的牧者

My Shepherd Will Supply My Need

My beloved is mine and I am his; he feedeth among the lilies.
— Song of Solomon 2:16

Psalm 23, paraphrased
Isaac Watts

RESIGNATION
Traditional American Melody
Arranged by Fred Bock

1. 耶 和 華 是 我 的 牧 者，我 必 一 無 缺
2. 當 我 經 過 死 蔭 幽 谷，祂 常 與 我 同
3. 主 有 豐 盛 慈 愛 恩 惠，夠 我 使 用 一
1 My Shep-herd will sup-ply my need: Je - ho-vah is His
2 When I walk through the shades of death His pres-ence is my
3 The sure pro - vi - sions of my God At - tend me all my

1. 欠； 祂 使 我 躺 臥 青 草 地，領 我 安
2. 在； 主 用 話 語 安 慰 扶 持，使 我 不
3. 生； 我 願 長 久 住 在 殿 中，歌 頌 讚
1 name: In pas-tures fresh He makes me feed, Be - side the
2 stay; One word of His sup-port-ing grace Drives all my
3 days; O may Thy house be my a - bode, And all my

1. 歇 水 邊。 當 我 徬 徨 失 喪 之 時，
2. 至 遭 害。 在 我 衆 敵 人 的 面 前，
3. 美 主 恩。 祢 的 稱 讚 滿 足 我 心，
1 liv - ing stream. He brings my wan-dering spir - it back
2 fears a - way. His hand, in sight of all my foes,
3 work be praise. There would I find a set - tled rest,

1. 祂 帶 領 我 歸 回； 救 主 滿 有 慈
2. 為 我 擺 設 筵 席； 祢 用 油 膏 了
3. 我 願 與 祢 相 親； 當 我 走 完 世
1 When I for - sake His ways, And leads me, for His
2 Doth still my ta - ble spread; My cup with bless - ings
3 While oth - ers go and come; No more a strang - er,

1. 悲 憐 憫， 引 導 我 走 義 路。
2. 我 的 頭， 使 我 福 杯 滿 溢。 阿 們
3. 上 路 程， 天 家 永 享 安 寧。
1 mer - cy's sake, In paths of truth and grace.
2 o - ver - flows, His oil a - noints my head.
3 nor a guest, But like a child at home. A - men.

I am the good shepherd. The good shepherd lays down his life for the sheep.
I am the good shepherd, I know my sheep and my sheep know me.

— John 10:11, 14. NIV

24

耶和華是我的牧者
The Lord Is My Shepherd

That . . . He might show the exceeding riches of His grace in His kindness . . .

— Ephesians 2:7

Psalm 23
Eng. Tran. by Marshall Huang
Chinese Traditional Melody
1. 耶和華是我的牧者，我必不至缺乏，祂使我躺臥在青草地上，領我在可安歇的水邊，祂使我的靈魂
2. 我雖然行過死蔭的幽谷，也不怕遭害，因為祢與我同在，祢的杖，祢的竿，都安慰我，在我敵人面前，祢為
3. 我一生一世，我一生一世，必有恩惠慈愛隨着我，我一生一世，我一生一世，必有恩惠慈愛隨着我，必有恩惠慈愛
1. Be - cause the Lord is my Shep - herd, I have everything that I need He lets me rest in the pasture green, And He leads me by the qui - et stream, He keeps on giv - ing
2. E - ven though I walk, thru the Vale of death, Yet I'll not fear For You are close be- side me. You use your rod, and your staff to com - fort me. You have spread a feast for me be-
3. Sure - ly all my life, all my days shall be filled with your good- ness and mer - cies, Surely all my life all my days shall be filled With your good - ness

1. 甦　醒，為自己的名　引導我走義路，
2. 我擺設筵席，祢用油，膏了我的頭，
3. 隨着我，我且要住在　耶和華的殿中，
1. life to me, And helps me do what hon-ors Him most
2. for my e-ne- mies, You use oil to a- noint me,
3. and mer - cies, And I shall dwell in your home for e- ver,

1. 為自己的名　引導我走義路，引導我走義　路。
2. 使我的福杯滿　溢，我的福杯滿　溢。
3. 我且要住在　耶和華的殿中，直　到　永　遠。
1. And helps me do what hon-ors Him most, hon - - ors Him most.
2. Till with bless-ing o - - ver flow-ing, o - - ver flow - ing.
3. And I shall dwell in your home for e - ver, for - - e - ver.

我是好牧人，好牧人為羊捨命。
我認識我的羊，我的羊也認識我。

約翰福音十章
11，14

25

如羊需牧人
Like a Lamb Who Needs the Shepherd

He shall feed His flock like a shepherd; He shall gather His lambs with His arms.
— Isaiah 40:11
Ralph Carmichael
LIKE A LAMB
Ralph Carmichael
1. 我願隨主一路同行，祂必指引我前路，有主引領前途光明，若我今願跟隨主；我如迷羊需要牧人，今願緊緊靠近主，經過
2. 人生道路曲折不平，前途茫茫無人知，有時引到蔭涼草地，有時領到曠野地；我如迷羊需要牧人，黑夜路求主指示，人生
3. 當我經過死蔭幽谷，或登高山遇艱險，雖有陰冷灰雲遮天，主賜我夠用恩典；我如迷羊需要牧人，主必常在我身邊，伴我
1 Where He leads me I must fol - low, With - out Him I'd lose my way. I will see a bright to - mor - row If I fol - low Him to - day. Like a lamb who needs the Shep-herd, At His side I'll al - ways stay. Through the
2 Life is like a wind - ing path - way, Who can tell what lies a - head? Will it lead to shad - y pas - tures, Or to wild - er - ness in - stead? Like a lamb who needs the Shep-herd, When in - to the night I go, Help me
3 Though you walk through dark - est val - leys And the sky is cold and gray, Though you climb the steep - est moun - tains He will nev - er let you stray. Like a lamb who needs the Shep-herd, By your side He'll al - ways stay. 'Til the

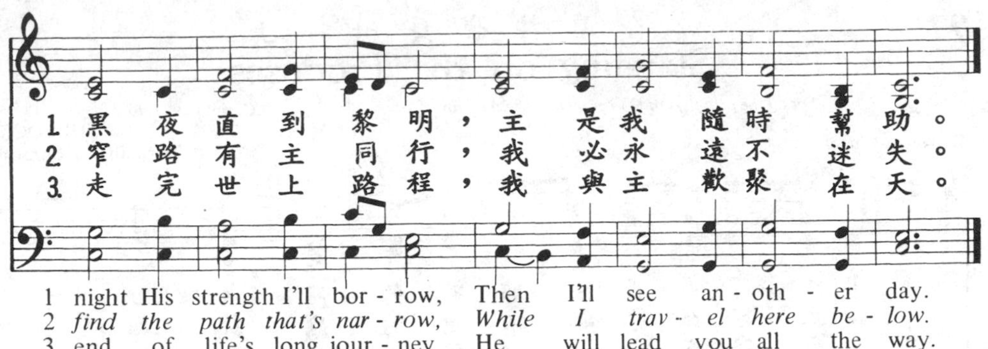
1. 黑夜直到黎明，主是我隨時幫助。
2. 窄路有主同行，我必永遠不迷失。
3. 走完世上路程，我與主歡聚在天。
1 night His strength I'll bor - row, Then I'll see an - oth - er day.
2 *find the path that's nar - row, While I trav - el here be - low.*
3 end of life's long jour - ney He will lead you all the way.

26

天父兒女

Children of the Heavenly Father

TRYGGARE KAN INGEN VARA
Swedish Folk Melody

Lina Sandell
Tr. by Ernst W. Olson

As a father pitieth his children, so the Lord pitieth . . . .
Psalm 103:13

1. 天父兒女蒙祂愛憐，聚集環抱在祂胸前；
2. 父神最愛祂的聖民，親自扶養看顧他們；
3. 不論生死遇福或苦，主的兒女永遠屬主；
4. 讚美天父慈愛真神，祂的保護永不打盹；
5. 無論賜與或是收取，天父自有祂的美意；

1 Chil - dren of the heaven - ly Fa - ther Safe - ly in His bos - om gath - er;
2 *God His own doth tend and nour - ish, In His ho - ly courts they flour - ish;*
3 Nei - ther life nor death shall ev - er From the Lord His chil - dren sev - er;
4 *Praise the Lord in joy - ful num - bers, Your Pro - tect - or nev - er slum - bers;*
5 Though He giv - eth or He tak - eth, God His chil - dren ne'er for - sak - eth;

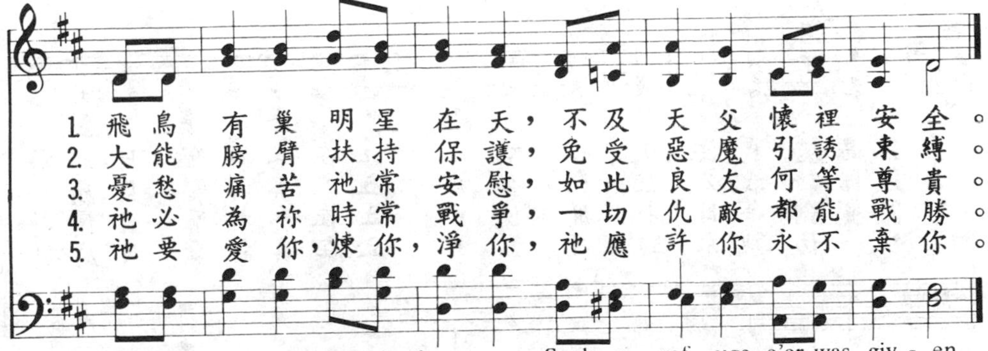
1. 飛鳥有巢明星在天，不及天父懷裡安全。
2. 大能膀臂扶持保護，免受惡魔引誘束縛。
3. 憂愁痛苦祂常安慰，如此良友何等尊貴。
4. 祂必為祢時常戰爭，一切仇敵都能戰勝。
5. 祂要愛你，煉你，淨你，祂應許你永不棄你。

1 Nest - ling bird nor star in heav - en Such a ref - uge e'er was giv - en.
2 *From all e - vil things He spares them, In His might - y arms He bears them.*
3 Un - to them His grace He show - eth, And their sor - rows all He know - eth.
4 *At the will of your De - fend - er Ev - ery foe - man must sur - ren - der.*
5 His the lov - ing pur - pose sole - ly To pre - serve them pure and ho - ly.

27 立在真神寶貝應許上

Standing on the Promises

For all the promises of God are "yes," and in him "Amen" . . . . — II Corinthians 1:20

R. Kelso Carter

TURLOCK
Norman E. Johnson

Unison
1. 立定在我主耶穌的應許上，
2. 立定在耶穌不變的應許上，
3. 立定在我主耶穌的應許上，
4. 立在主的應許上必不動搖，
1 Stand - ing on the prom - is - es of Christ my King,
2 Stand - ing on the prom - is - es that can - not fail
3 Stand - ing on the prom - is - es of Christ the Lord,
4 Stand - ing on the prom - is - es I can - not fall,
1. 直到永永遠遠讚美主不忘！榮耀在最
2. 必不疑惑也不懼怕風與浪，靠着生命
3. 永遠繫在救主堅固慈繩上，藉着聖靈
4. 時刻留心傾聽聖靈的教導，救主是我
1 Through e - ter - nal a - ges let His prais - es ring! Glo - ry in the
2 When the howl - ing storms of doubt and fear as - sail; By the liv - ing
3 Bound to Him e - ter - nal - ly by love's strong cord, O - ver - com - ing
4 Lis - tening ev - ery mo - ment to the Spir - it's call, Rest - ing in my
1. 高處我要大聲唱，立在真神寶貝應許
2. 話語我必能堅強，立在真神寶貝應許
3. 寶劍每日打勝仗，立在真神寶貝應許
4. 一切祂永遠可靠，立在真神寶貝應許
1 high - est I will shout and sing— Stand - ing on the prom - is - es of
2 word of God I shall pre - vail— Stand - ing on the prom - is - es of
3 dai - ly with the Spir - it's sword— Stand - ing on the prom - is - es of
4 Sav - ior as my all in all— Stand - ing on the prom - is - es of

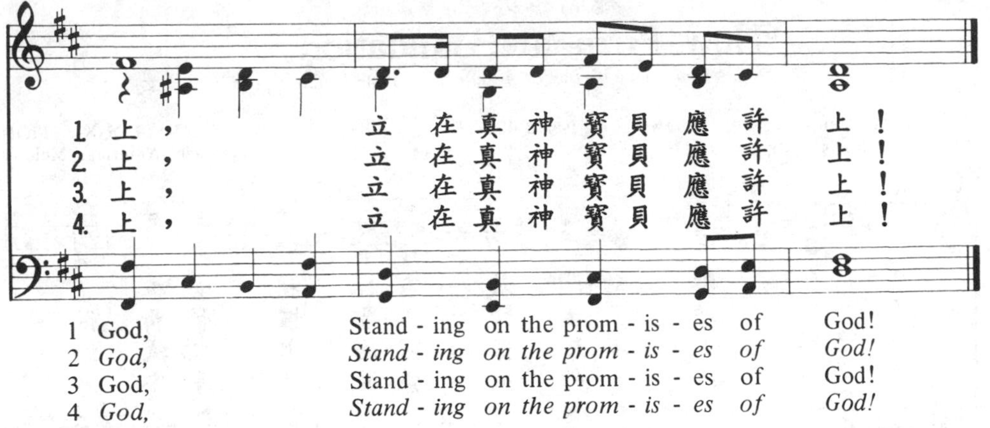
1. 上，立在真神寶貝應許上！
2. 上，立在真神寶貝應許上！
3. 上，立在真神寶貝應許上！
4. 上，立在真神寶貝應許上！
1 God, Stand - ing on the prom - is - es of God!
2 God, Stand - ing on the prom - is - es of God!
3 God, Stand - ing on the prom - is - es of God!
4 God, Stand - ing on the prom - is - es of God!

哈利路亞(1) 28

Alleluia

And I heard as it were the voices of a great multitude . . .
saying Alleluia for the Lord God omnipotent reigneth. — Revelation 19:6

ALLELUIA

Traditional text — Traditional melody

1. 哈利路亞，哈利路亞，哈利路亞，哈利路亞，
2. 祂是救主，祂是救主，祂是救主，祂是救主，
3. 讚美耶穌，讚美耶穌，讚美耶穌，讚美耶穌，
1 Al - le - lu - ia, al - le - lu - ia, Al - le - lu - ia, al - le - lu - ia,
2 He's my Sav - ior, He's my Sav - ior, He's my Sav - ior, He's my Sav - ior,
3 I will praise Him, I will praise Him, I will praise Him, I will praise Him,

1. 哈利路亞，哈利路亞，哈利路亞，哈利路亞。
2. 祂是救主，祂是救主，祂是救主，祂是救主。
3. 讚美耶穌，讚美耶穌，讚美耶穌，讚美耶穌。
1 Al - le - lu - ia, al - le - lu - ia, Al - le - lu - ia, al - le - lu - ia.
2 He's my Sav - ior, He's my Sav - ior, He's my Sav - ior, He's my Sav - ior.
3 I will praise Him, I will praise Him, I will praise Him, I will praise Him.

29

穩當根基

How Firm a Foundation

. . . And my God is the rock of my refuge. — Psalm 94:22

Based on II Timothy 2:19; Hebrews 13:5; Isaiah 43:1-2
"K" in Rippon's *Selection,* 1787

FOUNDATION
Early American Melody

1. 耶穌的門徒，有極穩當根基，
2. 請聽救主說："不要懼怕驚慌，
3. "雖然有患難，經過水火試煉，
4. "靠近我的人，靈魂必享安息，

1 How firm a foun - da - tion, ye saints of the Lord,
2 *"Fear not, I am with thee; O be not dis - mayed,*
3 "When through fier - y tri - als thy path - way shall lie,
4 *"The soul that on Je - sus hath leaned for re - pose*

1. 是神的言語，在聖經有所記！
2. 因為我是神，我必賜你力量；
3. 我必賜給你，豐富足夠恩典；
4. 在我懷中的，我永遠不丟棄：

1 Is laid for your faith in His ex - cel - lent Word!
2 *For I am thy God, and will still give thee aid;*
3 My grace, all suf - fi - cient, shall be thy sup - ply:
4 *I will not, I will not de - sert to its foes;*

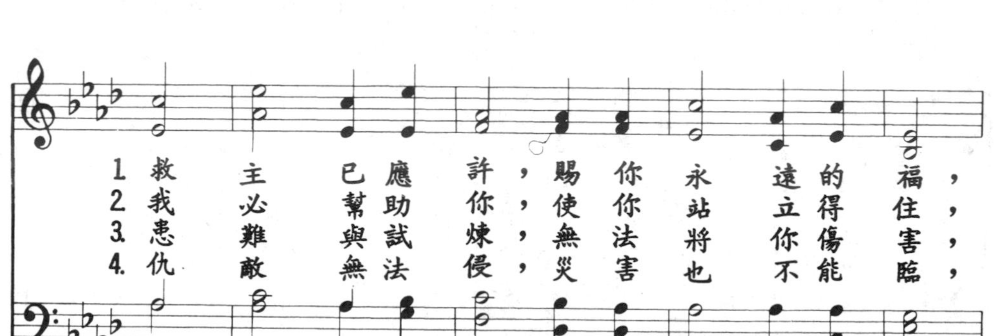
1. 救主已應許，賜你永遠的福，
2. 我必幫助你，使你站立得住，
3. 患難與試煉，無法將你傷害，
4. 仇敵無法侵，災害也不能臨，

1 What more can He say than to you He hath said,
2 *I'll strength - en thee, help thee, and cause thee to stand,*
3 The flame shall not hurt thee; I on - ly de - sign
4 *That soul, though all hell should en - deav - or to shake,*

1. 投靠你救主，祂必定要保護。
2. 用我全能手，時常將你扶助。
3. 你必成精金，必永遠不朽壞。
4. 我必常保護，一直到無窮盡！"
1 To you who for ref - uge to Je - sus have fled?
2 *Up - held by My right - eous, om - nip - o - tent hand.*
3 Thy dross to con - sume and thy gold to re - fine.
4 *I'll nev - er, no, nev - er, no, nev - er for - sake!"*

奇妙聖經

30

Holy Bible, Book Divine

Thy word is a lamp unto my feet, and a light unto my path. — Psalm 119:105

ALETTA
William B. Bradbury

John Burton

1. 奇妙聖經，神言語，是我真理寶藏庫；
2. 常警誡我免失足，一生引導並保護；
3. 當我苦悶它安慰，曠野行走它開路；
4. 主示我得救福樂，我若悖逆必沉淪；

1 Ho - ly Bi - ble, book di - vine, Pre - cious treas - ure, thou art mine;
2 *Mine to chide me when I rove; Mine to show a Sav - ior's love;*
3 Mine to com - fort in dis - tress, Suf - fering in this wil - der - ness;
4 *Mine to tell of joys to come, And the reb - el sin - ner's doom;*

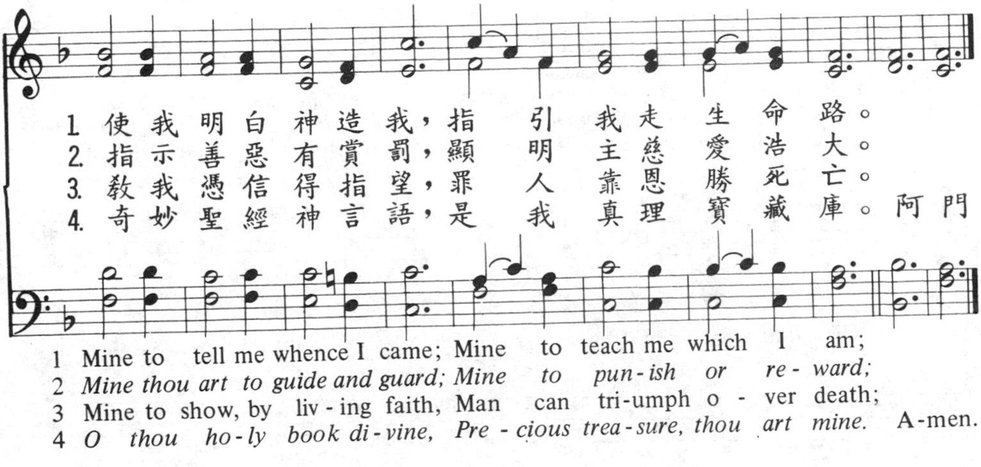

1. 使我明白神造我，指引我走生命路。
2. 指示善惡有賞罰，顯明主慈愛浩大。
3. 教我憑信得指望，罪人靠恩勝死亡。
4. 奇妙聖經神言語，是我真理寶藏庫。阿門

1 Mine to tell me whence I came; Mine to teach me which I am;
2 *Mine thou art to guide and guard; Mine to pun - ish or re - ward;*
3 Mine to show, by liv - ing faith, Man can tri - umph o - ver death;
4 *O thou ho - ly book di - vine, Pre - cious trea - sure, thou art mine.* A-men.

31

流淚撒種
They That Sow in Tears

Gloria Gaither
William J. Gaither

They that sow in tears shall reap in joy. — Psalm 126:5

THEY THAT SOW IN TEARS
William J. Gaither

1 雖有時你祈禱似乎都無效，你的
2 雖有時心絕望天色似茫茫，你是
3 禱告時你曾否心中有懷疑？這世
1 Though it seems that your prayers have been in vain, Though your
2 Though the mists of de-spair cloud the sky a-bove, Do you
3 Does your heart fill with doubt when a-lone you pray? Does the
1 信心幾乎被毀掉，你的心極憂傷，似乎
2 否仍不住在祈禱？你是否知道主在寶
3 界是否令你煩惱？當舉目仰望主，祂就
1 faith the world would de-stroy, Though your heart should ache 'til it
2 pray 'til His face ap-pears? In your heart do you know that you've
3 world your soul an-noy? Lift your sights! Look be-yond! God is
1 已破碎，但流淚撒種，必歡呼收割。
2 座施恩？流淚撒種的，必歡呼收割。
3 在身旁，流淚撒種的，必歡呼收割。
1 breaks in two, They that sow in tears shall reap in joy.
2 touched the throne? They shall reap in joy who sow in tears.
3 stand-ing near! They that sow in tears shall reap in joy.
流淚撒種必歡呼收割，因神仍
They that sow in tears shall reap in joy, For God is

坐 寶 座， 你的 心 似破 碎—因不
on His throne, Though you've prayed 'til it seems that your
停 祈 禱，但流淚 撒種，必 歡呼 收割！
heart would break, They that sow in tears shall reap in joy!

試煉

忍受痛苦與折磨，是成功者的座右銘。

艱苦可以磨鍊志，貧困可以證驗節操。

危身奉上曰忠，艱危莫奪曰節。

如果大地千篇一律，沒有高山大海，沒有狹谷深淵，那樣的世界是多麼單調。

如果一年沒有春夏秋冬，沒有風霜雨雪，那樣的日子是多麼無味平凡。

人生一如大地起伏不平，一如天氣變化無常，人的價值常在痛苦與不幸中。

顯出：「時窮節乃見」，「歲寒知松柏」。

不嘗艱苦，那知喜悅的味道？

32

靠近神的懷中

Near to the Heart of God

Draw nigh to God and He will draw nigh to you. — James 4:8

Cleland B. McAfee

McAFEE
Cleland B. McAfee

1. 有一安息恬靜之處，靠近神的懷中；
2. 有一安慰溫暖之處，靠近神的懷中；
3. 有一完全釋放之處，靠近神的懷中；
1 There is a place of qui - et rest, Near to the heart of God;
2 There is a place of com-fort sweet, Near to the heart of God;
3 There is a place of full re - lease, Near to the heart of God;
1. 罪惡不能侵擾之處，靠近神的懷中。
2. 我們與主相會之處，靠近神的懷中。
3. 平安喜樂充滿之處，靠近神的懷中。
1 A place where sin can - not mo-lest, Near to the heart of God.
2 A place where we our Sav - ior meet, Near to the heart of God.
3 A place where all is joy and peace, Near to the heart of God.
慈愛的救主耶穌，降世自父懷中，
O Je - sus, blest Re - deem - er, Sent from the heart of God,
求主使我蒙保守，靠近神的懷中。
Hold us, who wait be - fore Thee, Near to the heart of God.

無一朋友像主耶穌
No One Understands Like Jesus

ARIZONA

. . . But He knoweth the way that I take. — Job 23:10

John W. Peterson　　John W. Peterson

1. 無一朋友像主耶穌，祂比衆友更可靠；
2. 無一朋友像主耶穌，你有痛苦祂同情；
3. 無一朋友像主耶穌，若遇到敵人攻擊；
4. 無一朋友像主耶穌，一生道路祂引領；
1 No one un-der-stands like Je - sus, He's a friend be-yond com-pare;
2 No one un-der-stands like Je - sus, Ev - ery woe He sees and feels;
3 No one un-der-stands like Je - sus, When the foes of life as - sail;
4 No one un-der-stands like Je - sus, When you fal - ter on the way,
1. 快來到主施恩座前，祂正在向你呼召。
2. 祂用慈愛溫柔話語，安慰醫治破碎心。
3. 你切莫要失去勇氣，主必保佑你到底。
4. 我們縱然向祂失信，主有憐憫赦罪恩。
1 Meet Him at the throne of mer - cy, He is wait - ing for you there.
2 Ten-der - ly He whis-pers com-fort, And the bro-ken heart He heals.
3 You should nev-er be dis - cour-aged, Je - sus cares and will not fail.
4 Tho you fail Him, sad - ly fail Him, He will par-don you to - day.
無一朋友像主耶穌，當你有艱難困苦；
No-one un-der-stands like Je - sus, When the days are dark and grim;
無人如此可靠，像主耶穌，事事都有祂看顧。
No one is so near, so dear as Je - sus— Cast your ev - ery care on Him.

34

要告訴耶穌
I Must Tell Jesus

. . . by prayer . . . with thanksgiving let your requests be made known unto God.
— Philippians 4:6

Elisha A. Hoffman

ORWIGSBURG
Elisha A. Hoffman

1. 我一切苦楚，要告訴耶穌，我不能獨自
2. 我一切難處，要告訴耶穌，祂是我良友
3. 當試探來臨，我需要救主，祂能幫助我
4. 黑暗的世界，罪惡極深重，我心靈脆弱
1 I must tell Je - sus all of my tri - als, I can - not bear these
2 I must tell Je - sus all of my trou - bles, He is a kind, com -
3 Tempt - ed and tried, I need a great Sav - ior, One who can help my
4 O how the world of e - vil al - lures me! O how my heart is
1. 担當重負；我在患難中主親手攙扶，
2. 慈愛溫柔；我若向祂求祂必定拯救，
3. 担當重負；我要告訴主要告訴耶穌，
4. 不能勝過！我要告訴主祂能幫助我，
1 bur - dens a - lone; In my dis - tress He kind - ly will help me,
2 pas - sion - ate friend; If I but ask Him, He will de - liv - er,
3 bur - dens to bear; I must tell Je - sus, I must tell Je - sus,
4 tempt - ed to sin! I must tell Je - sus, and He will help me
1. 屬主的兒女主常看顧。
2. 主解決難處主解我憂。
3. 惟有主耶穌看顧保護。
4. 得勝世上的一切惡魔。
要告訴耶穌
1 He al - ways loves and cares for His own.
2 Make of my trou - bles quick - ly an end.
3 He all my cares and sor - rows will share.
4 O - ver the world the vic - tory to win.
I must tell Je - sus!

要告訴耶穌！我不能 獨自担當重負；要告訴
I must tell Je-sus! I can-not bear my bur-dens a-lone; I must tell
耶穌！要告訴耶穌！惟有主耶穌，祂能幫助 。
Je-sus! I must tell Je-sus! Je-sus can help me, Je-sus a-lone.

耶和華阿，我從深處向你求告。

主阿，求你聽我的聲音，願你側耳聽我懇求的聲音。

主耶和華阿，你若究察罪孽，誰能站得住呢？

但在你有赦免之恩，要叫人敬畏你。

我等候耶和華，我的心等候，我也仰望祂的話。

詩篇一百三十篇
1 — 5

Out of the depths I cry to you O Lord;
  O Lord, hear my voice.
Let your ears be attentive
  to my cry for mercy.

If you, O Lord, kept a record of sins,
  O Lord, who could stand?
But with you there is forgiveness;
  therefore you are feared.

I wait for the Lord, my soul waits,
  and in his word I put my hope.

— Pslam 130:1-5. NIV

35

只要相信
Only Believe

It is Thy Father's good pleasure to give you the kingdom.
— Luke 12:32

Paul Rader

ONLY BELIEVE
Paul Rader

1 群羊不要怕，牧者已復活，祂曾釘十
2 群羊不要怕，牧者引你路，你當跟從
3 群羊不要怕，不論是禍與福，縱使門已
1 Fear not, lit-tle flock, from the cross to the throne, From death in-to
2 Fear not, lit-tle flock, He go-eth a-head, Your Shep-herd se-
3 Fear not, lit-tle flock, what-ev-er your lot; He en-ters all

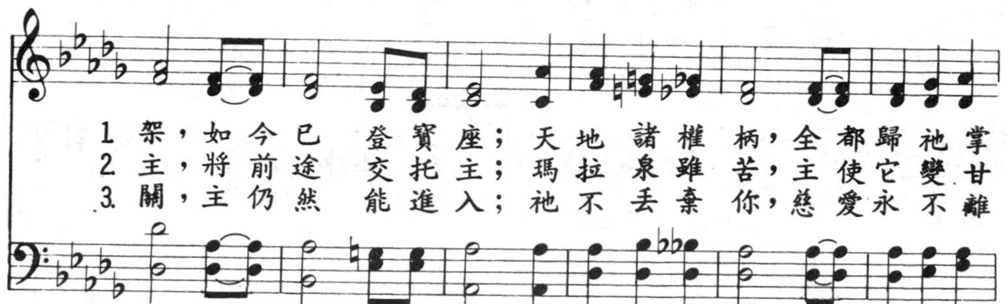
1 架，如今已登寶座；天地諸權柄，全都歸祂掌
2 主，将前途交托主；瑪拉泉雖苦，主使它變甘
3 關，主仍然能進入；祂不丟棄你，慈愛永不離
1 life He went for His own; All pow-er in earth, all pow-er a-
2 lect-eth the path you must tread; The wa-ters of Ma-rah He'll sweeten for
3 rooms, "the doors be-ing shut." He nev-er for-sakes, He nev-er is

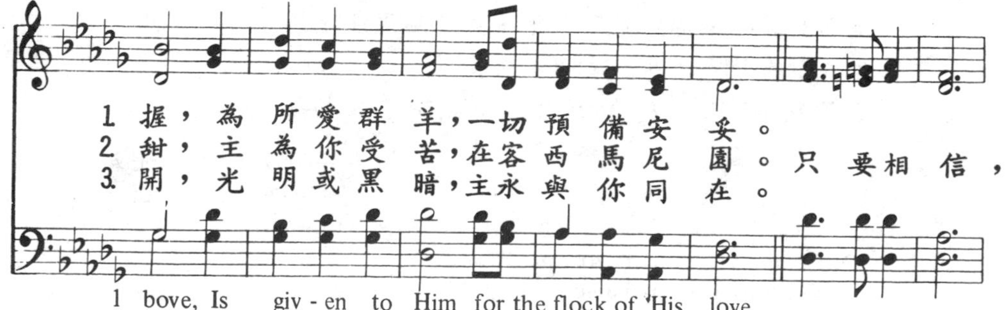
1 握，為所愛群羊，一切預備安妥。
2 甜，主為你受苦，在客西馬尼園。只要相信，
3 開，光明或黑暗，主永與你同在。
1 bove, Is giv-en to Him for the flock of His love.
2 thee—He drank all the bit-ter in Geth-sem-a-ne. On-ly be-lieve,
3 gone—So count on His pres-ence in dark-ness and dawn.

只要相信；凡事必能成就，只要相信；
on-ly be-lieve; All things are pos-si-ble, on-ly be-lieve;

只要相信，只要相信；凡事必能成就，只要相信
On - ly be - lieve, on - ly be - lieve; All things are pos-si-ble, on -ly be-lieve.

讚美三一真神 36

Praise Ye the Triune God

. . . The Father, the Word, and the Holy Spirit, and these three are one.
I John 5:8

FLEMMING

Elizabeth Rundle Charles

Friedrich F. Flemming

1. 讚美我天父，祂有豐富慈愛，何等溫
2. 讚美我救主，滿有慈悲憐憫，何等親
3. 讚美神聖靈，以色列安慰者，被父子

1 Praise ye the Fa - ther for His lov-ing - kind - ness; Ten - der - ly
2 *Praise ye the Sav - ior— great is His com - pas - sion; Gra - cious - ly*
3 Praise ye the Spir - it, Com - fort - er of Is - rael, Sent of the

1. 柔的看顧祂的兒女，天上衆天使，
2. 切的愛那被揀選者，不分男和女，
3. 所差為要賜福我們，讚美我天父，

1 cares He for His err - ing chil - dren; Praise Him, ye an - gels,
2 *cares He for His cho - sen peo - ple; Young men and maid - ens,*
3 Fa - ther and the Son to bless us; Praise ye the Fa - ther,

1. 一齊高聲讚美，讚美耶和華神！
2. 也不分老和幼，讚美救主耶穌！
3. 讚美聖子，聖靈，讚美三一真神！阿們
1 praise Him in the heav - ens, Praise ye Je - ho - vah!
2 *old - er folks and chil - dren, Praise ye the Sav - ior!*
3 Son, and Ho - ly Spir - it, Praise ye the Tri - une God! A - men.

37

我靈鎮靜
Be Still My Soul

Katharina von Schlegel
Tr. by Jane L. Borthwick

Be still and know that I am God. — Psalm 46:10

FINLANDIA
Jean Sibelius

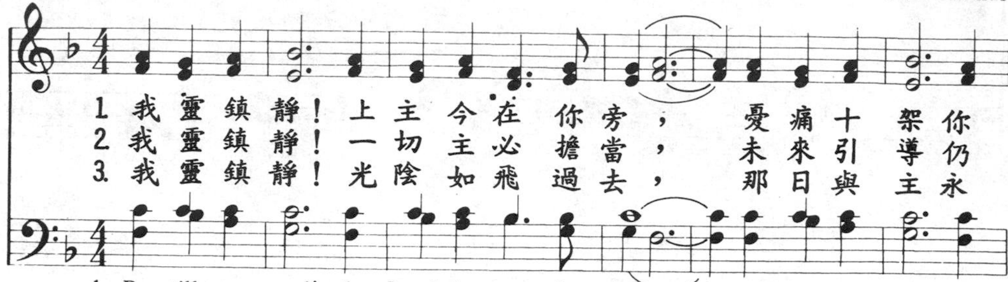

1 我靈鎮靜！上主今在你旁， 憂痛十架你
2 我靈鎮靜！一切主必擔當， 未來引導仍
3 我靈鎮靜！光陰如飛過去， 那日與主永
1 Be still, my soul! the Lord is on thy side; Bear pa - tient - ly the
2 Be still, my soul! thy God doth un - der - take To guide the fu - ture
3 Be still, my soul! the hour is has - tening on When we shall be for -

1 要忍耐擔當； 信靠天父為你安排主張，
2 似過去一樣； 莫讓何事動搖希望信仰，
3 遠同在一處； 失望驚慌那日都要消除，
1 cross of grief or pain; Leave to thy God to or - der and pro - vide;
2 as He has the past. Thy hope, thy con - fi - dence let noth - ing shake;
3 ev - er with the Lord, When dis - ap - point - ment, grief, and fear are gone,

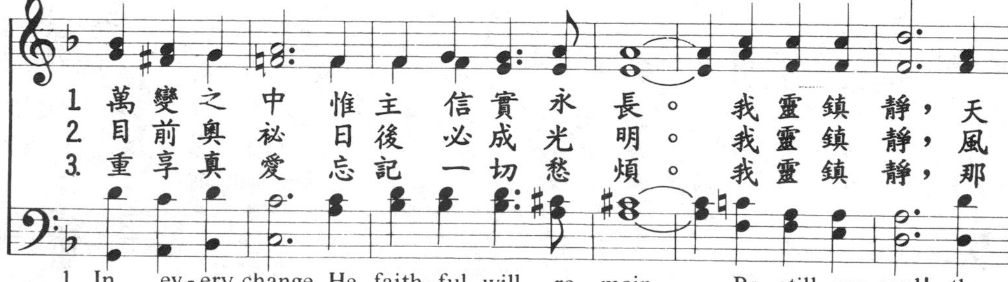

1 萬變之中惟主信實永長。 我靈鎮靜，天
2 目前奧祕日後必成光明。 我靈鎮靜，風
3 重享真愛忘記一切愁煩。 我靈鎮靜，那
1 In ev - ery change He faith - ful will re - main. Be still, my soul! thy
2 All now mys - te - rious shall be bright at last. Be still, my soul! the
3 Sor - row for - got, love's pur - est joys re - stored. Be still, my soul! when

1 友最是善良， 經過荊棘引到歡樂地方。
2 浪依舊聽命， 救主當年所發吩咐之聲。
3 日眼淚抹乾， 將來歡聚大家永享平安。
1 best, thy heaven - ly Friend Through thorny ways leads to a joy - ful end.
2 waves and winds still know His voice who ruled them while He dwelt be - low.
3 change and tears are past, All safe and bless - ed we shall meet at last.

生命之道

Wonderful Words of Life

WORDS OF LIFE
Philip P. Bliss

Philip P. Bliss, alt.

Lord, to whom shall we go? Thou hath the words of eternal life. — John 6:68

1.請再為我歌唱傳講，奇妙生命之道；
2.基督耶穌為人捨命，奇妙生命之道；
3.快將福音傳給世人，奇妙生命之道；

1 Sing them o-ver a-gain to me, Won-der-ful words of life;
2 *Christ, the bless-ed One, gives to all Won-der-ful words of life;*
3 Sweet-ly ech-o the gos-pel call, Won-der-ful words of life;

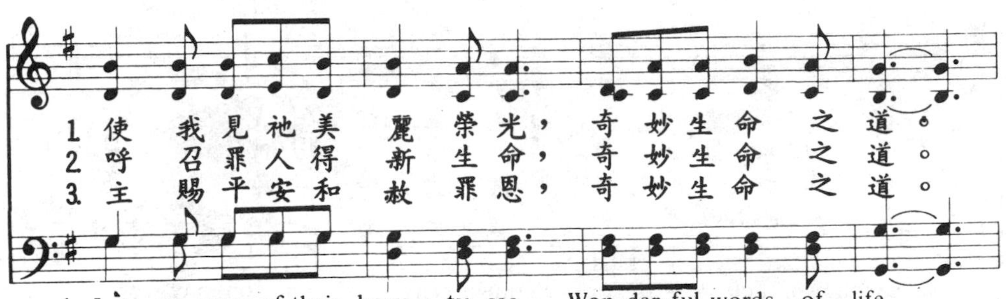
1.使我見祂美麗榮光，奇妙生命之道。
2.呼召罪人得新生命，奇妙生命之道。
3.主賜平安和赦罪恩，奇妙生命之道。

1 Let me more of their beau-ty see, Won-der-ful words of life.
2 *Lis-ten well to the lov-ing call, Won-der-ful words of life.*
3 Of-fer par-don and peace to all, Won-der-ful words of life.

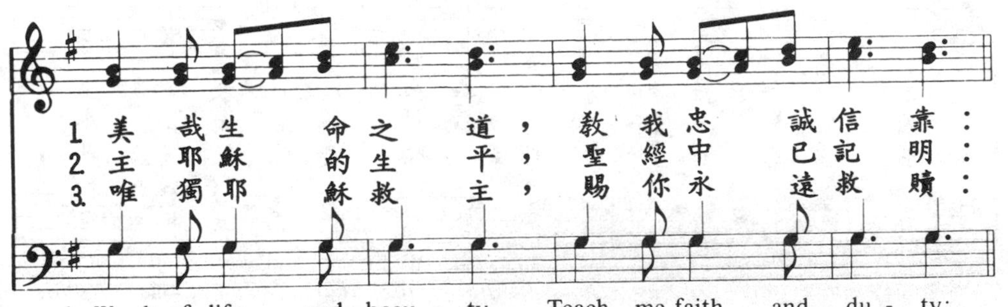
1.美哉生命之道，教我忠誠信靠：
2.主耶穌的生平，聖經中已記明：
3.唯獨耶穌救主，賜你永遠救贖：

1 Words of life and beau-ty, Teach me faith and du-ty:
2 *All the won-drous sto-ry, Show-ing us His glo-ry:*
3 Je-sus, on-ly Sav-ior, Sanc-ti-fy for-ev-er:

1
2
美哉主道，奇哉主道，生命之道奇妙。妙。
Beau-ti-ful words, won-der-ful words, Won-der-ful words of Life. Life.

39 我聽耶穌柔聲説

I Heard the Voice of Jesus Say

Come unto Me all ye who labor and are heavy laden and I will give you rest. — Matthew 11:28
Horatius Bonar
VOX DILECTI
John B. Dykes
1. 我 聽 耶 穌 柔 聲 的 説，“來 就 我 得 安 息；
2. 我 聽 耶 穌 柔 聲 的 説，“我 有 生 命 活 泉；
3. 我 聽 耶 穌 柔 聲 的 説，“我 是 暗 世 之 光；
1 I heard the voice of Je - sus say, “Come un - to me and rest;
2 I heard the voice of Je - sus say, “Be - hold, I free - ly give
3 I heard the voice of Je - sus say, “I am this dark world’s light;
1. 身 心 疲 倦 困 乏 的 人，靠 首 在 我 懷 裡。”
2. 乾 渴 切 慕 滋 潤 的 人，我 必 賜 祂 活 泉。”
3. 來 就 我 的 得 見 晨 光，全 路 程 必 照 亮。”
1 Lay down, thou wea-ry one, lay down Thy head up - on my breast.”
2 The liv - ing wa - ter—thirst - y one, Stoop down, and drink, and live.”
3 Look un - to me—thy morn shall rise, And all thy day be bright.”
1. 我 本 勞 苦 疲 倦 憂 愁，我 既 前 來 歸 主；
2. 我 心 乾 渴 來 就 耶 穌，祂 賜 生 命 活 水；
3. 我 舉 目 仰 望 主 耶 穌，祂 是 晨 星 朝 陽；
1 I came to Je - sus as I was, Wea - ry, and worn, and sad;
2 I came to Je - sus, and I drank Of that life - giv - ing stream;
3 I looked to Je - sus, and I found In Him my star, my sun;
1. 在 主 懷 裡 我 得 安 息 祂 使 我 心 歡 欣。
2. 心 得 滋 潤 靈 得 甦 醒 我 今 靠 主 而 活。
3. 在 祂 光 中 欣 然 前 往 行 完 在 世 路 程。
1 I found in Him a rest - ing place, And He has made me glad.
2 My thirst was quenched, my soul re - vived, And now I live in Him.
3 And in that light of life I’ll walk, ’Til trav - eling days are done.

基列的乳香
There Is a Balm in Gilead

Go up to Gilead and take balm . . . . — Jeremiah 46:11

BALM IN GILEAD
Traditional Spiritual
Jeremiah 8:22
在基列地有乳香，能醫治人創傷；
There is a balm in Gil - e - ad to make the wound-ed whole;
Fine
在基列地有乳香能醫罪人的心。
There is a balm in Gil - e - ad to heal the sin - sick soul.
1. 有時我真覺失望，為主作工落空，
2. 雖不像彼得保羅，會講道能禱告，
1 Some - times I feel dis - cour - aged, And think my work's in vain,
2 If you can't preach like Pe - ter, If you can't pray like Paul,
D.C. al Fine
1. 那時慈悲的聖靈，再復興我心靈。
2. 但你可傳講耶穌，為愛世人受死。
1 But then the Ho - ly Spir - it Re - vives my soul a - gain.
2 Just tell the love of Je - sus, And say He died for all.

41

将你的重擔卸給主

Cast Thy Burden upon the Lord

Cast thy burden upon the Lord . . . . — Psalm 55:22
CAST THY BURDEN
From *Elijah*
Felix Mendelssohn
Based on Psalm 55:22
将 你 的 重 担 都 卸 給 主， 祂 必 定 撫
Cast thy bur - den up - on the Lord, and He shall sus -
養 你，他 必 保 守 你 使 你 永 不 動 摇，
tain thee; He nev - er will suf - fer the right-eous to fall:
祂 常 在 你 右 邊。我 主 慈 愛 無
He is at thy right hand. Thy mer - cy, Lord, is
邊， 深 遠 超 過 諸 天， 在 祢 面 前 等
great and far a - bove the heav'ns: Let none be made a -
候 的， 必 永 不 蒙 羞。
sham - ed that wait up - on Thee. A-men.

我賜你平安

Peace I Leave with You

42

Thou wilt keep him in perfect peace whose mind is stayed on Thee.
Isaiah 26:3

Richard Maxwell

PEACE I GIVE
William Wirges

1. 我賜你平安，將我的平安給你。這平安不像世人所賜的，
2. 我賜你平安，將我的平安給你。你們若愛我當遵守誡命，
1 Peace I leave with you; My peace I give un-to you. Not as the world giv-eth, give I un-to you;
2 Peace I leave with you; My peace I give un-to you. Keep my com-mand-ments if you love me;
1. 這平安不像世人所賜的，你們心裡不要憂愁，也不要膽怯，我賜你平安；將我的平安給你。
2. 你們若愛我，當遵守誡命，我必不撇下你們，我必要再來，我賜你平安；將我的平安給你。
1 Not as the world giv-eth, give I un-to you. Let not your heart be trou-bled; Nei-ther let it be a-fraid. Peace I leave with you; My peace I give un-to you.
2 Keep my com-mand-ments, if you love Me. For I will not leave you com-fort-less; I will come un-to you. Peace I leave with you; My peace I give un-to you.
阿們。
A-men.

43

安穩港口
The Haven of Rest

I will put thee in a cleft of the rock, and I will cover thee with my hand. — Exodus 33:22

H. L. Gilmour
GOOD SHIP
George D. Moore
1. 我靈曾漂蕩在人生大海中，罪惡重擔使我痛苦，但聞救主慈聲說道："來就近我，"我便進入安穩的港口。
2. 我將自己完全投入祂懷裡，以信心緊握祂應許，我的罪鏈得脱我靈如錨抛牢，在主安穩港口無所懼。
3. 我靈要歌唱因救主醫治我，何等蒙福救恩故事，誰願得救來就耶穌必蒙引領，安穩港口天家享安息。
1 My soul, in sad exile, was out on life's sea. So burdened with sin and distressed, 'Til I heard a sweet voice saying, "Make me your choice," And I entered the haven of rest.
2 I yielded myself to His tender embrace, And, faith taking hold of the Word, My fetters fell off, and I anchored my soul, The haven of rest is my Lord.
3 The song of my soul, since the Lord made me whole, Has been the old story so blest Of Jesus, who'll save whosoever will have A home in the haven of rest.
我將我靈魂抛錨安穩港口，不再自己隨處漂流；雖有風暴
I've anchored my soul in the haven of rest, I'll sail the wide seas no more; The tempest may

攻擊，我已有所靠，安穩在主裡到永久。
sweep o'er the wild, storm-y deep, In Je-sus I'm safe ev-er-more.

生命路程 44

Where Cross the Crowded Ways of Life

And unto you which believe He is precious. . . . — I Peter 2:7

GERMANY
William Gardiner's *Sacred Melodies*

Frank M. North

1. 生命路程分岐之處，種族階級爭鬧紛紛，
2. 困苦艱難常臨之處，黑暗墮落驚恐之中，
3. 奉主之名杯水濟人，主的恩惠依舊清新；
4. 主啊求祢儘快下山，醫治衆人破碎心懷，
5. 直到世人瞭解主愛，跟隨我主脚踪前行，

1 Where cross the crowd-ed ways of life, Where sound the cries of race and clan,
2 *In haunts of wretch-ed-ness and need, On shad-owed thresh-olds dark with fears,*
3 The cup of wa-ter given for Thee Still holds the fresh-ness of Thy grace;
4 *O Mas-ter, from the moun-tain side, Make haste to heal these hearts of pain,*
5 'Til sons of men shall learn Thy love And fol-low where Thy feet have trod:

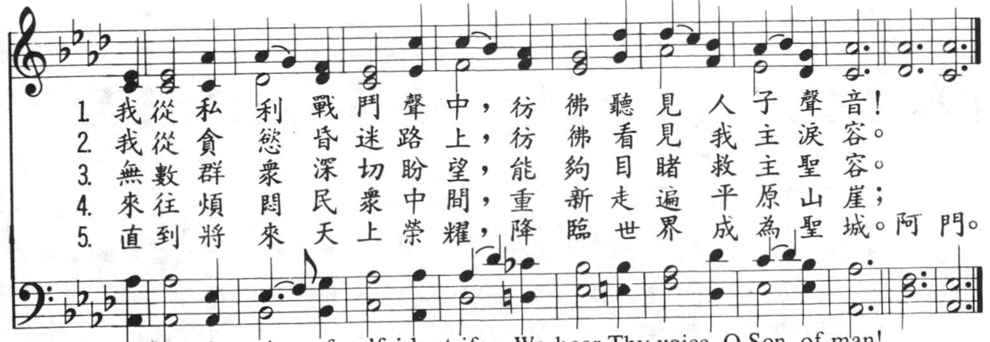

1. 我從私利戰鬥聲中，彷彿聽見人子聲音！
2. 我從貪慾昏迷路上，彷彿看見我主淚容。
3. 無數群衆深切盼望，能夠目睹救主聖容。
4. 來往煩悶民衆中間，重新走遍平原山崖；
5. 直到將來天上榮耀，降臨世界成為聖城。阿門。

1 A-bove the noise of self-ish strife, We hear Thy voice, O Son of man!
2 *From paths where hide the lures of greed, We catch the vi-sion of Thy tears.*
3 Yet long these mul-ti-tudes to see The sweet com-pas-sion of Thy face.
4 *A-mong these rest-less throngs a-bide, O tread the cit-y's streets a-gain;*
5 'Til glo-rious from Thy heaven a-bove Shall come the cit-y of our God. A-men.

45 重擔皆脱下在各各他
Burdens Are Lifted at Calvary

For when we were yet without strength Christ died for the ungodly. — Romans 5:6

John M. Moore
BURDENS LIFTED
John M. Moore
Slowly
1. 日 日 充 滿 憂 傷 掛 慮，心 裡 寂 寞 苦 悶；
2. 你 掛 慮 速 交 托 耶 穌，放 下 懼 怕 憂 情；
3. 困 苦 者 你 憂 傷 眼 淚，救 主 已 經 看 見；
1 Days are filled with sor-row and care, Hearts are lone-ly and drear;
2 Cast your care on Je-sus to-day, Leave your wor-ry and fear;
3 Trou-bled soul, the Sav-ior can see Ev - ery heart-ache and tear;
1. 重 擔 皆 脱 下 在 各 各 他，耶 穌 何 等 親 近。
2. 重 擔 皆 脱 下 在 各 各 他，耶 穌 何 等 親 近。
3. 重 擔 皆 脱 下 在 各 各 他，耶 穌 何 等 親 近。
1 Bur-dens are lift-ed at Cal-va-ry, Je-sus is ver-ry near.
2 Bur-dens are lift-ed at Cal-va-ry, Je-sus is ver-ry near.
3 Bur-dens are lift-ed at Cal-va-ry, Je-sus is ver-ry near.
重 擔 皆 脱 下 在 各 各 他，各 各 他，各 各 他；
Bur-dens are lift-ed at Cal-va-ry, Cal-va-ry, Cal-va-ry;
重 擔 皆 脱 下 在 各 各 他，耶 穌 何 等 親 近。
Bur-dens are lift-ed at Cal-va-ry, Je-sus is ver-y near.

天父必看顧你
God Will Take Care of You

. . . I will never leave thee or forsake thee. — Hebrews 13:5

GOD CARES
Civilla D. Martin, alt. W. Stillman Martin

1. 任遭何事不要驚怕，天父必看顧你；
2. 有時勞苦心中失望，天父必看顧你；
3. 你雖缺乏祂是豐富，天父必看顧你；
4. 無論遇見何等試煉，天父必看顧你；
1 Be not dis-mayed what-e'er be-tide, God will take care of you;
2 Through days of toil when your heart doth fail, God will take care of you;
3 All you may need He will pro-vide, God will take care of you;
4 No mat-ter what may be the test, God will take care of you;
1. 必将你藏祂恩翅下，天父必看顧你。
2. 危險臨到無處躲藏，天父必看顧你。
3. 你受試煉祂必開路，天父必看顧你。
4. 軟弱困倦靠祂胸前，天父必看顧你。
1 Be-neath His wings of love a-bide, God will take care of you.
2 When dan-gers fierce your path as-sail, God will take care of you.
3 Noth-ing you ask will be de-nied, God will take care of you.
4 Lean, wea-ry one, up-on His breast, God will take care of you.
天父必看顧你，時時看顧，處處看顧；
God will take care of you, Through ev-ery day, o'er all the way;
祂必要看顧你，天父必看顧你。
He will take care of you, God will take care of you.

47 耶穌是否仍然看顧？

Does Jesus Care?

He hath sent me to heal the brokenhearted; — Isaiah 61:1

Frank E. Graeff

J. Lincoln Hall

1. 耶 穌 是 否 仍 然 看 顧 我 ？當 我 心 中 充
2. 耶 穌 是 否 仍 然 看 顧 我 ？有 時 黑 雲 滿
3. 耶 穌 是 否 仍 然 看 顧 我 ？當 我 難 勝 試
4. 耶 穌 是 否 仍 然 看 顧 我 ？當 親 人 將 離
1. Does Je - sus care when my heart is pained Too deep - ly for
2. Does Je - sus care when my way is dark With a name - less
3. Does Je - sus care when I've tried and failed To re - sist some temp-
4. Does Je - sus care when I've said good-bye To the dear - est on
1. 滿 痛 苦 — 前 途 滿 荊 棘，魔 鬼 來 攻 擊，
2. 天 密 佈， 當 我 心 驚 恐，充 滿 了 苦 衷，
3. 探 來 臨， 我 心 極 憂 傷，痛 苦 難 承 當，
4. 我 而 去， 我 心 似 已 碎，安 慰 去 找 誰？
1. mirth and song— As the bur - dens press, and the cares dis - tress,
2. dread and fear? As the day - light fades in - to deep night shades,
3. ta - tion strong? When for my deep grief I find no re - lief,
4. earth to me, And my sad heart aches till it near - ly breaks—
1. 主 耶 穌 是 否 仍 看 顧 ？
2. 主 耶 穌 是 否 仍 看 顧 ？
3. 當 黑 夜 我 淚 流 滿 襟 ！
4. 憂 傷 心 誰 使 它 痊 癒 ？
祂 必 看 顧，祂
O yes, He cares— I
1. And the way grows wea - ry and long?
2. Does He care e - nough to be near?
3. Tho my tears flow all the night long?
4. Is It aught to Him? does He see?

必 看顧！因 祂 同情我痛 苦； 白晝
know He cares! His heart is touched with my grief; When the
雖 有痛苦，黑 夜覺凄楚，但 救主必看顧。
days are wea-ry, the long nights drear-y, I know my Sav - ior cares.

47–1 Plans While in Prison

"The most important part of our task will be to tell everyone who will listen that Jesus is the only answer to the problems that are disturbing the hearts of men and nations. We shall have the right to speak because we can tell from our experience that His light is more powerful than the deepest darkness. . . How wonderful that the reality of His presence is greater than the reality of the hell about us."

–Betsie ten Boom, to her sister, Corrie

48

每時每刻
Moment by Moment

But the Lord is faithful, who shall stablish you and keep you . . . .
— II Thessalonians 3:3

Daniel W. Whittle

WHITTLE
May W. Moody

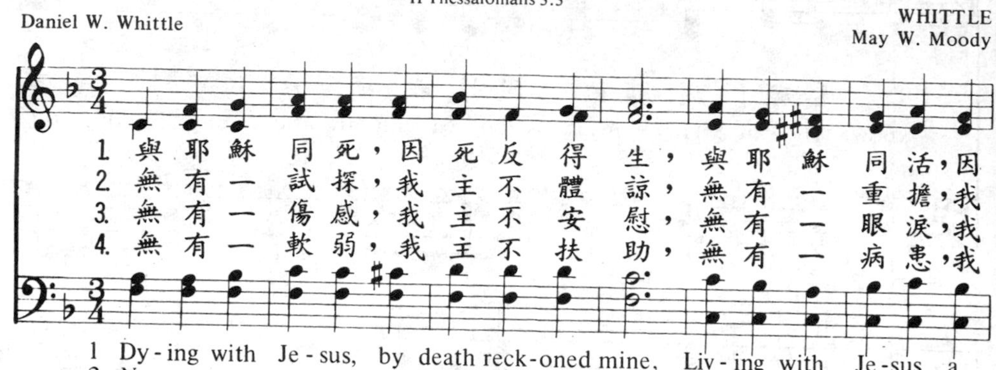

1. 與耶穌同死，因死反得生，與耶穌同活，因
2. 無有一試探，我主不體諒，無有一重擔，我
3. 無有一傷感，我主不安慰，無有一眼淚，我
4. 無有一軟弱，我主不扶助，無有一病患，我
1 Dy-ing with Je-sus, by death reck-oned mine, Liv-ing with Je-sus a
2 Nev-er a tri-al that He is not there, Nev-er a bur-den that
3 Nev-er a heart-ache and nev-er a groan, Nev-er a tear-drop and
4 Nev-er a weak-ness that He doth not feel, Nev-er a sick-ness that

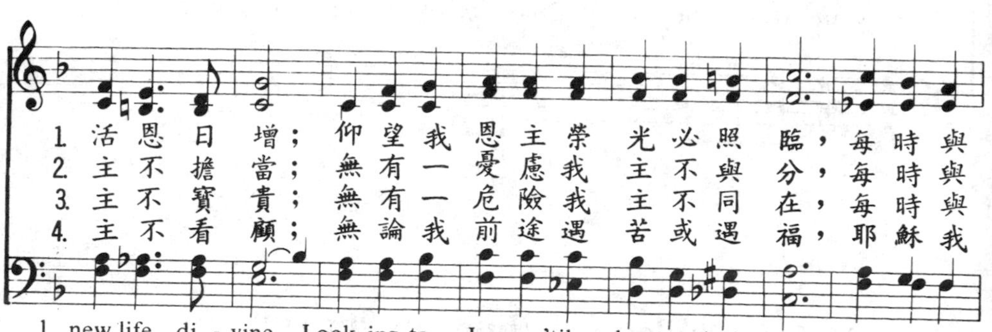

1. 活恩日增；仰望我恩主榮光必照臨，每時與
2. 主不擔當；無有一憂慮我主不與分，每時與
3. 主不寶貴；無有一危險我主不同在，每時與
4. 主不看顧；無論我前途遇苦或遇福，耶穌我
1 new life di-vine, Look-ing to Je-sus 'til glo-ry doth shine,—Mo-ment by
2 He doth not bear, Nev-er a sor-row that He doth not share,—Mo-ment by
3 nev-er a moan; Nev-er a dan-ger, but there on the throne, Mo-ment by
4 He can-not heal; Mo-ment by mo-ment, in woe or in weal, Je-sus, my

1. 每刻，我蒙主鴻恩。
2. 每刻，我蒙主鴻恩。
3. 每刻，我得主恩愛。
4. 救主，必時常保護。
每時每刻我蒙主之保佑，
Mo-ment by mo-ment I'm kept in His love,
1 mo-ment, O Lord, I am Thine.
2 mo-ment, I'm un-der His care.
3 mo-ment, He thinks of His own.
4 Sav-ior, a-bides with me still.

每時每刻我因主能得救；仰望主耶穌榮
Mo-ment by mo-ment I've life from a - bove; Look-ing to Je - sus 'til
光必照臨，每時與每刻，我為主子民。
glo - ry doth shine, Mo-ment by mo-ment, O Lord, I am Thine.

靜默

你最完美的思想發生在清靜單獨和默想的時候。

當你舒暢和深思之時，你給你最內在的力量一種最好的顯現機會。

不斷的行動和發表等於直接支用你的精神存款。

若欲繼續增加和積蓄有益的思想，你應該常有精神舒暢、專心和靜默的機會。謹防匆忙和浪費的現代趨勢。

你為了沉靜和智慧的默想而所費的時間一定能得到相當的酬報。

培養沉靜、心理的平衡和從容。

在內心沉靜的時間，你最能聽到神的聲音，並且知道神的旨意。

在那個時間你最容易感覺神靈的存在和祂的力量。

49

我只要信靠我主
I Just Keep Trusting My Lord

John W. Peterson . . . *And on Mine arm shall they trust.* — Isaiah 51:5 John W. Peterson

1. 我只要信靠我主，走生命道路，
2. 我只要信靠我主，走人生窄路，
1. I just keep trust-ing my Lord as I walk a - long,
2. I just keep trust - ing my Lord on the nar - row way,
1. 我只要信靠我主，一生歌頌主；
2. 我只要信靠我主，祂引領前途；
1. I just keep trust - ing my Lord and He gives a song;
2. I just keep trust - ing my Lord as He leads each day;
1 雖有風暴幽暗天空，遮掩我前路，
2 雖然有時疲倦困苦，滿心是憂愁，
(D.S.) Tho the storm-clouds dark-en the sky o'er the heav'n-ly trail,
(D.S.) Tho the road is wea-ry at times and I'm sad and blue,
Fine
1 我只要信靠我主—祂必定幫助！
2 我只要信靠我主—祂與我同走！
1. I just keep trust-ing my Lord— He will nev - er fail!
2. I just keep trust - ing my Lord— He will see me through!

1. 祂是我良友，忠實的良友，
2. 祂是我嚮導，忠實的嚮導，
1. He's a faith - ful friend, such a faith - ful friend,
2. He's a faith - ful guide, such a faith - ful guide,
D.S.
1. 我能信靠祂，一直到永久；
2. 常在我身旁，扶持與引導；
1. I can count on Him to the ver - y end;
2. He is al - ways there walk - ing by my side;

Christ Be with Me

I arise today
Through God's strength to pilot me:
God's might to uphold me,
God's wisdom to guide me,
God's eye to look before me,
God's ear to hear me,
God's word to speak for me,
God's hand to guard me,
God's way to lie before me,
God's shield to protect me.

Christ be with me, Christ before me, Christ behind me,
Christ in me, Christ beneath me, Christ above me,
Christ on my right, Christ on my left,
Christ when I lie down, Christ when I sit down, Christ when I arise,
Christ in the heart of every man who thinks of me,
Christ in the mouth of every one who speaks of me,
Christ in every eye that sees me,
Christ in every ear that hears me.

–St. Patrick

50 有福的確據
Blessed Assurance, Jesus Is Mine

. . . . Whereof He hath given assurance unto all men that He hath raised Him from the dead. — Acts 17:31
Fanny J. Crosby
ASSURANCE
Phoebe P. Knapp
1. 有福的確據，耶穌屬我！我今得先嚐主
2. 完全的順服，快樂無比，天堂的榮耀顯
3. 完全的順服，完全安息，何等的歡欣我
1 Bless-ed as-sur-ance, Je-sus is mine! O what a fore-taste of
2 Per-fect sub-mis-sion, per-fect de-light, Vi-sions of rap-ture now
3 Per-fect sub-mis-sion, all is at rest, I in my Sav-ior am
1. 榮耀喜樂！為神的後嗣，救贖功成，
2. 在我心裡；天使帶信息，由天而來，
3. 在基督裡；儆醒而禱告，等主回來，
1 glo-ry di-vine! Heir of sal-va-tion, pur-chase of God,
2 burst on my sight; An-gels de-scend-ing bring from a-bove
3 hap-py and blest; Watch-ing and wait-ing, look-ing a-bove,
1. 由聖靈重生，寶血洗淨。
2. 報明主憐憫，述說主愛。這是我信息，我的詩
3. 滿有主恩賜，暢我心懷。This is my sto-ry, this is my
1 Born of His Spir-it, washed in His blood.
2 Ech-oes of mer-cy, whis-pers of love.
3 Filled with His good-ness, lost in His love.
歌，讚美我救主，晝夜唱和；這是我信息，
song, Prais-ing my Sav-ior all the day long; This is my sto-ry,

我的詩歌，讚美我救主晝夜唱和。
this is my song, Prais - ing my Sav - ior all the day long.

我主耶穌，我依靠祢

I Am Trusting Thee, Lord Jesus

51

Trust in the Lord and do good, so shall thou dwell in the land. . . . and be fed. — Psalm 37:3

BULLINGER

Frances Ridley Havergal

Ethelbert W. Bullinger

1. 我主耶穌我依靠祢—惟獨倚靠祢；
2. 倚靠救主親手領我—惟獨跟從主；
3. 倚靠救主賜我力量—主能力無窮；
4. 我主耶穌我今靠祢—惟獨倚靠祢；
1 I am trust - ing Thee, Lord Je - sus— Trust - ing on - ly Thee;
2 I am trust - ing Thee to guide me— Thou a - lone shalt lead,
3 I am trust - ing Thee for pow - er— Thine can nev - er fail;
4 I am trust - ing Thee, Lord Je - sus— Nev - er let me fall;

1. 靠祢寶血將罪塗抹，全塗抹。
2. 時時刻刻主必賜我所需用。
3. 主所賜我恩惠應許不落空。
4. 倚靠救主直到永遠，到永遠。阿門。
1 Trust - ing Thee for full sal - va - tion, Great and free.
2 Ev - ery day and hour sup - ply - ing All my need.
3 Words which Thou Thy - self shalt give me Must pre - vail.
4 I am trust - ing Thee for - ev - er, And for all. A - men.

52

藏身主裡

Hiding in Thee

For Thou has been a shelter for me, and a strong tower from the enemy.
— Psalm 61:3
William O. Cushing
HIDING IN THEE
Ira D. Sankey
1. 我靈在憂傷痛苦掙扎之時，願
2. 無論在平靜或憂傷孤單時，無
3. 仇敵常侵擾，掙扎中真苦惱，速
1 O safe to the Rock that is high - er than I My
2 In the calm of the noon - tide, in sor - row's lone hour, In
3 How oft - en in con - flict, when pressed by the foe, I have
1. 飛往至高磐石中得安息；我罪雖衆
2. 論受試探或遇敵攻擊時；或遇暴風
3. 奔避難所可以陳述求告；試煉臨近
1 soul in its con - flicts and sor - rows would fly; So sin - ful, so
2 times when temp - ta - tion casts o'er me its power, In the tem - pests of
3 fled to my Ref - uge and breathed out my woe; How oft - en, when
1. 多，但我深願屬祢：祢是“萬古磐石，”我
2. 雨，在海中飄搖時，祢是“萬古磐石，”我
3. 身，好像海中風濤，藏身在磐石裡，我
1 wea - ry—Thine, Thine would I be: Thou blest “Rock of A - ges,” I'm
2 life, on its wide, heav - ing sea, Thou blest “Rock of A - ges,” I'm
3 tri - als like sea - bil - lows roll, Have I hid - den in Thee, O Thou
1. 藏身主裡。
2. 藏身主裡。
3. 靈得安逸。
藏身主裡，藏身主
Hid - ing in Thee, Hid - ing in
1 hid - ing in Thee.
2 hid - ing in Thee.
3 Rock of my soul.

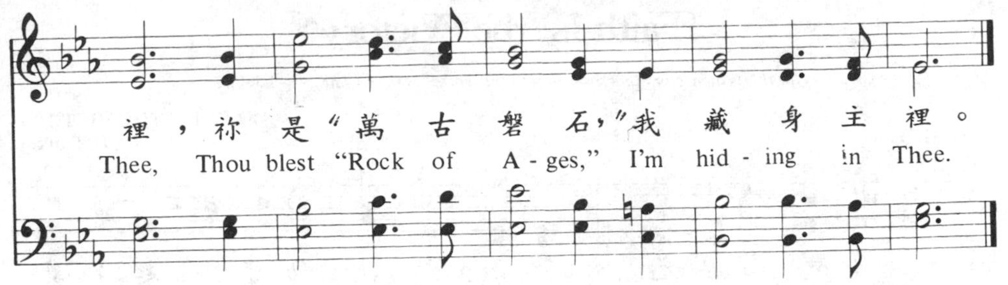
裡，祢是"萬古磐石，"我藏身主裡。
Thee, Thou blest "Rock of A - ges," I'm hid - ing in Thee.

53

主是我牧者，我必不缺乏

The Lord's My Shepherd, I'll Not Want

He shall feed His flock like a shepherd. Isaiah 40:11

Based on Psalm 23
Scottish Psalter

CRIMOND
Jessie S. Irvine

(FIRST TUNE)

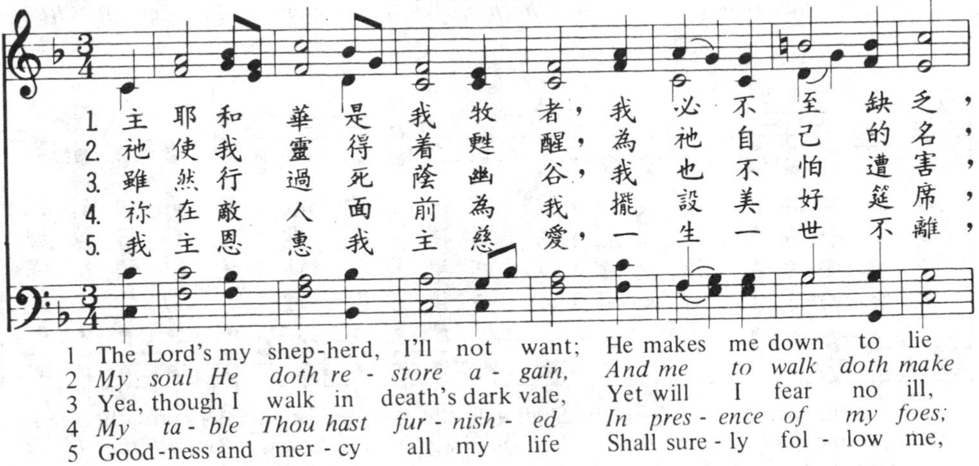

1. 主耶和華是我牧者，我必不至缺乏，
2. 祂使我靈得着甦醒，為祂自己的名，
3. 雖然行過死蔭幽谷，我也不怕遭害，
4. 祢在敵人面前為我擺設美好筵席，
5. 我主恩惠我主慈愛，一生一世不離，

1 The Lord's my shep-herd, I'll not want; He makes me down to lie
2 *My soul He doth re - store a - gain, And me to walk doth make*
3 Yea, though I walk in death's dark vale, Yet will I fear no ill,
4 *My ta - ble Thou hast fur - nish - ed In pres - ence of my foes;*
5 Good-ness and mer - cy all my life Shall sure - ly fol - low me,

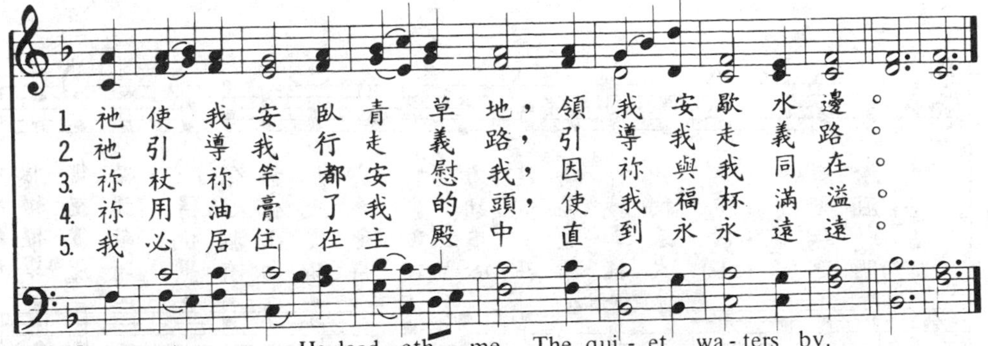
1. 祂使我安臥青草地，領我安歇水邊。
2. 祂引導我行走義路，引導我走義路。
3. 祢杖祢竿都安慰我，因祢與我同在。
4. 祢用油膏了我的頭，使我福杯滿溢。
5. 我必居住在主殿中直到永永遠遠。

1 In pas-tures green; He lead - eth me The qui - et wa - ters by.
2 *With-in the paths of right-eous-ness, E'en for His own name's sake.*
3 For Thou art with me, and Thy rod And staff me com-fort still.
4 *My head Thou dost with oil a - noint, And my cup o - ver-flows.*
5 And in God's house for - ev - er - more My dwell-ing place shall be. A-men.

54

信心使我得勝
Faith Is the Victory

. . . . for this is the victory that overcometh the world, even our faith. — I John 5:4

John H. Yates

FAITH IS THE VICTORY
Ira D. Sankey

1. 營壘高築光明聖山，信徒勃然興起；莫
2. 主以仁愛為我旌旗，聖言為我寶劍；昔
3. 四周都有仇敵圍住，預備向我攻擊；不
4. 得勝仇敵的衆聖徒，将穿聖潔白衣；天
1 En-camped a-long the hills of light, Ye Chris-tian sol-diers, rise, And
2 His ban-ner o-ver us is love, Our sword the Word of God; We
3 On ev-ery hand the foe we find Drawn up in dread ar-ray; Let
4 To him that o-ver-comes the foe, White rai-ment shall be-given; Be-

1. 待黃昏日落天暗，趁早一鼓破敵；奮勇向前抵
2. 日聖徒都因相信，高唱得勝凱歌；勇猛好像旋
3. 要安居在帳棚裡，應到爭戰之區；救恩頭盔保
4. 使面前盡都知名，天軍俱來歡迎；努力行走光
1 press the bat-tle ere the night Shall veil the glow-ing skies. A-gainst the foe in
2 tread the road the saints a-bove With shouts of tri-umph trod. By faith they like a
3 tents of ease be left be-hind, And on-ward to the fray. Sal-va-tion's hel-met
4 fore the an-gels he shall know His name con-fessed in heaven. Then onward from the

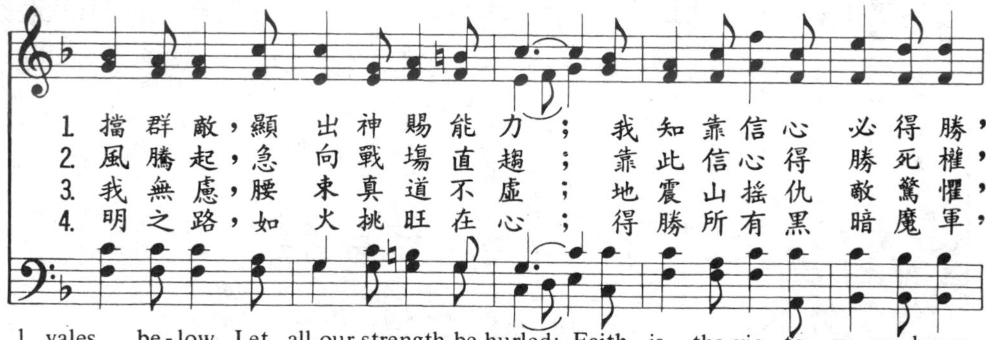

1. 擋群敵，顯出神賜能力；我知靠信心必得勝，
2. 風騰起，急向戰場直趨；靠此信心得勝死權，
3. 我無慮，腰束真道不虛；地震山搖仇敵驚懼，
4. 明之路，如火挑旺在心；得勝所有黑暗魔軍，
1 vales be-low Let all our strength be hurled; Faith is the vic-to-ry, we know,
2 whirlwind's breath, Swept on o'er ev-ery field; The faith by which they conquer'd death
3 on each head, With truth all girt a-bout, The earth shall tremble 'neath our tread,
4 hills of light, Our hearts with love a-flame; We'll van-quish all the hosts of night,

1. 信心可勝世界。
2. 我可安然無慮。
3. 歡呼聲迴響應。
4. 全靠耶穌聖名。
信心使我得勝！信心使
Faith is the vic-to-ry! Faith is the
1 That o-ver-comes the world.
2 Is still our shin-ing shield.
3 And ech-o with our shout.
4 In Je-sus' con-qu'ring name.

我得勝！啊！榮耀的大得勝，信心可勝世界。
vic-to-ry! O glo-ri-ous vic-to-ry, That o-ver-comes the world.

我倚靠神，我要讚美祂的話，我倚靠耶和華，我要讚美祂的話
我倚靠神，必不懼怕。

詩篇五十六篇
10 — 11

In God, whose word I praise,
in the Lord, whose word I praise —
in God I trust; I will not be afraid.
What can man do to me?

Psalm 56 : 10-11. NIV

天城珠門為我開

He the Pearly Gates Will Open

They that do His commandments . . . may enter through the gates into the city. — Revelation 22:14

Fred Blom
Tr. by Nathaniel Carlson

PEARLY GATES
Elsie Ahlwen

1. 主 愛 何 等 奇 妙 偉 大，高 深 純 淨 而 莊 嚴，
2. 我 如 雛 鴿 受 到 驚 駭，又 如 幼 鹿 受 創 傷，
3. 主 愛 何 等 奇 妙 偉 大！我 罪 雖 多 主 赦 免，
4. 日 落 黃 昏 今 生 將 盡，我 願 等 主 親 相 迎，

1 Love di-vine, so great and won-drous, Deep and might-y, pure, sub-lime,
2 *Like a dove when hunt-ed, frightened, As a wound-ed fawn was I;*
3 Love di-vine, so great and won-drous! All my sins He then for-gave.
4 *In life's e-ven-tide, at twi-light, At His door I'll knock and wait;*

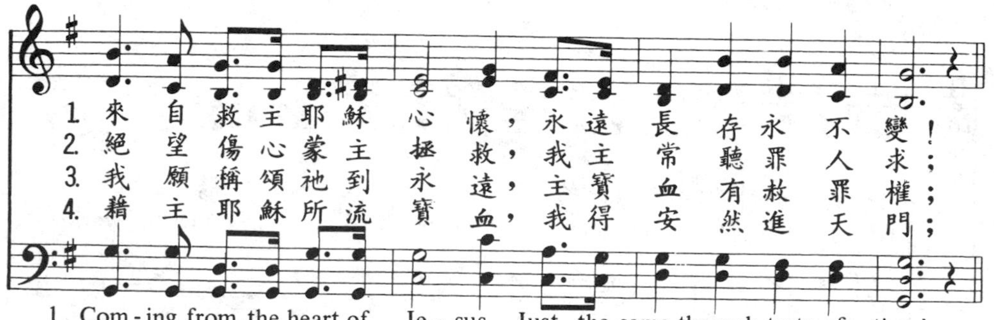
1. 來 自 救 主 耶 穌 心 懷，永 遠 長 存 永 不 變！
2. 絕 望 傷 心 蒙 主 拯 救，我 主 常 聽 罪 人 求；
3. 我 願 稱 頌 祂 到 永 遠，主 寶 血 有 赦 罪 權；
4. 藉 主 耶 穌 所 流 寶 血，我 得 安 然 進 天 門；
1 Com-ing from the heart of Je-sus, Just the same through tests of time!
2 Bro-ken-heart-ed, yet He healed me. He will heed the sin-ner's cry.
3 I will sing His praise for-ev-er, For His blood, His power to save.
4 By the pre-cious love of Je-sus, I shall en-ter heav-en's gate.

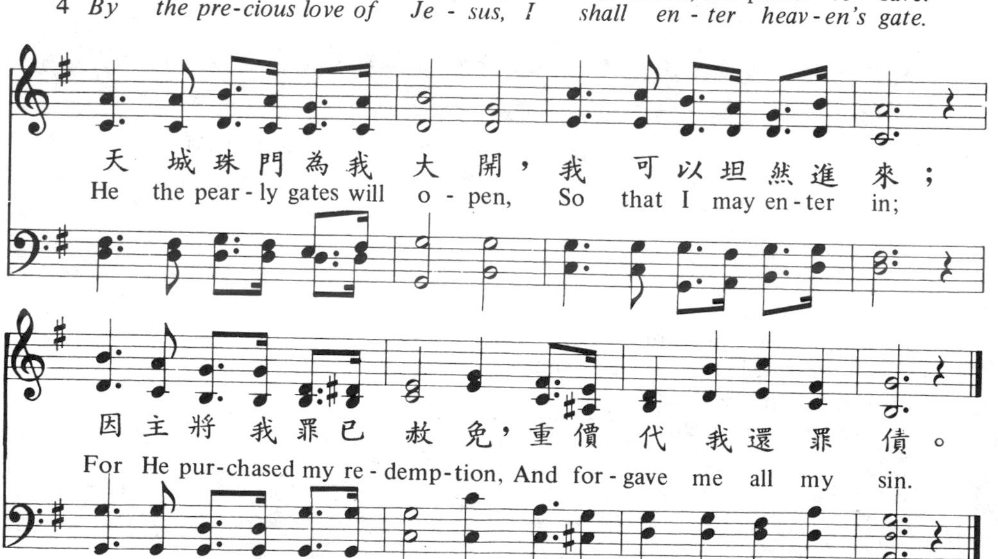
天 城 珠 門 為 我 大 開，我 可 以 坦 然 進 來；
He the pear-ly gates will o-pen, So that I may en-ter in;
因 主 將 我 罪 已 赦 免，重 價 代 我 還 罪 債。
For He pur-chased my re-demp-tion, And for-gave me all my sin.

我心所信，確有根基
My Faith Has Found a Resting Place

Let us labor, therefore, to enter into that rest. — Hebrews 4:11

Lidie H. Edmunds

NO OTHER PLEA
Norwegian Melody

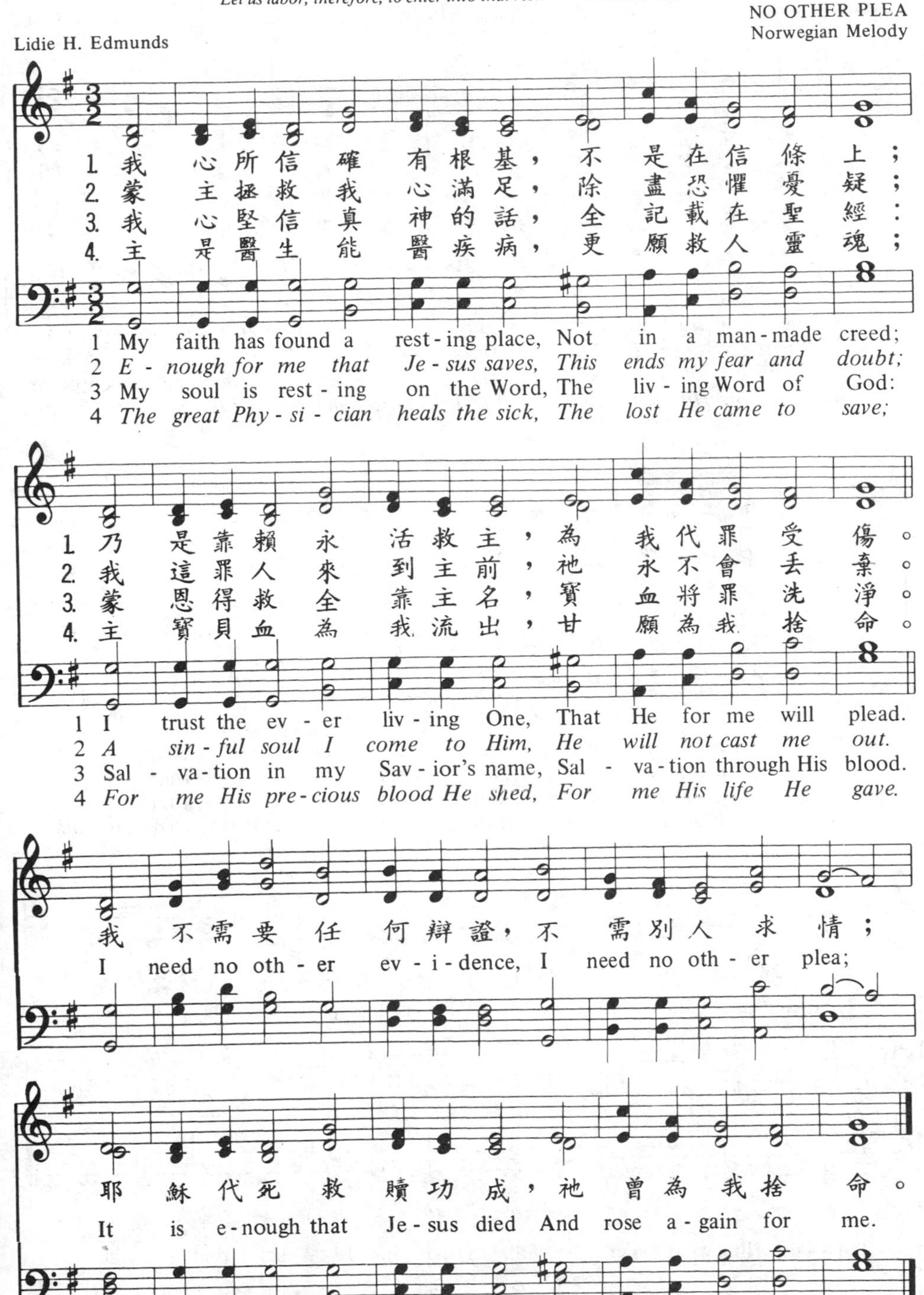
1. 我 心所信 確 有根基，不 是在信 條 上；
2. 蒙 主拯救 我 心滿足，除 盡恐懼 憂 疑；
3. 我 心堅信 真 神的話，全 記載在 聖 經：
4. 主 是醫生 能 醫疾病，更 願救人 靈 魂；
1 My faith has found a rest-ing place, Not in a man-made creed;
2 *E-nough for me that Je-sus saves, This ends my fear and doubt;*
3 My soul is rest-ing on the Word, The liv-ing Word of God:
4 *The great Phy-si-cian heals the sick, The lost He came to save;*
1. 乃 是靠賴 永 活救主，為 我代罪 受 傷。
2. 我 這罪人 來 到主前，祂 永不會 丟 棄。
3. 蒙 恩得救 全 靠主名，寶 血將罪 洗 淨。
4. 主 寶貝血 為 我流出，甘 願為我 捨 命。
1 I trust the ev-er liv-ing One, That He for me will plead.
2 *A sin-ful soul I come to Him, He will not cast me out.*
3 Sal-va-tion in my Sav-ior's name, Sal-va-tion through His blood.
4 *For me His pre-cious blood He shed, For me His life He gave.*
我 不需要 任 何辯證，不 需別人 求 情；
I need no oth-er ev-i-dence, I need no oth-er plea;
耶 穌代死 救 贖功成，祂 曾為我 捨 命。
It is e-nough that Je-sus died And rose a-gain for me.

57 信靠耶穌
Trusting Jesus

Commit thy way into the Lord; trust also in Him . . . .
Psalm 37:5

Edgar P. Stites

TRUSTING JESUS
Ira D. Sankey

1. 我平時當靠救主，遇難事求主救助；
2. 求聖靈照亮我心，叫我心滿得光明；
3. 路平安當頌主名，路黑暗有主同行；
4. 靠耶穌渡過今世，靠耶穌能行萬事；
1 Sim - ply trust - ing ev - ery day, Trust - ing through a storm - y way;
2 Bright - ly doth His Spir - it shine In - to this poor heart of mine;
3 Sing - ing if my way is clear, Pray - ing if the path be drear;
4 Trust - ing Him while life shall last, Trust - ing Him 'til earth be past;
1. 我信心雖還不足，惟要信靠我救主。
2. 求主領我走正路，惟要信靠我救主。
3. 若危險主必保護，惟要信靠我救主。
4. 我離世即往天堂，惟要信靠我救主。
1 E - ven when my faith is small, Trust - ing Je - sus– that is all.
2 While He leads I can - not fall, Trust - ing Je - sus– that is all.
3 If in dan - ger, for Him call, Trust - ing Je - sus– that is all.
4 'Til I hear His fi - nal call, Trust - ing Je - sus– that is all.
靠耶穌渡過今世，靠耶穌能行萬事；
Trust - ing as the mo - ments fly, Trust - ing as the days go by;
我不論走何險路，惟要信靠我救主。
Trust - ing Him what - e'er be - fall, Trust - ing Je - sus– that is all.

我以信心仰望祢

My Faith Looks Up to Thee

Then Peter said unto him, Lord . . . . Thou hast the words of eternal life. — John 6:68

OLIVET
Lowell Mason

Ray Palmer

1. 我以信心仰望，祢在十字架上，
2. 主賜能力恩惠，在我軟弱心內，
3. 我今行走世路，四圍痛苦密佈，
4. 人生短夢一過，死河要起寒波，
1 My faith looks up to Thee, Thou Lamb of Cal - va - ry,
2 May Thy rich grace im - part Strength to my faint - ing heart,
3 While life's dark maze I tread And griefs a - round me spread,
4 When ends life's pass - ing dream, When death's cold, threat-ening stream
1 我的耶穌！求祢聽我禱告！將我罪
2 熱情鼓舞；祢既為我流血，我要愛
3 求祢引領；擦乾我的眼淚，保守我
4 將我淹沒，那時求主恩惠，除我疑
1 Sav - ior di - vine! Now hear me while I pray, Take all my
2 My zeal in - spire; As Thou has died for me, O may my
3 Be Thou my guide; Bid dark - ness turn to day, Wipe sor - row's
4 Shall o'er me roll, Blest Sav - ior, then, in love, Fear and dis -
1. 過寬饒，使我從今到老永屬救主！
2. 祢深切，真摯長久，純潔如火如荼！
3. 不懊悔，拯救我不犯罪貽羞祢名。
4. 惑驚畏，帶我平安而歸永遠快樂！阿門。
1 guilt a - way, O let me from this day Be whol - ly Thine!
2 love to Thee Pure, warm, and change-less be, A liv - ing fire!
3 tears a - way, Nor let me ev - er stray From Thee a - side.
4 trust re - move; O lift me safe a - bove, A ran - somed soul! A - men.

59

靠主耶穌得勝
Victory in Jesus

And this is the victory that overcometh the world, even our faith. — I John 5:4

Eugene M. Bartlett

HARTFORD
Eugene M. Bartlett

1. 我 曾 聽 過 一 故 事，救 主 如 何 由 天 降 臨，
2. 祂 曾 在 世 行 奇 事，顯 出 祂 的 醫 治 大 能，
3. 我 深 知 主 在 天 家，為 我 預 備 榮 耀 住 處，

1 I heard an old, old sto - ry, how a Sav - ior came from glo - ry,
2 *I heard a - bout His heal - ing, of His cleans - ing power re - veal - ing,*
3 I heard a - bout a man - sion He has built for me in glo - ry,

1. 祂 曾 捨 命 在 加 略 山 頂，為 救 我 這 罪 人；
2. 祂 使 瘸 腿 的 跳 躍 行 走，使 瞎 眼 能 看 見；
3. 遙 遠 望 見 那 明 亮 彼 岸，黃 金 街 碧 玉 城；

1 How He gave His life on Cal - va - ry to save a wretch like me;
2 *How He made the lame to walk a - gain and caused the blind to see;*
3 And I heard a - bout the streets of gold be - yond the crys - tal sea;

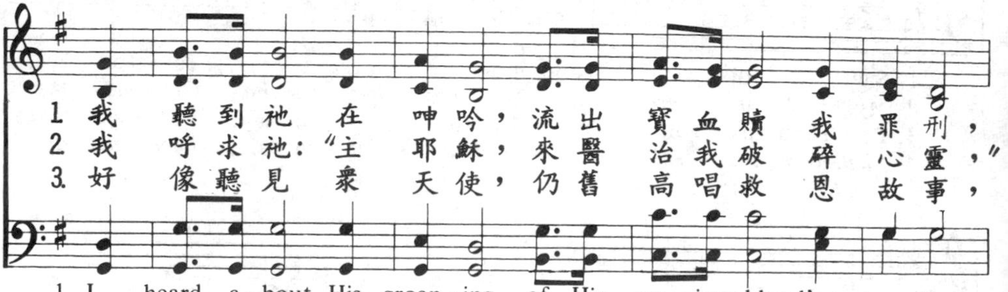
1. 我 聽 到 祂 在 呻 吟，流 出 寶 血 贖 我 罪 刑，
2. 我 呼 求 祂：“主 耶 穌，來 醫 治 我 破 碎 心 靈，”
3. 好 像 聽 見 衆 天 使，仍 舊 高 唱 救 恩 故 事，
1 I heard a - bout His groan - ing, of His pre - cious blood's a - ton - ing,
2 *And then I cried, "Dear Je - sus, come and heal my bro - ken spir - it,"*
3 A - bout the an - gels sing - ing and the old re - demp - tion sto - ry,

1. 我 即 刻 悔 改 歸 向 神 祂 使 我 大 得 勝。
2. 主 聽 我 祈 求 前 來 救 我 使 我 大 得 勝。
3. 到 那 日 我 必 在 那 邊 同 唱 得 勝 凱 歌。
1 Then I re - pent - ed of my sins and won the vic - to - ry.
2 *And some - how Je - sus came and brought to me the vic - to - ry.*
3 And some sweet day I'll sing up there the song of vic - to - ry.

靠主耶穌我救主，能得勝到永遠，主慈愛尋
O vic-to-ry in Je-sus, my Sav-ior, for-ev-er! He sought me and
找我，賜我贖罪之恩；我深知道祂愛我，我
bought me with His re-deem-ing blood; He loved me ere I knew Him, and
願全心愛我主，主寶血已潔淨我，使我永遠得勝
all my love is due Him—He plunged me to vic-to-ry be-neath the cleans-ing flood.

來阿，我們要向耶和華歌唱，向拯救我們的磐石歡呼。
我們要來感謝祂用詩歌向祂歡呼。
因耶和華為大神、為大王，超乎萬神之上。
地的深處在祂手中，山的高峯也屬祂。
海洋屬祂，是祂造的，旱地也是祂手造的。
來阿，我們要屈身敬拜，在造我們的耶和華面前跪下。
因為祂是我們的 神，我們是祂草場的羊，是祂手下的民。
惟願你們今天聽祂的話。

詩篇九十五篇
1－7節

尊主為神

Let God Be God

Bryan Jeffery Leech

Therefore Thou art great, O Lord God, for there is none like Thee. . . . — II Samuel 7:22

CARLA
Bryan Jeffery Leech

Unison
1. 尊主為神，當我們同心聚集，稱祂為主一切由
2. 尊主為神，每日要忠心事奉，完成祂所托付的
3. 基督是主，祂有復活的大能，慈善的聖靈今活
4. 尊主為王，儆醒的等候祂來，向世人傳講祂是

1 Let God be God, in this our pres-ent mo-ment. Let God be mas-ter hold-ing
2 *Let God be God, or we shall nev - er fin - ish The task to which He calls us*
3 Let Christ be Lord in all His ris - en pow - er; His gra-cious Spir-it un - sup
4 *Let this be ours as we a - wait His com - ing, To tell the world of Him our*

1. 祂管理，生命與氣息都是祂的賞賜；
2. 大事工，赦免我過犯使我信心加增；
3. 在我心，重新的改造賜我新的生命；
4. 主是王，讓我們齊聲歡呼擁祂為王；
1 in con - trol All parts of life as gifts of His be - stow - ment
2 ev - ery day; Lest, err - ing, we in un - be - lief di - min - ish
3 pressed and free; Our Fa - ther, re - cre - ate us for this hour
4 Lord and King; O let us march to this, the dis - tant drum-ming

CODA (after stanza 4)
1. 蒙祂的恩世人得着福氣。
2. 主在我身彰顯祂大權能。
3. 在世人面前為祂做見證。
4. 聲達天庭向祂高聲頌揚。尊主為神，尊主為王！

1 For mak-ing men now bro-ken strong and whole.
2 *The force, the power He wish-es to dis-play.*
3 In - to the men You wish for us to be.
4 *Which in cres-cend-o soon will roar and ring.* *Let God be God, let Christ be King!*

61

救主威容

Majestic Sweetness Sits Enthroned

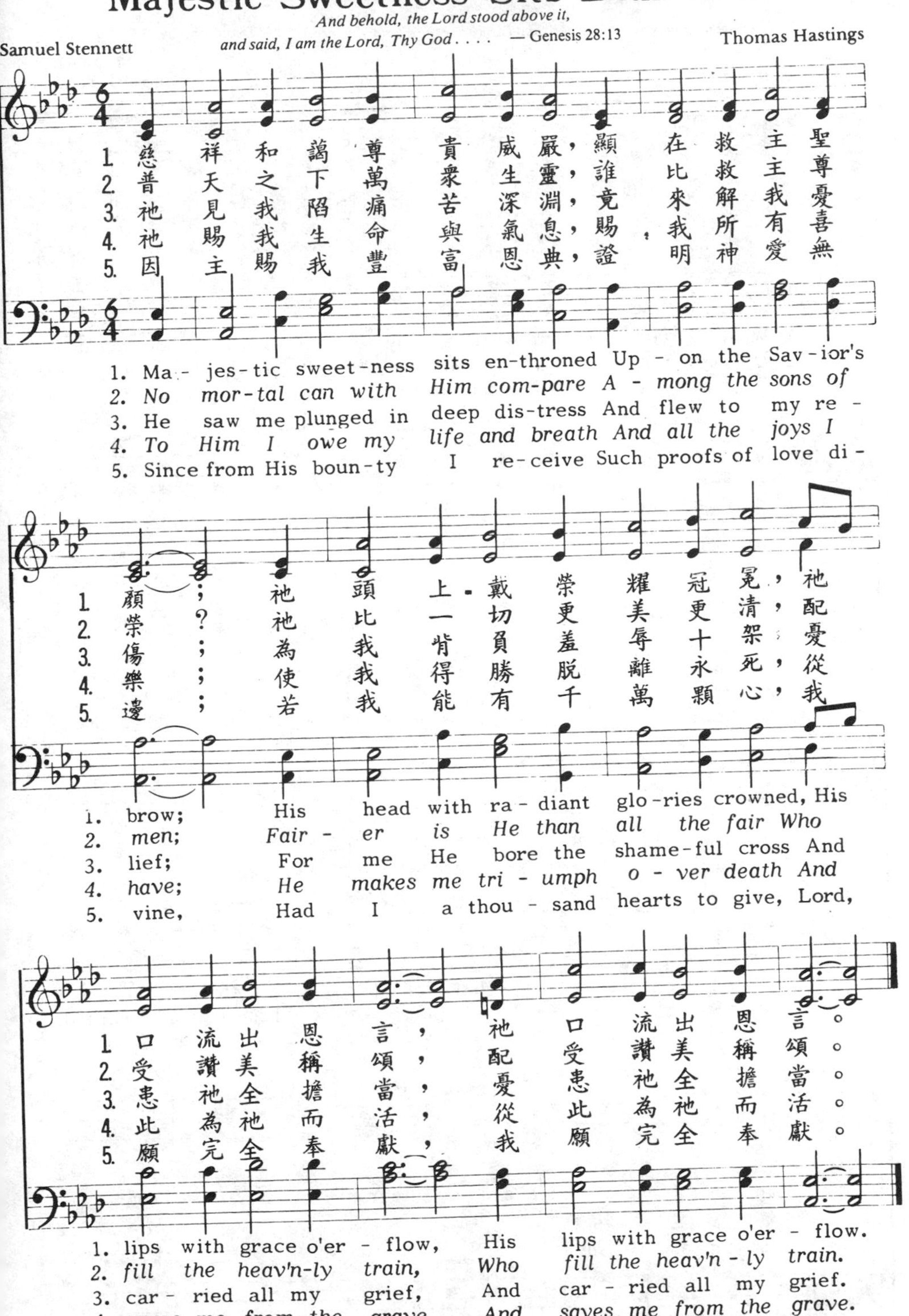

And behold, the Lord stood above it,
and said, I am the Lord, Thy God . . . . — Genesis 28:13
Samuel Stennett
Thomas Hastings
1. 慈祥和藹尊貴威嚴，顯在救主聖顏；祂頭上戴榮耀冠冕，祂口流出恩言，祂口流出恩言。
2. 普天之下萬衆生靈，誰比救主尊榮？祂比一切更美更清，配受讚美稱頌，配受讚美稱頌。
3. 祂見我陷痛苦深淵，竟來解我憂傷；祂為我背負羞辱十架，憂患祂全擔當，憂患祂全擔當。
4. 祂賜我生命與氣息，賜，我所有喜樂；使我得勝脫離永死，從此為祂而活，從此為祂而活。
5. 因主賜我豐富恩典，證明神愛無邊；若我能有千萬顆心，我願完全奉獻，我願完全奉獻。
1. Ma - jes-tic sweet-ness sits en-throned Up - on the Sav-ior's brow; His head with ra-diant glo-ries crowned, His lips with grace o'er - flow, His lips with grace o'er - flow.
2. No mor-tal can with Him com-pare A - mong the sons of men; Fair - er is He than all the fair Who fill the heav'n-ly train, Who fill the heav'n - ly train.
3. He saw me plunged in deep dis-tress And flew to my re - lief; For me He bore the shame-ful cross And car - ried all my grief, And car - ried all my grief.
4. To Him I owe my life and breath And all the joys I have; He makes me tri - umph o - ver death And saves me from the grave, And saves me from the grave.
5. Since from His boun-ty I re-ceive Such proofs of love di - vine, Had I a thou - sand hearts to give, Lord, they should all be Thine, Lord, they should all be thine.

62

倚靠主永遠膀臂
Leaning on the Everlasting Arms

The eternal God is our refuge and underneath are the everlasting arms. — Deuteronomy 33:27
Elisha A. Hoffman
SHOWALTER
Anthony J. Showalter
1. 何 等 的 深 交，何 等 的 歡 喜，倚 靠 主 耶 穌 永
2. 我 滿 心 歡 喜，行 走 這 天 路，倚 靠 主 耶 穌 永
3. 我 不 用 畏 懼，我 不 用 驚 慌，倚 靠 主 耶 穌 永
1 What a fel - low-ship, what a joy di - vine, Lean - ing on the ev - er -
2 O how sweet to walk in this pil - grim way, Lean - ing on the ev - er -
3 What have I to dread, what have I to fear, Lean - ing on the ev - er -
1. 遠 膀 臂； 何 等 的 平 安， 何 等 的 福 氣，
2. 遠 膀 臂； 每 日 有 榮 光， 照 亮 我 旅 途，
3. 遠 膀 臂； 我 滿 有 平 安， 主 在 我 身 旁，
1 last - ing arms; What a bless - ed - ness, what a peace is mine,
2 last - ing arms; O how bright the path grows from day to day,
3 last - ing arms? I have bless - ed peace with my Lord so near,
1. 倚 靠 主 耶 穌 永 遠 膀 臂。 倚 靠，
2. 倚 靠 主 耶 穌 永 遠 膀 臂。 Lean - ing,
3. 倚 靠 主 耶 穌 永 遠 膀 臂。
1 Lean - ing on the ev - er - last - ing arms. 倚 靠 主 耶 穌，
2 Lean - ing on the ev - er - last - ing arms. Lean-ing on Je - sus,
3 Lean - ing on the ev - er - last - ing arms.
倚 靠， 平 安 穩 妥，危 險 遠 離； 倚
lean - ing, Safe and se-cure from all a - larms; Lean
倚 靠 主 耶 穌， 倚 靠 主
lean-ing on Je - sus, Lean-ing on

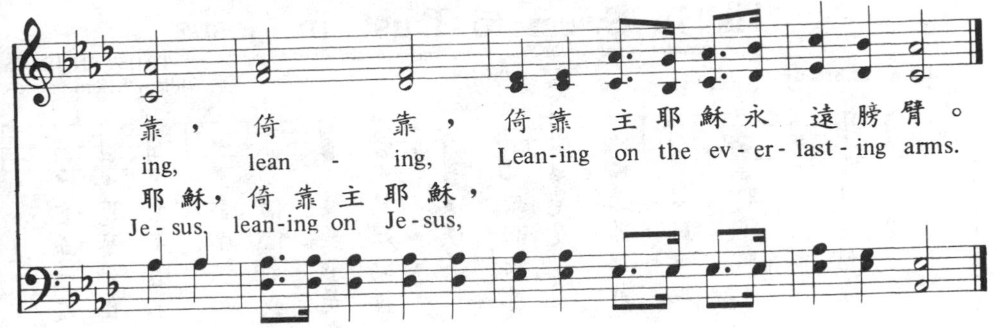

靠，倚 靠，倚靠主耶穌永遠膀臂。
ing, lean - ing, Lean-ing on the ev-er-last-ing arms.
耶穌，倚靠主耶穌，
Je-sus, lean-ing on Je-sus,

63

昨日，今日，到永遠
Yesterday, Today, Forever

. . . A chief cornerstone, elect, precious; and he that believeth on Him shall not be confounded. — I Peter 2:6

NYACK
J. H. Burke

Albert B. Simpson

昨日，今日，直到永遠，耶穌不改變；天地萬物
Yes-ter-day, to-day, for-ev-er, Je-sus is the same, All may change, but

都要改變，耶穌不改變！榮耀歸主名！榮耀
Je-sus nev-er! Glo-ry to His name! Glo-ry to His name! Glo-ry

歸主名！天地萬物都要改變，耶穌不改變！
to His name! All may change, but Je-sus nev-er! Glo-ry to His name!

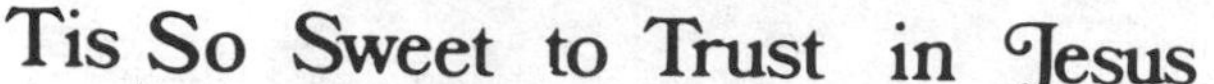
信靠耶穌真是甜美

'Tis So Sweet to Trust in Jesus

. . . because we trust in the living God, who is the Savior of all men.
I Timothy 4:10

Louisa M. R. Stead

TRUST IN JESUS
William J. Kirkpatrick

1. 信靠耶穌真是甜美，只要信靠主恩言，
2. 信靠耶穌真是甜美，只要信靠主寶血，
3. 信靠耶穌真是甜美，助我将罪惡離棄，
4. 感謝主助我信靠祢，祢是我救主良友，

1 'Tis so sweet to trust in Je - sus, Just to take Him at His word,
2 *How I love to trust in Je - sus, Just to trust His cleans-ing blood,*
3 Yes, I've learned to trust in Je - sus, And from sin and self to cease,
4 *I'm so glad I learned to trust Him, Pre - cious Je - sus, Sav - ior, Friend;*

1. 只要站在主應許上，信靠主蒙福無邊。
2. 只要憑着純一信心，能洗罪污白如雪！
3. 得着耶穌得着一切，生命喜樂和安息。
4. 我深信祢與我同在，從今時直到永久。

1 Just to rest up - on His prom - ise, Just to know, "Thus saith the Lord."
2 *Just in sim - ple faith to plunge me 'Neath the heal - ing, cleans-ing flood!*
3 Now from Je - sus sim - ply tak - ing Life and rest and joy and peace.
4 *And I know that He is with me, He'll be with me to the end.*

耶穌，耶穌，何等可靠！多少事上已證明！

Je - sus, Je - sus, how I trust Him! How I've proved Him o'er and o'er!

耶穌，耶穌，寶貴耶穌！願我信心更堅定！

Je - sus, Je - sus, pre - cious Je - sus! O for grace to trust Him more!

主是我的盼望

My Hope Is in the Lord

WAKEFIELD

Norman J. Clayton

Christ, in you the hope of Glory. — Colossians 1:27

Norman J. Clayton

1. 主是我的盼望，祂曾為我捨己，
2. 我無善行可陳，主震怒在我身，
3. 今日在父右邊，主為我付代價，
4. 恩典為我預備，因信便能得着，
1 My hope is in the Lord Who gave Him-self for me,
2 No mer-it of my own His an-ger to sup-press,
3 And now for me He stands Be-fore the Fa-ther's throne,
4 His grace has planned it all, 'Tis mine but to be-lieve,
1. 釘死十架為贖我罪在髑髏地。
2. 一切盼望惟靠基督公義之恩。
3. 顯示雙手釘痕宣告我永屬祂。
4. 接受基督承認主愛完成救贖。
1 And paid the price of all my sin at Cal-va-ry.
2 My on-ly hope is found in Je-sus' right-eous-ness.
3 And shows His wound-ed hands, and names me as His own.
4 And rec-og-nize His work of love and Christ re-ceive.
主死為我，主活為我，
For me He died, For me He lives,
主死為我，主活為我，
For me He died, For me He lives,
永遠生命與光明白白賜給我。
And ev-er-last-ing life and light He free-ly gives.

66

我知誰掌管明天
I Know Who Holds Tomorrow

Fear ye not . . ye are of more value than many sparrows . . . .
Matthew 10:31

Ira F. Stanphill

I KNOW
Ira F. Stanphill

1. 我不知明天的道路，每一天只為主活；我不借明天的太陽，因明天或許陰暗。我不要為將來憂慮，因我信主的應許；我今天
2. 每一步越走越光明，像攀登黃金階梯；每重擔越挑越輕省，每朵雲披上銀衣。在那裡陽光常普照，在那裡沒有眼淚；在美麗
3. 我不知明天的道路，或遭遇生活苦楚；但那位養活麻雀者．祂必然也看顧我。祂是我旅途的良伴，或經過水火之災；但救主
1 I don't know a-bout to-mor-row, I just live from day to day; I don't bor-row from its sun-shine, For its skies may turn to gray. I don't wor-ry o'er the fu-ture, For I know what Je-sus said; And to-day
2 Ev-ery step is get-ting bright-er As the gold-en stairs I climb; Ev-ery bur-den's get-ting light-er, Ev-ery cloud is sil-ver-lined. There the sun is al-ways shin-ing, There no tear will dim the eye; At the end-
3 I don't know a-bout to-mor-row, It may bring me pov-er-ty; But the one who feeds the spar-row, Is the one who stands by me. And the path that is my por-tion, May be through the flame or flood; But His pres-

1. 要與主同行，因祂知前面如何。
2. 彩虹的盡頭，衆山嶺與天相連。
3. 必與我同在，祂寶血把我遮蓋。
1 I'll walk be - side Him, For He knows what is a - head.
2 ing of the rain - bow, Where the moun - tains touch the sky.
3 ence goes be - fore me, And I'm cov - ered with His blood.
有許多未來的事情，我現在不能識透；但我知誰掌管明天，我也知誰牽我手。
Man - y things a - bout to - mor - row I don't seem to un - der - stand; But I know who holds to - mor - row, And I know who holds my hand.

67 在十架
At the Cross

For the preaching of the cross is . . . . unto us who are saved the power of God. — 1 Corinthians 1:18

Isaac Watts
Refrain added by Ralph E. Hudson

HUDSON
Ralph E. Hudson

1. 可 嘆，我 主 流 出 寶 血，甘 願 為 我 捨 身！
2. 我 主 受 苦 在 十 字 架，為 我 所 犯 罪 愆，
3. 正 當 基 督 造 物 的 主，為 人 罪 過 身 亡，
4. 我 雖 流 盡 傷 心 眼 淚，難 還 主 愛 的 債，
1 A - las, and did my Sav - ior bleed? And did my Sov-ereign die?
2 Was it for crimes that I have done, He suf-fered on the tree?
3 Well might the sun in dark - ness hide And shut his glo - ries in,
4 But drops of grief can ne'er re - pay The debt of love I owe:

1. 忍 受 痛 苦 歷 盡 艱 辛，救 我 卑 微 罪 人！
2. 何 等 慈 悲 無 量 恩 典，主 愛 廣 大 無 邊！
3. 輝 煌 紅 日 也 被 隱 藏，天 地 黑 暗 無 光；
4. 只 將 身 心 獻 為 活 祭，藉 報 救 主 大 愛！
1 Would He de - vote that sa - cred head For some - one such as I?
2 A - maz - ing pit - y! grace un-known! And love be - yond de - gree!
3 When Christ, the might-y Mak - er, died For man the crea - ture's sin.
4 Here, Lord, I give my - self a - way, 'Tis all that I can do!

在 十 架，在 十 架，我 一 見 主 恩 光，我 心
At the cross, at the cross where I first saw the light, And the
中 罪 孽 重 擔 皆 脫 落，在 我 主 十 架，
bur - den of my heart rolled a - way, It was there by faith

我因 信眼明亮，如 今我心 常歡喜 快樂！
I re-ceived my sight, And now I am hap-py all the day!

我為祂活

I'll Live for Him

68

That they might live . . . unto Him who died for them. II Corinthians 5:15

DUNBAR

Ralph E. Hudson C. R. Dunbar

1. 我将身心 奉獻給祢，神的羔羊曾為我死；
2. 我今相信 祢接納我，因祢受死我得存活；
3. 在髑髏地 祢為我死，救我靈魂從罪得釋；

1 My life, my love I give to Thee, Thou Lamb of God who died for me;
2 *I now be-lieve Thou dost re-ceive, For Thou hast died that I might live;*
3 O Thou who died on Cal-va-ry, To save my soul and make me free,

副歌 祂為我死 我為祂活，生命充滿無限喜樂！
Ref. *I'll live for Him who died for me, How hap-py then my life shall be!*

D.C. Refrain

1. 我願向祢忠心到底，我救主我的神！
2. 我願一生靠祢而活，我救主我的神！
3. 我今願意奉獻自己，我救主我的神！

1 O may I ev-er faith-ful be, My Sav-ior and my God!
2 *And now hence-forth I'll trust in Thee, My Sav-ior and my God!*
3 I'll con-se-crate my life to Thee, My Sav-ior and my God!

副歌 祂為我死我為祂活，我救主我的神！
Ref. *I'll live for Him who died for me, My Sav-ior and my God!*

69
堅固磐石
The Solid Rock
They who trust in the Lord shall be as Mount Zion, which cannot be moved. . . —Psalm 125:1
Edward Mote
SOLID ROCK
William B. Bradbury
1. 我心所望別無根基，惟有救主流血公義；除此以外虛空無憑，我獨靠主耶穌聖名。
2. 有時黑雲遮沒我面，耶穌恩典永無改變；大風巨浪我亦不怕，因望如錨海底抛牢。
3. 主曾流血立此新約，應許救我扶助軟弱；良朋蜜友雖都遠離，我靠救主安慰到底。
4. 末日聽見號筒聲音，與主相遇永遠相親；穿上救主雪白義袍，無瑕無疵同受榮耀。
立在基督磐石堅固，其餘根基全是沙土，其餘根基全是沙土。
1 My hope is built on noth-ing less Than Je-sus' blood and right-eous-ness; I dare not trust the sweet-est frame, But whol-ly lean on Je-sus' name.
2 When dark-ness veils His love-ly face, I rest on His un-chang-ing grace; In ev-ery high and storm-y gale, My an-chor holds with-in the veil.
3 His oath, His cov-e-nant, His blood, Sup-port me in the whelm-ing flood; When all a-round my soul gives way, He then is all my hope and stay.
4 When He shall come with trum-pet sound, O may I then in Him be found; Dressed in His right-eous-ness a-lone, Fault-less to stand be-fore the throne.
On Christ, the sol-id Rock, I stand; All oth-er ground is sink-ing sand, All oth-er ground is sink-ing sand.
© Copyright 1976 by Paragon Associates, Inc. All rights reserved.

永久磐石

Rock of Ages, Cleft for Me

. . . Hide me in the rock that is higher than I. — Psalm 61:2

TOPLADY

Augustus M. Toplady — Thomas Hastings

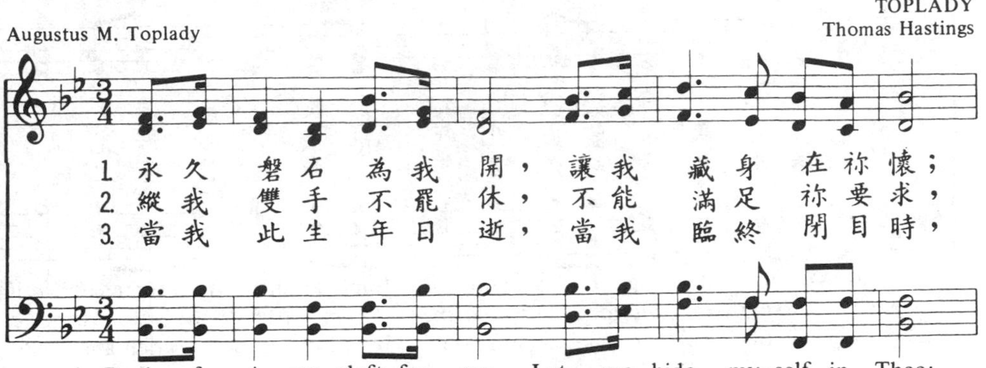
1. 永久磐石為我開，讓我藏身在祢懷；
2. 縱我雙手不罷休，不能滿足祢要求，
3. 當我此生年日逝，當我臨終閉目時，

1 Rock of A - ges, cleft for me, Let me hide my-self in Thee;
2 *Could my tears for - ev - er flow, Could my zeal no lan-guor know,*
3 While I draw this fi - nal breath, When my eyes shall close in death,

1. 願祢所流水與血，解決我的衆罪孽，
2. 縱我熱心能持久，縱我眼淚永遠流，
3. 當我飛進永世間，當我到祢寶座前，

1 Let the wa - ter and the blood, From Thy wound-ed side which flowed,
2 *These for sin could not a - tone— Thou must save, and Thou a - lone:*
3 When I rise to worlds un-known, And be - hold Thee on Thy throne,

1. 贖我免去罪永刑，救我脱離罪權能。
2. 仍不足以贖愆尤，必須祢來施拯救。
3. 永久磐石為我開，讓我藏身在祢懷。阿門

1 Be of sin the dou-ble cure, Save from wrath and make me pure.
2 *In my hand no price I bring, Sim - ply to Thy cross I cling.*
3 Rock of A - ges, cleft for me, Let me hide my-self in Thee. A-men.

71

我心得滿足
Satisfied

As the heart panteth after the waterbrook so panteth my soul after Thee, O God.
— Psalm 42:1

Clara T. Williams

SATISFIED
Ralph E. Hudson

1. 我的生命渴望已久，能飲於清涼水泉，
2. 我心欲求豐盛生命，能使我心得充盈，
3. 活水泉源永流不息，生命靈糧靠主賜，
1 All my life long I had pant - ed For a drink from some cool spring
2 *Feed-ing on the food a - round me 'Til my strength was al-most gone,*
3 Well of wa - ter, ev - er spring - ing, Bread of life, so rich and free,

1. 除去我心如火憂情，解我乾渴的心靈。
2. 但我所得都如煙雲，惟使我心更虛空。
3. 豐富恩典永遠基業，都在救主基督裡。
1 That I hoped would quench the burn-ing Of the thirst I felt with - in.
2 *Longed my soul for some-thing bet - ter, On-ly still to hun-ger on.*
3 Un - told wealth that nev - er fail - eth, My Re - deem - er is to me.

哈利路亞！我已尋見我心所渴慕的主！
Hal - le - lu - jah! I have found Him—Whom my soul so long has craved!
靠祂寶血我得拯救；使我心靈得滿足。
Je - sus sat - is - fies my long - ings; Through His blood I now am saved.

72

在各各他
At Calvary

And when they were come to . . . Calvary they crucified Him .
— Luke 23:33

CALVARY

William R. Newell

Daniel B. Towner

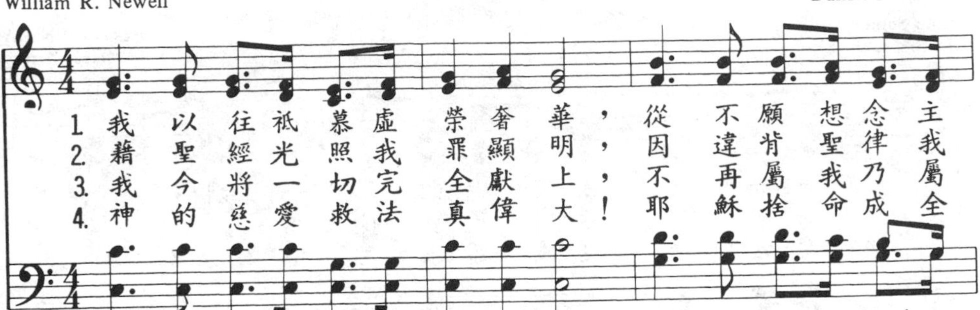

1. 我以往祇慕虛榮奢華，從不願想念主
2. 藉聖經光照我罪顯明，因違背聖律我
3. 我今將一切完全獻上，不再屬我乃屬
4. 神的慈愛救法真偉大！耶穌捨命成全

1 Years I spent in van - i - ty and pride, Car - ing not my Lord was
2 *By God's Word at last my sin I learned; Then I trem-bled at the*
3 Now I've given to Je - sus ev - ery - thing; Now I glad - ly own Him
4 *O the love that drew sal - va - tion's plan! O the grace that brought it*

1. 釘十架，從不知我主是為我死在各各他。
2. 甚戰兢，我這罪人今來懇求主在各各他。
3. 主我王，我心靈快樂讚美歌唱在各各他。
4. 神計劃，除去神與人之間隔膜在各各他。
1 cru - ci - fied, Know - ing not it was for me He died On Cal - va - ry.
2 law I'd spurned, 'Til my guilt - y soul im - plor - ing turned To Cal - va - ry.
3 as my King; Now my rap - tured soul can on - ly sing Of Cal - va - ry.
4 down to man! O the might - y gulf that God did span At Cal - va - ry.

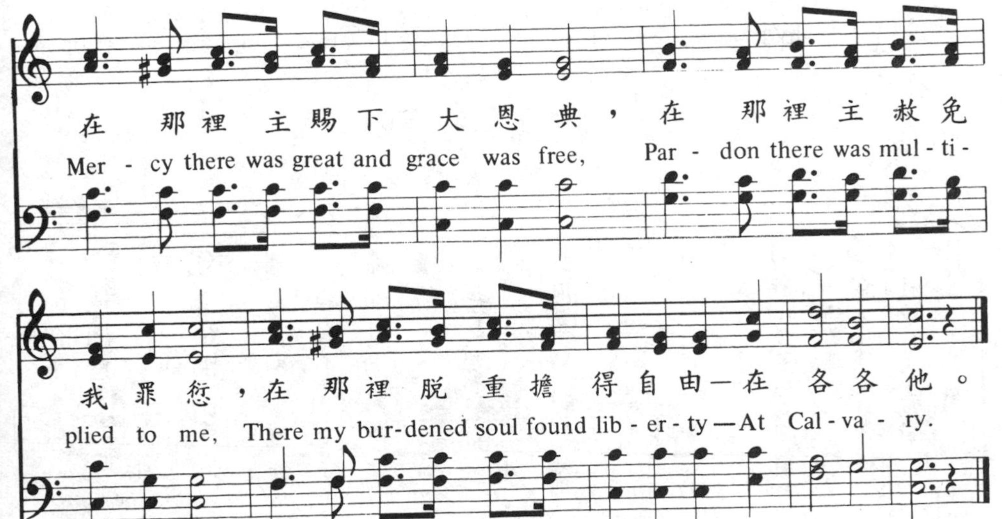

在那裡主賜下大恩典，在那裡主赦免
Mer - cy there was great and grace was free, Par - don there was mul - ti -
我罪愆，在那裡脫重擔得自由—在各各他。
plied to me, There my bur - dened soul found lib - er - ty—At Cal - va - ry.

73

每一天所渡過的每一刻

Day By Day and With Each Passing Moment

As thy days so shall thy strength be. — Deuteronomy 33:25

Lina Sandell
Tr. by A. L. Skoog

BLOTT EN DAG
Oscar Ahnfelt

1. 每 一 天 所 渡 過 的 每 一 刻 ， 我 得
2. 每 一 天 主 自 己 與 我 相 親 ， 每 時
3. 每 當 遭 遇 患 難 求 主 搭 救 ， 全 靠
1 Day by day and with each pass - ing mo - ment, Strength I
2 Ev - ery day the Lord Him-self is near me With a
3 Help me then in ev - ery trib - u - la - tion So to

1. 着 能 力 勝 過 試 探 ； 我 依 靠 天 父 週 詳 的
2. 刻 賜 下 格 外 憐 憫 ； 我 掛 慮 主 願 安 慰 與
3. 我 主 真 誠 的 應 許 ； 我 確 信 主 的 體 貼 與
1 find to meet my tri - als here; Trust - ing in my Fa-ther's wise be -
2 spe - cial mer- cy for each hour; All my cares He fain would bear, and
3 trust Thy prom-is - es, O Lord, That I lose not faith's sweet con-so-

1. 供 應 ， 我 不 用 再 恐 慌 與 掛 念 。 祂 的
2. 擔 當 ， 祂 的 名 是 策 士 與 權 能 。 祂 保
3. 安 慰 ， 深 信 聖 經 應 許 不 落 空 。 懇 求
1 stow - ment, I've no cause for wor - ry or for fear. He whose
2 cheer me, He whose name is Coun-sel - lor and Power. The pro -
3 la - tion Of - fered me with - in Thy ho - ly word. Help me

1. 心 極仁慈無可測度，祂每天都
2. 護祂的兒女與珍寶，祂熱心必
3. 主 患難困苦中拯救，平穩與試
1 heart is kind be - yond all meas - ure Gives un - to each
2 tec - tion of His child and treas - ure Is a charge that
3 Lord, when toil and trou - ble meet - ing, E'er to take, as

1. 有最好安排，不論憂或喜祂慈愛
2. 要成全這事；“你日子如何力量也
3. 煉皆由父旨，我一生年日便如飛
1 day what He deems best— Lov - ing - ly, its part of pain and
2 on Him - self He laid; "As thy days, thy strength shall be in
3 from a fa - ther's hand, One by one, the days, the mo - ments

1. 顯明，勞苦中祂賜平安。
2. 如何，”這是祂向我應許。
3. 而去，直待進應許美地。阿門。
1 pleas - ure, Min - gling toil with peace and rest.
2 meas - ure," This the pledge to me He made.
3 fleet - ing, 'Til I reach the prom - ised land. A - men.

74

恩典大過我罪
Grace Greater Than Our Sin

. . . But where sin abounded, grace did much more abound. — Romans 5:20

Julia H. Johnston
MOODY
Daniel B. Towner
1. 慈愛主滿有奇異恩典，恩典遠超過
2. 罪惡絕望如寒冷風浪，威脅生命將
3. 罪惡衆多雖不能洗淨，罪惡污點也
4. 奇異無限無量大恩典，白白賜給凡
1 Mar-vel-ous grace of our lov-ing Lord, Grace that ex-ceeds our
2 Sin and de-spair, like the sea-waves cold, Threat-en the soul with
3 Dark is the stain that we can-not hide, What can a-vail to
4 Mar-vel-ous, in-fi-nite, match-less grace, Free-ly be-stowed on
1. 我的罪惡！各各他山上寶血傾流—
2. 永遠沉淪；幸有救主無量大恩典—
3. 無法遮蓋；但有一處寶血泉湧流，
4. 信祂的人！你若渴想見救主榮面，
1 sin and our guilt! Yon-der on Cal-va-ry's mount out-poured—
2 in-fi-nite loss; Grace that is great-er— yes, grace un-told—
3 wash it a-way? Look! There is flow-ing a crim-son tide—
4 all who be-lieve! You that are long-ing to see His face,
1. 羔羊血能洗淨衆罪污。
2. 指向十架得贖罪救恩。
3. 今日洗你罪比雪更白。
4. 願否今日接受祂救恩？
真神
Grace, grace,
1 There where the blood of the Lamb was spilt.
2 Points to the Ref-uge, the might-y Cross.
3 Whit-er than snow you may be to-day.
4 Will you this mo-ment His grace re-ceive?
恩典，恩典能赦免將心洗淨；真
God's grace, Grace that will par-don and cleanse with-in; Grace,

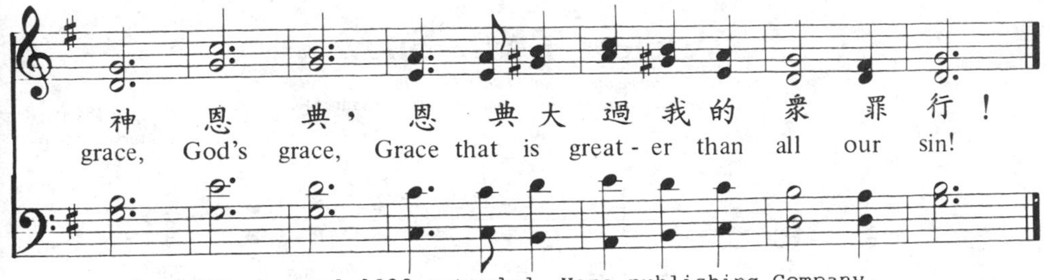

神恩典，恩典大過我的衆罪行！
grace, God's grace, Grace that is great - er than all our sin!

75

奇異恩典

Amazing Grace! How Sweet the Sound

For by grace are ye saved through faith . . . — Ephesians 2:8

AMAZING GRACE
American Melody
Carrell and Clayton's *Virginia Harmony*
Harmonized by Edwin O. Excell

John Newton
John P. Rees, stanza 5

1. 奇異恩典，何等甘甜，我罪已得赦免！
2. 如此恩典，使我敬畏，使我心得安慰；
3. 救主應許，愛我真切，使我今得盼望；
4. 歷經艱險，勞苦奔走，我今來到主前；
5. 住在天家，千萬年世，如日無限光亮；

1 A - maz-ing grace! How sweet the sound–That saved a wretch like me!
2 *'Twas grace that taught my heart to fear, And grace my fears re-lieved;*
3 The Lord has prom-ised good to me, His word my hope se-cures;
4 *Through man-y dan-gers, toils, and snares, I have al - read - y come;*
5 When we've been there ten thou-sand years, Bright shin-ing as the sun,

1. 前我失喪，今被尋回，瞎眼今得看見。
2. 初信之時，我蒙恩惠，真是何等寶貴！
3. 主是盾牌，是我產業，是我生命保障。
4. 全靠主恩，扶持保佑，恩典帶進永久。
5. 時時頌讚，永不止息，仍像凱歌初唱。

1 I once was lost but now am found, Was blind but now I see.
2 *How pre - cious did that grace ap - pear The hour I first be-lieved!*
3 He will my shield and por - tion be As long as life en-dures.
4 *'Tis grace hath brought me safe thus far, And grace will lead me home.*
5 We've no less days to sing God's praise Than when we'd first be - gun.

76

比雪更白
Whiter Than Snow

Purge me . . . and I shall be clean; wash me and I shall be whiter than snow. — Psalm 51:7

James Nicholson

FISCHER
William G. Fischer

1. 耶 穌我救主，我今切慕近祢；願
2. 耶 穌我救主，從祢寶座之上；垂
3. 耶 穌我救主，我謙卑的懇求；在
4. 耶 穌我救主，我耐心的等候；求

1 Lord Je - sus, I long to be per - fect - ly whole; I
2 *Lord Je - sus, look down from Your throne in the skies And*
3 Lord Je - sus, for this I most hum - bly en - treat; I
4 *Lord Je - sus, You see as I pa - tient - ly wait; Come*

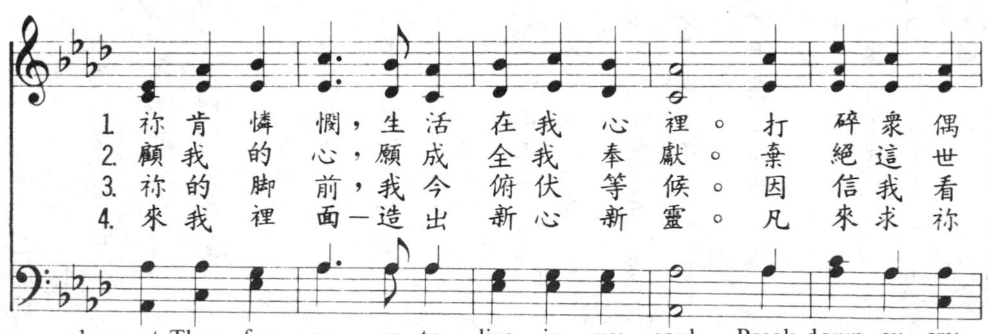

1. 祢肯憐憫，生活在我心裡。打碎眾偶
2. 顧我的心，願成全我奉獻。棄絕這世
3. 祢的腳前，我今俯伏等候。因信我看
4. 來我裡面—造出新心新靈。凡來求祢
1 want Thee for - ev - er to live in my soul. Break down ev - ery
2 help me to make a com - plete sac - ri - fice. I give up my-
3 wait, bless - ed Lord, at Thy cru - ci - fied feet. By faith, for my
4 now and with - in me a new heart cre - ate. To those who have

1. 像，仇敵全數擊敗—祢若將我洗，我就
2. 界和我一切喜愛—祢若將我洗，我就
3. 見祢血洗我清潔—祢若將我洗，我就
4. 的，從來祢都恩待—祢若將我洗，我就

1 i - dol, cast out ev- ery foe— Now wash me and I shall be
2 *self and what - ev - er I know— Now wash me and I shall be*
3 cleans - ing I see Your blood flow— Now wash me and I shall be
4 *sought You, You nev - er said, "No"— Now wash me and I shall be*

比 雪更 白。 比雪更 白，是，比雪更
whit - er than snow. Whit - er than snow, yes, whit - er than
白一祢 若将 我 洗，我就 比 雪更 白。
snow— Now wash me and I shall be whit - er than snow.

The Supremacy of Christ

He is the image of the invisible God, the firstborn over all creation. For by Him all things were created: things in heaven and on earth, visible and invisible, whether thrones or powers or rulers or authorities; all things were created by Him and for Him. He is before all things, and in Him all things hold together. And He is the head of the body, the church; He is the beginning and the firstborn from among the dead, so that in everything He might have the supremacy. For God was pleased to have all His fullness dwell in Him, and through Him to reconcile to Himself all things, whether things on earth or things in heaven, by making peace through His blood, shed on the cross.

Once you were alienated from God and were enemies in your minds because of your evil behavior. But now He has reconciled you by Christ's physical body through death to present you holy in His sight, without blemish and free from accusation–if you continue in your faith, established and firm, not moved from the hope held out in the gospel. This is the gospel that you heard and that has been proclaimed to every creature under heaven, and of which I, Paul, have become a servant.

–Colossians 1:15-23 (NIV)

77

祂賜更多恩典
He Giveth More Grace

God is able to make all grace abound toward you — II Corinthians 9 :8

HE GIVETH MORE GRACE
Annie Johnson Flint
Hubert Mitchell
1. 當 重 擔 加 增 祂 賜 更 多 的 恩 典 ，當 勞 苦 加
2. 當 我 們 用 盡 所 有 內 在 的 耐 力 ，當 日 落 之
1 He giv-eth more grace when the burdens grow greater, He send-eth more
2 When we have ex-haust-ed our store of en-dur-ance, When our strength has
1. 深 ，祂 的 力 量 加 添 ； 更 多 的 愛 更 多 的
2. 前 ，所 有 力 量 已 失 ， 當 人 生 的 道 路 走
1 strength when the la-bors in-crease; To add-ed af-flic-tion He
2 failed ere the day is half done, When we reach the end of our
1. 慈 悲 與 憐 憫，主 賜 更 多 平 安 當 試 煉 來 臨。
2. 到 盡 頭 之 時，天 父 的 恩 典 仍 不 斷 的 供 應。
1 add-eth His mer-cy, To mul-ti-plied tri-als, His mul-ti-plied peace.
2 hoard-ed re-sourc-es, Our Fa-ther's full giv-ing is on-ly be-gun.
主 有 豐 富 慈 愛，恩 典 取 之 不 盡，主 能 力 超
His love has no lim-it, His grace has no meas-ure, His power has no

過世人 所能測 度；在 基督耶 穌裡有
bound-a - ry known un - to men; For out of His in - fi - nite
無限的豐盛，主 供應，常供應，不 斷的供應！
rich - es in Je-sus, He giv - eth, and giv - eth, and giv - eth a - gain!

The Love of Christ

Here is love,
that God sent His Son,
His Son that never offended,
His Son that was always His delight.
Herein is love, that He sent Him to save sinners;
to save them by bearing their sins,
by bearing their curse, by dying their death, and by carrying their sorrows.
Here is love, in that while we were yet enemies, Christ died for us;
yes, here is love,
in that while we were yet without strength, Christ died for the ungodly.

–John Bunyan

78

耶穌奇妙的救恩
Wonderful Grace of Jesus

For by grace are ye saved, through faith . . . . — Ephesians 2:8

Haldor Lillenas

WONDERFUL GRACE
Haldor Lillenas

1. 耶穌奇妙的救恩，超過我衆過犯，
2. 耶穌奇妙的救恩，臨到失喪之人，
3. 耶穌奇妙的救恩，施與罪惡之人，

1 Won-der-ful grace of Je-sus, Great-er than all my sin;
2 *Won-der-ful grace of Je-sus, Reach-ing to all the lost,*
3 Won-der-ful grace of Je-sus, Reach-ing the most de-filed.

1. 我口舌怎能述說，更將從何頌讚？
2. 藉救恩我罪得赦，並拯救我靈魂；
3. 靠主的大能救助，使我順服歸神；

1 How shall my tongue de-scribe it, Where shall its praise be-gin?
2 *By it I have been par-doned, Saved to the ut-ter-most;*
3 By its trans-form-ing pow-er Mak-ing him God's dear child,

1. 祂除我罪擔憂愁，使我得着自由，
2. 主為我解脱捆綁，使我得着釋放，
3. 蒙主賜平安滿足，得享天堂永福，

1 Tak-ing a-way my bur-den, Set-ting my spir-it free,
2 *Chains have been torn a-sun-der, Giv-ing me lib-er-ty,*
3 Pur-chas-ing peace and heav-en For all e-ter-ni-ty—

1. 耶穌奇妙的救恩使我得拯救。
2. 耶穌奇妙的救恩使我得拯救。
3. 耶穌奇妙的救恩使我得拯救。

1 For the won-der-ful grace of Je-sus reach-es me.
2 *For the won-der-ful grace of Je-sus reach-es me.*
3 And the won-der-ful grace of Je-sus reach-es me.

主耶穌奇妙無比的救恩，深過波濤滾滾大海
Won-der-ful the matchless grace of Je - sus, Deep-er than the might-y roll - ing
洋；高過最高山嶺，美過最美泉源，
sea; High - er than the moun - tain, spark - ling like a foun - tain,
奇妙救恩足夠我需用；闊過我一生所行的
All suf - fi - cient grace for e - ven me; Broad-er than the scope of my trans -
過犯，大過我一切罪污邪情；我
gres - sions, Great - er far than all my sin and shame; O
要稱揚主聖名，我要讚美主·聖名！
mag - ni - fy the pre - cious name of Je - sus, Praise His name!

79

暴風雨中之避難所
A Shelter in the Time of Storm

There is none as holy as the Lord, . . .
neither is there any rock like our God. — I Samuel 2:2
Vernon J. Charlesworth
Adapted by Ira D. Sankey
SHELTER
Ira D. Sankey
1. 主是磐石容我藏躲，暴風雨中之避難所；
2. 日間遮蔭夜間保護，暴風雨中之避難所；
3. 驚風海濤浪潮擊身，暴風雨中之避難所；
4. 神聖磐石容身之處，暴風雨中之避難所；
1 The Lord's our rock, in Him we hide, A shel-ter in the time of storm;
2 A shade by day, de-fense by night, A shel-ter in the time of storm;
3 The rag-ing storms may 'round us beat, A shel-ter in the time of storm;
4 O Rock di-vine, O Ref-uge dear, A shel-ter in the time of storm;
1. 災禍來臨我得穩妥，暴風雨中之避難所。
2. 無事可驚無事可怖，暴風雨中之避難所。
3. 永遠藏身主裡安穩，暴風雨中之避難所。
4. 何時有難主卽幫助，暴風雨中之避難所。
1 Se-cure what-ev-er ill be-tide, A shel-ter in the time of storm.
2 No fears a-larm, no fears af-fright, A shel-ter in the time of storm.
3 We'll nev-er leave our safe re-treat, A shel-ter in the time of storm.
4 Be Thou our help-er ev-er near, A shel-ter in the time of storm.
主耶穌是磐石我之避難所，如
O Je-sus is a rock in a wea-ry land, A
沙漠地，有蔭涼所；主耶穌是磐
wea-ry land, a wea-ry land; O, Je-sus is a

石 我 之 避 難 所，暴 風 雨 中 之 避 難 所。
rock in a wea - ry land, A shel - ter in the time of storm.

80

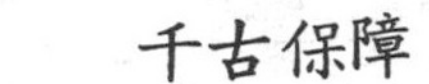
千古保障

O God, Our Help in Ages Past

Psalm 90
Isaac Watts

Our soul waiteth for the Lord; He is our help . . . . — Psalm 33:20

ST. ANNE
William Croft

1. 上 主 是 我 昔 日 幫 助，是 我 将 來 盼 望；
2. 在 主 寶 座 蔭 庇 之 下，聖 徒 常 得 安 住；
3. 太 初 之 時 天 地 未 闢，山 川 尚 未 安 定；
4. 似 箭 光 陰 如 川 不 息，世 人 瞬 間 即 逝；
5. 恩 主 是 我 昔 日 幫 助，是 我 将 來 盼 望；

1 O God, our help in a - ges past, Our hope for years to come,
2 *Un - der the shad - ow of Thy throne Still may we dwell se - cure;*
3 Be - fore the hills in or - der stood, Or earth re - ceived her frame,
4 *A thou - sand a - ges in Thy sight Are like an eve - ning gone;*
5 O God, our help in a - ges past, Our hope for years to come,

1. 每 遇 風 波 是 避 難 處，是 我 安 宅 保 障！
2. 我 主 膀 臂 能 力 極 大，時 常 将 我 保 護。
3. 無 始 以 來 神 是 無 比，直 到 永 世 無 盡。
4. 猶 如 曉 夢 醒 時 難 覓，不 復 為 人 所 識。
5. 我 若 遇 難 求 主 保 護，作 我 安 宅 保 障！阿 門。

1 Our shel - ter from the storm - y blast, And our e - ter - nal home!
2 *Suf - fi - cient is Thine arm a - lone, And our de - fense is sure.*
3 From ev - er - last - ing Thou art God, To end - less years the same.
4 *Short as the watch that ends the night, Be - fore the ris - ing sun.*
5 Be Thou our guide while life shall last, And our e - ter - nal home! A-men.

81

堅固保障
A Mighty Fortress Is Our God

The Lord is my rock, my fortress, and my deliverer . . . — Psalm 18:2

Based on Psalm 46
Martin Luther
Tr. by Frederick H. Hedge

EIN' FESTE BURG
Martin Luther

1. 上 主 是 我 堅 固 保 障，是 我 山 寨 和 避 難 所；
2. 我 若 單 靠 己 力 行 走，每 遇 戰 爭 必 要 退 後；
3. 若 全 世 界 充 滿 鬼 魔，救 主 聖 徒 仍 能 安 妥；
4. 主 言 有 權 高 過 萬 王，世 上 帝 王 不 能 相 比；

1 A might-y for-tress is our God, A bul-wark nev-er fail - ing;
2 *Did we in our own strength con-fide, Our striv-ing would be los - ing,*
3 And though this world with dev-ils filled, Should threat-en to un-do us,
4 *That word a-bove all earth-ly powers, No thanks to them, a-bid - eth;*

1. 苦 海 汪 洋 主 為 救 星，四 無 生 門 我 仍 有 望。
2. 須 有 能 者 隨 時 幫 助，即 神 設 立 救 贖 恩 主。
3. 仇 敵 降 災 設 下 網 羅，主 為 道 路 助 我 勝 過。
4. 聖 靈 恩 賜 全 備 可 信，降 於 我 身 何 等 希 奇。

1 Our help-er He a-mid the flood Of mor-tal ills pre-vail - ing.
2 *Were not the right man on our side, The man of God's own choos - ing.*
3 We will not fear, for God hath willed His truth to tri-umph through us.
4 *The Spir-it and the gifts are ours Through Him who with us sid - eth.*

1. 雖 有 兇 惡 仇 敵，攻 擊 不 留 餘 力，對 我 仇 恨 刺
2. 若 問 所 設 為 誰？乃 主 耶 穌 基 督，又 稱 萬 有 主
3. 幽 暗 魔 王 興 起，我 靠 救 主 能 抵，敵 怒 不 能 久
4. 名 利 任 其 失 去，生 命 我 也 無 慮，身 家 雖 然 失

1 For still our an-cient foe Doth seek to work us woe— His craft and power are
2 *Dost ask who that may be? Christ Je-sus, it is He— Lord Sab-a-oth His*
3 The prince of dark-ness grim, We trem-ble not for him— His rage we can en-
4 *Let goods and kin-dred go, This mor-tal life al-so— The bod-y they may*

1. 骨，常用狡猾引誘，但我救主將我保護。
2. 牢，到永遠不更改，祂已得勝做我元帥。
3. 長，敵迫我能忍受，主言一出敵即敗退
4. 喪，主道終必興旺，救主之國存到永遠。阿門
1 great, And, armed with cru-el hate, On earth is not His e - qual.
2 name, From age to age the same, And He must win the bat - tle.
3 dure, For lo, his doom is sure: One lit-tle word shall fell him.
4 kill; God's truth a-bid-eth still: His king-dom is for-ev - er. A-men.

永世的君王 Now unto the King

81-1

Now to the King eternal, immortal, invisible, the only God, be honor. 1 Tim. 1:17

William David Young

William David Young

祢是永世的君王，永不朽壞，不能看見，獨
Now un-to the King e - ter-nal, im - mor-tal, in - vis - i - ble, the
一的眞神，願尊貴，榮耀歸祢到永遠。阿門。
on-ly wise God, be hon-or, and glo-ry for-ev-er-more. A - men.

82

祂藏我靈

He Hideth My Soul

I will put thee in a cleft of the Rock, and will cover thee with My hand. — Exodus 33:22

Fanny J. Crosby

HE HIDETH MY SOUL
William J. Kirkpatrick

1. 奇 妙 的 救 主 就 是 耶 穌 我 主 ， 這
2. 奇 妙 的 救 主 就 是 耶 穌 我 主 ， 祂
3. 每 時 每 刻 祂 賜 我 恩 惠 無 窮 ， 祂
4. 穿 上 主 所 賜 聖 潔 光 榮 衣 裳 ， 將
1 A won - der - ful Sav - ior is Je - sus my Lord, A
2 A won - der - ful Sav - ior is Je - sus my Lord, A
3 With num - ber - less bless - ings each mo - ment He crowns, He
4 When clothed in His bright - ness trans - port - ed I rise And, To

1. 奇 妙 的 救 主 屬 我 ； 祂 藏 我 靈 魂 在 於
2. 將 我 的 重 擔 挪 去 ； 扶 持 保 守 我 使 我
3. 靈 又 充 滿 我 心 中 ； 當 我 被 提 時 我 願
4. 與 救 主 空 中 相 見 ； 願 與 衆 聖 徒 一 齊
1 won - der - ful Sav - ior to me; He hid - eth my soul in the
2 tak - eth my bur - den a - way; He hold - eth me up, and I
3 filled with His full - ness di - vine, I sing in my rap - ture, "O
4 meet Him in clouds of the sky, His per - fect sal - va - tion, His

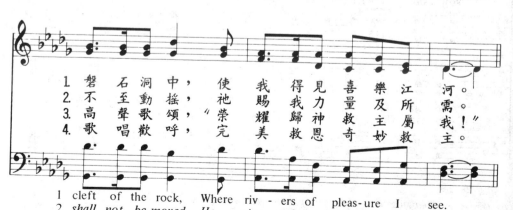

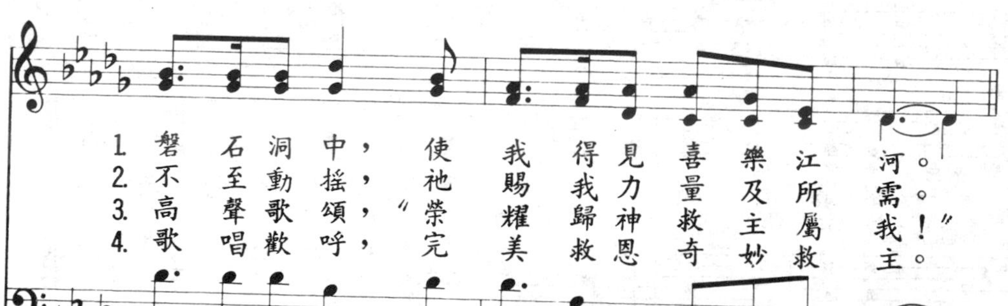

1. 磐 石 洞 中 ， 使 我 得 見 喜 樂 江 河 。
2. 不 至 動 搖 ， 祂 賜 我 力 量 及 所 需 。
3. 高 聲 歌 頌 ， " 榮 耀 歸 神 救 主 屬 我 ！ "
4. 歌 唱 歡 呼 ， 完 美 救 恩 奇 妙 救 主 。
1 cleft of the rock, Where riv - ers of pleas - ure I see.
2 shall not be moved, He giv - eth me strength for each day.
3 glo - ry to God For such a Re - deem - er as mine!"
4 won - der - ful love, I'll shout with the mil - lions on high.

祂 藏我靈魂 在磐 石洞 穴裡，如 乾渴之
He hid-eth my soul in the cleft of the rock That shad-ows a
地得蔭 庇；祂 藏我生命 在祂 大慈愛 裡，
dry, thirst-y land; He hid-eth my life in the depths of His love,
用 祂全能手來 扶 持， 用 祂全能手來扶 持。
And cov-ers me there with His hand, And cov-ers me there with His hand.

但我要歌頌你的力量，早晨要高唱你的慈愛，因為你作過我的高臺，在我急難的日子，作過我的避難所。
我的力量阿，我要歌頌你，因為 神是我的高臺，是賜恩與我的 神。

詩篇五十九篇
16—17節

83

面對面

Face to Face

Carrie E. Breck
For now we see through a glass darkly; . . .
—I Corinthians 13:12
FACE TO FACE
Grant C. Tullar
1. 與救主基督面對面，何等榮耀的相見—
2. 如今因有黑雲遮掩，不能清晰見主面，
3. 主同在時何等快樂，憂傷痛苦全消除，
4. 面對面有福的良辰！面對面萬事知清，
1 Face to face with Christ my Sav - ior, Face to face—what will it be—
2 On - ly faint-ly now I see Him, With the dark-ened veil be-tween,
3 What re-joic-ing in His pres-ence When are ban-ished grief and pain,
4 Face to face! O bliss-ful mo - ment! Face to face— to see and know;
1. 因祂曾為我罪釘死，我羨慕見祂慈面。
2. 但那榮耀日必來臨，我必要見主榮面。
3. 彎曲道路全都修直，隱密事都要顯露。
4. 面對面見我救贖主，祂的愛何等豐盛。
1 When with rap-ture I be-hold Him, Je-sus Christ who died for me?
2 But a bless-ed day is com - ing When His glo - ry shall be seen.
3 When the crook-ed ways are straight-ened And the dark things shall be plain.
4 Face to face with my Re-deem - er, Je-sus Christ who loves me so.
面對面我與主相見，在那遙遠的青天；
Face to face I shall be-hold Him, Far be-yond the star-ry sky;
面對面在主榮耀中，我必親見主榮面！
Face to face in all His glo-ry, I shall see Him by and by!

84

當我們回到天家

When We All Get to Heaven

Then we, . . . shall be caught up together with the Lord . . .
and so shall we ever be with the Lord. — I Thessalonians 4:17

Eliza E. Hewitt

HEAVEN
Emily D. Wilson

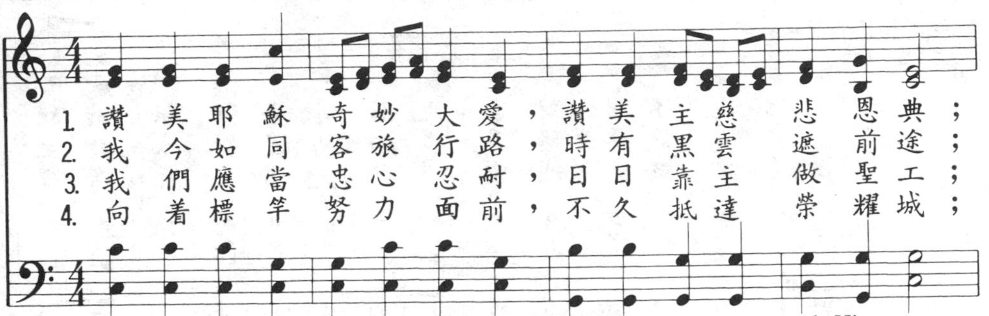

1. 讚美耶穌奇妙大愛，讚美主慈悲恩典；
2. 我今如同客旅行路，時有黑雲遮前途；
3. 我們應當忠心忍耐，日日靠主做聖工；
4. 向着標竿努力面前，不久抵達榮耀城；

1 Sing the won-drous love of Je - sus, Sing His mer - cy and His grace;
2 *While we walk the pil-grim path-way Clouds will o - ver - spread the sky;*
3 Let us then be true and faith-ful, Trust-ing, serv - ing ev - ery day;
4 *On - ward to the prize be-fore us! Soon His beau - ty we'll be - hold:*

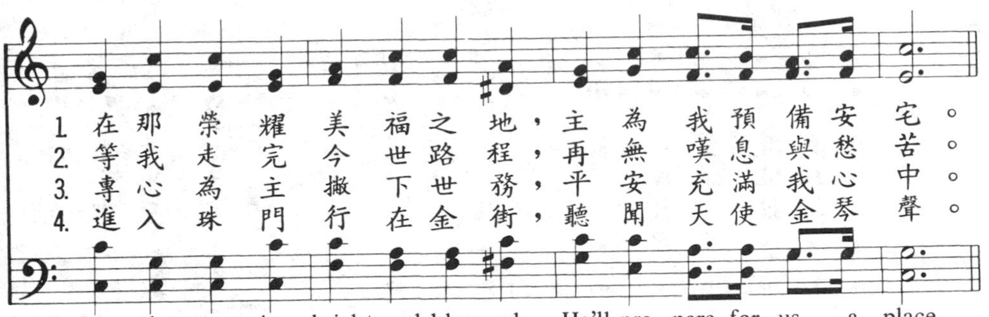

1. 在那榮耀美福之地，主為我預備安宅。
2. 等我走完今世路程，再無嘆息與愁苦。
3. 專心為主撇下世務，平安充滿我心中。
4. 進入珠門行在金街，聽聞天使金琴聲。

1 In the man-sions bright and bless-ed He'll pre - pare for us a place.
2 *But when trav-eling days are o - ver Not a shad-ow, not a sigh.*
3 Just one glimpse of Him in glo - ry Will the toils of life re - pay.
4 *Soon the pearl - y gates will o - pen— We shall tread the streets of gold.*

當我們回到天家，那日期真歡喜，極大福
When we all get to heav - en, What a day of re-joic-ing that will
氣！當我們見耶穌，我們要唱得勝凱歌！
be! When we all see Je - sus, We'll sing and shout the vic - to - ry!

85

是否記下我的名？
Is My Name Written There?

And another Book was opened which is the Book of Life . . . — Revelation 20:12

Mary A. Kidder

IS MY NAME
Frank M. Davis

1. 主啊，我不求財富，也不求金和銀，我願
2. 主啊，我罪惡雖多，多如海邊塵沙，但主
3. 華美燦爛天城中，多少光明居所，榮耀

1 Lord, I care not for rich - es, Nei - ther sil - ver nor gold, I would
2 *Lord, my sins they are man - y, Like the sands of the sea, But Thy*
3 O that beau - ti - ful cit - y With its man-sions of light, With its

1. 有真實憑據，將來天家能進；在主永生的
2. 寶血能洗淨，使我無疵無瑕；因主曾向我
3. 裡的眾聖徒，穿上潔白衣袍；在那聖潔的
1 make sure of heav - en, I would en - ter the fold. In the book of Thy
2 blood, O my Sav - ior, Is suf - fi - cient for me; For Thy prom - ise is
3 glo - ri - fied be - ings In pure gar - ments of white; Where no e - vil thing

1. 國裡，莊嚴生命册上，請問耶穌我救主，是否
2. 應許，並且明確寫下，“你的罪雖如硃紅，必定
3. 境地，罪惡不再侵襲，眾天使圍觀之下，我的
1 king - dom, With its pag - es so fair, Tell me, Je - sus, my Sav - ior, Is my
2 writ - ten In bright let - ters that glow, "Though your sins be as scar - let, I will
3 com - eth To de - spoil what is fair; Where the an - gels are watch - ing, Yes, my

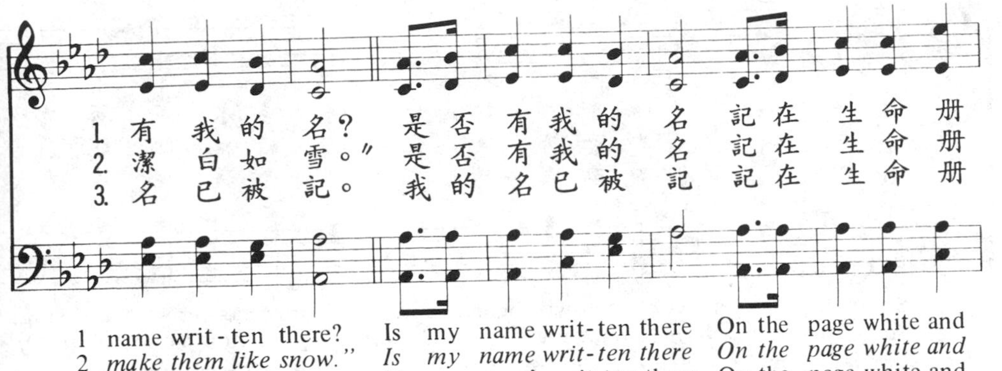
1. 有 我 的 名？ 是 否 有 我 的 名 記 在 生 命 册
2. 潔 白 如 雪。" 是 否 有 我 的 名 記 在 生 命 册
3. 名 已 被 記。 我 的 名 已 被 記 記 在 生 命 册
1 name writ - ten there? Is my name writ-ten there On the page white and
2 *make them like snow." Is my name writ-ten there On the page white and*
3 name's writ-ten there. Yes, my name's writ-ten there On the page white and

1. 上？ 在 天 國 生 命 册 上，是 否 記 下 我 名？
2. 上？ 在 天 國 生 命 册 上，是 否 記 下 我 名？
3. 上！ 在 天 國 生 命 册 上，我 的 名 已 被 記！

1 fair? In the book of Thy king-dom, Is my name writ-ten there?
2 *fair? In the book of Thy king-dom, Is my name writ-ten there?*
3 fair! In the book of Thy king-dom, Yes, my name's writ-ten there!

神阿，求你按你的慈愛憐恤我，按你豐盛的慈悲塗抹我的過犯。
求祢將我的罪孽洗除淨盡，並潔除我的罪。

詩篇五十一篇
1 — 2節

靠恩得救

Saved By Grace

Fanny J. Crosby

God forbid that I should glory, save in the Cross . . . .
— Galatians 6:14

George C. Stabbins
Arr. by Donald P. Hustad

1 塵世網羅我将脱掉，生前苦味永不再嚐；
2 地上帳棚将要衰殘，不知何時就臨眼前；
3 信徒務要儆醒等待，把燈剔亮望主快來，

1. Some day the sil-ver cord will break, And I no more as now shall sing;
2. *Some day my earth-ly house will fall, I can-not tell how soon 'twill be;*
3. Some day, when fades the gold-en sun Be-neath the ro - sy tint-ed west,

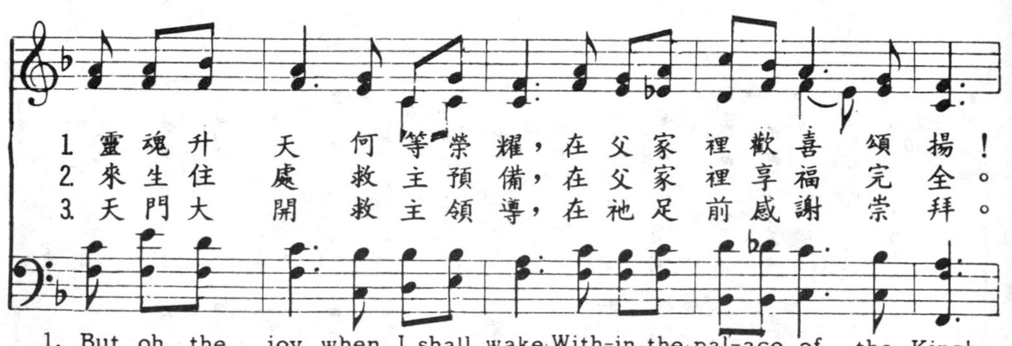

1 靈魂升天何等榮耀，在父家裡歡喜頌揚！
2 來生住處救主預備，在父家裡享福完全。
3 天門大開救主領導，在祂足前感謝崇拜。

1. But oh, the joy when I shall wake With-in the pal-ace of the King!
2. *But this I know my All in All Has now a place in heav'n for me.*
3. My bless-ed Lord will say, "Well done!" And I shall en - ter in - to rest.

我必要見主面對面，永遠歌唱救我恩典；
And I shall see Him face to face, And tell the sto-ry—Saved by grace;
我必要見主面對面，永遠歌唱救我恩典。
And I shall see Him face to face, And tell the sto-ry—Saved by grace.

豈可空手回天府？

Must I Go and Empty Handed?

"In My Father's house are many mansions." — John 14:2
Charles C. Luther
George C. Stabbins
1. 主若今日接我靈魂，我能坦然見主否？
2. 今日見主復有何憂，因主耶穌已救我；
3. 追想昔日虛度光陰，現時豈願再虛度？
4. 我實甘願竭盡心才，殷勤作工趁現在；
1. "Must I go, and emp - ty hand - ed," Thus my dear Re-deem - er meet?
2. Not at death I shrink nor fal - ter, For my Sav-iour saves me now;
3. O the years in sin - ning wast-ed, Could I but re - call them now,
4. O ye saints, a-rouse, be earn-est, Up and work while yet 'tis day;
1. 缺少珍寶向主獻陳，贖罪大恩白白受。
2. 惟有一事使我懷憂，空佔地土未結果。
3. 我今奉獻全身全心，聽主命令行其路。
4. 黑夜已深白晝將近，儆醒救人等主來。
1. Not one day of serv-ice give Him, Lay no tro-phy at His feet?
2. But to meet Him emp-ty hand-ed, Tho't of that now clouds my brow.
3. I would give them to my Sav - iour, To His will I'd glad - ly bow.
4. Ere the night of death o'er-take thee, Strive for souls while still you may.
工尚未成，我卽去乎；何能如此見恩主？
"Must I go, and emp-ty hand-ed?" Must I meet my Sav - iour so?
未領一人來歸耶穌，豈可空手回天府？
Not one soul with which to greet Him: Must I emp- ty hand- ed go?

88

日落之那邊

Beyond the Sunset
For now we see through a glass darkly; but then face to face. — I Corinthians 13:12
SUNSET
Virgil P. Brock
Blanche Kerr Brock
1. 日落之那邊，賜福之早晨，在天堂
2. 日落之那邊，雲霧盡消去，無風暴
3. 日落之那邊，主親手引領，到父寶
4. 日落之那邊，故人樂團圓，親愛者
1 Be-yond the sun-set, O bliss-ful morn-ing, When with our
2 Be-yond the sun-set no clouds will gath-er, No storms will
3 Be-yond the sun-set a hand will guide me To God the
4 Be-yond the sun-set, O glad re-un-ion, With our dear
1. 樂境，與主相親；勞碌盡完畢，榮耀之
2. 威脅，無憂無慮；榮耀快樂日，永遠快
3. 座前，見父榮面；同在榮耀中，主伸手
4. 久別，歡喜相見；在天家美地，不再有
1 Sav-ior heaven is be-gun; Earth's toil-ing end-ed, O glo-rious
2 threat-en, no fears an-noy; O day of glad-ness, O day un-
3 Fa-ther, whom I a-dore; His glo-rious pres-ence, His words of
4 loved ones who've gone be-fore; In that fair home-land we'll know no
1. 黎明，日落之那邊，永遠歡欣。
2. 樂日，日落之那邊，歡樂不息！
3. 相迎，美麗的那邊，直到萬年。
4. 別離，日落之那邊，歡樂永遠！
1 dawn-ing, Be-yond the sun-set, when day is done.
2 end-ing, Be-yond the sun-set, e-ter-nal joy!
3 wel-come, Will be my por-tion on that fair shore.
4 part-ing, Be-yond the sun-set, for-ev-er-more!

89

與主同住

Abide With Me

And now, . . . abide in Him, that when He shall appear we may have confidence, and not be ashamed . . . — I John 2:28

EVENTIDE

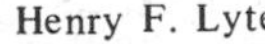
Henry F. Lyte

William H. Monk

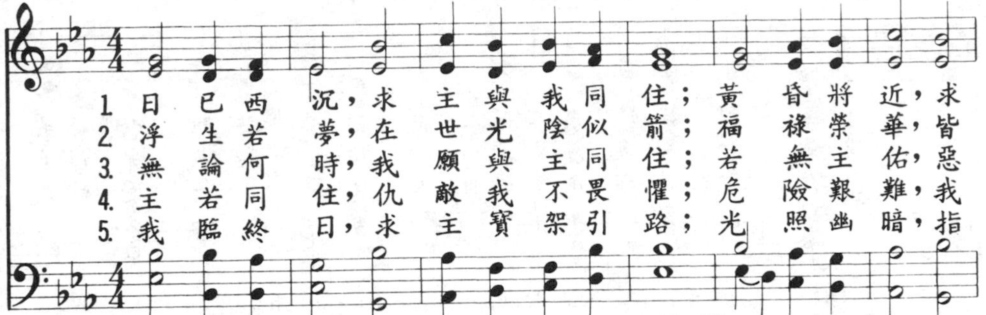

1. 日已西沉，求主與我同住；黃昏將近，求
2. 浮生若夢，在世光陰似箭；福祿榮華，皆
3. 無論何時，我願與主同住；若無主佑，惡
4. 主若同住，仇敵我不畏懼；危險艱難，我
5. 我臨終日，求主寶架引路；光照幽暗，指

1 A - bide with me— fast falls the e - ven - tide; The dark-ness deep-ens—
2 *Swift to its close ebbs out life's lit - tle day; Earth's joys grow dim, its*
3 I need Thy pres-ence ev - ery pass - ing hour; What but Thy grace can
4 *I fear no foe, with Thee at hand to bless; Ills have no weight and*
5 Hold Thou Thy cross be - fore my clos - ing eyes; Shine thru the gloom and

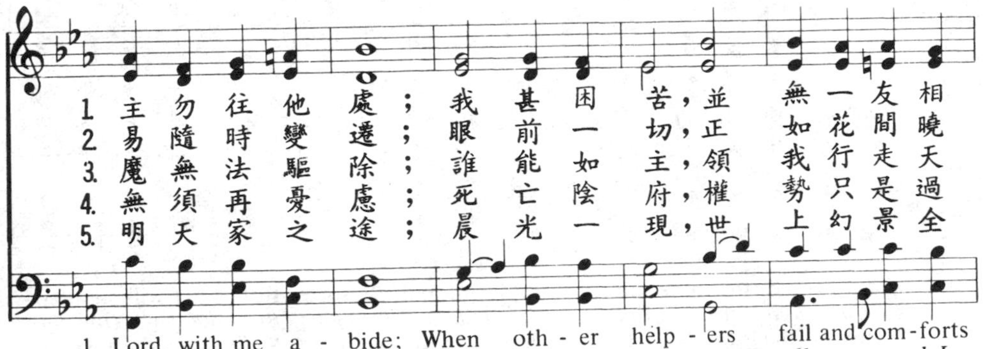

1. 主勿往他處；我甚困苦，並無一友相
2. 易隨時變遷；眼前一切，正如花間曉
3. 魔無法驅除；誰能如主，領我行走天
4. 無須再憂慮；死亡陰府，權勢只是過
5. 明天家之途；晨光一現，世上幻景全

1 Lord, with me a - bide; When oth - er help - ers fail and com-forts
2 *glo - ries pass a - way; Change and de - cay in all a-round I*
3 foil the temp-ter's power? Who like Thy - self my guide and stay can
4 *tears no bit - ter - ness; Where is death's sting? where, grave, thy vic - to -*
5 point me to the skies; Heaven's morn-ing breaks and earth's vain shad-ows

1. 助；無能無友，求主與我同住。
2. 露；惟主不變，求主與我同住。
3. 路？不論陰晴，求主與我同住。
4. 度；主必得勝，因主與我同住。
5. 無；或生或死，求主與我同住。阿門。

1 flee, Help of the help-less, O a - bide with me.
2 *see; O Thou who chang-est not, a - bide with me.*
3 be? Through cloud and sun - shine, O a - bide with me.
4 *ry? I tri - umph still if Thou a - bide with me.*
5 flee; In life, in death, O Lord, a - bide with me. A-men.

90

當我見主時

When We See Christ

. . . We shall be like Him for we shall see Him as He is.
— I John 3:2

Esther Kerr Rusthoi

WHEN WE SEE CHRIST
Esther Kerr Rusthoi

1. 每當試煉來臨，時日痛苦難當，我
2. 每當長夜漫漫，四境昏暗無光，我
3. 生命瞬即消逝，人生風暴將過，我

1 Oft - times the day seems long, our tri - als hard to bear, We're
2 *Some-times the sky looks dark with not a ray of light, We're*
3 Life's day will soon be o'er, all storms for - ev - er past, We'll

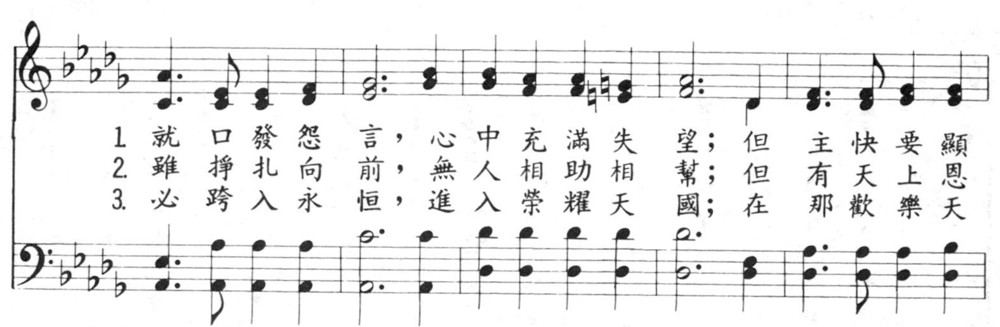
1. 就口發怨言，心中充滿失望；但主快要顯
2. 雖掙扎向前，無人相助相幫；但有天上恩
3. 必跨入永恒，進入榮耀天國；在那歡樂天
1 tempt - ed to com-plain, to mur-mur and de - spair; But Christ will soon ap -
2 tossed and driv - en on, no hu-man help in sight; But there is One in
3 cross the great di - vide to glo - ry, safe at last. We'll share the joys of

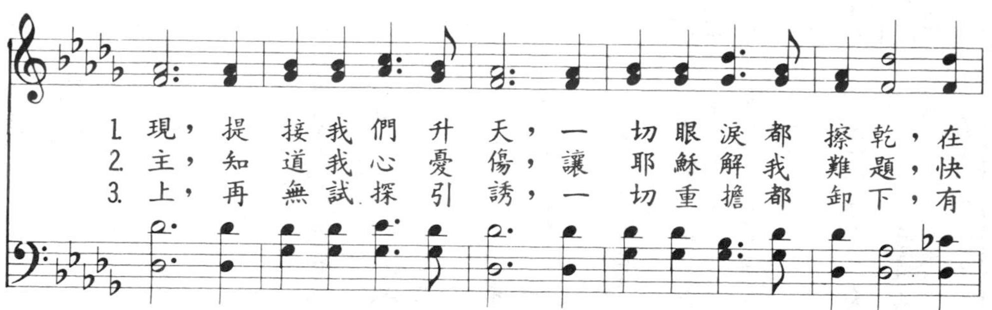
1. 現，提接我們升天，一切眼淚都擦乾，在
2. 主，知道我心憂傷，讓耶穌解我難題，快
3. 上，再無試探引誘，一切重擔都卸下，有
1 pear to catch His Bride a - way, All tears for - ev - er o - ver in
2 heaven who knows our deep-est care, Let Je-sus solve your prob-lem—just
3 heaven— a harp, a home, a crown, The tempt-er will be ban-ished, we'll

1. 神永恒裡面。
2. 來向祂求告。
3. 冠冕為我留。
一切都得報償，當我見
It will be worth it all when we see
1 God's e - ter - nal day.
2 go to Him in prayer.
3 lay our bur-den down.
主時，因此我不介意，當我見主；
Je - sus, Life's trials will seem so small when we see Christ;
一見祂的榮面，一切憂慮丟棄，
One glimpse of His dear face all sor-row will e-rase,
我仍勇往直前，到見主面。
So brave - ly run the race 'til we see Christ.

91

我的榮耀

O, That Will be Glory for Me

But when the multitude saw it, they marvelled and glorified God
Matthew 9:8
Charles H. Gabriel
GLORY SONG
Charles H. Gabriel
1. 當 我 作 完 主 交 付 的 聖 工 ，得 見 恩 主 面 得
2. 我 主 賜 我 無 限 無 量 恩 典 ，得 脫 屬 地 帳 蓬
3. 在 榮 耀 中 與 衆 聖 徒 相 見 ，快 樂 像 江 河 環
1 When all my la-bors and tri-als are o'er, And I am safe on that
2 When by the gift of His in-fi-nite grace, I am ac-cord-ed in
3 Friends will be there I have loved long a-go; Joy like a riv-er a-
1. 進 榮 耀 中 ， 住 在 彼 岸 得 享 福 樂 無 窮 ，
2. 回 家 在 天 ， 我 得 站 在 主 前 見 祂 榮 面 ，
3. 繞 我 身 邊 ， 更 寶 貴 是 我 得 見 主 笑 臉 ，
1 beau-ti-ful shore, Just to be near the dear Lord I a-dore
2 heav-en a place, Just to be there and to look on His face
3 round me will flow; Yet, just a smile from my Sav-ior, I know,
1. 這 就 是 我 永 遠 的 大榮 耀 。我 的 榮 耀 ，
2. 這 就 是 我 永 遠 的 大 榮 耀 。O, that will be
3. 這 就 是 我 永 遠 的 大 榮 耀 。我 的 榮
O, that will
1 Will through the a-ges be glo-ry for me.
2 Will through the a-ges be glo-ry for me.
3 Will through the a-ges be glo-ry for me.
我 的 榮 耀 ， 我 的 榮 耀 ， 我 的 榮 耀 ， 靠 着 主
glo-ry for me, Glo-ry for me, glo-ry for me; When by His
耀 ， 我 的 榮 耀 ， 我 的 榮 耀 ， 我 的 榮 耀 ，
be glo-ry for me, Glo-ry for me, glo-ry for me;

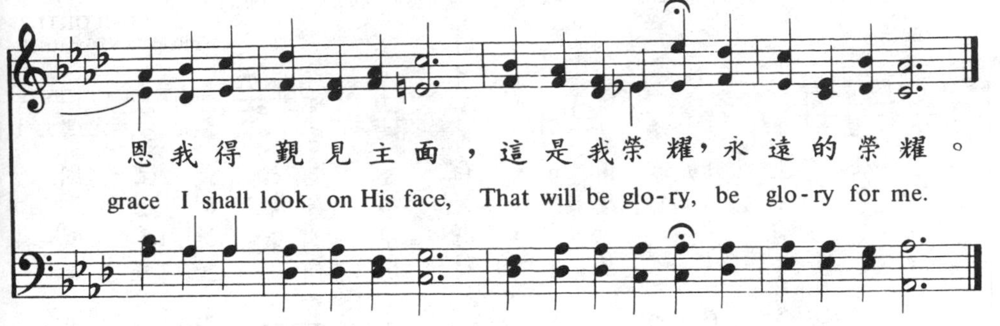
恩我得 覲見主面，這是我榮耀，永遠的榮耀。
grace I shall look on His face, That will be glo-ry, be glo-ry for me.

榮耀頌

92

Gloria Patri

And He said unto them, . . . how much more shall your heavenly Father give the Holy Spirit . . . Luke 11 :13

GLORIA PATRI
Henry W. Greatorex

Source unknown

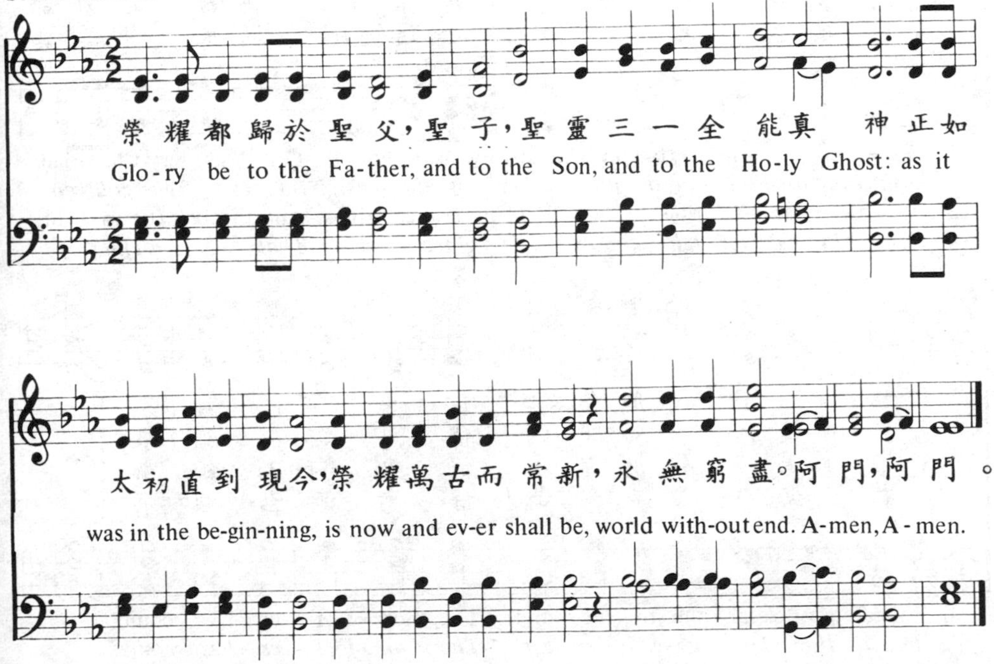

榮耀都歸於聖父，聖子，聖靈三一全能真 神正如
Glo-ry be to the Fa-ther, and to the Son, and to the Ho-ly Ghost: as it

太初直到現今，榮耀萬古而常新，永無窮盡。阿門，阿門。
was in the be-gin-ning, is now and ev-er shall be, world with-out end. A-men, A-men.

8

93

保惠師已經來
The Comforter Has Come

I will pray the Father and He will give you another Comforter. — John 14:16

Frank Bottome

COMFORTER
William J. Kirkpatrick

1. 願主助我傳道，任憑主領何往，因為人心黑暗，罪惡束縛煩惱；勿以福音為恥，只管大胆傳揚：保惠師已經來！
2. 願主教會復興，兄弟姊妹同心，到處傳揚主名，拯救遠近罪人；脱離黑暗權勢，進入奇妙光明！保惠師已經來！
3. 基督是我牧者，捨命為我迷羊，我前流離失所，祢今將我尋回；仇敵能力都敗，高唱得勝凱歌：保惠師已經來！
4. 今手已經扶犂，往事何必重提？等候有福指望，忍耐忠心到底；同聲讚美真神，聖哉聖哉聖哉！保惠師已經來！
1 O spread the ti-dings 'round wher-ev-er man is found, Wher-ev-er hu-man hearts and hu-man woes a-bound; Let ev-ery Chris-tian tongue pro-claim the joy-ful sound: The Com-fort-er has come!
2 The long, long night is past, the morn-ing breaks at last, And hushed the dread-ful sound and fu-ry of the blast, As o-ver gold-en hills the day ad-vanc-es fast! The Com-fort-er has come!
3 Lo, the great King of kings, with heal-ing in His wings, To ev-ery cap-tive soul a full de-liv-erance brings; And through the va-cant cells the song of tri-umph rings: The Com-fort-er has come!
4 O bound-less love di-vine! How shall this tongue of mine To won-dering mor-tals tell the match-less grace di-vine— That I, a child of hell, should in His im-age shine? The Com-fort-er has come!

保惠師已經來，保惠師已經來！聖
The Com-fort-er has come, the Com-fort-er has come! The
靈由天降臨，天父應許是真；願主助我傳
Ho-ly Ghost from Heaven, the Fa-ther's pro-mise given; O spread the ti-dings
道，任憑主領何往，保惠師已經來！
'round wher-ev-er man is found—The Com-fort-er has come!

聖靈居衷

Blessed Quietness

He shall give you another comforter that He may abide with you forever. — John 14:16

BLESSED QUIETNESS
W. S. Marshall
Arranged by James M. Kirk

Manie P. Ferguson

1. 歡喜快樂如同江河，因為聖靈復興我；
2. 復活生命在我心中，榮耀喜樂大奮興；
3. 聖靈來臨啓迪我心，如同旱地得甘霖；
4. 有如田園被水澆灌，公義善果滿處結；
5. 奇妙救恩聖哉救主，是我榮耀與豐富；
1 Joys are flow - ing like a riv - er Since the Com - fort-er has come;
2 *Bring-ing life and health and glad - ness All a - round, this heav'n-ly Guest*
3 Like the rain that falls from heav - en, Like the sun - light from the sky,
4 *See, a fruit - ful field is grow - ing, Bless - ed fruit of right-eous - ness;*
5 What a won - der - ful sal - va - tion, Where we al - ways see His face!

1. 聖靈榮光將我充滿，主以我心為聖所。
2. 刪去不信解去疑心，惟順從主與主親。
3. 聖靈下降照耀輝煌，如同太陽發光明。
4. 又如生命活水泉源，湧流於荒涼原野。
5. 有主同在何等甘甜，得享安息與美福！
1 He a - bides with us for - ev - er, Makes the trust - ing heart His home.
2 *Ban-ished un - be - lief and sad - ness, Changed our wea - ri - ness to rest.*
3 So the Ho - ly Ghost is giv - en, Com - ing on us from on high.
4 *And the streams of life are flow - ing In the lone - ly wil - der - ness.*
5 What a per - fect hab - i - ta - tion, What a qui - et rest - ing place!

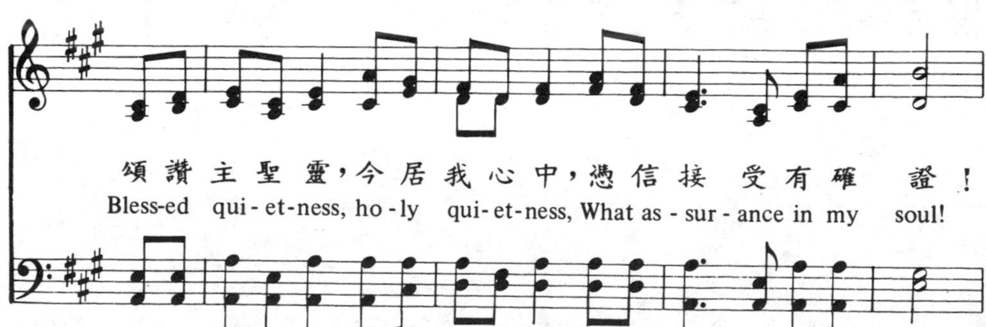
頌讚主聖靈，今居我心中，憑信接受有確證！
Bless-ed qui - et - ness, ho - ly qui - et - ness, What as - sur - ance in my soul!

海浪雖翻騰，我心却鎮靜，萬事如雲無踪影！
On the storm-y sea He speaks peace to me, How the bil-lows cease to roll!

懇求聖靈如鴿降臨

Come, Holy Spirit, Heavenly Dove

95

And I saw the Spirit, descending like a dove and it abode upon Him. John 1:32

GRÄFENBERG
Praxis Pietatis Melica
Johann Crüger

Isaac Watts

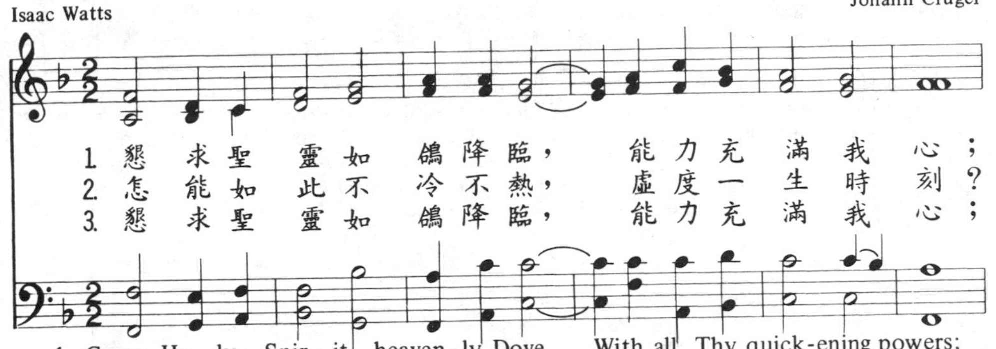
1. 懇求聖靈如鴿降臨，能力充滿我心；
2. 怎能如此不冷不熱，虛度一生時刻？
3. 懇求聖靈如鴿降臨，能力充滿我心；
1 Come, Ho-ly Spir-it, heaven-ly Dove, With all Thy quick-ening powers;
2 Dear Lord, and shall we ev-er live At this poor, dy-ing rate?
3 Come, Ho-ly Spir-it, heaven-ly Dove, With all Thy quick-ening powers;

1. 我心冷淡願主施恩，日日與主更親。
2. 愛主之心如此冷漠，主愛却深難測！
3. 願與人分享主慈愛，我靈再得復興。阿門
1 Kin-dle a flame of sa-cred love In these cold hearts of ours.
2 Our love so faint, so cold to Thee, And Thine to us so great!
3 Come, shed a-broad the Sav-ior's love, And that shall kin-dle ours. A-men.

96

聖哉！聖哉！

Holy, Holy

They rest not day and night,
saying holy, holy, holy, Lord God almighty.
— Revelation 4:8

Jimmy Owens

HOLY, HOLY
Jimmy Owens

1. 聖哉，聖哉，聖哉，聖哉，聖哉，聖哉，
2. 慈愛天父，慈愛天父，何等福氣成為
3. 寶貴耶穌，寶貴耶穌，感謝祢已救贖
4. 至善聖靈，至善聖靈，求祢重新充滿
5. 聖哉，聖哉，聖哉，聖哉，聖哉，聖哉，
6. 哈利路亞，哈利路亞，哈利路亞，
1 Ho - ly, ho - ly, ho - ly, ho - ly, Ho - ly, ho - ly,
2 Gra-cious Fa - ther, gra - cious Fa - ther, We're so blest to be your
3 Pre-cious Je - sus, pre - cious Je - sus, We're so glad that You've re -
4 Ho - ly Spir - it, Ho - ly Spir - it, Come and fill our hearts a -
5 Ho - ly, ho - ly, ho - ly ho - ly, Ho - ly, ho - ly,
6 Hal - le - lu - jah, hal - le - lu - jah, Hal - le - lu - jah,

1. 全能大主宰；我們誠心向祢敬拜，以愛
2. 兒女，慈愛天父；我們抬頭向祢敬拜，以愛
3. 我們，寶貴耶穌；我們舉手向祢敬拜，以愛
4. 我們，至善聖靈；我們高聲稱頌敬拜，以愛
5. 全能大主宰；我們誠心向祢敬拜，以愛
6. 哈利路亞；我們誠心向祢敬拜，以愛
1 Lord God Al - might - y; And we lift our hearts be - fore You as a
2 chil - dren, gra - cious Fa - ther; And we lift our heads be - fore You as a
3 deemed us, pre - cious Je - sus; And we lift our hands be - fore You as a
4 new, Ho - ly Spir - it; And we lift our voice be - fore You as a
5 Lord God Al - might - y; And we lift our hearts be - fore You as a
6 hal - le - lu - jah; And we lift our hearts be - fore You as a

1. 為 祭 獻 於 主，聖 哉，聖 哉，聖 哉，聖 哉。
2. 為 祭 獻 於 主，慈 愛 天 父，慈 愛 天 父。
3. 為 祭 獻 於 主，寶 貴 耶 穌，寶 貴 耶 穌。
4. 為 祭 獻 於 主，至 善 聖 靈，至 善 聖 靈。
5. 為 祭 獻 於 主，聖 哉，聖 哉，聖 哉，聖 哉。
6. 為 祭 獻 於 主，哈 利 路 亞，哈 利 路 亞。
1 to - ken of our love, Ho - ly, ho - ly, ho - ly, ho - ly.
2 *to - ken of our love, Gra - cious Fa - ther, gra - cious Fa - ther.*
3 to - ken of our love, Pre - cious Je - sus, pre - cious Je - sus.
4 *to - ken of our love, Ho - ly Spir - it, Ho - ly Spir - it.*
5 to - ken of our love, Ho - ly, ho - ly, ho - ly, ho - ly.
6 *to - ken of our love, Hal - le - lu - jah, hal - le - lu - jah.*

97

神真美好

God Is So Good

Unknown

African melody

Unison

1. 神 真 美 好，神 真 美 好，
1. God is so good, God is so good,

神 真 美 好，祂 對 我 真 好。
God is so good — He's so good to me.

2. 祂看顧我——時常看顧我。
3. 我願順服——順服祂旨意。
4. 祂真愛我——祂真是愛我。

2. *He cares for me ——*
3. I'll do His will ——
4. *He loves me so ——*

98

求聖靈降臨

Come, Holy Spirit

My grace is sufficient for thee; for my strength is made perfect in weakness. — II Corinthians 12:9
Gloria Gaither
William J. Gaither
COME, HOLY SPIRIT
William J. Gaither
1. 求 慈 善 聖 靈 今 降 臨， 扶 持 我 軟 弱 心
2. 聖 靈 能 力 能 除 憂 情， 能 使 病 痛 得 醫
3. 聖 靈 好 像 荒 漠 甘 泉， 能 滋 潤 枯 乾 心
1 Come as a wis-dom to child-ren, Come as new sight to the
2 Come as a rest to the wea-ry, Come as a balm for the
3 Come like a spring in the de-sert, Come to the with-ered of
1. 靈 ； 像 孩 童 得 着 了 智 慧， 像 瞎 眼
2. 治 ； 像 甘 露 能 滋 潤 我 心， 使 我 喜
3. 田 ； 求 聖 靈 醫 治 的 大 能， 使 我 靈
1 blind, Come, Lord, as strength to my weak-ness, Take me: soul,
2 sore, Come as a dew to my dry-ness: Fill me with
3 soul; O let Your sweet heal-ing pow-er Touch me and
1. 重 見 光 明 。
2. 樂 不 止 息 ， 求 慈 善 聖 靈，今 降 臨，
3. 能 得 完 全 。 Come, Ho-ly Spir-it, I need You,
1 bod-y and mind.
2 joy ev-er-more,
3 make me whole.
求 聖 靈 住 我 心； 我 需 要 聖 靈 的
Come, sweet Spir-it, I pray; Come in Your strength and Your

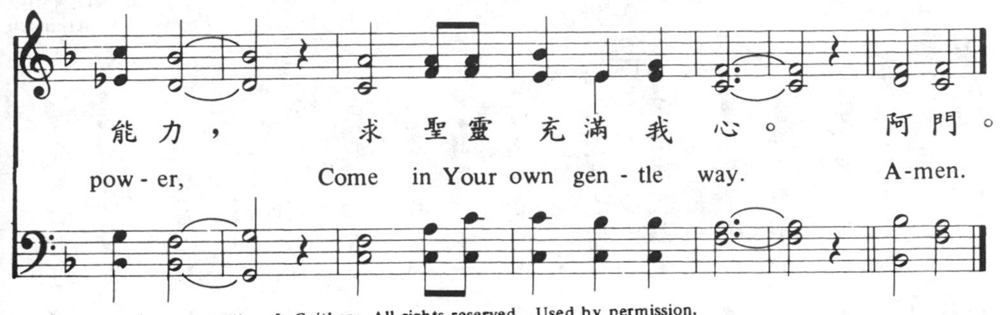
能力， 求聖靈充滿我心。 阿門。
pow - er, Come in Your own gen - tle way. A-men.

99

聖靈光芒

Holy Ghost, With Light Divine

MERCY
Louis M. Gottschalk
Adapted by Edwin P. Parker

Andrew Reed

. . . ye do well that ye heed, as unto a light that shineth in a dark place . . . — II Peter 1:19

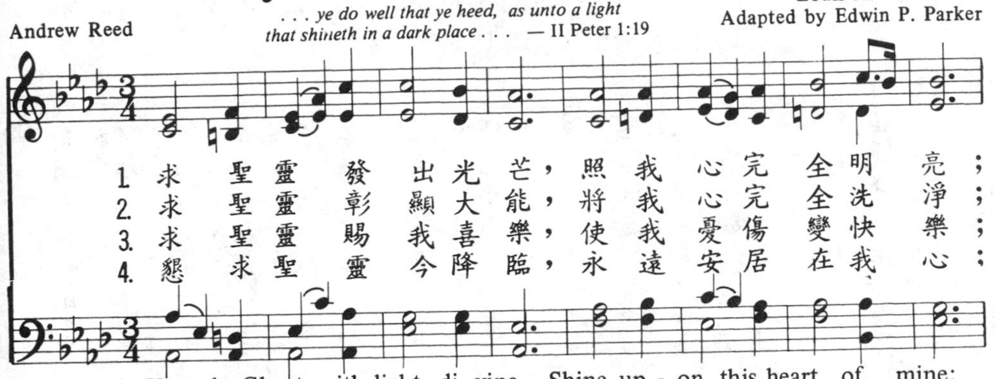
1. 求聖靈發出光芒，照我心完全明亮；
2. 求聖靈彰顯大能，将我心完全洗淨；
3. 求聖靈賜我喜樂，使我憂傷變快樂；
4. 懇求聖靈今降臨，永遠安居在我心；
1 Ho - ly Ghost, with light di - vine, Shine up - on this heart of mine;
2 *Ho - ly Ghost, with power di - vine, Cleanse this guilt - y heart of mine;*
3 Ho - ly Ghost, with joy di - vine, Cheer this sad - dened heart of mine;
4 *Ho - ly Spir - it, all di - vine, Dwell with - in this heart of mine;*

1. 使黑暗陰影驅走，化黑夜變為白晝。
2. 願我罪惡被盡除，我靈魂歸祢管束。
3. 不使愁苦臨近我，醫我創痛使我活。
4. 使我将偶像除盡，惟獨祢是至尊君。阿們。
1 Chase the shades of night a - way, Turn my dark - ness in - to day.
2 *Long hath sin with - out con - trol Held do - min - ion o'er my soul.*
3 Bid my man - y woes de - part, Heal my wound - ed, bleed - ing heart.
4 *Cast down ev - ery i - dol - throne, Reign su - preme and reign a - lone.* A-men.

100

上主之靈，懇求降臨

Spirit of God, Descend upon My Heart

And thou shalt love the Lord, thy God, with all thy heart, and soul. . . . — Mark 12:30

George Croly

MORECAMBE
Frederick C. Atkinson

1. 上主之靈，懇求降臨我心，默化我心，潛移世俗邪情；體恤我軟弱，彰顯祢能力，使我能愛祢照祢旨意行。
2. 我不妄求先知異夢經歷，也不求身軀突然相分離，不望天開，不求天使降臨，只求恩主除我心中陰影。
3. 主命令我：當愛主祢的神，當盡心盡意當竭盡心力！仰望十架，我心願歸向祢，求使我在祢光中尋見祢！
4. 教我確知一祢時刻在身旁，心靈重擔，教我知如何當；能除疑慮，能平無知反抗，有求未應仍存耐心盼望。
5. 教我能愛祢，像天使一樣，聖潔的熱情，充滿我全身；聖靈來臨，如鴿由天下降，主愛如火焰燒我心壇上。阿們。

1 Spirit of God, descend upon my heart;
Wean it from earth, through all its pulses move;
Stoop to my weakness, mighty as Thou art,
And make me love Thee as I ought to love.

2 *I ask no dream, no prophet ecstasies,*
No sudden rending of the veil of clay,
No angel visitant, no opening skies;
But take the dimness of my soul away.

3 Hast Thou not bid us love Thee, God and King?
All, all Thine own—soul, heart and strength and mind!
I see Thy cross—there teach my heart to cling:
O let me seek Thee, and O let me find!

4 *Teach me to feel that Thou art always nigh;*
Teach me the struggles of the soul to bear,
To check the rising doubt, the rebel sigh;
Teach me the patience of unanswered prayer.

5 Teach me to love Thee as Thine angels love,
One holy passion filling all my frame;
The baptism of the heaven-descended Dove:
My heart an altar, and Thy love the flame. Amen.

充滿我
Fill Me Now

And to know the love of Christ, . . . that ye might be filled . . .
— Ephesians 3:19

Elwood R. Stokes

FILL ME NOW
John R. Sweney

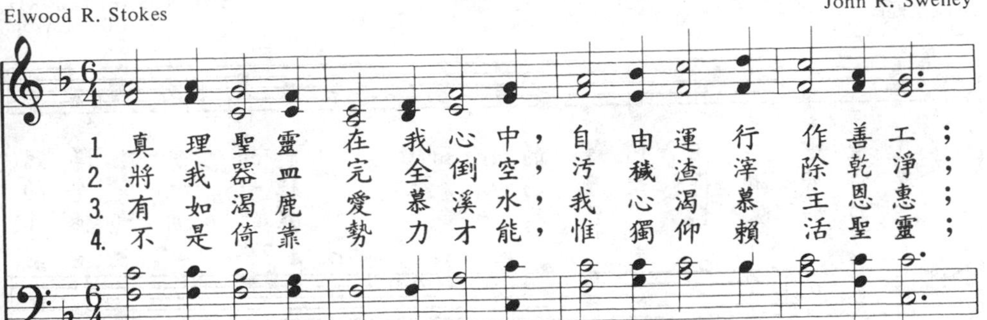
1. 真理聖靈在我心中，自由運行作善工；
2. 将我器皿完全倒空，污穢渣滓除乾淨；
3. 有如渴鹿愛慕溪水，我心渴慕主恩惠；
4. 不是倚靠勢力才能，惟獨仰賴活聖靈；

1 Hov - er o'er me, Ho - ly Spir - it, Bathe my trem-bling heart and brow;
2 *Thou canst fill me, gra-cious Spir - it, Though I can - not tell Thee how;*
3 I am weak-ness, full of weak-ness, At Thy sa - cred feet I bow;
4 *Cleanse and com-fort, bless and save me, Bathe, O bathe my heart and brow;*

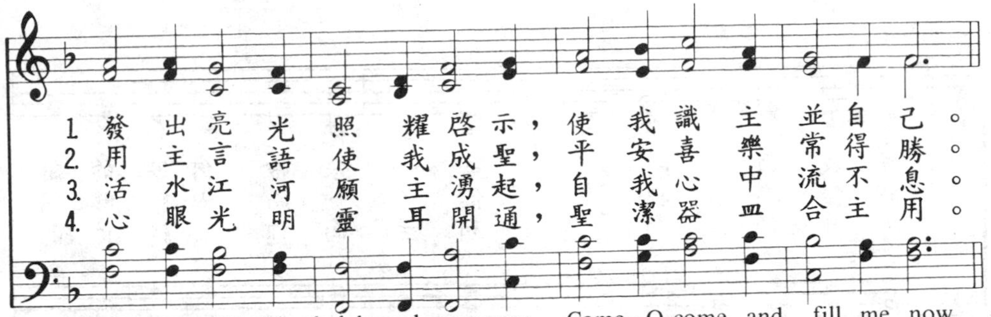
1. 發出亮光照耀啓示，使我識主並自己。
2. 用主言語使我成聖，平安喜樂常得勝。
3. 活水江河願主湧起，自我心中流不息。
4. 心眼光明靈耳開通，聖潔器皿合主用。

1 Fill me with Thy hal-lowed pres-ence, Come, O come and fill me now.
2 *But I need Thee, great - ly need Thee, Come, O come and fill me now.*
3 Blest, di - vine, e - ter - nal Spir - it, Fill with power, and fill me now.
4 *Thou art com - fort - ing and sav - ing, Thou art sweet - ly fill - ing now.*

充滿我，充滿我，耶穌今來充滿我；
Fill me now, fill me now, Je - sus, come and fill me now;
榮耀聖靈今充滿我，願主現今充滿我。
Fill me with Thy hal-lowed pres-ence–Come, O come and fill me now.

102

聖靈同在，何等甘甜
Sweet, Sweet Spirit

I will not leave you comfortless; I will come to you. — John 14:18

Doris Akers

SWEET, SWEET SPIRIT
Doris Akers

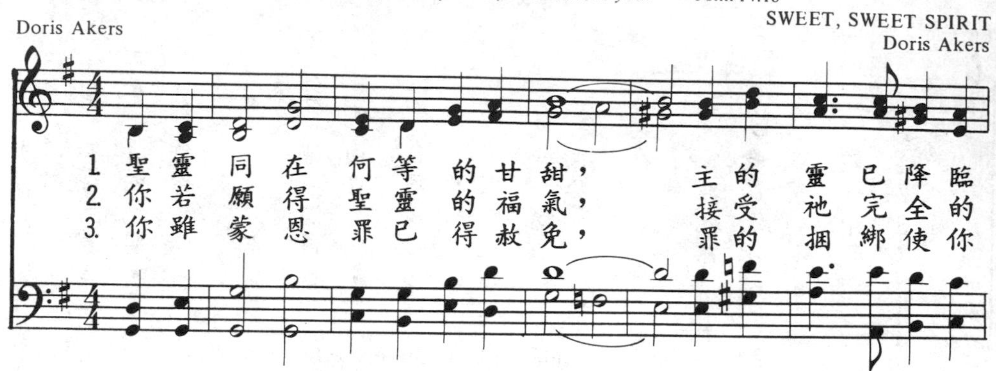
1. 聖 靈 同 在 何 等 的 甘 甜， 主 的 靈 已 降 臨
2. 你 若 願 得 聖 靈 的 福 氣， 接 受 祂 完 全 的
3. 你 雖 蒙 恩 罪 已 得 赦 免， 罪 的 捆 綁 使 你

1 There's a sweet, sweet Spir-it in this place, And I know that it's the
2 *There are bless-ings you can-not re-ceive 'Til you know Him in His*
3 If you say He saved you from your sin, Now you're weak, you're bound and

1. 在 我 們 中 間； 每 一 張 臉 何 等 的 甜
2. 相 信 依 靠 祂； 你 若 一 路 與 耶 穌 同
3. 心 靈 仍 軟 弱； 到 主 面 前 承 認 你 的

1 Spir-it of the Lord; There are sweet ex-pres-sions on each
2 *full-ness and be-lieve; You're the one to prof-it when you*
3 can-not en-ter in; You can make it right if you will

1. 美， 我 深 知 主 親 自 在 我 們 中 間。
2. 行， 你 必 親 自 體 會 主 恩 何 等 大。
3. 罪， 聖 靈 必 充 滿 你 使 你 為 祂 活。

1 face, And I know they feel the pres-ence of the Lord.
2 *say, "I am going to walk with Je-sus all the way."*
3 yield— You'll en-joy the Ho-ly Spir-it that we feel.

聖 靈 的 降 臨 ， 何 等 的 甘 甜 ， 與 我 們
Sweet Ho-ly Spir-it, Sweet heav-en-ly Dove, Stay right here
同 在 ， 充 滿 着 祢 的 愛 ； 感 謝 讚
with us, Fill-ing us with Your love; And for these
美 祢 ， 因 祢 賜 下 福 氣： 我 們 深 深 相 信 ，
bless-ings We lift our hearts in praise: With-out a doubt we'll know
確 知 祢 已 降 臨 ， 我 們 得 大 復 興 。
that we have been re-vived, When we shall leave this place.

主的聖靈在此
The Spirit of Jesus Is in This Place

Gloria Gaither
William J. Gaither

SPIRIT OF JESUS
William J. Gaither

主的聖靈在這裡大顯能力，
O, the Spir - it of Je - sus is in this place,
我見到衆人的臉都覺歡喜；
I can see the change He's mak-ing on each face;
當天上有能力降臨，就必有美好的
When the power of Heaven is tapped, then, some-thing good is bound to
事情，因為聖靈在這裡大顯能力。
hap - pen, for the Spir - it of Je - sus is in this place.
朋友，我願你知道祂就在這裡，
O my friend, He is so near that we could touch Him,

聖 靈 同在 使你 心 甚覺 甜 蜜；
His sweet pres-ence this old world could ne'er re - place;
願你 接 受祂 的 能力，祂用 大 愛來改
Won't you let His Spir - it warm you, let His might - y love trans-
變你，主的 聖 靈在 這 裡 大顯能 力。
form you, while the Spir - it of Je - sus is in this place.

你們要讚美耶和華　因歌頌我們的神為善為美，

讚美的話是合宜的。

我們的主為大，最有能力，他的智慧，無法測度

詩篇一百四十七篇

1，5

Praise the Lord!
For it is good to sing praise to our God;
for he is gracious, and a song of praise is seemly.
Great is our Lord, and abundant in power;
his understanding is beyond measure.

Psalms 147:1,5 RSV

104

懇求聖靈充滿我

Holy Spirit, Flow Through Me

Walt Mills

. . . But if ye through the Spirit do mortify the deeds of the body, ye shall live. — Romans 8:13

MILLS
Walt Mills

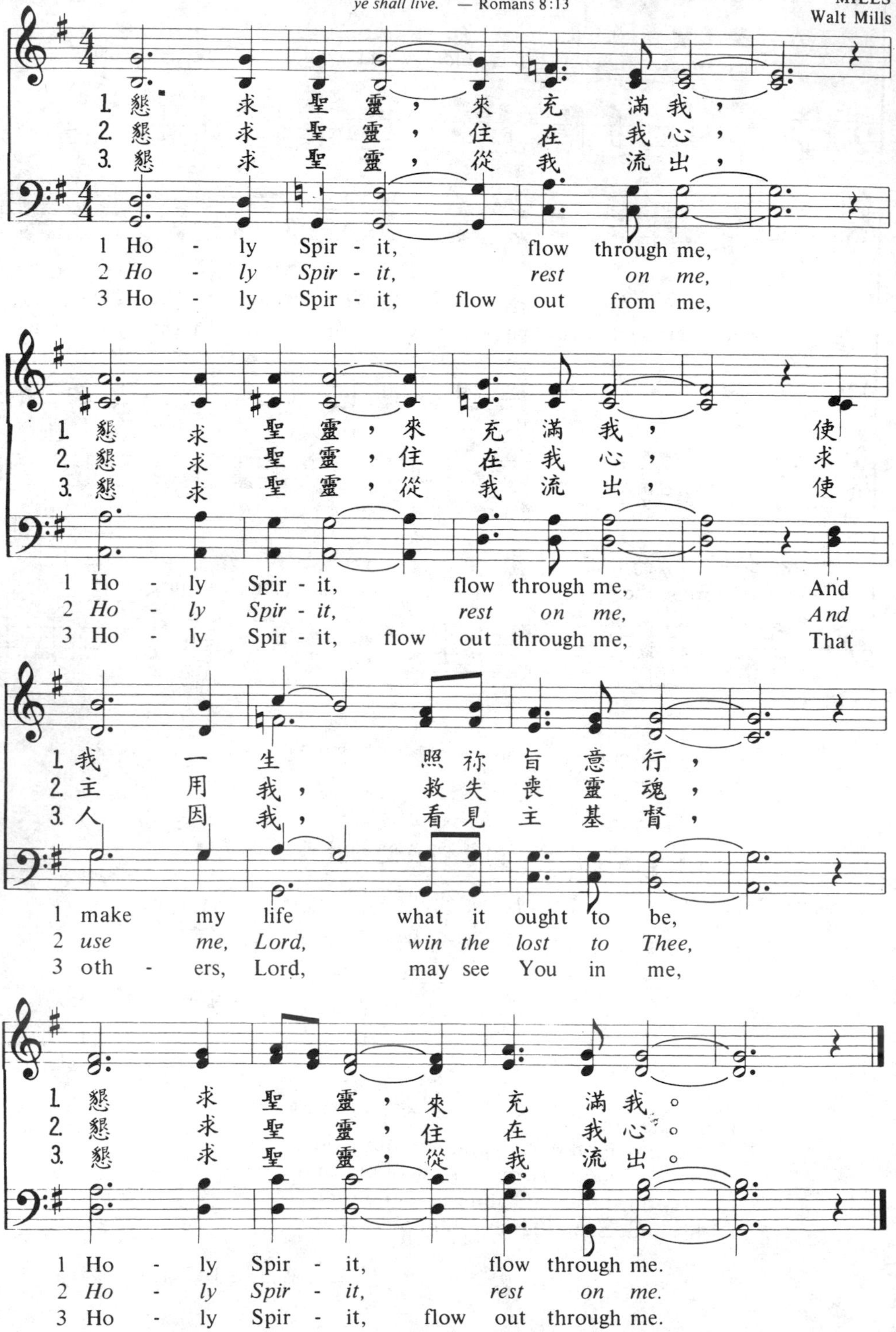

1. 懇求聖靈，來充滿我，懇求聖靈，來充滿我，使我一生照祢旨意行，懇求聖靈，來充滿我。
2. 懇求聖靈，住在我心，懇求聖靈，住在我心，求主用我，救失喪靈魂，懇求聖靈，住在我心。
3. 懇求聖靈，從我流出，懇求聖靈，從我流出，使人因我，看見主基督，懇求聖靈，從我流出。

1 Holy Spirit, flow through me,
Holy Spirit, flow through me,
And make my life what it ought to be,
Holy Spirit, flow through me.

2 *Holy Spirit, rest on me,*
Holy Spirit, rest on me,
And use me, Lord, win the lost to Thee,
Holy Spirit, rest on me.

3 Holy Spirit, flow out from me,
Holy Spirit, flow out through me,
That others, Lord, may see You in me,
Holy Spirit, flow out through me.

無論那裡有兩三人相聚

Where Two or Three Are Gathered

John W. Peterson
And be renewed in the spirit of your mind. — Ephesians 4:23
John W. Peterson
1. 無 論 那 裡 有 兩 三 人，奉 主 的 名 相 聚 ，
2. 今 日 我 們 在 此 相 聚，願 主 名 得 榮 耀 ；
1. Where two or three are gath-ered, Gath-ered in Je - sus' name,
2. In Your name and for Your glo - ry We are met to - day;
1. 主 必 同 在 賜 下 聖 靈，這 是 主 的 應 許 。
2. 使 我 心 靈 熱 忱 敬 拜，教 我 如 何 禱 告 。
1. In the midst he'll be— He prom-ised, Kin-dling a ho - ly flame.
2. Stir our hearts to praise and wor-ship, Teach us how to pray.
1. 求 主 耶 穌 來，帶 着 能 力 與 愛 ；
2. 求 主 耶 穌 來，來 與 我 們 同 住 ；
1. Come, come, Lord Je - sus, Come in love and pow'r;
2. Come, come, Lord Je - sus, Be our hal - lowed guest;
1. 我 們 在 祢 面 前 靜 候— 求 主 現 在 就 來 。
2. 聖 靈 吹 入 我 們 心 中— 使 每 顆 心 蒙 福 。
1. Qui-et- ly we wait be - fore You—Make this a sa - cred hour.
2. Breathe Your ho- ly breath up - on us— May ev - 'ry heart be blest.

106 以馬内利來臨
O Come, O Come, Emmanuel

Behold, a virgin shall . . . bear a Son and shall call His name Immanuel.
Isaiah 7:14
Latin: c. 9th Century
Tr. by John M. Neale, stanzas 1, 2, alt.
Tr. by Henry S. Coffin, stanzas 3, 4, alt.
VENI EMMANUEL
Adapted from Plainsong, Mode I
Thomas Helmore
Unison
1. 以馬内利懇求降臨，救贖解放以色列民；淪落異邦寂寞傷心，引頸渴望神子降臨。
2. 清晨日光懇求降臨，藉主降臨歡慰衆心；衝開長夜幽暗愁雲，驅散死亡深沉黑影。歡欣！歡欣！以
3. 榮耀君王懇求降臨，統治萬物協和萬民；懇求顯示智慧大能，指領群生步步遵循。
4. 萬邦所望懇求降臨，團結萬民一志一心；永息兵戈妒忌紛爭，充滿世界天賜和平。
1 O come, O come, Em - man - u - el, And ran-som cap-tive Is - ra - el, That mourns in lone - ly ex - ile here, Un - til the Son of God ap - pear.
2 *O come, Thou Day-spring, come and cheer Our spir - its by Thine ad - vent here; Dis - perse the gloom - y clouds of night, And death's dark shad-ows put to flight.*
3 O come, Thou Wis-dom from on high, And or - der all things, far and nigh; To us the path of knowl - edge show, And cause us in her ways to go.
4 *O come, De - sire of na - tions, bind In one the hearts of all man - kind; Bid Thou our sad di - vi - sions cease, And be Thy-self our King of peace.*
Re - joice! Re - joice! Em -

色 列 民，以 馬 內 利，定 要 降 臨！阿 門。
man - u - el Shall come to thee, O Is - ra - el! A-men.

萬口歡唱

107

O for a Thousand Tongues to Sing

My tongue shall speak . . . praise all the day long. — Psalm 35:28

AZMON
Carl G. Gläser

Charles Wesley

1. 哦，千 萬 口 舌 齊 歌 唱，讚 美 救 主 我 神，
2. 哦，我 的 神 慈 愛 的 主，賜 我 力 量 傳 揚，
3. 耶 穌 聖 名 能 除 畏 懼，能 安 慰 我 愁 煩，
4. 耶 穌 能 消 滅 罪 權 勢，使 罪 人 得 自 由；
5. 耳 聾 的 人 來 聽 主 言，啞 吧 讚 美 主 名；

1 O for a thou-sand tongues to sing My great Re-deem-er's praise,
2 *My gra-cious Mas - ter and my God, As - sist me to pro - claim,*
3 Je - sus! the name that charms our fears, That bids our sor - rows cease,
4 *He breaks the power of can-celled sin, He sets the pris-oner free;*
5 Hear Him, ye deaf; His praise, ye dumb, Your loos-ened tongues em-ploy;

1. 讚 美 我 主 榮 耀 的 王，讚 美 救 主 恩 深。
2. 走 遍 地 上 世 界 各 處，宣 揚 主 名 榮 光。
3. 罪 人 聽 見 好 像 音 樂，主 是 生 命 平 安。
4. 主 寶 血 能 洗 清 罪 漬，主 寶 血 為 我 流。
5. 瞎 眼 的 能 看 見 主 面，瘸 腿 跳 躍 歡 欣。阿 門。
1 The glo - ries of my God and King, The tri-umphs of His grace!
2 To spread through all the earth a-broad The hon-ors of Thy name.
3 'Tis mu - sic in the sin-ner's ears, 'Tis life and health and peace.
4 His blood can make the foul-est clean, His blood a - vailed for me.
5 Ye blind, be-hold your Sav-ior come; And leap, ye lame, for joy! A - men.

來讚美
Come and Praise

Traditional
Stanzas 2ab, 3b by E.B.

The Lord reigneth; let the earth rejoice.
— Psalm 97:1

Traditional
Arr. by Eldon Burkwall

1. 基督降生伯利恒，哈利路亞，神愛
成為一嬰孩，哈利路亞，屬世
2. 成為人子受勞苦，哈利路亞，以愛
天父的旨意，哈利路亞，滿有

1. Christ was born in Beth-le-hem, Hal-le-lu-jah! Son of
up an earth-ly child, Hal-le-lu-jah! Of the
2. As a man He toiled and taught, Hal-le-lu-jah! And in
Fa-ther's will de-fined, Hal-le-lu-jah! Grace and

副歌 (來讚) 美救主我王，哈利路亞，來讚
Refr.: (Come and) praise the Lord our King, Hal-le-lu-jah! Come and

1. 子道成肉身，哈利路亞，降生
界但不敗壞，哈利路亞，來讚
2. 尋人得救贖，哈利路亞，完成
恩典與真理，哈利路亞，來讚

1. God and Son of Man, Hal-le-lu-jah! He grew
world but un-de-filed, Hal-le-lu-jah! Come and
2. love our souls He sought. Hal-le-lu-jah! He His
truth in Him com-bined, Hal-le-lu-jah! Come and

美救主我王，哈利路亞！
praise the Lord our King, Hal-le-lu-jah!

3. 救主捨命各各他，哈利路亞，
從死復活回父家，哈利路亞，
寶血流出賜世人，哈利路亞，
世人因此蒙神恩，哈利路亞。
副歌

3. Jesus died at Calvary, . . .
Rose again triumphantly, . . .
Thru the gift of His own blood, . . .
Reconciling us to God, . . .
Refrain

4. 主能洗清我罪污，哈利路亞，
只要全心信靠主，哈利路亞，
那日必與主相見，哈利路亞，
永遠同住在高天，哈利路亞。
副歌

4. He will cleanse us from our sin, . . .
If we come by faith to Him, . . .
Then we'll live with Him some day, . . .
And forever with Him stay, . . .
Refrain

這日子
This Is The Day
Psalm 118:24
Sing unto the Lord, Bless His Name, ... — Psalm 96:2
Unknown
Unison
這日子是，這日子是耶和華定的，耶和
This is the day, this is the day that the Lord hath made, that the
華定的。我們應當在其中要高
Lord hath made; We will re-joice, we will re-joice and be
興歡喜，高興歡喜。這日子是耶和
glad in it, and be glad in it. This is the day that the
華定的，我們在其中要高興歡喜；
Lord hath made, We will re-joice and be glad in it;
這日子是，這日子是耶和華定的。
This is the day, this is the day that the Lord hath made.

110

凡有血氣皆當靜默
Let All Mortal Flesh Keep Silence

Let all mortal flesh keep silent.

— Habakkuk 2:20

Liturgy of St. James
Tr. by Gerard Moultrie

PICARDY
French Carol

Unison
1. 凡有血氣皆當靜默，謙卑敬畏同肅立，
2. 萬王之王藉童女生，虛心捨己為世人，
3. 天使撒拉弗嗘嚕啪，儆醒侍立主腳前，
1 Let all mor-tal flesh keep si - lence, And with fear and trem-bling stand;
2 King of kings, yet born of Mar - y, As of old on earth He stood,
3 At His feet the six-winged ser - aph; Cher - u - bim with watch-ful eye,

1. 切勿思慮世俗事物，因主親手賜福氣；
2. 萬主之主道成肉身，甘願作人賜人恩；
3. 兩翅遮面大聲歡呼，歌聲充滿主聖殿；
1 Pon-der noth-ing world - ly mind - ed, For with bless-ing in His hand
2 Lord of lords in hu - man na - ture, In the bod-y and the blood,
3 Veil their fac - es to His Pres - ence, As with cease-less voice they cry,

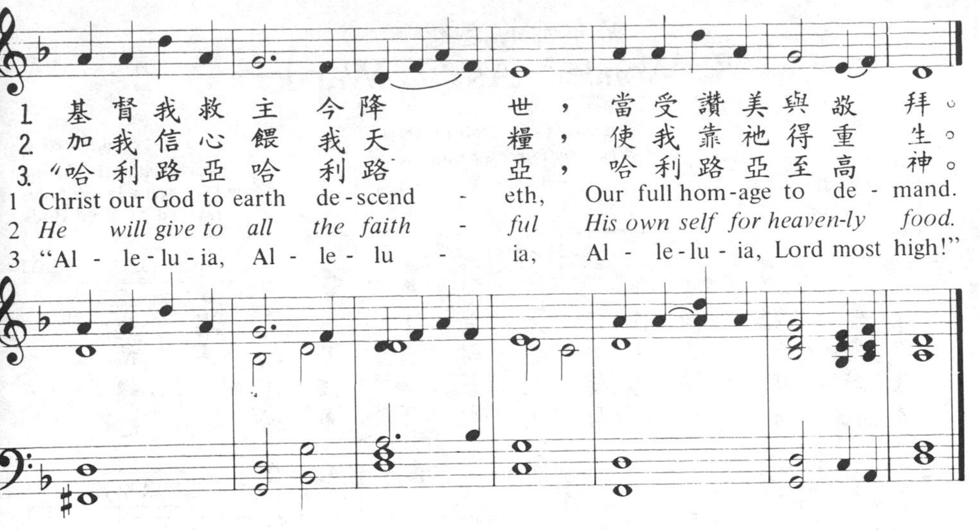

1. 基督我救主今降世，當受讚美與敬拜。
2. 加我信心餵我天糧，使我靠祂得重生。
3. “哈利路亞哈利路亞，哈利路亞至高神。
1 Christ our God to earth de-scend - eth, Our full hom-age to de - mand.
2 He will give to all the faith - ful His own self for heaven-ly food.
3 “Al - le-lu-ia, Al - le-lu - ia, Al - le-lu - ia, Lord most high!”

神愛世上的人

111

For God So Loved the World

Based on John 3:16
Frances Townsend

While we were yet sinners, Christ died for us.
— Romans 5:8

GOD LOVED THE WORLD
Alfred B. Smith

Unison

神極愛世上人，賜下獨生愛子，加略山上受死，使我脱罪權勢；一日祂要再來，那是何等榮耀，救主愛我真奇妙。

For God so loved the world He gave His on-ly Son To die on Cal-vary's tree, From sin to set me free; Some day He's com-ing back, What glo - ry that will be! Won-der-ful His love to me.

我希奇的思想
I Wonder As I Wander

As He spake by His Holy Prophets
which have been since the world began.
— Luke 1:70
Appalachian carol
Collected by John Jacob Niles
I WONDER
Appalachian Folksong
Adapted by John Jacob Niles
Arranged by Fred Bock
Unison
1. 我徘徊在日光之下希奇思想，
2. 馬利亞生耶穌在卑微馬槽，
3. 若耶穌想要天下事任何一樣：
4. 我徘徊在日光之下希奇思想，
1 I won - der as I wan - der out un - der the sky,
2 When Ma - ry birthed Je - sus, 'twas in a cows' stall,
3 If Je - sus had want - ed for an - y wee thing:
4 I won - der as I wan - der out un - der the sky,
1. 主耶穌竟為我受死由天降，為
2. 有博士農夫牧人遠地來到，有
3. 或天上衆星辰或飛鳥歌唱，或
4. 主耶穌竟為我受死由天降，為
1 How Je - sus, the Sav - ior, did come for to die. For
2 With wise - men and far - mers and shep - herds and all. But
3 A star in the sky, or a bird on the wing; Or
4 How Je - sus, the Sav - ior did come for to die. For
1. 你，為我，困苦罪人而心傷，我
2. 奇星發大光從高天照耀，自
3. 天上衆天使高聲的讚揚，祂
4. 你，為我，困苦罪人而心傷，我
1 poor, or - nery peo - ple like you and like I— I
2 high from God's heav - en a star's light did fall, And the
3 all of God's an - gels in heav - en to sing, He
4 poor, or - nery peo - ple like you and like I— I

1. 徘 徊 在 日 光 下，希 奇 的 思 想。
2. 古 已 有 的 應 許，今 向 人 傳 報。
3. 能 擁 有 這 一 切，因 為 祂 是 王！
4. 徘 徊 在 日 光 下，希 奇 的 思 想。
1 won - der as I wan - der, Out un - der the sky.
2 prom-ise of a - ges It then did re - call.
3 sure - ly could have had it, 'Cause He was the King!
4 won - der as I wan - der, Out un - der the sky.

113

安靜思想我是真神
Be Still and Know That I Am God

Blessed is that nation whose God is the Lord. — Psalm 33:12

Psalm 46:10

Unknown

1. 安 靜 思 想：我 是 真 神。安 靜 思
2. 我 是 救 主，能 醫 治 你。我 是 救

1. Be still and know that I am God. Be still and
2. *I am the Lord that heal - eth thee. I am the*

1. 想：我 是 真 神。安 靜 思 想：我 是 真 神。
2. 主，能 醫 治 你。我 是 救 主，能 醫 治 你。

1. know that I am God. Be still and know that I am God.
2. *Lord that heal - eth thee. I am the Lord that heal - eth thee*

114 主曾離寶座
Thou Didst Leave Thy Throne

He came unto His own and His own received Him not.
— John 1:11

Emily E. S. Elliott

MARGARET
Timothy R. Matthews

1. 在昔日，我主為罪人降生，撇榮
2. 天軍皆稱頌，天樂響天空，宣揚
3. 狐狸尚有洞，飛鳥亦有巢，困乏
4. 救主來世間，賜真理聖言，使人
5. 當主再來臨，天樂振天庭，為迎

1 Thou didst leave Thy throne and Thy king - ly crown When Thou
2 *Heav - en's arch - es rang when the an - gels sang, Pro -*
3 The fox - es found rest, and the birds their nest In the
4 *Thou cam - est, O Lord, with the liv - ing word That should*
5 When the heavens shall ring and the an - gels sing At Thy

1. 寃離天上寶座；在大衛之城，一窮
2. 主無量大尊榮；主竟肯虛己，降生
3. 時能安然居住；惟我主耶穌，順父
4. 得生命脫罪權；人却戲笑主，荊棘
5. 接得勝君歡喜；主向我施恩，對我

1 cam - est to earth for me, But in Beth - le-hem's home there was
2 *claim - ing Thy roy - al de - gree, But in low - ly birth didst Thou*
3 shade of the for - est tree, But Thy couch was the sod, O Thou
4 *set Thy peo - ple free, But with mock - ing scorn and with*
5 com - ing to vic - to - ry, Let Thy voice call me home, say - ing,

1. 苦馬棚，有空處作為主居所。求來到我
2. 貧苦地，為世人受痛苦貧窮。求來到我
3. 旨辛苦，在世間無枕首之處。求來到我
4. 冠刺主，釘死救主在加略山。求來到我
5. 發慈聲：“在我旁有空處為你！”我心甚快
1 found no room For Thy ho - ly na - tiv - i - ty. O come to my
2 *come to earth And in great hu - mil - i - ty. O come to my*
3 Son of God, In the des - erts of Gal - i - lee. O come to my
4 *crown of thorn They bore Thee to Cal - va - ry. O come to my*
5 "Yet there is room, There is room at my side for thee." And my heart shall re-

1. 心，主 耶 穌：在 我 心 有 空 處 為 祢！
2. 心，主 耶 穌：在 我 心 有 空 處 為 祢！
3. 心，主 耶 穌：在 我 心 有 空 處 為 祢！
4. 心，主 耶 穌：在 我 心 有 空 處 為 祢！
5. 樂，主 耶 穌：因 主 來 也 肯 召 呼 我！阿 門。
1 heart, Lord Je - sus: There is room in my heart for Thee!
2 heart, Lord Je - sus: There is room in my heart for Thee!
3 heart, Lord Je - sus: There is room in my heart for Thee!
4 heart, Lord Je - sus: There is room in my heart for Thee!
5 joice, Lord Je - sus, When Thou com - est and call - est me. A-men.

借

基督沒有自己的牀舖，
　　降世時，客店借他一把乾草；
基督沒有自己的墳墓，
　　離世時，財主借他一個石洞。

基督沒有存款，
　　行神蹟用的餅魚，是小孩子獻的；
基督沒有動產，
　　當講壇用的漁船，是小村民借的。

基督沒有車子，
　　進耶路撒冷時借了驢駒一頭；
基督沒有房子，
　　告別的晚宴擺在別人的樓房。

一無所有是基督：
　　沒有高帽和金冠，只有荊棘在頭上，
　　沒有戒指和手套，只有釘子在手上。
一無所留更是基督：
　　身外的全是借的，身內的全數盡傾；

借——是他的記號，
給——却是他的人生！

問耕改寫

115

聖誕佳音

The First Noel

And there were in that same country, Shepherds . . . in the field. . . .

— Luke 2:8

THE FIRST NOEL

English Carol

English Melody

From Sandys' *Christmas Carols*

1. 天 使 初 報 聖 誕 佳 音，先 向 田
2. 牧 人 抬 頭 見 一 景 星，遠 在 東
3. 博 士 三 人 因 見 星 光，遠 道 而
4. 景 星 導 引 渡 漠 越 荒，到 伯 利
5. 博 士 尋 見 欣 喜 同 往，屈 膝 跪
6. 信 徒 都 當 高 聲 歡 呼，同 心 歌
1 The first no - el the an-gel did say Was to cer-tain poor
2 *They look - ed up and saw a star Shin-ing in the*
3 And by the light of that same star, Three wise men
4 *This star drew nigh to the north-west, O - ver Beth - le -*
5 Then en - tered in those wise men three, Full rev - erent-
6 *Then let us all with one ac - cord Sing prais - es*

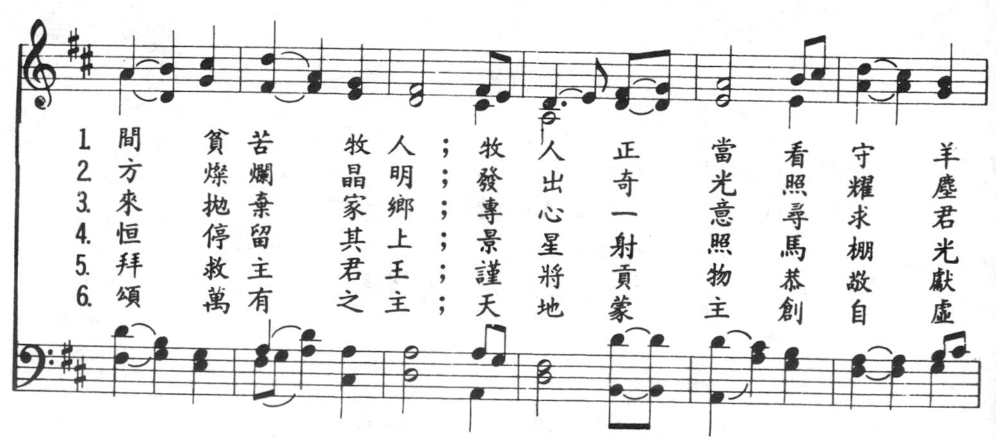
1. 間 貧 苦 牧 人；牧 人 正 當 看 守 羊
2. 方 燦 爛 晶 明；發 出 奇 光 照 耀 塵
3. 來 拋 棄 家 鄉；專 心 一 意 尋 求 君
4. 恒 停 留 其 上；景 星 射 照 馬 棚 光
5. 拜 救 主 君 王；謹 將 貢 物 恭 敬 獻
6. 頌 萬 有 之 主；天 地 蒙 主 創 自 虛
1 shep-herds in fields as they lay— In fields where they lay keep-ing their
2 *east, be - yond them far; And to the earth it gave great*
3 came from coun - try far: To seek for a king was their in -
4 *hem it took its rest; And there it did both stop and*
5 ly up - on their knee, And of - fered there, in His pres -
6 *to our heaven - ly Lord, That hath made heaven and earth of*

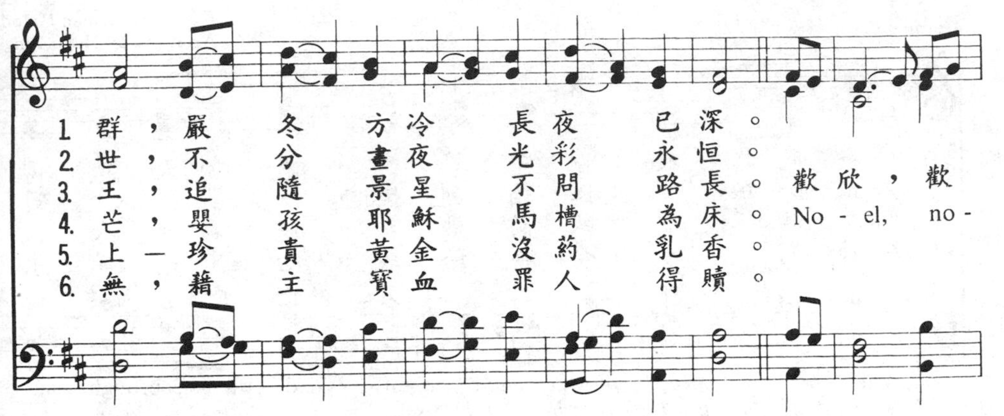
1. 群，嚴 冬 方冷 長夜 已深。
2. 世，不 分 晝夜 光彩 永恒。
3. 王，追 隨 景星 不問 路長。 歡欣，歡
4. 芒，嬰 孩 耶穌 馬槽 為床。 No - el, no -
5. 上一珍 貴 黃金 沒葯 乳香。
6. 無，藉 主 寶血 罪人 得贖。

1 sheep, On a cold win-ter's night that was so deep.
2 *light, And so it con - tin-ued both day and night.*
3 tent, And to fol-low the star wher - ev - er it went.
4 *stay, Right o - ver the place where Je - sus lay.*
5 ence, Their gold and myrrh and frank - in-cense.
6 *naught, And with His blood man-kind hath bought.*

欣！歡 欣，歡 欣 ！天國君 王 今日 降生！
el! No - el, no - el! Born is the King of Is - ra - el!

116

何等喜樂
How Great Our Joy!

Therefore with joy shall they draw water out of the wells of salvation . . . . — Isaiah 12:3

JUNGST
German Carol
German Melody
Arranged by Hugo Jungst
1. 夜 間 牧 人 看 守 羊 群， 忽 聞 天 使 傳
2. 正 如 預 言 在 伯 利 恒， 一 嬰 孩 今 日
3. 馬 槽 裡 安 臥 的 嬰 孩， 將 為 世 人 代
4. 神 將 愛 子 今 賜 給 我， 心 中 充 滿 永
1 While by the sheep we watched at night, Glad tid - ings brought an
2 There shall be born, so he did say, In Beth - le - hem a
3 There shall the Child lie in a stall, This Child who shall re -
4 This gift of God we'll cher - ish well, That ev - er joy our
f
p echo
1. 報 喜 訊。 何 等 喜 樂！ 大 喜 樂！
2. 已 降 生。 何 等 喜 樂！ 大 喜 樂！
3. 還 罪 債。 何 等 喜 樂！ 大 喜 樂！
4. 遠 喜 樂。 何 等 喜 樂！ 大 喜 樂！
1 an - gel bright. How great our joy! Great our joy!
2 Child to - day. How great our joy! Great our joy!
3 deem us all. How great our joy! Great our joy!
4 hearts shall fill. How great our joy! Great our joy!
f
p echo
f
1. 大 喜 樂！ 大 喜 樂！ 至 高 之 處 讚
2. 大 喜 樂！ 大 喜 樂！ 至 高 之 處 讚
3. 大 喜 樂！ 大 喜 樂！ 至 高 之 處 讚
4. 大 喜 樂！ 大 喜 樂！ 至 高 之 處 讚
1 Joy, joy, joy! Joy, joy, joy! Praise we the Lord in
2 Joy, joy, joy! Joy, joy, joy! Praise we the Lord in
3 Joy, joy, joy! Joy, joy, joy! Praise we the Lord in
4 Joy, joy, joy! Joy, joy, joy! Praise we the Lord in

p echo
1. 美 真 神！至 高 之 處 讚 美 真 神！
2. 美 真 神！至 高 之 處 讚 美 真 神！
3. 美 真 神！至 高 之 處 讚 美 真 神！
4. 美 真 神！至 高 之 處 讚 美 真 神！
1 heaven on high! Praise we the Lord in heaven on high!
2 heaven on high! Praise we the Lord in heaven on high!
3 heaven on high! Praise we the Lord in heaven on high!
4 heaven on high! Praise we the Lord in heaven on high!

在伯利恒的野地裡，有牧羊的人，夜間按着更次看守羊群。有主的使者站在他們旁邊，主的榮光四面照着他們，牧羊的人就甚懼怕。那天使對他們說，不要懼怕，我報給你們大喜的信息，是關乎萬民的，因今天在大衛的城裡，為你們生了救主，就是主基督。你們要看見一個嬰孩，包着布，臥在馬槽裡，那就是記號了。忽然有一大隊天兵，同那天使讚美神說：在至高之處榮耀歸與神，在地上平安歸與祂所喜悦的人。

路加福音二章
8 — 14

And there were shepherds living out in the fields nearby, keeping watch over their flocks at night. An angel of the Lord appeared to them, and the glory of the Lord shone around them, and they were terrified. But the angel said to them, "Do not be afraid. I bring you good news of great joy that will be for all the people. Today in the town of David a Savior has been born to you; he is Christ the Lord. This will be a sign to you: You will find a baby wrapped in strips of cloth and lying in a manger."

Suddenly a great company of the heavenly hosts appeared with the angel, praising God and saying,

> Glory to God in the highest,
> and on earth peace to men on whom his favor rests."

— Luke 2:8-14. NIV

117

普世歡騰
Joy to the World!

For unto you is born this day . . . a Savior . . . .
— Luke 2:11

Psalm 98
Adapted by Isaac Watts

ANTIOCH
George Friedrich Handel
Arranged by Fred Bock
and Ralph Carmichael

C
F
G
1. 普世歡騰！救主下降，大地接
2. 普世歡騰！主治萬方，民衆都
3. 罪惡憂愁，不容再長，世途荊
4. 主藉真理，恩治萬方，要使萬
1 Joy to the world! the Lord is come: Let earth re-
2 Joy to the world! the Savior reigns: Let men their
3 No more let sins and sorrows grow, Nor thorns in-
4 He rules the world with truth and grace, And makes the
C
1. 她君王；惟願衆心預備地
2. 當歌唱；沃野洪濤山石平
3. 棘消亡；化詛為恩無遠弗
4. 邦證明，我主公義無限光
1 ceive her King; Let every heart prepare Him
2 songs employ; While fields and floods, rocks, hills, and
3 fest the ground; He comes to make His blessings
4 nations prove The glories of His righteous-
G
1. 方，諸天萬物歌唱，諸天萬物歌唱，諸
2. 原，響應歌聲嘹亮，響應歌聲嘹亮，響
3. 達，到處主澤流長，到處主澤流長，到
4. 榮，主愛奇妙莫名，主愛奇妙莫名，主
1 room, And heaven and nature sing, And heaven and nature sing, And
2 plains Repeat the sounding joy, Repeat the sounding joy, Re-
3 flow Far as the curse is found, Far as the curse is found, Far
4 ness, And wonders of His love, And wonders of His love, And

1. 天，諸天萬物歌唱。
2. 應，響應歌聲嘹亮。
3. 處，到處主澤流長。
4. 愛，主愛奇妙莫名。阿門。
1 heaven, and heaven and na - ture sing.
2 peat, re - peat the sound - ing joy.
3 as, far as the curse is found.
4 won - ders, won - ders of His love. A - men.

進入祂的門

118

I Will Enter His Gates

Psalm 100:4

Unknown

Unison

我必向主稱謝，進入祂的門我必

I will en - ter His gates with thanks-giv-ing in my heart, I will

讚美進入祂的院 —— 因為這日子

en - ter His courts with praise; —— I will say. "This is the

是耶和華定的 我必高興，因祂使我歡喜。

day that the Lord hath made, I will re-joice for He hath made me glad."

119

聽啊，天使高聲唱

Hark! the Herald Angels Sing

And suddenly there was with the Angel a multitude of the Heavenly Host praising God. . . .
— Luke 2:13

Charles Wesley

MENDELSSOHN
Felix Mendelssohn
Descant by Paul Liljestrand

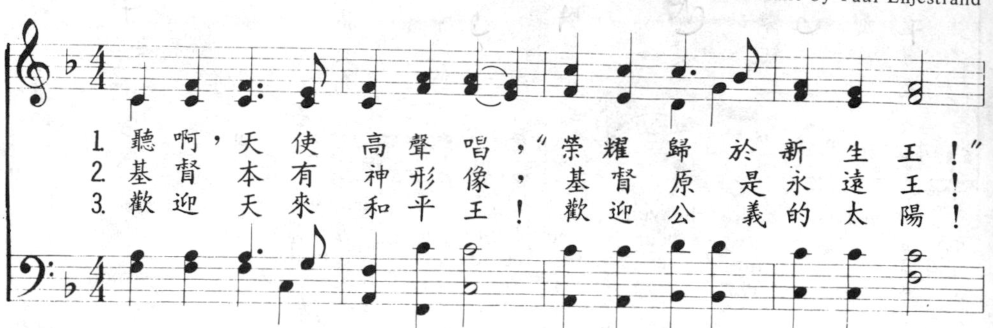
1. 聽 啊，天 使 高 聲 唱，“榮 耀 歸 於 新 生 王！”
2. 基 督 本 有 神 形 像，基 督 原 是 永 遠 王！
3. 歡 迎 天 來 和 平 王！歡 迎 公 義 的 太 陽！

1 Hark! the her - ald an - gels sing, "Glo - ry to the new-born King:
2 *Christ, by high - est heaven a - dored; Christ, the ev - er - last - ing Lord!*
3 Hail the heaven-born Prince of Peace! Hail the Sun of Right-eous-ness!

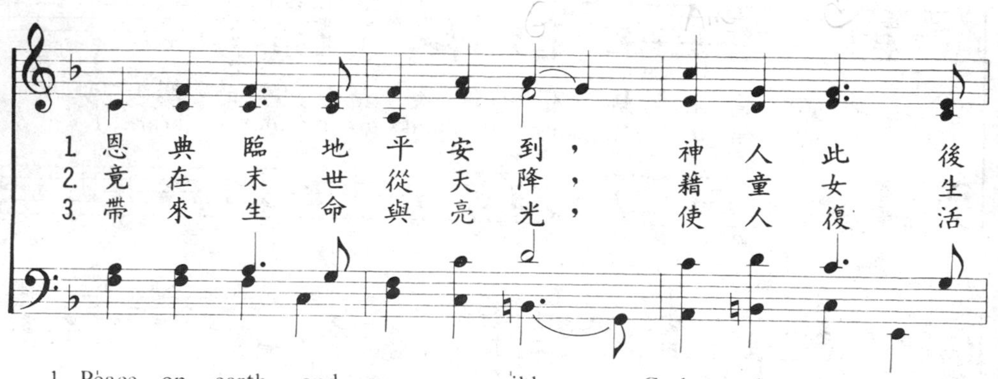
1. 恩 典 臨 地 平 安 到， 神 人 此 後
2. 竟 在 末 世 從 天 降， 藉 童 女 生
3. 帶 來 生 命 與 亮 光， 使 人 復 活

1 Peace on earth, and mer - cy mild, God and sin - ners
2 *Late in time be - hold Him come, Off - spring of the*
3 Light and life to all He brings, Risen with heal - ing

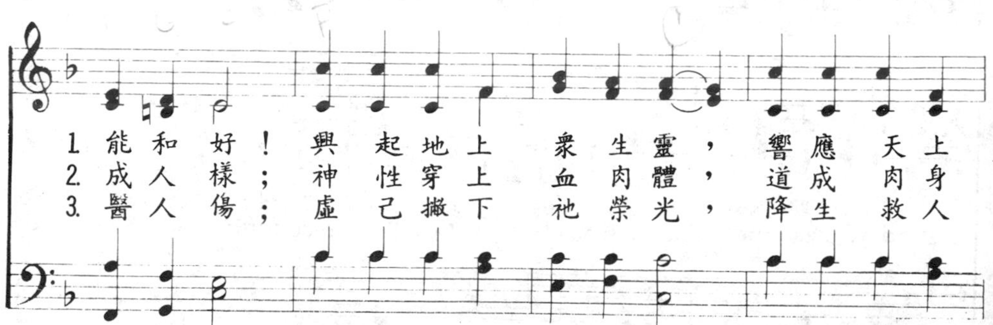
1. 能 和 好！興 起 地 上 衆 生 靈，響 應 天 上
2. 成 人 樣；神 性 穿 上 血 肉 體，道 成 肉 身
3. 醫 人 傷；虛 己 撇 下 祂 榮 光，降 生 救 人

1 rec - on - ciled!" Joy - ful, all ye na-tions, rise, Join the tri-umph
2 *Vir-gin's womb. Veiled in flesh the God-head see; Hail th' in-car - nate*
3 in His wings. Mild He lays His glo - ry by, Born that man no

1. 讚　美　聲；　天　唱　地　和　樂　歡　騰：
2. 何　奧　祕；　甘　願　作　人　同　人　住，
3. 免　死　亡；　降　生　使　人　得　重　生，

1 of the skies; With the an - gel - ic host pro - claim,
2 *De - i - ty, Pleased as man with men to dwell,*
3 more may die; Born to raise the sons of earth,

1.“基　督　降　生　伯　利　恒！”　聽　啊，天　使
2. 以　馬　内　利　是　耶　穌。　聽　啊，天　使
3. 降　生　使　人　能　高　升。　聽　啊，天　使

1 “Christ is born in Beth - le - hem!” Hark! the her - ald
2 *Je - sus, our Em - man - u - el. Hark! the her - ald*
3 Born to give them sec - ond birth. Hark! the her - ald

1. 高　聲　唱，“榮　耀　歸　於　新　生　王。”
2. 高　聲　唱，“榮　耀　歸　於　新　生　王。”
3. 高　聲　唱，“榮　耀　歸　於　新　生　王。”阿　門。
1 an - gels sing, “Glo - ry to the new - born King.”
2 *an - gels sing, “Glo - ry to the new - born King.”*
3 an - gels sing, “Glo - ry to the new - born King.” A-men.

馬槽歌(1)

Away in a Manger

Source unknown, stanzas 1, 2
John Thomas McFarland, stanza 3

... there was no room for them in the inn.
— Luke 2:7

AWAY IN A MANGER
James R. Murray

Unison
(FIRST TUNE)
1. 遠 遠 在 馬 槽 裡，無 枕 也 無 床，小 小 的 主
2. 衆 牲 畜 鳴 鳴 叫，聖 嬰 忽 驚 醒，小 小 的 主
3. 恭 敬 求 主 耶 穌，靠 近 我 身 旁，愛 護 我 接
1 A - way in a man-ger, no crib for a bed, The lit - tle Lord
2 The cat - tle are low-ing, the ba - by a - wakes, The lit - tle Lord
3 Be near me, Lord Je-sus! I ask Thee to stay Close by me for -

1. 耶 穌，睡 覺 很 安 康；衆 明 星 都 望 着 主
2. 耶 穌，却 無 啼 哭 聲；我 真 愛 主 耶 穌 敬
3. 受 我，做 主 的 小 羊；也 保 護 衆 孩 童 一
1 Je - sus laid down His sweet head. The stars in the sky all looked
2 Je - sus, no cry - ing He makes. I love Thee, Lord Je - sus! Look
3 ev - er, and love me, I pray. Bless all the dear chil - dren in

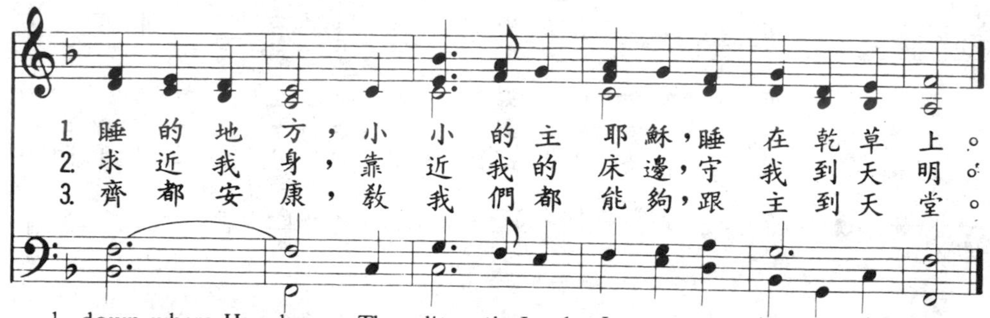
1. 睡 的 地 方，小 小 的 主 耶 穌，睡 在 乾 草 上。
2. 求 近 我 身，靠 近 我 的 床 邊，守 我 到 天 明。
3. 齊 都 安 康，教 我 們 都 能 夠，跟 主 到 天 堂。
1 down where He lay, The lit - tle Lord Je - sus, a - sleep on the hay.
2 down from the sky, And stay by my side un - til morn - ing is nigh.
3 Thy ten - der care, And fit us for heav - en, to live with Thee there.

馬槽歌(2)
Away in a Manger

"Ye shall find the babe . . . lying in a manger." — Luke 2:12

CRADLE SONG

Source unknown, stanzas 1, 2
John Thomas McFarland, stanza 3

(SECOND TUNE)

William J. Kirkpatrick

Unison
1. 遠 遠 在 馬 槽 裡，無 枕 也 無 床，小 小 的 主
2. 衆 牲 畜 鳴 鳴 叫，聖 嬰 忽 驚 醒，小 小 的 主
3. 恭 敬 求 主 耶 穌，靠 近 我 身 旁，愛 護 我 接
1 A - way in a man-ger, no crib for a bed, The lit - tle Lord
2 The cat - tle are low - ing, the ba - by a - wakes, But lit - tle Lord
3 Be near me, Lord Je - sus! I ask Thee to stay Close by me for -

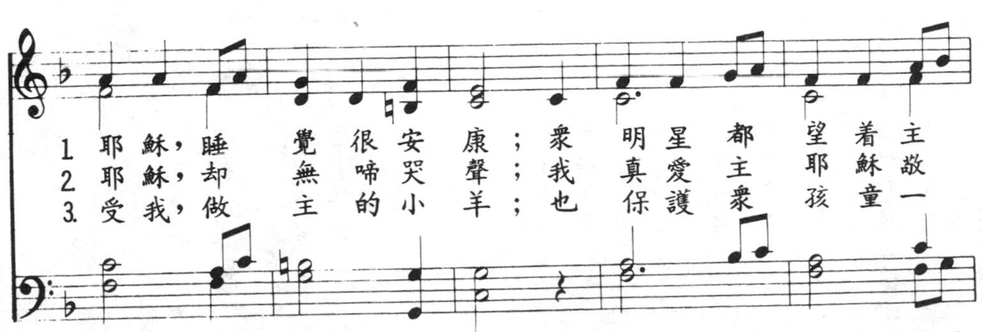
1. 耶 穌，睡 覺 很 安 康；衆 明 星 都 望 着 主
2. 耶 穌，却 無 啼 哭 聲；我 真 愛 主 耶 穌 敬
3. 受 我，做 主 的 小 羊；也 保 護 衆 孩 童 一
1 Je - sus laid down His sweet head. The stars in the bright sky looked
2 Je - sus, no cry - ing He makes. I love Thee, Lord Je - sus! Look
3 ev - er, and love me, I pray. Bless all the dear chil - dren in

1. 睡 的 地 方，小 小 的 主 耶 穌，睡 在 乾 草 上。
2. 求 近 我 身，靠 近 我 的 床 邊，守 我 到 天 明。
3. 齊 都 安 康，敎 我 們 都 能 夠，跟 主 到 天 堂。
1 down where He lay, The lit - tle Lord Je-sus, a - sleep on the hay.
2 down from the sky, And stay by my side un - til morn - ing is nigh.
3 Thy ten - der care, And fit us for heav - en, to live with Thee there.

122

小伯利恒
O Little Town of Bethlehem

But thou, Bethlehem, out of thee shall come He forth . . . a ruler in Israel. — Micah 5:2

Phillips Brooks

ST. LOUIS
Lewis H. Redner

1. 美哉小城小伯利恒，你是何等清靜！
2. 因馬利亞誕生聖嬰，天上衆軍齊集，
3. 宏愛上主至大恩典，普賜相信的人，
4. 哦，伯利恒至聖嬰孩，懇求今再降臨！
1 O lit - tle town of Beth - le - hem, How still we see thee lie!
2 For Christ is born of Ma - ry, And gath-ered all a - bove,
3 How si - lent - ly, how si - lent - ly, The won-drous gift is given!
4 O ho - ly Child of Beth - le - hem! De - scend to us, we pray;

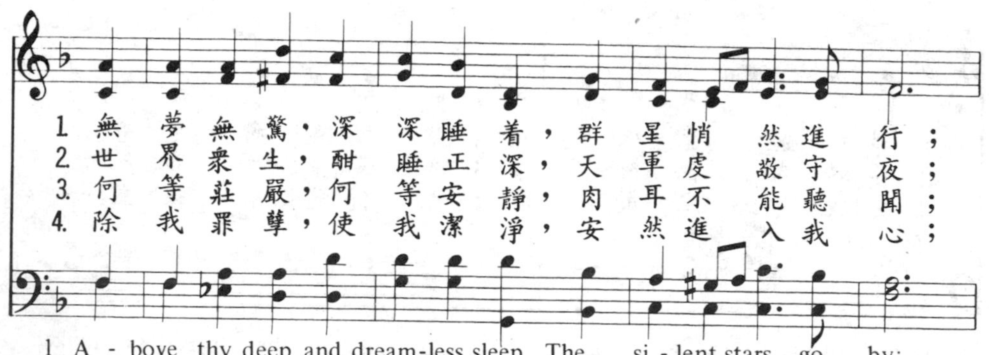
1. 無夢無驚，深深睡着，群星悄然進行；
2. 世界衆生，酣睡正深，天軍虔敬守夜；
3. 何等莊嚴，何等安靜，肉耳不能聽聞；
4. 除我罪孽，使我潔淨，安然進入我心；
1 A - bove thy deep and dream-less sleep The si - lent stars go by;
2 While mor - tals sleep, the an - gels keep Their watch of won-dering love.
3 So God im - parts to hu-man hearts The bless-ings of His heaven.
4 Cast out our sin and en - ter in, Be born in us to - day.

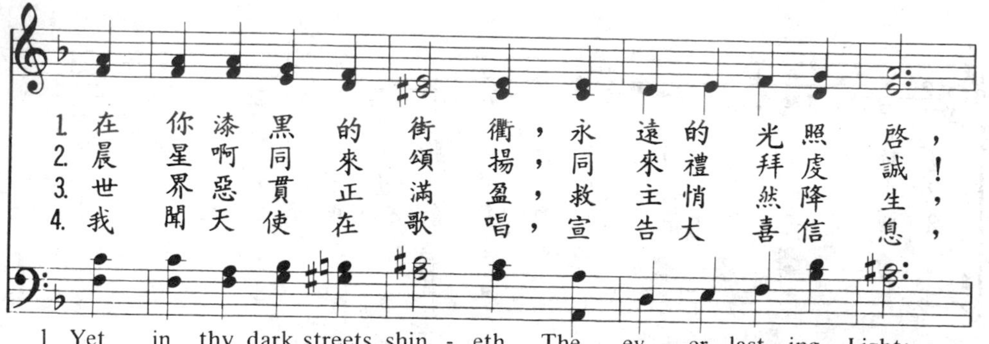
1. 在你漆黑的街衢，永遠的光照啓，
2. 晨星啊同來頌揚，同來禮拜虔誠！
3. 世界惡貫正滿盈，救主悄然降生，
4. 我聞天使在歌唱，宣告大喜信息，
1 Yet in thy dark streets shin - eth The ev - er - last - ing Light:
2 O morn-ing stars, to - geth - er Pro - claim the ho - ly birth!
3 No ear may hear His com - ing, But in this world of sin,
4 We hear the Christ-mas an - gels The great glad ti - dings tell;

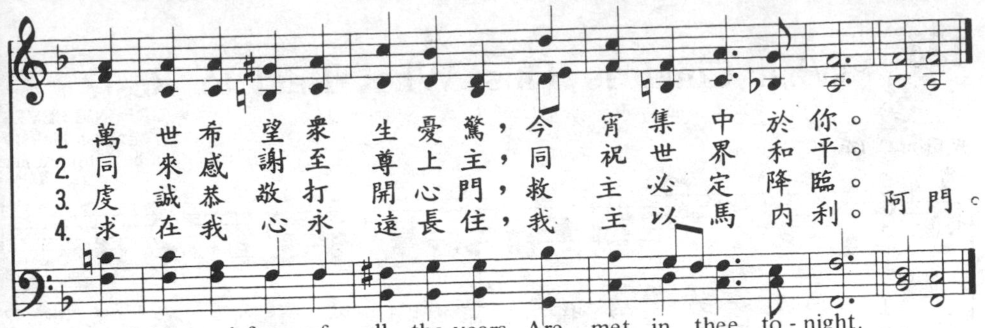

1. 萬世希望衆生憂驚，今宵集中於你。
2. 同來感謝至尊上主，同祝世界和平。
3. 虔誠恭敬打開心門，救主必定降臨。
4. 求在我心永遠長住，我主以馬內利。阿門。

1 The hopes and fears of all the years Are met in thee to-night.
2 *And prais-es sing to God the King, And peace to men on earth.*
3 Where meek souls will re-ceive Him still, The dear Christ en-ters in.
4 *O come to us, a-bide with us, Our Lord Em-man-u-el!* A-men.

122-1

耶穌，何等奇妙的主

Jesus, What A Wonder You Are

Your eyes will see the King in His beauty. Isa. 33:17

Dave Bolton — Dave Bolton

Unison

耶穌，何等奇妙的主，
Je - sus, what a won-der You are,

溫柔和謙卑，聖潔與慈祥。
You are so gen-tle, so pure and so kind.

又如晨星燦爛發光。
You shine like the morn-ing star.

耶穌，何等奇妙的主。
Je - sus, what a won-der You are.

123

是何嬰孩？
What Child Is This, Who, Laid to Rest?

What manner of child shall this be? — Luke 1:66

GREENSLEEVES
English Melody
Harmonized by John Stainer

William C. Dix

1. 這 位 奇 妙 嬰 孩 是 誰，安 臥 馬 利 亞 懷 中？
2. 為 何 看 來 窮 苦 微 賤，牛 馬 就 在 祂 旁 邊？
3. 獻 上 乳 香 沒 葯 黃 金，衆 人 當 齊 來 拜 祂；

1 What child is this, who, laid to rest, On Ma-ry's lap is sleep-ing?
2 *Why lies He in such mean es-tate Where ox and ass are feed-ing?*
3 So bring Him in-cense, gold, and myrrh, Come peas-ant, king, to own Him;

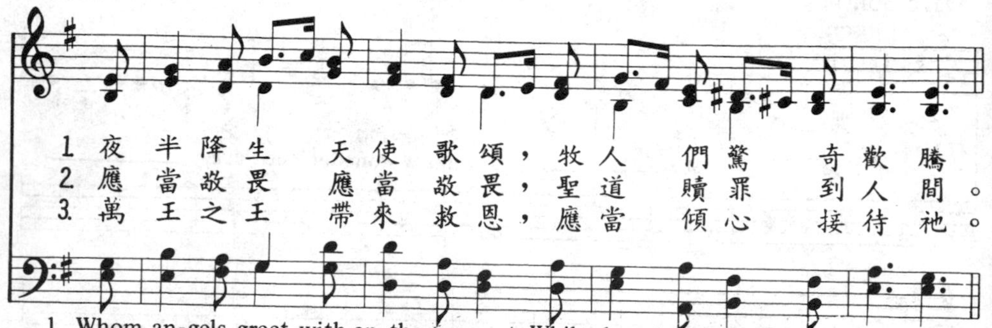

1. 夜 半 降 生 天 使 歌 頌，牧 人 們 驚 奇 歡 騰
2. 應 當 敬 畏 應 當 敬 畏，聖 道 贖 罪 到 人 間。
3. 萬 王 之 王 帶 來 救 恩，應 當 傾 心 接 待 祂。
1 Whom an-gels greet with an-thems sweet, While shep-herds watch are keep-ing?
2 Good Chris-tian, fear: for sin-ners here The si - lent Word is plead-ing.
3 The King of kings sal - va-tion brings, Let lov - ing hearts en-throne Him.

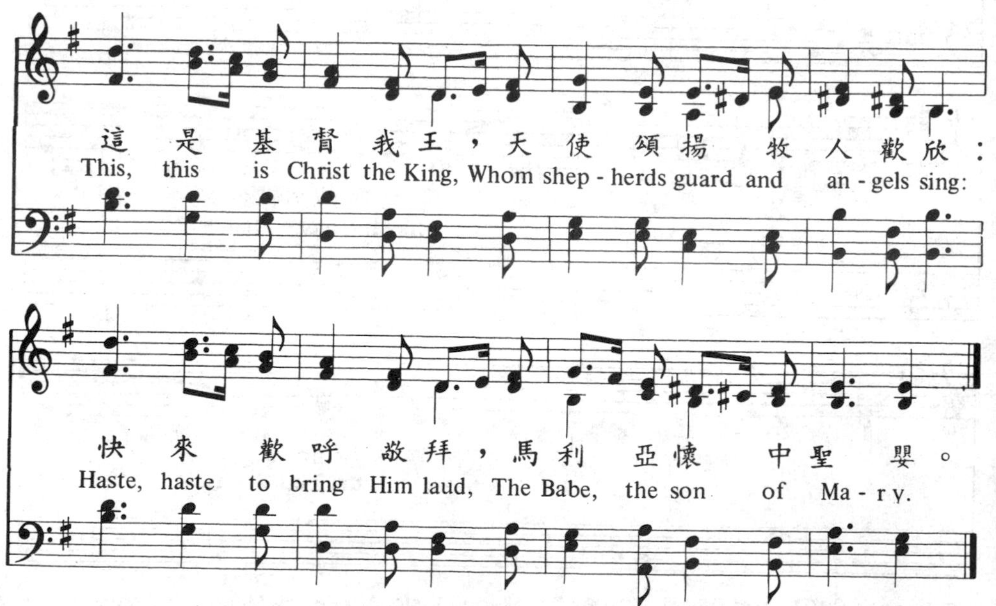

這 是 基 督 我 王，天 使 頌 揚 牧 人 歡 欣：
This, this is Christ the King, Whom shep - herds guard and an - gels sing:
快 來 歡 呼 敬 拜，馬 利 亞 懷 中 聖 嬰。
Haste, haste to bring Him laud, The Babe, the son of Ma - ry.

聖嬰柔和，聖嬰謙卑

Infant Holy, Infant Lowly

Paraphrase by Edith M. G. Reed

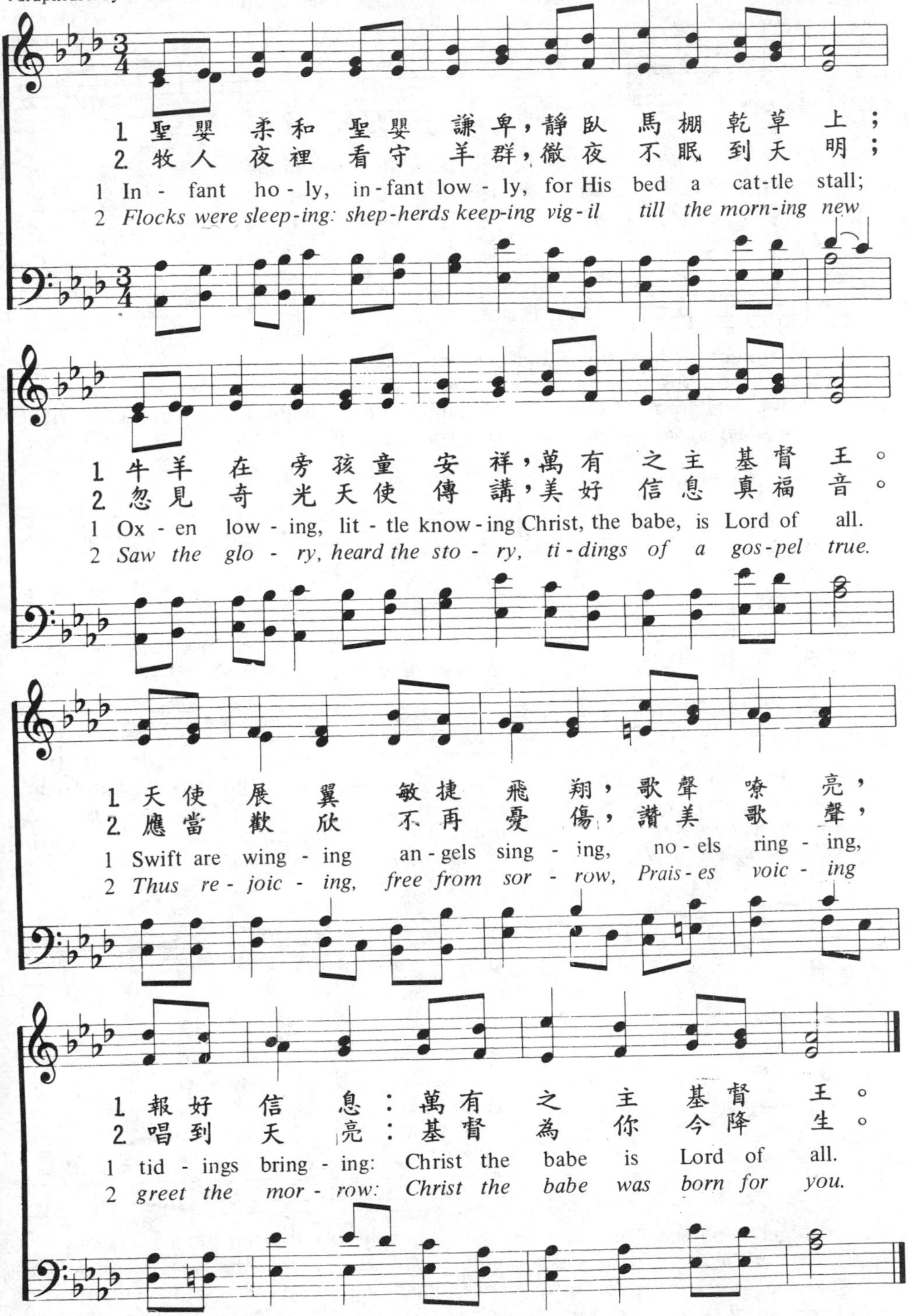

W ZLOBIE LEZY
Polish Carol

1. 聖嬰柔和聖嬰謙卑，靜臥馬棚乾草上；
2. 牧人夜裡看守羊群，徹夜不眠到天明；

1 In - fant ho - ly, in - fant low - ly, for His bed a cat - tle stall;
2 *Flocks were sleep - ing: shep - herds keep - ing vig - il till the morn - ing new*

1. 牛羊在旁孩童安祥，萬有之主基督王。
2. 忽見奇光天使傳講，美好信息真福音。

1 Ox - en low - ing, lit - tle know - ing Christ, the babe, is Lord of all.
2 *Saw the glo - ry, heard the sto - ry, ti - dings of a gos - pel true.*

1. 天使展翼敏捷飛翔，歌聲嘹亮，
2. 應當歡欣不再憂傷，讚美歌聲，

1 Swift are wing - ing an - gels sing - ing, no - els ring - ing,
2 *Thus re - joic - ing, free from sor - row, Prais - es voic - ing*

1. 報好信息：萬有之主基督王。
2. 唱到天亮：基督為你今降生。

1 tid - ings bring - ing: Christ the babe is Lord of all.
2 *greet the mor - row: Christ the babe was born for you.*

125

明星燦爛

Midnight Sleeping Bethlehem

Yang Ching-Tsiu
Eng. Tr. by Marshall Huang

When they saw the star, they rejoiced . . . — Matthew 2:10

Liang Chi-Fang
"Huan Sha Chi"
Chinese melody

1. 明星燦爛夜深沉，伯利恒城在睡鄉；
2. 明星燦爛夜深沉，孤燈熒熒照客窗；
3. 東方竟有三博士，仰瞻異星發光芒；
4. 天人相隔因罪孽，罪心潛滋道心亡；

1. Mid-night sleep - ing Beth-le-hem, Bright Thy stars in so - lemn night
2. *Now sleep - ing Beth - le - hem, There in sta-ble lan - tern's glow;*
3. Scho - lars from the ori - ent came, Led by light from yon star bright,
4. *Sin has man from God dis - join, Death its fruit our lives de - filed,*

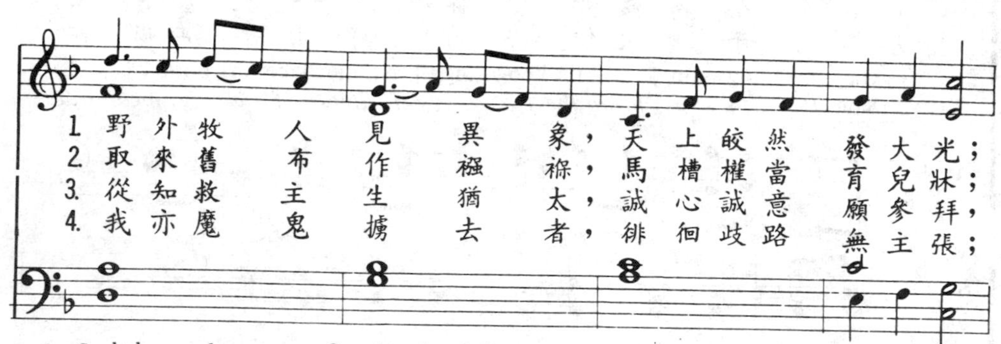

1. 野外牧人見異象，天上皎然發大光；
2. 取來舊布作襁褓，馬槽權當育兒牀；
3. 從知救主生猶太，誠心誠意願參拜，
4. 我亦魔鬼擄去者，徘徊歧路無主張；

1. Sud-den glo - ry floods thy hill - side, Start-led Sheph-erds wake in fright;
2. *Lies a Ho-ly Babe, midst the ox and ass, Gent - ly swathed in man - ger low;*
3. Know-ing there was born, From a-mong the Jews, God of glo - ry, God of might,
4. *On this night of night, Christ in - car - nate came, God and sin - ners re - con - ciled,*

1. 天使列隊同歌唱，牧人見狀真驚惶，
2. 為欲拯救衆罪人，道成人身真理彰，
3. 借彼明駝千里足，跋涉荒漠朝君王，
4. 神已為我立善牧，我豈依舊作亡羊？

1. An - gel mes - sen - gers ap - pear, She-pherd lis - ten first in fear,
2. *Hea - ven's one of match - less worth, Liv - ing word thru hum - ble birth,*
3. Trav'ling miles and miles from hence, Pass - ing de - sert so im - mense,
4. *Christ my she - pherd He must be, how can I stray far from Thee?*

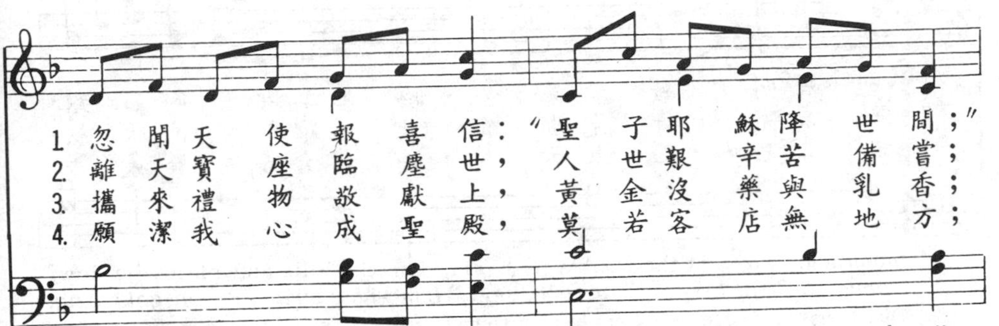
1. 忽 聞 天 使 報 喜 信："聖 子 耶 穌 降 世 間；"
2. 離 天 寶 座 臨 塵 世，人 世 艱 辛 苦 備 嘗；
3. 攜 來 禮 物 敬 獻 上，黃 金 沒 藥 與 乳 香；
4. 願 潔 我 心 成 聖 殿，莫 若 客 店 無 地 方；

1. Till they hear these words of cheer: "God own Son is gi - ven here";
2. *Come to ran - som sons of earth, Come to rid our souls of dearth;*
3. Bring - ing gifts of great ex - pense, Gold and myrrh and frank - in - cense;
4. *Cleanse my heart a tem - ple be, Not like the inn no room for Thee;*

1. 至 高 榮 耀 歸 上 主！全 地 人 民 福 無 疆！
2. 至 高 榮 耀 歸 上 主！全 地 人 民 福 無 疆！
3. 至 高 榮 耀 歸 上 主！全 地 人 民 福 無 疆！
4. 願 潔 我 心 成 聖 殿，莫 若 客 店 無 地 方。
1. High - est glo - ry, Lord to Thee, Bound - less joy to all men be.
2. High - est glo - ry, Lord to Thee, Bound - less joy to all men be.
3. High - est glo - ry, Lord to Thee, Bound - less joy to all men be.
4. Cleanse my heart a tem - ple be, Not like the inn no room for Thee

Peace on Earth

This is God's Christmas greeting.
In the beautiful story of Jesus' birth,
it was sung by a chorus of angelic voices.
Heard at first only by Judean shepherds outside the town of Bethlehem,
nevertheless, it is a message that the whole world should hear.
On each Christmas Day,
God repeats His greeting.

—Anonymous

126

明月寒星

The Moon and Stars on Christmas Eve

Tien Ching-Fu

Eng. Tr. by Marshall Huang

When they saw the star they rejoiced with exceeding great joy.

Matthew 2:10

Bliss Wiant

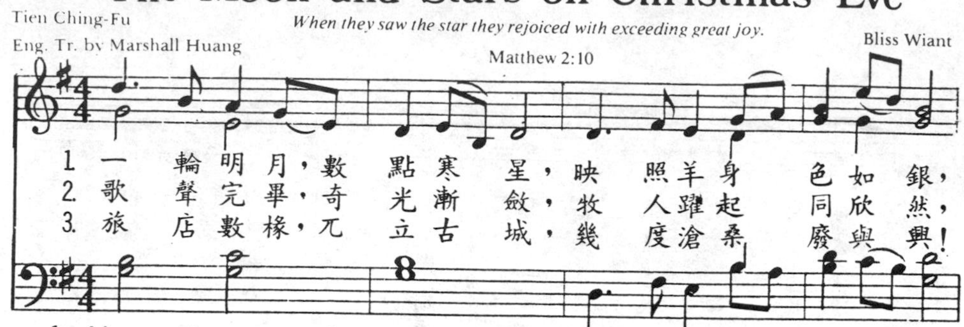

1. 一輪明月，數點寒星，映照羊身色如銀，
2. 歌聲完畢，奇光漸斂，牧人躍起同欣然，
3. 旅店數椽，兀立古城，幾度滄桑廢與興！

1. Moon and star cast their sil-ver beam, On the hills and plains be-low,
2. *Come to Beth-le- hem and see, Him whose birth the an-gels sing,*
3. Qui- et lit-tle Beth-le-hem town, In a sta-ble, one little Child,

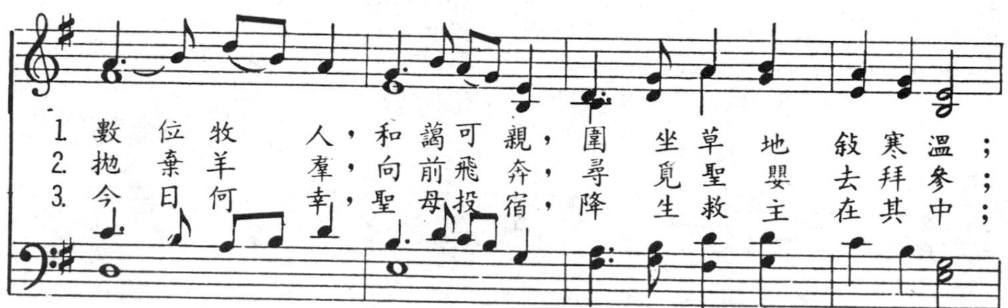

1. 數位牧人，和藹可親，圍坐草地敘寒溫；
2. 拋棄羊羣，向前飛奔，尋覓聖嬰去拜參；
3. 今日何幸，聖母投宿，降生救主在其中；

1. While Shepherds keep wat-ching o'er the sheep, Round a campfire's friend-ly glow;
2. *Leave your sheep and rams, goats and gentle lambs, Worship Him, our new born King;*
3. Hum-ble low- ly shed, in a man-ger bed, Rests the King, a Babe so mild;

1. 奇光燦爛，歌聲悠揚，牧人俯伏奇且驚！
2. 人聲鼎沸，佳報頻傳，滿城歡樂齊頌讚，
3. 東方學者，不遠千里，來獻禮物豐且隆；

1. Won-drous light shone the hea-vens bright, An-ge-lic hosts bade them come;
2. *From the east kings and ma-gi came, Bring-ing their gifts to this Child;*
3. Come a-dore on bend-ed knee, Glo- ry and grace to a- dorn;

1. 雲中天使，同聲報告，神子已生伯利恒。
2. 農工良友，平民救星，今日降生人世間。
3. 博愛救主，和平真神，今日降生伯利恒！

1. Peace and good will be to all men, Christ is born in Beth-le-hem.
2. *All the world this day re- joice, God and sin-ners re-con-ciled.*
3. Lord of Lords and King of Kings, God of all Cre-a-tion born.

最美麗聖名
The Beautiful Name

And it shall be to Me a name of joy, a praise and honor before all the nations. — Jeremiah 33:9
Jean Perry, Alt.
Mabel Johnston Camp
1. 我 知 一 聖 名，最 美 麗 聖 名，由 天 使 送
2. 我 知 一 聖 名，最 美 麗 聖 名，賜 給 一 可
1. I know of a Name, A beau-ti-ful Name, That an-gels bro't
2. I know of a Name, A beau-ti-ful Name, That un-to a
1. 達 人 間； 昔 年 有 一 夜，天 使 向 童 女，
2. 愛 聖 嬰； 昔 年 歡 樂 夜，景 星 放 光 明，
1. down to earth; They whis-pered it low, One night long a-go,
2. Babe was giv'n; The stars glit-tered bright Thro'-out that glad night,
1. 細 語 此 名，樂 無 限。
2. 衆 天 使 讚 美 不 停。
最 美 麗 聖 名，最
1. To a maid-en of low-ly birth.
2. And an-gels praised God in heav'n.
That beau-ti-ful Name, That
美 麗 聖 名，使 我 脱 罪 與 痛 苦 最 美 麗 聖
beau-ti-ful Name, From sin has pow-er to free us! That beau-ti-ful
名，最 奇 妙 聖 名，最 大 之 名 是 耶 穌。
Name, That won-der-ful Name, That match-less Name is Je-sus!

東方三博士
We Three Kings of Orient Are

Now when Jesus was born in Bethlehem
. . . there came wise men from the East . . . . — Matthew 2:1

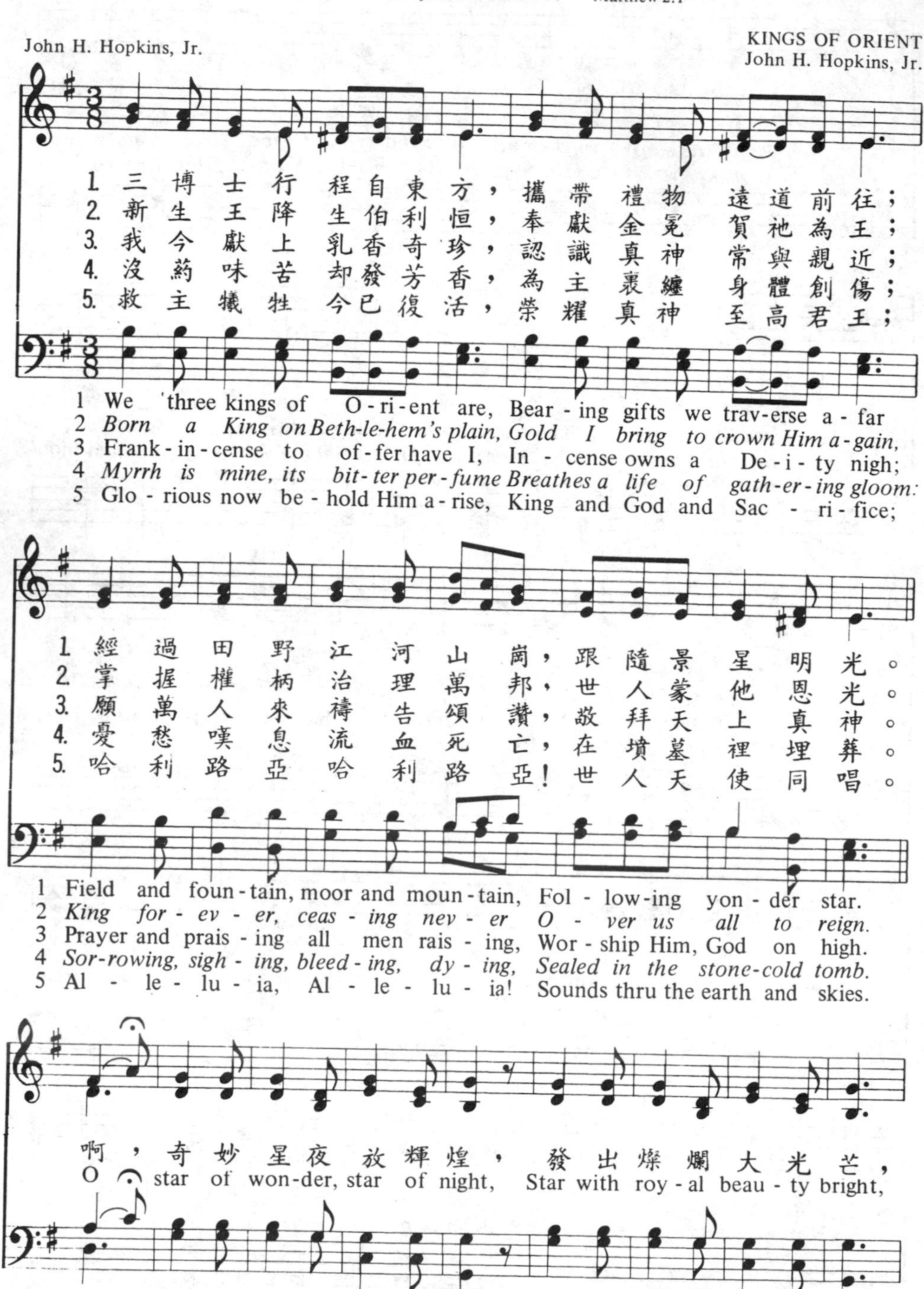
John H. Hopkins, Jr.
KINGS OF ORIENT
John H. Hopkins, Jr.
1. 三博士行程自東方，攜帶禮物遠道前往；
2. 新生王降生伯利恒，奉獻金冕賀祂為王；
3. 我今獻上乳香奇珍，認識真神常與親近；
4. 沒葯味苦却發芳香，為主裹纏身體創傷；
5. 救主犧牲今已復活，榮耀真神至高君王；
1 We three kings of O-ri-ent are, Bear-ing gifts we trav-erse a-far
2 Born a King on Beth-le-hem's plain, Gold I bring to crown Him a-gain,
3 Frank-in-cense to of-fer have I, In-cense owns a De-i-ty nigh;
4 Myrrh is mine, its bit-ter per-fume Breathes a life of gath-er-ing gloom:
5 Glo-rious now be-hold Him a-rise, King and God and Sac-ri-fice;
1. 經過田野江河山崗，跟隨景星明光。
2. 掌握權柄治理萬邦，世人蒙他恩光。
3. 願萬人來禱告頌讚，敬拜天上真神。
4. 憂愁嘆息流血死亡，在墳墓裡埋葬。
5. 哈利路亞哈利路亞！世人天使同唱。
1 Field and foun-tain, moor and moun-tain, Fol-low-ing yon-der star.
2 King for-ev-er, ceas-ing nev-er O-ver us all to reign.
3 Prayer and prais-ing all men rais-ing, Wor-ship Him, God on high.
4 Sor-rowing, sigh-ing, bleed-ing, dy-ing, Sealed in the stone-cold tomb.
5 Al-le-lu-ia, Al-le-lu-ia! Sounds thru the earth and skies.
啊，奇妙星夜放輝煌，發出燦爛大光芒，
O star of won-der, star of night, Star with roy-al beau-ty bright,

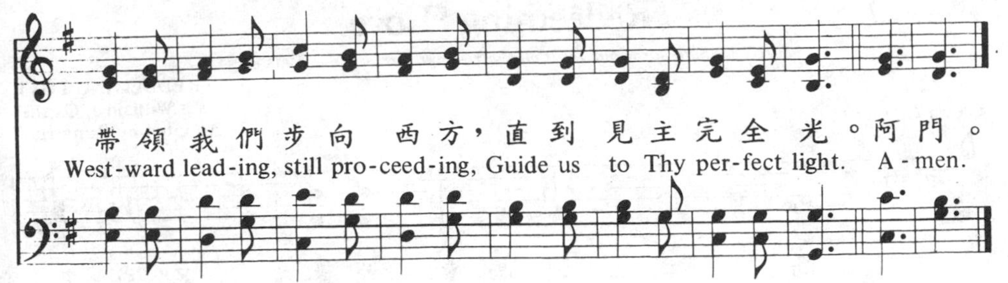
帶領我們步向 西方，直到 見主完全 光。阿門。
West-ward lead-ing, still pro-ceed-ing, Guide us to Thy per-fect light. A-men.

129

向前走
March On Forward

Based on Luk. 9:62
Eng. Tr. by Marshall Huang

Chinese melody

向前走呀，努力向前走，一去不回頭。
March on for-ward Press on for the Lord, Go and don't look back.

向前走呀，努力向前走，前進莫退後。
March on for-ward Press on for the Lord, Go and don't turn back.

手扶着犂向後看的人，不配進神國。
He who puts his hand to the plow and looks back, Is not fit for Heav'n

向前走呀，努力向前走，主就在前頭。
March on for-ward Press on for the Lord. He will lead us on.

救贖大愛
Redeeming Love

Surely He hath borne our griefs and carried our sorrows. — Isaiah 53:4

Gloria Gaither

REDEEMING LOVE
William J. Gaither
Adapted by Ronn Huff

1 自高天降生到馬槽，原為富足成貧
2 來自至高慈愛父神，降到世上無人
1 From God's heav-en to a man-ger, From great rich-es to the
2 From a lov-ing heaven-ly Fa-ther, To a world that knew Him
1 窮，聖嬰孩是神愛子，耶穌基督；
2 知，憂傷人子是耶穌，基督我主；
1 poor, Came the ho-ly Son of God, a lit-tle Child;
2 not, Came a man of sor-rows, Je-sus Christ, the Lord;
1 原住在美麗的青天，今却以乾草為床，
2 迷失中主將我尋着，主大愛改變了我，
1 From the a-zure halls of heav-en To a low-ly man-ger stall,
2 In my wan-dering Je-sus found me, Touched my life with His great love,
1 耶穌來，是為你我將生命捨。
2 聖嬰孩耶穌是我生命的主。
1 Je-sus came, and here He gave His life for all.
2 And this Babe has grown to be my sov-ereign Lord.

救贖大愛，這愛直存到萬代；救贖大
Re-deem-ing love, a love that knows no lim - it; Re-deem-ing
愛，這愛無窮無限；我靈歌唱直唱到千萬
love, a love that nev - er dies; My soul shall sing through-out the end-less
年代。我俯伏敬拜至高無比的愛。
a - ges, The ad - o - ra-tion of this great love on high.

太初有道，道與 神同在，道就是 神。這道太初與 神同在。

約翰福音第一章
1—2節

道成了肉身，住在我們中間，充充滿滿的有恩典有真理。我們也見過他的榮光，正是父獨生子的榮光。

約翰福音第一章
14節

131

榮耀天軍

Angels from the Realms of Glory

. . . We have come to worship Him. — Matthew 2:2

James Montgomery

REGENT SQUARE
Henry T. Smart

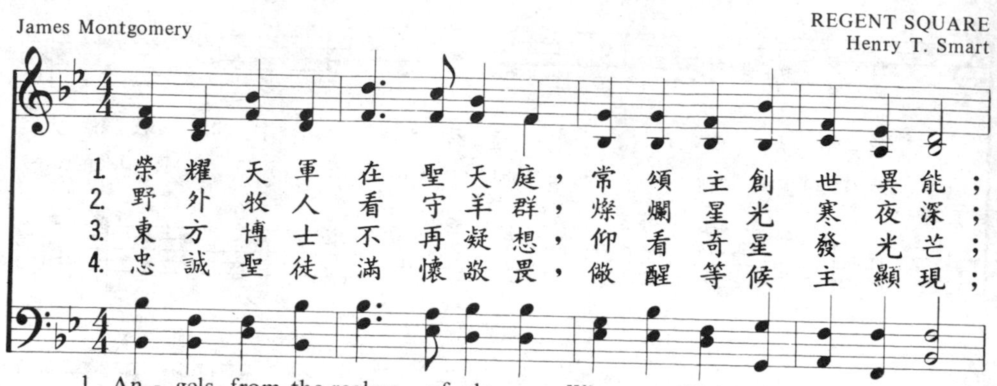
1. 榮 耀 天 軍 在 聖 天 庭，常 頌 主 創 世 異 能；
2. 野 外 牧 人 看 守 羊 群，燦 爛 星 光 寒 夜 深；
3. 東 方 博 士 不 再 凝 想，仰 看 奇 星 發 光 芒；
4. 忠 誠 聖 徒 滿 懷 敬 畏，儆 醒 等 候 主 顯 現；
1 An - gels, from the realms of glo - ry, Wing your flight o'er all the earth;
2 *Shep-herds, in the fields a - bid - ing, Watch - ing o'er your flocks by night,*
3 Wise men, leave your con - tem - pla - tion, Bright - er vi - sions beam a - far;
4 *Saints be - fore the al - tar bend - ing, Watch - ing long in hope and fear,*

1. 今 日 展 翅 飛 向 大 地，傳 揚 救 世 主 降 生。
2. 聖 嬰 降 生 榮 光 普 照，神 人 同 居 當 歡 欣。
3. 今 日 得 見 萬 民 所 望，迅 速 起 身 去 尋 訪。
4. 至 聖 救 主 忽 然 臨 到，榮 光 充 滿 主 聖 殿。
1 Ye who sang cre - a - tion's sto - ry, Now pro - claim Mes - si - ah's birth:
2 *God with man is now re - sid - ing, Yon - der shines the in - fant light:*
3 Seek the great De - sire of na - tions, Ye have seen His na - tal star:
4 *Sud - den - ly the Lord, de - scend - ing, In His tem - ple shall ap - pear:*

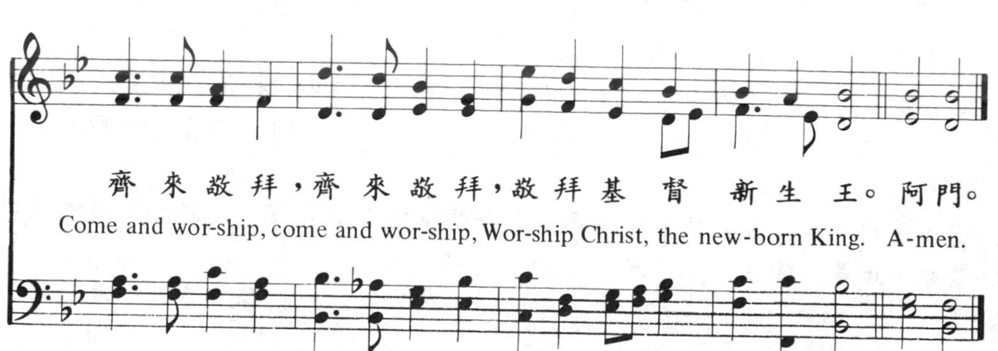
齊 來 敬 拜，齊 來 敬 拜，敬 拜 基 督 新 生 王。阿 門。
Come and wor-ship, come and wor-ship, Wor-ship Christ, the new-born King. A-men.

信徒們當歡欣

Good Christian Men, Rejoice
Latin Carol
Tr. by John M. Neale
When they saw the star they rejoiced. — Matthew 2:10
IN DULCI JUBILO
German Melody
1. 信 徒 們 當 歡 欣， 發 出 讚 美 聲 音；
2. 信 徒 們 當 歡 欣， 發 出 讚 美 聲 音；
3. 信 徒 們 當 歡 欣， 發 出 讚 美 聲 音；
1 Good Chris-tian men, re - joice With heart and soul and voice;
2 Good Chris-tian men, re - joice With heart and soul and voice;
3 Good Chris-tian men, re - joice With heart and soul and voice;
1. 請 聽 大 好 的 喜 訊 ： 喜 訊 ！ 耶 穌 基 督 今 降 生 ！
2. 請 聽 喜 樂 的 福 音 ： 喜 樂 ！ 耶 穌 為 此 而 降 生 ！
3. 不 再 懼 怕 死 亡 門 ： 平 安 ！ 耶 穌 為 救 我 降 生 ！
1 Give ye heed to what we say: News! news! Je-sus Christ is born to-day!
2 Now ye hear of end-less bliss: Joy! joy! Je-sus Christ was born for this!
3 Now ye need not fear the grave: Peace! peace! Je-sus Christ was born to save!
1. 牛 羊 在 祂 前 屈 膝， 救 主 安 臥 在 馬 槽 裡 。
2. 祂 為 我 開 天 堂 門， 世 人 從 此 蒙 主 宏 恩 。
3. 祂 今 向 世 人 呼 喚， 得 着 救 主 永 遠 平 安 。
1 Ox and ass be - fore Him bow, And He is in the man-ger now.
2 He has o-pened heav-en's door, And man is bless - ed ev - er-more.
3 Calls you one and calls you all To gain His ev - er - last - ing hall.
1. 基 督 今 降 生 ！ 基 督 今 降 生 ！
2. 基 督 為 此 生 ！ 基 督 為 此 生 ！
3. 基 督 今 降 生 ！ 基 督 今 降 生 ！
1 Christ is born to - day! Christ is born to - day!
2 Christ was born for this! Christ was born for this!
3 Christ was born to save! Christ was born to save!

133

牧人聞信

While Shepherds Watched Their Flocks by Night

Nahum Tate

Fear not, for I bring you good tidings of great joy. — Luke 2:10

CHRISTMAS
Arranged from George Friedrich Handel

1. 牧人夜間看守羊群，彼此對坐地上，忽然使者從天降臨，榮光四圍照亮，榮光四圍照亮。
2. 牧人一見駭然大驚，天使囑咐勿懼："我來傳報大喜之音，關乎萬民好處，關乎萬民好處。
3. 按古預言大衛城中，今日降生救主，乃主基督又名耶穌，今有記號賜你，今有記號賜你。
4. 至尊嬰孩今在那城，你可親眼看見，裹布於身就是記號，躺臥馬槽裡面，躺臥馬槽裡面。
5. 榮耀全歸至高真神，平安充滿全地，天上恩門從今大開，直到永世無盡！直到永世無盡！"
1 While shep-herds watched their flocks by night, All seat-ed on the ground, The an-gel of the Lord came down, And glo-ry shone a-round, And glo-ry shone a-round.
2 "Fear not!" said he, for might-y dread Had seized their trou-bled mind; "Glad ti-dings of great joy I bring To you and all man-kind, To you and all man-kind.
3 "To you in Da-vid's town this day Is born, of Da-vid's line, The Sav-ior, who is Christ the Lord, And this shall be the sign— And this shall be the sign:
4 "The heaven-ly Babe you there shall find To hu-man view dis-played, All mean-ly wrapt in swath-ing-bands And in a man-ger laid, And in a man-ger laid.
5 "All glo-ry be to God on high, And to the earth be peace: Good will hence-forth from heaven to men Be-gin and nev-er cease! Be-gin and nev-er cease!"

夜半歌聲

It Came upon the Midnight Clear

Through the tender mercies of our God . . . the dayspring from on high hath visited us.
Luke 1:78

CAROL

Edmund H. Sears

Richard S. Willis

1. 緬想當年時方夜半，忽來榮耀歌聲，
2. 世界萬千勞苦民衆，負擔重壓身心，
3. 因為歲月周行不息，世事積極前進，

1 It came up-on the mid-night clear, That glo-rious song of old,
2 *And ye, be-neath life's crush-ing load, Whose forms are bend-ing low,*
3 For lo, the days are has-tening on, By proph-et seen of old,

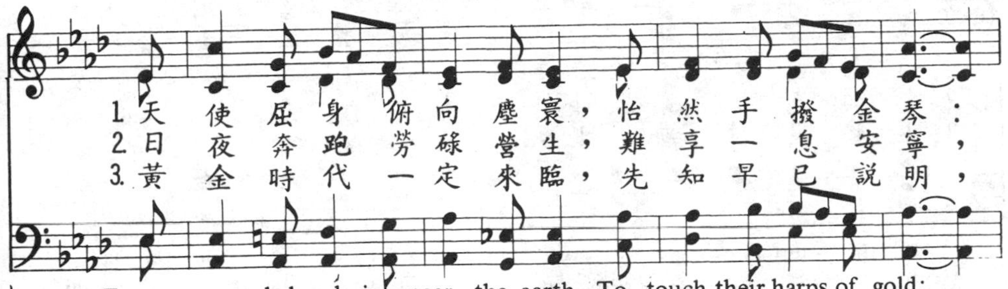
1. 天使屈身俯向塵寰，怡然手撥金琴：
2. 日夜奔跑勞碌營生，難享一息安寧，
3. 黃金時代一定來臨，先知早已說明，

1 From an-gels bend-ing near the earth To touch their harps of gold:
2 *Who toil a-long the climb-ing way With pain-ful steps and slow,*
3 When, with the ev-er-cir-cling years, Shall come the time fore-told,

1. "地上平安人增友誼，天賜特殊奇恩，"
2. 當知所望黃金時代，不久便要來臨，
3. 到時新天新地生靈，共戴和平之君，

1 "Peace on the earth, good-will to men, From heaven's all-gra-cious King":
2 *Look now! for glad and gold-en hours Come swift-ly on the wing:*
3 When the new heaven and earth shall own The Prince of Peace their King,

1. 當晚世界沉寂之中，靜聽天使歌聲。
2. 崎嶇道上請息片時，靜聽天使歌聲。
3. 普天之下齊聲響應，今日天使歌聲。

1 The world in sol-emn still-ness lay To hear the an-gels sing.
2 *O rest be-side the wea-ry load, And hear the an-gels sing.*
3 And the whole world send back the song Which now the an-gels sing.

135

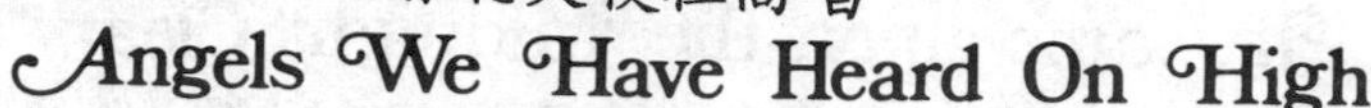
請聽天使在高唱

Angels We Have Heard On High

French Carol

. . . *Glory to God in the highest.* — Luke 2:14

GLORIA
French Carol

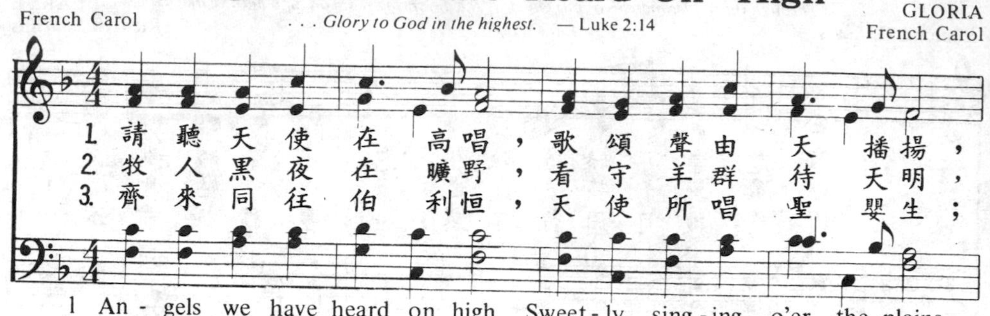
1. 請 聽 天 使 在 高唱，歌 頌 聲 由 天 播揚，
2. 牧 人 黑 夜 在 曠野，看 守 羊群 待 天明，
3. 齊 來 同 往 伯 利恒，天 使 所 唱 聖 嬰生；

1 An - gels we have heard on high Sweet - ly sing - ing o'er the plains,
2 *Shep-herds, why this ju - bi - lee? Why your joy - ous strains pro - long?*
3 Come to Beth - le - hem and see Him whose birth the an - gels sing;

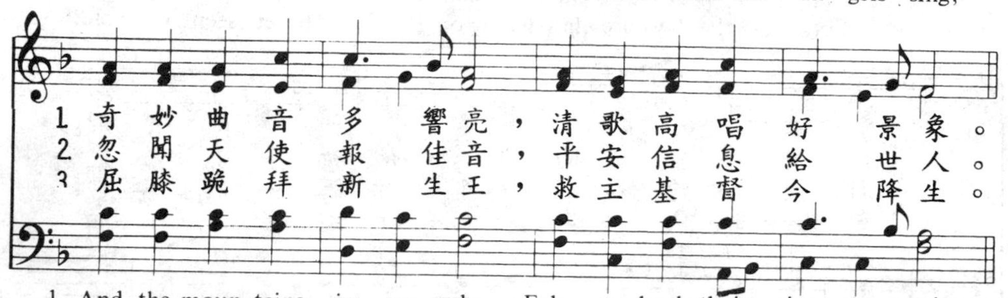
1. 奇 妙 曲 音 多 響亮，清 歌 高 唱 好 景 象。
2. 忽 聞 天 使 報 佳音，平 安 信 息 給 世 人。
3. 屈 膝 跪 拜 新 生王，救 主 基 督 今 降 生。

1 And the moun-tains in re - ply Ech - o back their joy - ous strains.
2 *Say what may the ti - dings be, Which in - spire your heaven - ly song?*
3 Come a - dore, on bend - ed knee, Christ, the Lord, the new - born King.

榮 ─ ─ ─ ─ ─ ─ ─ ─ ─ ─ 耀，榮 耀，
Glo - ─ ─ ─ ─ ─ ─ ─ ─ ─ ─ ri - a

榮 耀 歸 於 真 神，榮 ─ ─ ─
in ex - cel - sis De - o, Glo ─ ─ ─

─ ─ ─ ─ 耀，榮 耀．榮 耀 歸 於 真 神。
─ ri - a in ex - cel - sis De - o.

齊來，宗主信徒
O Come, All Ye Faithful

Let us go even unto Bethlehem. — Luke 2:15
Latin: John F. Wade
Tr. by Frederick Oakeley
ADESTE FIDELES
John F. Wade's Cantus Diversi
1. 齊來宗主信徒，快樂又歡欣，齊來，一齊來大家上伯利恒；來朝見聖嬰，天使王已降生；
2. 天使結成樂隊，歡然同歌唱，光明衆天軍來高聲同讚揚；至高的處所，榮耀歸於君王；
3. 救主生於今晨，我衆來歡迎，天人諸榮耀完全歸主一身；大哉父本像，藉聖子來顯明；
1 O come, all ye faith-ful, joy-ful and tri-um-phant, O come ye, O come ye to Beth-le-hem; Come and behold Him, born the King of an-gels;
2 Sing, choirs of an-gels, sing in ex-ul-ta-tion, O sing, all ye cit-i-zens of heaven a-bove; Glo-ry to God, all glo-ry in the high-est;
3 Yea, Lord, we greet Thee, born this hap-py morn-ing, O Je-sus, to Thee be all glo-ry given; Word of the Fa-ther, now in flesh ap-pear-ing;
齊來，虔誠同崇拜，齊來，虔誠同崇拜，
O come, let us a-dore Him, O come, let us a-dore Him,
齊來，虔誠同崇拜，主基督。阿門。
O come, let us a-dore Him, Christ, the Lord. A-men.

137

到各山嶺去傳揚

Go, Tell It on the Mountains

They made known abroad the saying . . . concerning this child.

— Luke 2:17

GO TELL IT ON THE MOUNTAINS
American Folk Song
Traditional
Unison
到各山嶺去傳揚，越過山崗到各地方；
Go, tell it on the moun-tains, O-ver the hills and ev-ery-where;
到各山嶺去傳揚，說基督已降生！
Go, tell it on the moun-tains That Je-sus Christ is born!
Fine
Harmony
1. 有牧羊人在野地，夜間看守群羊，忽
2. 牧羊人心裡戰兢，但聞天使歌聲，歡
3. 卑微低賤的馬棚，救主基督降生，帶
1 While shep-herds kept their watch-ing O'er si-lent flocks by night, Be-
2 The shep-herds feared and trem-bled When lo! A-bove the earth Rang
3 Down in a low-ly man-ger The hum-ble Christ was born, And
D.C.
1. 然自天上照耀，極聖潔的亮光。
2. 呼讚美聲嘹亮，救主今夜降生。
3. 來救恩好福音，主降生人蒙恩。
1 hold through-out the heav-ens There shone a ho-ly light.
2 out the an-gel cho-rus That hailed our Sav-ior's birth.
3 brought us God's sal-va-tion That bless-ed Christ-mas morn.

平安夜，聖善夜

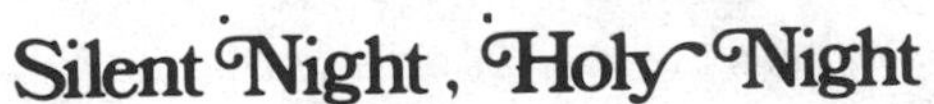
Silent Night, Holy Night

Joseph Mohr
Tr. by John F. Young

And they . . . found Mary and Joseph, and the baby . . . .
— Luke 2:16

STILLE NACHT
Franz Gruber

1. 平 安 夜，聖 善 夜，萬 暗 中，光 華 射，
2. 平 安 夜，聖 善 夜，牧 羊 人，在 曠 野，
3. 平 安 夜，聖 善 夜，神 子 愛，光 皎 潔，
1 Si - lent night, ho - ly night, All is calm, all is bright
2 Si - lent night, ho - ly night, Shep-herds quake at the sight.
3 Si - lent night, ho - ly night, Son of God, love's pure light

1. 照 着 聖 母 也 照 着 聖 嬰，多 少 慈 祥 也 多 少 天 真，
2. 忽 然 看 見 了 天 上 光 華，聽 見 天 使 唱 哈 利 路 亞，
3. 救 贖 宏 恩 的 黎 明 來 到，聖 容 發 出 來 榮 光 普 照，
1 Round yon vir - gin moth-er and child. Ho - ly in-fant so ten-der and mild,
2 Glo - ries stream from heav-en a - far, Heaven-ly hosts sing al - le - lu - ia;
3 Ra-diant beams from Thy ho - ly face, With the dawn of re - deem - ing grace,

1. 靜 享 天 賜 安 眠，靜 享 天 賜 安 眠。
2. 救 主 今 夜 降 生！救 主 今 夜 降 生！
3. 耶 穌 我 主 降 生，耶 穌 我 主 降 生。
1 Sleep in heav-en - ly peace, Sleep in heav - en - ly peace.
2 Christ the Sav - ior, is born! Christ, the Sav - ior, is born!
3 Je - sus, Lord, at Thy birth, Je - sus, Lord, at Thy birth.

啊！聖善夜
O Holy Night

And this shall be a sign unto you; you shall find the child . . .
— Luke 2:12

John S. Dwight
Revised by Avis B. Christiansen

Adolphe Adam
Arr. by Eldon Burkwall

1. 啊聖善夜！衆星照耀極光明，今夜良
2. 虔卑俯伏，恭敬崇拜聖嬰孩，是神所
3. 何等快樂，燦爛光明的日子，祂必再
1. O ho-ly night! the stars are bright-ly shin-ing— It is the
2. With hum-ble hearts we bow in ad-o-ra-tion Be-fore this
3. O day of joy, when in e-ter-nal splen-dor He shall re-
1. 辰親愛救主降生！世人沉淪，全地已
2. 賜無限慈愛禮物，賜我救恩，親自為
3. 來榮耀的掌王權，衆口同聲，讚美稱
1. night of the dear Sav-ior's birth! Long lay the world in sin and
2. Child, gift of God's match-less love, Sent from on high to pur-chase
3. turn in His glo-ry to reign, When ev-'ry tongue due praise to
1. 罪惡貫盈直到主來靈魂自覺奇
2. 我還罪債，使我將來與祂永遠同
3. 頌主恩賜，祂有權能全地都當宣
1. dark-ness pin-ing— Till He ap-peared, gift of in-fi-nite
2. our sal-va-tion— That we might dwell with Him ev-er a-
3. Him shall ren-der, His pow'r and might to all na-tions pro-

1. 珍！聖 嬰耶穌 卑 微馬 棚裡 安 歇，道
2. 住，何 等恩典 榮 耀無 比的 福 氣，為
3. 傳，困 倦世人 驟 獲希 望真 高 興，因
1. worth! Be- hold the Babe in yon-der man-ger low-ly— 'Tis
2. bove. What grace un-told— to leave the bliss of glo- ry And
3. claim! A thrill of hope our long-ing heart re-joic-es, For
1. 成肉身降 臨到人世間：恭 敬崇 拜 至
2. 救罪人救 主孤單受死：恭 敬崇 拜 高
3. 為迎接一 榮耀的清晨：恭 敬崇 拜 高
1. God's own Son come down in hu-man form: Fall on your knees be-
2. die for sin-ners guilt-y and for- lorn: Fall on your knees! re-
3. soon shall dawn that glad e-ter-nal morn: Fall on your knees! with
1. 高 聖潔的 救主，啊，聖 善 夜，聖
2. 聲 傳講主 故事，
3. 唱 快樂的 詩歌，
O night di-vine O
1. fore the Lord most ho- ly!
2. peat the won-drous sto- ry!
3. joy lift up your voic-es!
夜 基督降 生！啊，聖善 夜，聖夜，啊，聖善夜！
night when Christ was born! O night di-vine O night, O night di-vine!

鈴在摇，鐘在響

Ring The Bells

Looking for and hasting unto the coming of the Day of God.

— I John 3:12

Harry Bollback

Harry Bollback

鈴在摇，鐘在響，讓全地知道，多年前在

Ring the bells, ring the bells, Let the whole world know Christ was born in

伯利恒基督已降生．祂降生受死為我，

Beth-le-hem Man-y years a- go: Born to die that man might live,

賜我生命叫我活，在那遥遠的馬棚，

Came to earth new life to give, Born of Ma - ry, born so low,

主藉童女生。天父賜下獨生子，是祂唯一

Man-y years a - go. God the Fa - ther gave His Son, Gave His own be -

的愛子，到罪惡的世界來，要賜他們生命，與
lov - ed One . To this wick - ed, sin - ful earth, To bring man-kind His love, new
愛。鈴在搖，鐘在響，讓全地知道，
birth: Ring the bells, ring the bells, Let the whole world know
正如多年前一樣，救主今日仍活着。
Christ the Sav - ior lives to - day As He did so long a - go!

How proper it is that Christmas should follow Advent.
— For him who looks toward the future, the Manger is situated on Golgotha,
and the Cross has already been raised in Bethlehem.

— Dag Hammarskjold

141

但我知道

I Cannot Tell

The righteous shall be glad in the Lord, and shall trust in Him . . . — Psalm 64:10

W. Y. Fullerton
LONDONDERRY AIR
Traditional Irish Melody
1. 我不知道天使所拜的君王，為何這
2. 我不知道祂如何默然受苦，將祂平
3. 我不知道祂如何能得民心，如何承
4. 我不知道全地要如何敬拜，祂發一
1 I can-not tell why He, whom an-gels wor - ship Should set His
2 I can-not tell how si-lent-ly He suf - fered As with His
3 I can-not tell how He will win the na - tions, How He will
4 I can-not tell how all the lands shall wor - ship When at His
1. 樣愛憐世上罪人，為何又像牧人去尋找
2. 安安慰這流淚谷，祂又如何在十字架上
3. 受祂屬地的產業，無論何人不論何處或
4. 言立時風浪平靜，當人的心充滿豐富的
1 love up - on the sons of men, Or why, as Shep-herd, He should seek the
2 peace He graced this place of tears, Or how His heart up - on the cross was
3 claim His earth-ly her - i - tage, Or sat-is - fy the needs and as - pir -
4 bidd - ing ev - ery storm is stilled, Or who can say how great the ju - bi -
1. 迷羊，引領他們歸回祂的羊圈。
2. 心碎，三十三年換來痛苦冠冕。
3. 善惡，祂又如何滿足他們需要。
4. 主愛，誰能說盡其中極大喜悅。
1 wan-der-ers To bring them back, they know not how or when.
2 bro - ken, The crown of pain to three and thir-ty years.
3 a - tions Of east and west, of sin - ner and of sage.
4 la - tion When all the hearts of men with love are filled.

1. 但我知道，祂從馬利亞而生，卑微降
2. 但我知道，祂手醫治我心傷，除我罪
3. 但我知道，衆人必見祂榮光，所撒的
4. 但我知道，天空要響徹歡呼，千萬世
1 But this I know, that He was born of Ma - ry When Beth-lehem's
2 But this I know, He heals the bro - ken heart - ed And stays our
3 But this I know, all flesh shall see His glo - ry, And He shall
4 But this I know, the skies will thrill with rap - ture, And count-less
1. 生在伯利恒馬槽，居住長大在
2. 惡使我恐怖消散，凡擔重擔的
3. 種祂必親自收割，必有一日公
4. 人要引聲而高唱，天上傳揚地
1 man - ger was His on - ly home, And that He lived at
2 sin and calms our lurk-ing fear, And lifts the bur - den
3 reap the har - vest He has sown, And some glad day His
4 voic - es then will join to sing, And earth to heaven, and
1. 拿撒勒辛苦作工，我深知救主，為世人今已來到。
2. 人都能享受安息，因我的救主，為世人祂在這裡。
3. 義的日頭要普照，那時我救主，必定被世人知道。
4. 上衆口同聲說道，"必竟我救主，祂來到世上做王。
1 Naz - a-reth and la-bored, And so the Sav-ior, Sav-ior of the world, is come.
2 from the heav - y la - den, For yet the Sav-ior, Sav-ior of the world, is here.
3 sun will shine in splen-dor When He the Sav-ior, Sav-ior of the world, is known.
4 heaven to earth will an-swer: "At last the Sav-ior, Sav-ior of the world, is King!"

142

對我述說耶穌故事

Tell Me the Story of Jesus

Did not our hearts burn within us when He talked to us?
— Luke 24:32

Fanny J. Crosby

STORY OF JESUS
John R. Sweney

1. 對我述說耶穌故事，深印每句在我心；
2. 述說主飢渴在曠野，一生傳道救罪人；
3. 述說救主被釘十架，如何受極大苦楚；

1 Tell me the story of Jesus, Write on my heart every word;
2 *Fasting alone in the desert, Tell of the days that are past,*
3 Tell of the cross where they nailed Him, Writhing in anguish and pain;

副歌 對我述說耶穌故事，深印每句在我心；
Refrain: Tell me the story of Jesus, Write on my heart every word;

Fine

1. 對我述說寶貴故事，最奇妙可愛佳音。
2. 述說主受惡魔試探，堅忍不移終得勝。
3. 述說主被葬在墳墓，如何三日後復活。

1 Tell me the story most precious, Sweetest that ever was heard.
2 *How for our sins He was tempted, Yet was triumphant at last.*
3 Tell of the grave where they laid Him, Tell how He liveth again.

副歌 對我述說寶貴故事，最奇妙可愛佳音。
Refrain: Tell me the story most precious, Sweetest that ever was heard.

1. 述說天使如何歌頌，慶賀耶穌的降生：
2. 述說祂為世人辛勞，一生貧窮與孤獨，
3. 這故事中的大慈愛，我今已明白是真，

1 Tell how the angels in chorus Sang as they welcomed His birth,
2 *Tell of the years of His labor, Tell of the sorrow He bore,*
3 Love in that story so tender Clearer than ever I see:

D.C. for Refrain
1.“天上榮耀歸與真神！地下平安歸與人。”
2.被人藐視又被厭棄，受盡了憂傷痛苦。
3.説到主愛，為我贖價，我不禁流淚感恩。

1 “Glo - ry to God in the high - est! Peace and good ti - dings to earth.”
2 *He was de-spised and af - flict - ed, Home - less, re - ject - ed and poor.*
3 Lord, may I al - ways re - mem - ber Love paid the ran - som for me.

我是否要背負十架 143

Am I a Soldier of the Cross?

No soldier that wareth entangleth himself with the affairs of this life . . . . — II Timothy 2:4

ARLINGTON

Isaac Watts

Thomas A. Arne

1.我是否要背負十架，跟從神的羔羊？
2.別人苦戰要得榮耀，血汗滿被沙場，
3.難道我無仇敵當拒？我無破口當堵？
4.我要掌權就得爭戰，哦，主加我力量！

1 Am I a sol - dier of the cross, A fol - lower of the Lamb?
2 *Must I be car - ried to the skies On flow - ery beds of ease,*
3 Are there no foes for me to face? Must I not stem the flood?
4 *Sure I must fight if I would reign: In - crease my cour - age, Lord;*

1.我豈可以怕出代價，要得世界原諒？
2.我豈可以安坐花轎，盼望抬進天堂？
3.難道惡世也可相與，也可作我幫助？
4.我願受辱不畏艱難，靠祢話語剛強。阿門。

1 And shall I fear to own His cause Or blush to speak His name?
2 *While oth - ers fought to win the prize And sailed thru blood - y seas?*
3 Is this vile world a friend to grace, To help me on to God?
4 *I'll bear the toil, en - dure the pain, Sup - port - ed by Thy word.* A-men.

144

加利利陌生人
The Stranger of Galilee

Mrs. C.H. Morris

Jesus sayeth . . ., No man cometh unto the Father but by Me.
— John 14:6

Mrs. C.H. Morris

1. 彷佛當年在加利利海濱，眼望面前波光鱗
2. 祂言語慈祥面容現憐憫，哀我苦被罪孽壓
3. 遭顛沛為風暴所困的人，快來得祂完美救

1. In fan - cy I stood by the shore, one day, Of the beau - ti - ful murm'ring
2. *His look of com - pas - sion, His words of love, They shall nev - er for - got - ten*
3. Come ye, who are driv - en, and tempest - tossed, And His gra - cious sal - va - tion

1. 鱗；我見岸上群衆簇擁如雲，爭看加利利
2. 困；祂言語面容將永記我心，慈愛加利利
3. 恩！祂要平息風暴護你安穩，依靠加利利
1. sea; I saw the great crowds as they thronged the way Of the Stranger of
2. be, When sin - sick and helpless He saw me there, This Stranger of
3. see; He'll qui - et life's storms with His "Peace, be still!" This Stranger of

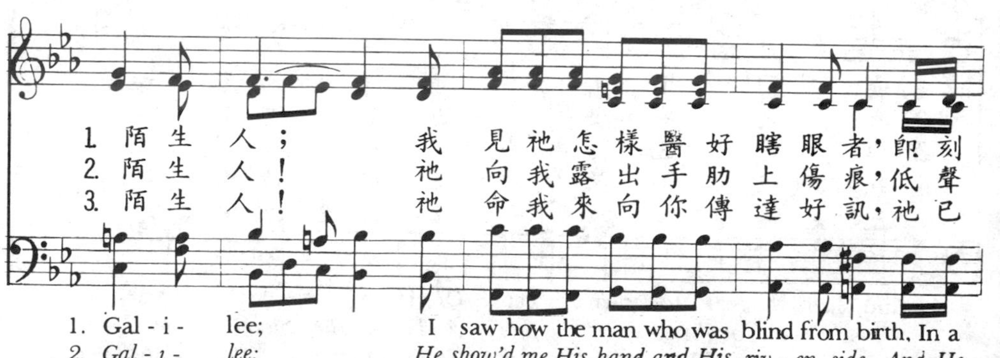

1. 陌生人；我見祂怎樣醫好瞎眼者，即刻
2. 陌生人！祂向我露出手肋上傷痕，低聲
3. 陌生人！祂命我來向你傳達好訊，祂已

1. Gal - i - lee; I saw how the man who was blind from birth, In a
2. *Gal - i - lee; He show'd me His hand and His riv - en side, And He*
3. Gal - i - lee; He bids me to go and the sto - ry tell What He

ff
p
1. 敎他重見光明， 又 施恩能敎瘸腿者前行，
2. 說道“這是為你！” 我 伏祂脚前重擔全脱離，
3. 為你 預備福分， 惟 要你肯謙卑與祂親近，
1. mo-ment was made to see; The lame was made whole by the matchless skill
2. whispered "It was for thee!" My bur-den fell off at the pierc-ed feet
3. ev-er to you will be, If on-ly you let Him with you a-bide,
1. 奇妙 加利利陌 生 人！ 1. 2. 那時 我便立意永遠
2. 感激 加利利陌 生 人！
3. 跟隨 加利利陌 生 人。 3. 朋友！你是否願永遠
1. Of the Stranger of Gal - i - lee. 1. 2. And I felt I could love Him for-
2. Of the Stranger of Gal - i - lee.
3. This Stranger of Gal - i - lee; 3. Oh, my friend, won't you love Him for-
1. 2. 愛 祂， 因 祂那樣溫柔憐 憫， 那
1. 2. ev - - - er, So gra-cious and ten-der was He! I
3. 愛 祂？ 祂 乃如此溫柔憐 憫！ 今
3. ev - - - er? So gra - cious and ten - der was He! Ac -
1. 2. 日便認祂為我救 主，信靠 加利利陌 生 人！
1. 2. claimed Him that day as my Sav- ior, This Strang er of Gal - i - lee.
3. 日使認祂為你救 主，信靠 加利利陌 生 人！
3. cept Him to-day as your Sav - ior, This Strang er of Gal - i - lee.

145

谷中百合花

The Lily of The Valley

I am the rose of Sharon, the lily of the valley. — Song of Solomon 2:1

Charles W. Fry

William S. Hays

1. 主 耶穌是我良友，有 主勝得萬有，萬人
2. 主 把我憂傷擔去，帶 走一切憂愁，當我
3. 主 永不把我捨棄；我 主何等仁慈，我要

1. I have found a friend in Je-sus, He's ev-ery thing to me, He's the
2. *He all my griefs has tak-en, and all my sor-rows borne; In temp-*
3. He will nev-er, nev-er leave me, nor yet for-sake me here, While I

1. 中救主是我最好靈 友；主 是谷中百合花，
2. 受試探時祂是我力 量；我 願盡心來愛祂，
3. 忠誠信靠遵行主旨 意；有 火焚燒我身旁，

1. fair-est of ten thou-sand to my soul; The Lil-y of the Val-ley,
2. *ta-tion He's my strong and migh-ty power; I have all for Him for-sak-en,*
3. live by faith and do His bless-ed will; A wall of fire a-bout me,

D. S. — 晨星燦爛光華，
Lil-y of the Val-ley,

Fine.
1. 我 惟一需要 祂，祂能 洗淨我使我聖潔無 瑕。
2. 毀 掉一切偶 像，祂有 能力保守我為祂而 活。
3. 任 遭何事不 慌，主賜 嗎哪餧養我靈得健 壯。

1. in Him a-lone I see All I need, to cleanse and make me ful-ly whole.
2. *and all my i-dols torn From my heart, and now He keeps me by His power.*
3. I've noth-ing now to fear, With His man-na He my hun-gry soul shall fill.

是 谷中百合花，萬人中救主最美好我愛 祂。
the Bright and Morn-ing Star, He's the fair-est of ten thou-sand to my soul.

1. 悲 傷時祂來解憂，患 難時祂保佑，
2. 那 日在天見主面，享 受主愛甘甜，
3. 縱 然世界棄絕我，撒 旦來試探我，
1. In sor-row He's my com-fort, in trou-ble He's my stay,
2. Though all the world for-sake me, and Sa - tan tempt me sore,
3. Then sweep-ing up to glo - ry to see His bless - ed face,
D. S.
1. 一 切憂慮全放在主肩頭；主是
2. 有 快樂江河長流至永年；主是
3. 靠 着耶穌能過得勝生活；主是
1. He tells me ev - ery care on Him to roll: He's the
2. Through' Je - sus I shall safe-ly reach the goal: He's the
3. Where riv - ers of de-light shall ev - er roll: He's the

145-1 Worship

Worship is the highest and noblest act that any person can do. When men worship, God is satisfied! "The Father seeketh such to worship Him." Amazing, isn't it? And when you worship, you are fulfilled! Think about this: why did Jesus Christ come? He came to make worshipers out of rebels. We who were once self-centered have to be completely changed so that we can shift our attention outside of ourselves and become able to worship Him.

—Raymond C. Ortlund

146

耶穌，愛我靈的主

Jesus, Lover of My Soul

For Thou hath been a shelter for me and a strong tower . . . .

— Psalm 61:3

Charles Wesley

ABERYSTWYTH
Joseph Parry

1. 耶 穌 愛 我 靈 的 主， 容 我 投 入 祢 懷 中，
2. 此 外 別 無 避 難 所， 惟 獨 救 主 能 保 護；
3. 救 主 恩 惠 極 豐 富， 遮 蓋 我 的 衆 罪 污；

1 Je - sus, lov - er of my soul, Let me to Thy bos - om fly,
2 *Oth - er ref - uge have I none, Hangs my help - less soul on Thee;*
3 Plen-teous grace with Thee is found, Grace to cov - er all my sin;

1. 可 畏 暴 雨 夾 狂 風， 波 濤 滾 滾 勢 洶 洶。
2. 莫 撇 棄 我 致 孤 單， 仍 舊 安 慰 與 扶 助。
3. 恩 典 浩 大 如 江 河， 洗 清 我 的 衆 罪 過。

1 While the near - er wa - ters roll, While the tem - pest still is high.
2 *Leave, O leave me not a - lone, Still sup - port and com - fort me.*
3 Let the heal - ing streams a - bound, Make and keep me pure with - in.

1. 懇 求 主 將 我 隱 藏， 直 到 風 靜 浪 平 穩；
2. 一 切 倚 靠 惟 有 主， 一 切 幫 助 從 主 來；
3. 祢 有 生 命 的 活 水， 竟 願 白 白 的 賜 給；
1 Hide me, O my Sav - ior, hide, 'Til the storm of life is past;
2 All my trust on Thee is stayed, All my help from Thee I bring;
3 Thou of life the foun - tain art, Free - ly let me take of Thee;

1. 使我安全無恐慌，至終接納我靈魂！
2. 可憐我身無蔭庇，願主恩翼常遮蓋。
3. 願在我心成泉源，湧流不止到永遠。阿門。

1 Safe in - to the ha-ven guide, O re - ceive my soul at last!
2 *Cov - er my de - fense-less head With the shad - ow of Thy wing.*
3 Spring Thou up with-in my heart, Rise to all e - ter-ni - ty. A-men.

普天之下萬族萬民

All People That on Earth Do Dwell

147

Let all the people praise thee, O God . . . — Psalm 67:3

OLD 100th
Genevan Psalter
Attributed to Louis Bourgeois

Based on Psalm 100
Attr. to William Kethe

1. 普天之下萬族萬民，都當向主歡呼頌揚；
2. 我們當曉得祂是神，祂用智慧創造世人；
3. 當稱謝進入祂的門，當讚美進入祂的院；
4. 至高真神祂本為善，祂的慈愛永遠常在；

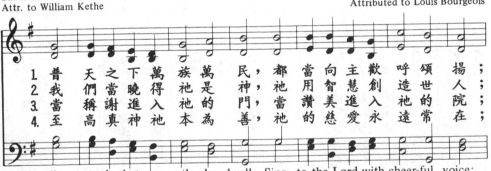

1 All peo-ple that on earth do dwell, Sing to the Lord with cheer-ful voice;
2 *Know that the Lord is God in - deed: With-out our aid He did us make;*
3 O en-ter then His gates with praise, Ap-proach with joy His courts un - to;
4 *For why? the Lord our God is good, His mer-cy is for - ev - er sure;*

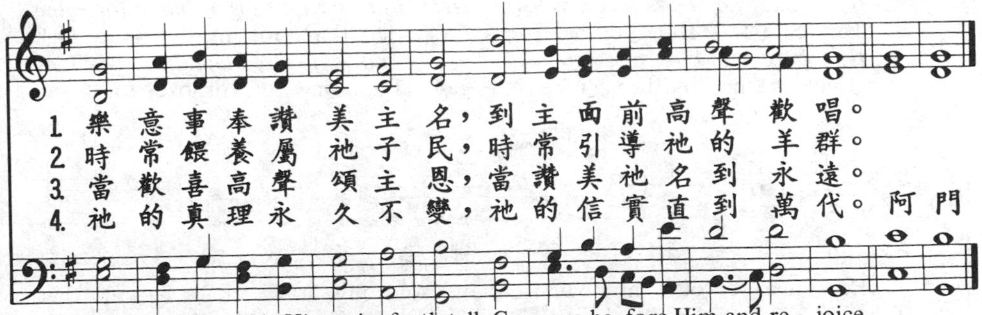

1. 樂意事奉讚美主名，到主面前高聲歡唱。
2. 時常餵養屬祂子民，時常引導祂的羊群。
3. 當歡喜高聲頌主恩，當讚美祂名到永遠。
4. 祂的真理永久不變，祂的信實直到萬代。阿門

1 Him serve with mirth, His praise forth tell, Come ye be-fore Him and re - joice.
2 *We are His folk, He doth us feed, And for His sheep He doth us take.*
3 Praise, laud, and bless His name al - ways, For it is seem-ly so to do.
4 *His truth at all times firm-ly stood, And shall from age to age en - dure.* A-men.

148

我真希奇

I Stand Amazed

God, who is rich in mercy, for His great love wherewith He loved us . . .

— Ephesians 2:4

Charles H. Gabriel

MY SAVIOR'S LOVE
Charles H. Gabriel

1. 我真希奇主的慈愛，竟如此廣大普遍；
2. 主在客西馬尼園內，為遵父旨意懇求；
3. 時當夜半救主孤單，為我靈魂受苦難；
4. 主為我承擔了憂傷，又為我罪受羞辱；
5. 在榮耀裡與衆聖徒，一同瞻仰主聖容；

1 I stand a-mazed in the pres-ence Of Je-sus the Naz-a-rene,
2 *For me it was in the gar-den He prayed, "Not my will, but Thine;"*
3 In pit-y an-gels be-held Him, And came from the world of light
4 *He took my sins and my sor-rows, He made them His ver-y own;*
5 When with the ran-somed in glo-ry His face I at last shall see,

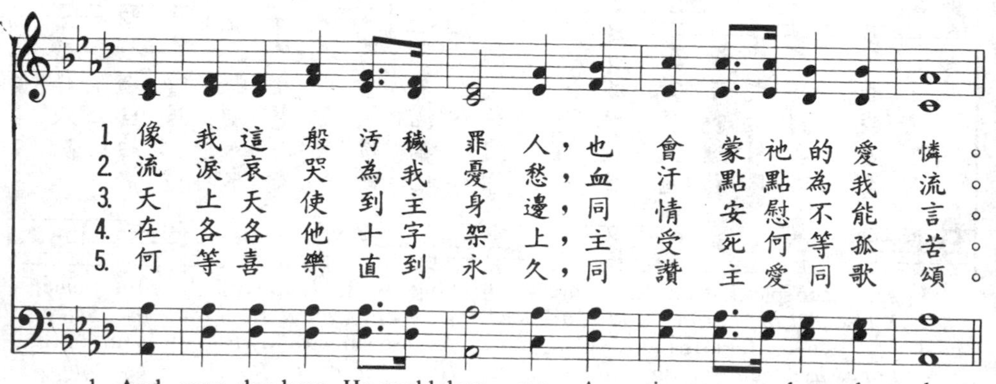
1. 像我這般污穢罪人，也會蒙祂的愛憐。
2. 流淚哀哭為我憂愁，血汗點點為我流。
3. 天上天使到主身邊，同情安慰不能言。
4. 在各各他十字架上，主受死何等孤苦。
5. 何等喜樂直到永久，同讚主愛同歌頌。

1 And won-der how He could love me, A sin-ner, con-demned, un-clean.
2 *He had no tears for His own griefs, But sweat drops of blood for mine.*
3 To com-fort Him in the sor-rows He bore for my soul that night.
4 *He bore the bur-den to Cal-vary, And suf-fered and died a-lone.*
5 'Twill be my joy through the a-ges To sing of His love for me.

何等希奇！何等奇妙！我要歌唱到永遠：
How mar-vel-ous! how won-der-ful! And my song shall ev-er be:

何等希奇！何等奇妙！我竟蒙救主愛憐！
How mar-vel-ous! how won-der-ful Is my Sav-ior's love for me!

我神，祢是何等奇妙

My God, How Wonderful Thou Art. 149

Heaven is my throne and the earth is my footstool — Isaiah 66:1

Frederick W. Faber

Thomas Hasting

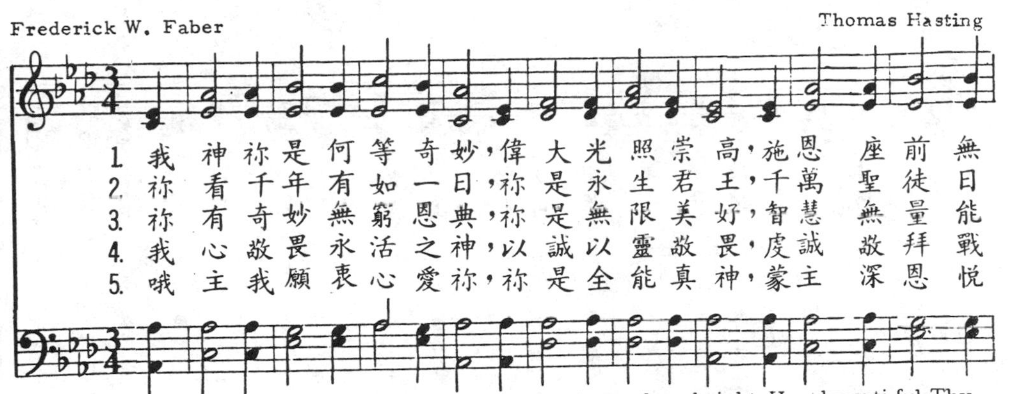
1. 我神祢是何等奇妙，偉大光照崇高，施恩座前無
2. 祢看千年有如一日，祢是永生君王，千萬聖徒日
3. 祢有奇妙無窮恩典，祢是無限美好，智慧無量能
4. 我心敬畏永活之神，以誠以靈敬畏，虔誠敬拜戰
5. 哦主我願衷心愛祢，祢是全能真神，蒙主深恩悅

1. My God, how wonder-ful Thou art, Thy maj-es-ty how bright, How beau-ti-ful Thy
2. *How dread are Thine e-ter-nal years, O ev-er-last-ing Lord: By pros-trate spir-its*
3. How won-der-ful, how beau-ti-ful, The sight of Thee must be, Thine end-less wis-dom,
4. *O how I fear Thee, liv-ing God, With deepest, tenderest fears, And worship Thee with*
5. Yet, I may love Thee, too, O Lord, Al-migh-ty as Thou art, For Thou hast stooped to

1. 限美好，光芒不斷照耀，光芒不斷照耀！
2. 夜祈禱，虔誠敬拜頌揚，虔誠敬拜頌揚！
3. 力豐富，極其聖潔崇高，極其聖潔崇高。
4. 兢事奉，流淚為罪懺悔，流淚為罪懺悔！
5. 納我心，我願愛祢更深，我願愛祢更深。阿們。

1. mer - cy seat, In depths of burn-ing light, In depths of burn-ing light!
2. *day and night In-cess-ant-ly a-dored, In-cess-ant-ly a-dored!*
3. bound-less power, And aw-ful pur-i-ty, And aw-ful pur-i-ty!
4. *tremb-ling hope, And pen-i-ten-tial tears, And pen-i-ten-tial tears!*
5. ask of me The love of my poor heart, The love of my poor heart. A-MEN.

150

若這不是愛

If That Isn't Love

So Christ was once offered to bear the sins of many. . . . Hebrews 9:28

Dottie Rambo

LOVE
Dottie Rambo

1 祂離棄天上的榮耀，竟甘心來到地上；祂孤單的在各各他山，為我捨命在十架上。
2 當祂臨死仍在關懷，那與他同掛的賊；祂用慈愛同情寬恕他，天堂樂園為他預備。
1 He left the splen-dor of heav-en, Know-ing His des-ti-ny Was the lone-ly hill of Gol-goth-a, There to lay down His life for me.
2 E-ven in death He re-mem-bered The thief hang-ing by His side; He spoke with love and com-pas-sion Then He took him to Par-a-dise.
若這不是愛，海洋水會乾，天空星不再閃，雀鳥無翼可
If that is-n't love the o-cean is dry, There's no star in the sky and the spar-row can't

展！ 若這不是愛， 天堂不存在，
fly! If that is-n't love then heav-en's a myth,
人間何處有愛， 若這不是愛。
There's no feel-ing like this, if that is-n't love.

150–1 His Love ...... Reaching

Right from the beginning God's love has reached, and from the beginning man has refused to understand. But love went on reaching, offering itself. Love offered the eternal . . . we wanted the immediate. Love offered deep joy . . . we wanted thrills. Love offered freedom . . . we wanted license. Love offered communion with God Himself . . . we wanted to worship at the shrine of our own minds. Love offered peace . . . we wanted approval for our wars. Even yet, love went on reaching. And still today, after two thousand years, patiently, lovingly, Christ is reaching out to us today. Right through the chaos of our world, through the confusion of our minds. He is reaching . . . longing to share with us . . . the very being of God.

His love still is longing, His love still is reaching, right past the shackles of my mind. And the Word of the Father became Mary's little Son. And His love reached all the way to where I was.

–Gloria Gaither

151

我要歌頌我救贖主

I Will Sing of My Redeemer

For I know that my Redeemer liveth . . . — Job 19:25
Philip P. Bliss
MY REDEEMER
James McGranahan
1. 我要 歌頌我救贖主，並祂救我的奇愛；
2. 我要 歌頌我救贖主，祂已贖盡我罪愆；
3. 我要 歌頌我救贖主，祂的大能我傳述；
4. 我要 歌頌我救贖主，豐滿救恩祂賞賜；
1 I will sing of my Re-deem-er And His won-drous love to me;
2 I will tell the won-drous sto-ry, How my lost es-tate to save,
3 I will praise my dear Re-deem-er, His tri-um-phant power I'll tell,
4 I will sing of my Re-deem-er, And His heaven-ly love to me;
1. 他在 十架受盡咒詛，為要 將我贖出來。
2. 祂有 豐富慈愛憐憫，今將 我罪全赦免。
3. 他使 我能得勝歡呼，勝過 罪死與陰府。
4. 使我 重生得享天福，與祂 同作神後嗣。
1 On the cru-el cross He suf-fered From the curse to set me free.
2 In His bound-less love and mer-cy, He the ran-som free-ly gave.
3 How the vic-to-ry He giv-eth O-ver sin and death and hell.
4 He from death to life hath brought me, Son of God, with Him to be.
歌頌，歌 頌我救贖 主。 祂的
Sing, O sing of my Re-deem-er, With His
歌頌我救贖主，歌頌，歌頌我救贖主，
sing of my Re-deem-er, Sing, O sing of my Re-deem-er,

寶 血為我流；十字
blood He pur-chased me; On the
血為我流，血為我流；為我流出，
He pur-chased me, He pur-chased me, He pur-chased me,
架 上受盡痛苦，還清
cross He sealed my par - don, Paid the
上受盡痛苦，十字架上受盡痛苦，
He sealed my par-don, On the cross He sealed my par - don,
罪 債把我贖。
debt and made me free.
債，還清罪債，祂把我贖。
and made me free, and made me free.

頌主大愛

Sweeter As The Years Go By

Enter into His gates with thanksgiving and into His courts with praise.
— Psalm 100:4

Lelta N. Morris | Lelta N. Morris

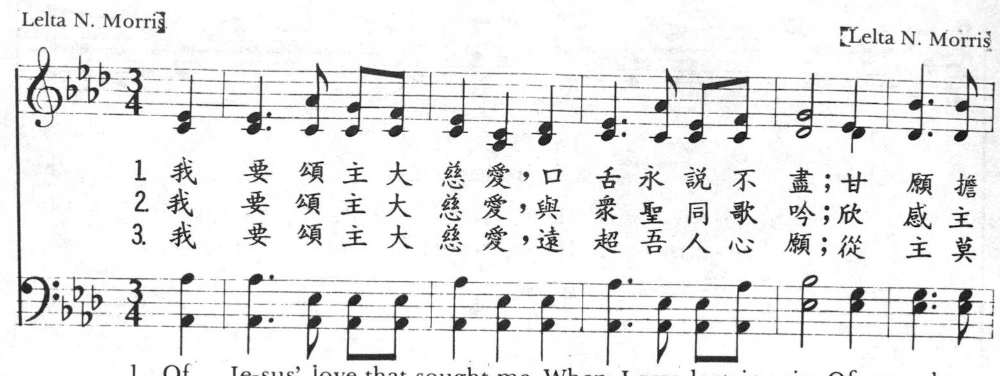
1. 我要頌主大慈愛，口舌永說不盡；甘願擔
2. 我要頌主大慈愛，與衆聖同歌吟；欣感主
3. 我要頌主大慈愛，遠超吾人心願；從主莫

1. Of Je-sus' love that sought me, When I was lost in sin; Of won-drous
2. He trod in old Ju - de - a, Life's path-way long a - go; The peo - ple
3. 'Twas wondrous love which led Him, For us to suf-fer loss— To bear with-

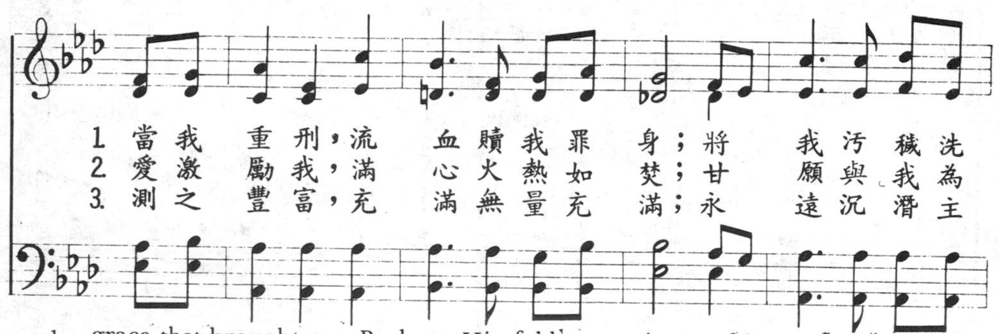
1. 當我重刑，流血贖我罪身；將我污穢洗
2. 愛激勵我，滿心火熱如焚；甘願與我為
3. 測之豐富，充滿無量充滿；永遠沉滑主

1. grace that brought me Back to His fold a - gain; Of heights and depths of
2. thronged a - bout Him His sav - ing grace to know; He healed the bro - ken -
3. out a mur - mur The an - guish of the cross; With saints re-deemed in

1. 潔淨，日日與神親近；身靈安居主愛裏，
2. 密友；彼此靈交日新；情意最厚恩無盡，
3. 愛中，時時有新效驗；愛我終必愛到底，

1. mer - cy, Far deep - er than the sea, And high - er than the heav - ens,
2. heart-ed, And caused the blind to see; And still His great heart yearn-eth
3. glo - ry Let us our voi - ces raise, Till heaven and earth re - ech-o

1. 永遠滿足我心。主的愛越久越深，
2. 主愛越久越深。
3. 主愛永不改變。Sweet-er as the years go by,
1. My theme shall ev-er be. 主的愛越久越深，救
2. In love for e-ven me. Sweet-er as the years go by, 'Tis
3. With our Re-deem-er's praise.
主的愛越久越深， 何等長濶高深，
Sweet-er as the years go by; Rich-er, full-er, deep-er,
主的愛越久越深，
Sweet-er as the years go by,
rit.
我要時時歌唱，主的愛越久越深！
Je-sus' love is sweet-er, Sweet-er as the years go by.

153

奇哉，耶穌愛我

Jesus Loves Even Me

Christ came into the world to save sinners of whom I am chief.
— I Timothy 1:15
Philip P. Bliss
GLADNESS
Philip P. Bliss
1. 我 今 甚 歡 喜 因 天 上 真 神， 明 明 的
2. 我 雖 然 遠 離 主，将 主 忘 記， 主 仍 是
3. 時 候 快 到 我 必 見 主 容 顏， 獻 上 我
1 I am so glad that my Fa - ther in heaven Tells of His
2 Though I for - get Him and wan - der a - way, Still Je - sus
3 O if there's on - ly one song I can sing, When in His
1. 説 道：祂 憐 愛 罪 人； 希 罕 的 事 中 最
2. 愛 我 不 把 我 丟 棄； 我 願 再 回 到 主
3. 歌 頌 在 主 的 面 前； 到 那 時 我 必 歡
1 love in the Book He has given; Won - der - ful things in the
2 loves me wher - ev - er I stray; Back to His dear lov - ing
3 beau - ty I see the great King, This shall my song in e -
1. 希 罕 不 過， 經 上 有 言 語 耶 穌 是 愛 我。
2. 慈 愛 懷 裡， 每 當 我 記 起 耶 穌 是 愛 我。
3. 喜 的 歌 唱， 哦，何 等 希 奇 耶 穌 是 愛 我！
1 Bi - ble I see— This is the dear - est, that Je - sus loves me.
2 arms I would flee, When I re - mem - ber that Je - sus loves me.
3 ter - ni - ty be: O, what a won - der that Je - sus loves me!"
我 甚 歡 樂 因 耶 穌 愛 我，耶 穌 愛 我，耶 穌 愛 我；
I am so glad that Je - sus loves me, Je - sus loves me, Je - sus loves me;

我甚歡樂因耶穌愛我，奇哉耶穌愛我。
I am so glad that Je-sus loves me, Je - sus loves e - ven me.

154

耶穌聖名何等美善

How Sweet the Name of Jesus Sounds

. . . He that loveth Me shall be loved of My Father, and I will love Him . . . — John 14:21

ST. PETER
Alexander R. Reinagle

John Newton

1. 耶穌聖名何等美善，猶如悅耳聲音！
2. 這名能治破碎心靈，安靜苦悶的心；
3. 耶穌是我牧人，朋友，先知，祭司，君王，
4. 我們愛心常常冷淡，感謝更是薄弱；
1 How sweet the name of Je-sus sounds In a be-liev-er's ear!
2 It makes the wound-ed spir-it whole And calms the trou-bled breast;
3 Je - sus! my Sav-ior, Shep-herd, Friend, My Proph-et, Priest, and King,
4 Weak is the ef-fort of my heart, And cold my warm-est thought;

1. 醫治憂悶安慰悲嘆，又將懼怕除盡。
2. 又是飢餓者的嗎哪，疲倦者得安寧。
3. 救主，生命，道路，真理；求接納我頌揚。
4. 但當我們見祢榮顏，我就歡唱樂歌。阿門。
1 It soothes his sor-rows, heals his wounds, And drives a-way his fear.
2 'Tis nour-ish-ment to hun-gry souls, And to the wea-ry rest.
3 My Lord, my Life, my Way, my End, Ac-cept the praise I bring.
4 But when I see Thee as Thou art, I'll praise Thee as I ought. A-men.

155

何等奇妙耶穌聖名

There's Something About That Name

The Spirit and the bride say, Come. And let him that heareth say, Come . . . . and whosoever will let him take of the water of life freely . . . . — Revelation 22:17

Gloria Gaither
William J. Gaither

THAT NAME
William J. Gaither

耶穌，耶穌，耶穌！何等奇妙耶穌聖名！
Je - sus, Je - sus, Je - sus! There's just some-thing a - bout that name!

基督，救主，耶穌！如同朝露潔淨芳香；
Mas - ter, Sav - ior, Je - sus! Like the fra - grance af - ter the rain;

耶穌，耶穌，耶穌！天上人間同聲頌揚；
Je - sus, Je - sus, Je - sus! Let all Heav - en and earth pro - claim:

歷代君王都将成過去，唯有耶穌聖名永存！
Kings and king - doms will all pass a - way, But there's some - thing a - bout that name!

156

耶穌必做萬國君王

Jesus Shall Reign Where'er the Sun

His kingdom is an everlasting kingdom,
and His dominion from generation to generation. — Daniel 4:3
Based on Psalm 72
Isaac Watts
DUKE STREET
John Hatton
1. 日 月 所 照 中 外 各 方，耶 穌 必 作 萬
2. 諸 國 君 王 文 武 大 臣，士 農 工 商 普
3. 家 家 戶 戶 早 晚 跪 拜，感 恩 頌 德 同
4. 天 下 萬 國 一 切 罪 人，蒙 主 引 領 能
1 Je - sus shall reign wher - e'er the sun Does His suc - ces - sive
2 *To Him shall end - less prayer be made, And end-less prais - es*
3 Peo - ple and realms of ev - ery tongue Dwell on His love with
4 *Let ev - ery crea - ture rise and bring His grate - ful hon - ors*
1. 國 君 王，從 南 至 北 從 西 至 東，
2. 天 下 人，同 來 聚 集 意 誠 心 虔，
3. 心 敬 愛，雖 是 嬰 孩 口 亦 能 言，
4. 進 天 門，天 使 高 聲 頌 主 聖 名，
1 jour - neys run, His king - dom spread from shore to shore,
2 *crown His head; His name like sweet per - fume shall rise*
3 sweet - est song; And in - fant voic - es shall pro - claim
4 *to our King; An - gels de - scend with songs a - gain,*
1. 四 海 萬 民 以 主 為 榮。
2. 共 獻 珍 寶 在 主 台 前。
3. 讚 美 話 語 也 能 說 全。
4. 地 上 萬 民 同 唱 阿 門！
1 'Til moons shall wax and wane no more.
2 *With ev - ery morn - ing sac - ri - fice.*
3 Their ear - ly bless - ings on His name.
4 *And earth re - peat the loud "A - men!"*

157

記念主名

Take the Name of Jesus with You

Neither is there salvation in any other. . . . — Acts 4:12

Lydia Baxter

PRECIOUS NAME
William H. Doane

1. 憂苦弟兄容我勸你，常常記念耶穌名；
2. 處處記念耶穌聖名，當作盾牌敵魔劍；
3. 耶穌名字馨香寶貴，我一聽聞就歡欣；
4. 經歷世途艱辛疾累，聽見主名心歡暢；
1 Take the name of Je-sus with you, Child of sor-row and of woe.
2 *Take the name of Je-sus ev-er As pro-tec-tion ev-ery-where;*
3 At the name of Je-sus bow-ing, When in heav-en we shall meet,
1. 這名使你煩悶變喜，疑懼消散心安平。
2. 衆惑環繞齊來攻逼，靠主聖名就得勝。
3. 但願人人得其安慰，同我稱頌主聖名。
4. 摘下冠冕主前伏拜，歡稱耶穌是我王。
1 It will joy and com-fort give you, Take it then wher-e'er you go.
2 *If temp-ta-tions 'round you gath-er, Breathe that ho-ly name in prayer.*
3 King of kings, we'll glad-ly crown Him When our jour-ney is com-plete.
名至寶，名最甜！地之望而天之樂
Pre-cious name, O how sweet! Hope of earth and joy of heaven,
名至寶，名最甜，地之望而天之樂。
Pre-cious name, O how sweet– Hope of earth and joy of heaven.

158

進入我心
Into My Heart

Blessed are the pure in heart for they shall see God.
Matthew 5:8

Harry D. Clarke — Harry D. Clarke

1. 進入我的心，親愛耶穌，求主來進入我的心；
2. 進入我的心，親愛耶穌，艱苦路上我需要主；
3. 進入我的心，親愛耶穌，求主潔淨光照我心；

1. Come in-to my heart, bless-ed Je-sus, Come in-to my heart, I pray;
2. *Come in-to my heart, bless-ed Je-sus, I need Thee thro' life's drear-y way;*
3. Come in-to my heart, bless-ed Je-sus, O cleanse and il-lu-mine my soul;

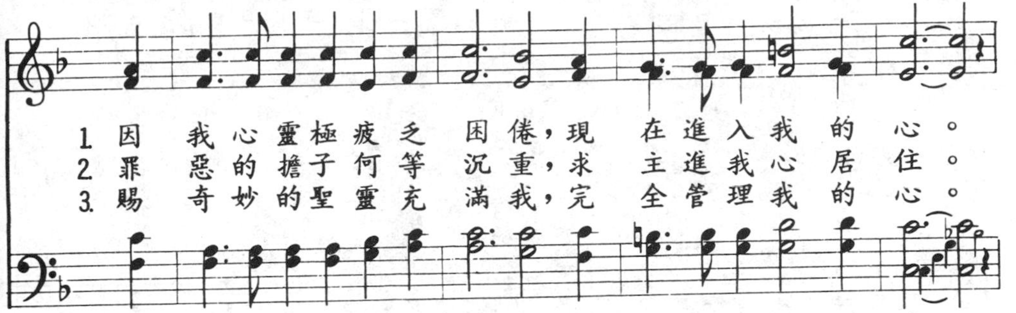

1. 因我心靈極疲乏困倦，現在進入我的心。
2. 罪惡的擔子何等沉重，求主進我心居住。
3. 賜奇妙的聖靈充滿我，完全管理我的心。

1. My soul is so troub-led and wea-ry, Come in-to my heart to-day.
2. *The bur-den of sin is so heav-y, Come in-to my heart to stay.*
3. Fill me with Thy won-der-ful Spir-it, Come in and take full con-trol.

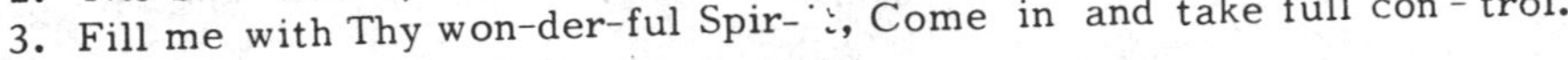

進入我心，進入我心，進入我的心，主耶穌；

In-to my heart, in-to my heart, Come in-to my heart, Lord Je-sus;

現在進來，永不離開，進入我的心，主耶穌。

Come in to-day, Come in to stay, Come in-to my heart, Lord Je-sus.

159

祂名稱為奇妙

His Name Is Wonderful

. . . Which is, and which was, and which is to come, the Almighty.
— Revelation 1:8
Audrey Mieir
MIEIR
Audrey Mieir
祂名稱為奇妙，祂名稱為奇妙，祂名稱
His name is Won-der-ful, His name is Won-der-ful, His name is
為奇妙，耶穌我主；祂是全能君王，
Won-der-ful, Je-sus, my Lord; He is the might-y King,
祂是萬有之主，祂名稱為奇妙，耶穌我主
Mas-ter of ev-ery-thing, His name is Won-der-ful, Je-sus, my Lord.
祂是好牧者，是萬古的磐石，祂是全
He's the great Shep-herd, the Rock of all a-ges, Al-might-y
能的神；當伏在主前，敬愛崇
God is He; Bow down be-fore Him, Love and a-

拜祂，祂名稱為奇妙，耶穌我主。
dore Him, His name is Won-der-ful, Je - sus, my Lord.

讚美耶穌聖名 160

Praise The Name Of Jesus

Mountains, and all hills, fruitful trees, fowls . . . let them praise the name of the Lord.

Psalm 148:9

Psalm 18:1

Roy Hicks, Jr.

Unison

讚美耶穌聖名，讚美耶穌聖名，
Praise the name of Je - sus, Praise the name of Je - sus,

祂是磐石，祂是我山寨，祂是我的拯救者，我
He's my rock, He's my for - tress, He's my de - liv - er - er, in

全心信靠祂；讚美耶穌聖名。
Him will I trust. Praise the name of Je - sus.

161

神是何等奇妙

God Is So Wonderful

They shall see the Son of man coming in the clouds of heaven . . . .

— Matthew 24:30

Virginia Marshall | Virginia Marshall

神是何等奇妙，我難說明，我
God is so won-der-ful I can't ex-plain, But
只能說，"榮耀哈利路亞，讚美主聖名!"哦！名！"
I can say, "Glo-ry, hal-le-lu-jah, praise His ho-ly name!" O name!
1 Only
2 & Final
1. 何等奇妙，因祂拯救我，何等奇妙，因祂赦
2. 将你重擔全卸在主肩，一切掛慮，放在主
1. It's won-der-ful be-cause he saved me, It's won-der-ful that He for-
2. I cast on Him my ev-'ry bur-den, Lay at his feet my ev-'ry
1. 免我；何等奇妙，真奇妙，真是何等奇妙，
2. 脚前；何等奇妙，真奇妙，真是何等奇妙，
1. gave me; It's won-der-ful, won-der-ful, so ver-y won-der-ful,
2. care, It's won-der-ful, won-der-ful, so ver-y won-der-ful,

D.C.
1. 主今屬我，真 奇 妙 ！
2. 主今屬我，真 奇 妙 ！ 哦 ！
1. Won-der-ful that He is mine!
2. Won-der-ful that He is mine! O
我活
I Live
162
Rich Cook
Rich Cook
1. 我 活，我 活，因 祂已經 復活！祂 赦罪大能 使 我 活；
2. 我 活，我 活，因 祂已經 復活，我 活着為要 敬拜我 主。
1. I live, I live be-cause He is ris-en, I live, I live with pow'r o-ver sin;
2. I live, I live be-cause He is ris-en, I live, I live to wor-ship Him.
感謝耶穌 感謝耶 穌，因 祢是活 着，因 祢是活 着，祢 為我活，我能活！
Thank You, Je-sus! Thank You, Je-sus! Be-cause You're a-live, be-cause You're a-live, Be-cause You're a-live, I live!
© 1976 by John T. Benson Publ. Co. All rights reserved.

163

救主耶穌，罪人良友
Jesus Is the Friend of Sinners

They that are whole need not a physician, but they that are sick.
— Matthew 9:12
John W. Peterson
FRIEND OF SINNERS
John W. Peterson
1. 救 主耶 穌 罪 人良 友，救 主耶 穌
2. 你 若信 祂，祂 必救 你，你 若信 祂
3. 祂 必一 路 與 你同 行，祂 必一 路
1 Je - sus is the friend of sin - ners, Friend of sin - ners,
2 If you trust Him, He will save you, He will save you,
3 He will walk a - long be - side you, Walk be - side you,
1. 罪 人 良 友；救 主耶 穌 罪 人良 友，
2. 祂 必 救 你；你 若信 祂，祂 必救 你，
3. 與 你 同 行；祂 必一 路 與 你同 行，
1 friend of sin - ners; Je - sus is the Friend of sin - ners;
2 He will save you; If you trust Him, He will save you,
3 Walk be - side you; He will walk a - long be - side you,
1-2
3
1. 使 你 得 自 由 。
2. 賜 你 新 生 命 。
3. 每 日 引 導 你。
4. 祂 必 領 你
4 He will lead you
1 He can set you free.
2 give you life a - new.
3 guide you day by day.
4. 進 入 榮 耀，祂 必領 你 進 入榮 耀；
4 on to glo - ry, On to glo - ry, on to glo - ry;

4. 祂 必領 你 進 入 榮 耀，永 遠 的 天 家！
4 He will lead you on to glo - ry, Home for - ev - er - more!

耶穌，每逢想念祢

164

Jesus, the Very Thought of Thee

For me to live is Christ, and to die is gain. — Philippians 1:21

Latin: 12th Century
Tr. by Edward Caswall

ST. AGNES
John B. Dykes

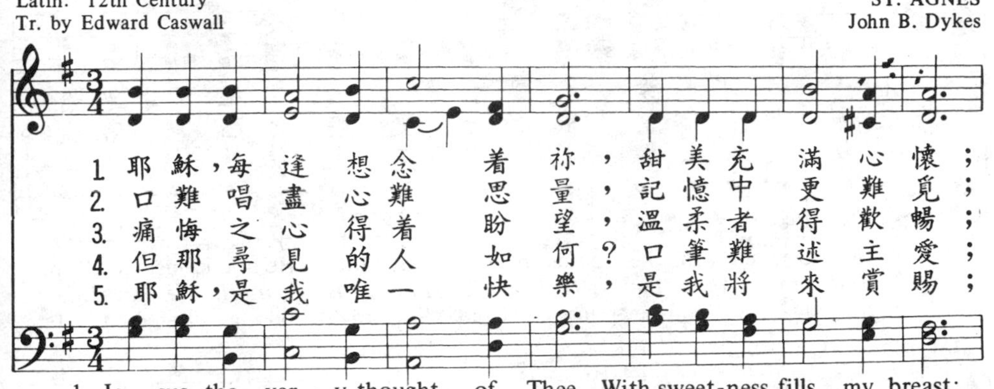
1. 耶 穌，每 逢 想 念 着 祢，甜 美 充 滿 心 懷；
2. 口 難 唱 盡 心 難 思 量，記 憶 中 更 難 覓；
3. 痛 悔 之 心 得 着 盼 望，溫 柔 者 得 歡 暢；
4. 但 那 尋 見 的 人 如 何？口 筆 難 述 主 愛；
5. 耶 穌，是 我 唯 一 快 樂，是 我 將 來 賞 賜；
1 Je - sus, the ver - y thought of Thee With sweet-ness fills my breast;
2 No voice can sing, no heart can frame, Nor can the mem-ory find
3 O hope of ev - ery con - trite heart, O joy of all the meek,
4 But what to those who find? Ah, this No tongue or pen can show;
5 Je - sus, our on - ly joy be Thou, As Thou our prize wilt be;

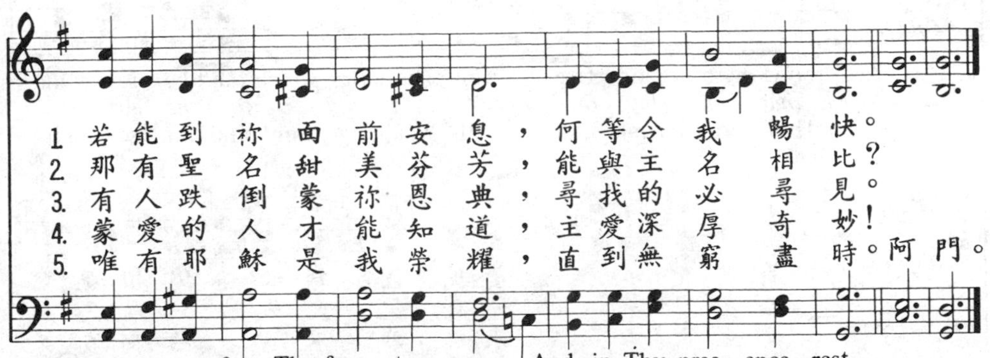
1. 若 能 到 祢 面 前 安 息，何 等 令 我 暢 快。
2. 那 有 聖 名 甜 美 芬 芳，能 與 主 名 相 比？
3. 有 人 跌 倒 蒙 祢 恩 典，尋 找 的 必 尋 見。
4. 蒙 愛 的 人 才 能 知 道，主 愛 深 厚 奇 妙！
5. 唯 有 耶 穌 是 我 榮 耀，直 到 無 窮 盡 時。阿 門。
1 But sweet-er far Thy face to see And in Thy pres - ence rest.
2 A sweet-er sound than Thy blest name, O Sav-ior of man - kind.
3 To those who fall, how kind Thou art! How good to those who seek!
4 The love of Je-sus, what it is None but His loved ones know.
5 Je - sus, be Thou our glo - ry now And through e - ter - ni - ty. A - men.

165

我有一友，何等良友

I've Found a Friend, O Such a Friend

A friend loveth at all times. — Proverbs 17:17

James G. Small

FRIEND

George C. Stebbins

1. 我有一友，何等良友！未識時已先愛我；
2. 我有一友，何等良友！流血捨身為救我；
3. 我有一友，何等良友！恩慈良善又溫柔；
1 I've found a Friend, O such a Friend! He loved me ere I knew Him;
2 *I've found a Friend, O such a Friend! He bled, He died to save me:*
3 I've found a Friend, O such a Friend! So kind, and true, and ten-der,

1. 慈繩引我愛索繫我，教我與祂相連合。
2. 賜我生命使我永活，更將自己賜給我。
3. 做我策士導我前路，用大能扶持保佑！
1 He drew me with the cords of love, And thus He bound me to Him.
2 *And not a-lone the gift of life, But His own self He gave me.*
3 So wise a Coun-se-lor and Guide, So might-y a De-fend-er!

1. 情深意切縈繞我心，願與恩主永不分；
2. 凡我所有不再屬己，願奉獻恩主良友；
3. 祂既愛我愛我到底，誰能使主我相隔？
1 And 'round my heart still close-ly twine Those ties which can't be sev-ered.
2 *Naught that I have my own I call, I hold it for the giv-er;*
3 From Him who loves me now so well, What power my soul can sev-er?

1. 我屬我友，我友屬我，直到永遠仍相親。
2. 我心我力，我命所有，完全屬主到永久。
3. 不論生死，今生來世，我永屬我的良友。
1 For I am His, and He is mine, For-ev-er and for-ev-er.
2 *My heart, my strength, my life, my all Are His, and His for-ev-er.*
3 Shall life or death, shall earth or hell? No! I am His for-ev-er.

無友可比
No, Not One!

There is a friend that sticketh closer than a brother. — Proverbs 18:24

Johnson Oatman, Jr.

NO, NOT ONE
George C. Hugg

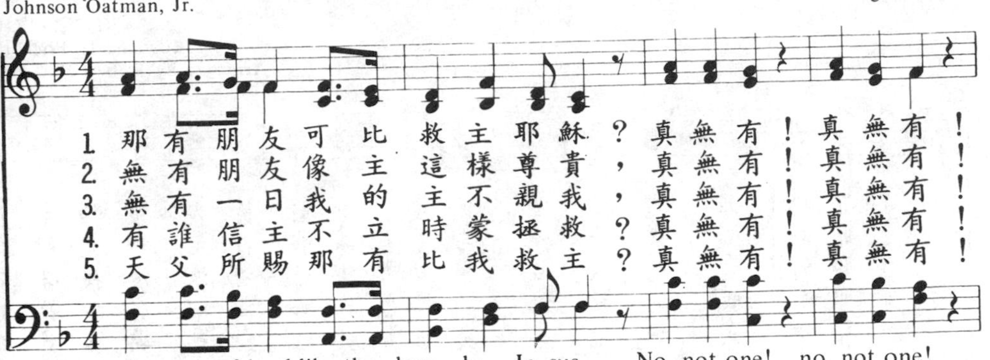

1. 那有朋友可比救主耶穌？真無有！真無有！
2. 無有朋友像主這樣尊貴，真無有！真無有！
3. 無有一日我的主不親我，真無有！真無有！
4. 有誰信主不立時蒙拯救？真無有！真無有！
5. 天父所賜那有比我救主？真無有！真無有！

1 There's not a friend like the low - ly Je-sus, No, not one! no, not one!
2 *No friend like Him is so high and ho-ly, No, not one! no, not one!*
3 There's not an hour that He is not near us, No, not one! no, not one!
4 *Did ev-er saint find this friend for-sake him? No, not one! no, not one!*
5 Was e'er a gift like the Sav-ior giv-en? No, not one! no, not one!

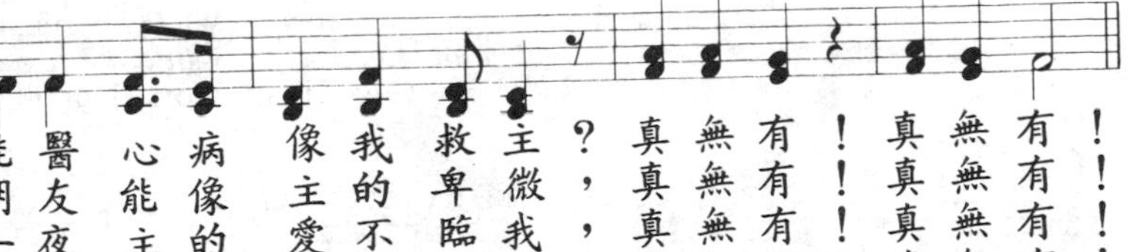

1. 那有能醫心病像我救主？真無有！真無有！
2. 無有朋友能像主的卑微，真無有！真無有！
3. 無有一夜主的愛不臨我，真無有！真無有！
4. 有誰悔改會被救主丟棄？真無有！真無有！
5. 那有信徒在天家無住處？真無有！真無有！

1 None else could heal all our soul's dis - eas - es, No, not one! no, not one!
2 *And yet no friend is so meek and low-ly, No, not one! no, not one!*
3 No night so dark but His love can cheer us, No, not one! no, not one!
4 *Or sin - ner find that He would not take him? No, not one! no, not one!*
5 Will He re-fuse us a home in heav-en? No, not one! no, not one!

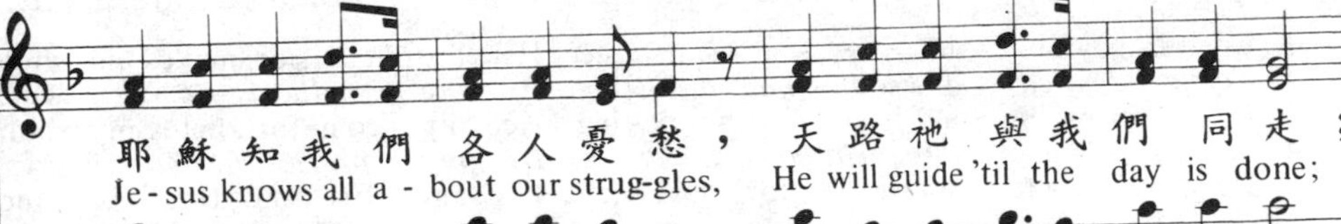

耶穌知我們各人憂愁，天路祂與我們同走；

Je - sus knows all a - bout our strug-gles, He will guide 'til the day is done;

那有朋友可比救主耶穌，真無有！真無友！

There's not a friend like the low - ly Je-sus, No, not one! no, not one!

167 耶穌，罪人奇妙良友

Jesus! What a Friend for Sinners

Behold, . . . a friend of publicans and sinners.

— Luke 7:34

HYFRYDOL

J. Wilbur Chapman

Rowland H. Prichard
Arranged by Robert Harkness

1. 耶穌！罪人奇妙良友！耶穌愛我靈的主！
2. 耶穌！弱者奇妙力量！讓我在主裡藏躲；
3. 耶穌！憂愁人的幫助！縱是海浪漫我身；
4. 耶穌！我的扶助前導！在海濤中有拯救；
5. 耶穌！我願意接受祢，發現祢恩典真多；
1 Je - sus! what a friend for sin-ners! Je - sus! lov-er of my soul!
2 Je - sus! what a strength in weak-ness! Let me hide my-self in Him;
3 Je - sus! what a help in sor-row! While the bil-lows o'er me roll;
4 Je - sus! what a guide and keep-er! While the tem-pest still is high;
5 Je - sus! I do now re-ceive Him, More than all in Him I find;
1. 友或離我敵或害我，但救主必定看顧。
2. 試探來臨有時跌倒，靠主力使我勝過。
3. 祂支持安慰破碎心，祂用慈愛來同行。
4. 狂風四吹星夜來臨，主是良伴聽我求。
5. 用祢寶血赦我罪孽，我屬祢，祢也屬我。
1 Friends may fail me, foes as-sail me, He, my Sav-ior, makes me whole.
2 Tempt-ed, tried, and some-times fail-ing, He, my strength, my vic-tory wins.
3 E - ven when my heart is break-ing, He, my com-fort, helps my soul.
4 Storms a-bout me, night o'er-takes me, He, my pi-lot, hears my cry.
5 He hath grant-ed me for-give-ness, I am His, and He is mine.
哈利路亞！奇妙救主！哈利路亞！我良友！
Hal-le-lu-jah! what a Sav-ior! Hal-le-lu-jah! what a friend!

救我，助我，護我，愛我，與我同在到永久。
Sav - ing, help - ing, keep - ing, lov - ing, He is with me to the end.

哈利路亞，奇妙救主 168

"Man of Sorrows," What a Name!

Who hath believed our report? And to whom is the arm of the Lord revealed? — Isaiah 53:1

HALLELUJAH! WHAT A SAVIOR

Philip P. Bliss

Philip P. Bliss

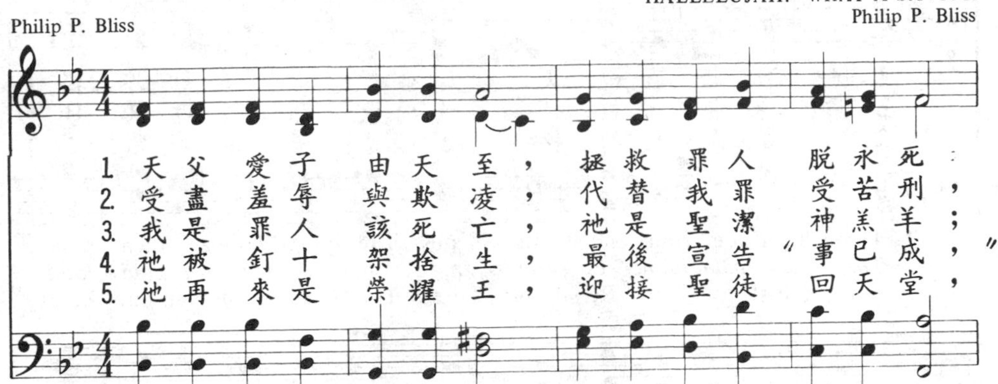
1. 天父愛子由天至，拯救罪人脱永死：
2. 受盡羞辱與欺凌，代替我罪受苦刑，
3. 我是罪人該死亡，祂是聖潔神羔羊；
4. 祂被釘十架捨生，最後宣告"事已成，"
5. 祂再來是榮耀王，迎接聖徒回天堂，
1 "Man of sor - rows!" what a name For the Son of God who came
2 *Bear - ing shame and scoff - ing rude, In my place con - demned He stood,*
3 Guilt - y, vile, and help - less we, Spot - less Lamb of God was He;
4 *Lift - ed up was He to die, "It is fin - ished," was His cry;*
5 When He comes, our glo - rious King, All His ran - somed home to bring,

1. 竟然稱為"憂患子！"哈利路亞，奇妙救主！
2. 藉寶血我罪洗清，哈利路亞，奇妙救主！
3. 我的罪債祂代償，哈利路亞，奇妙救主！
4. 今在高天榮美城，哈利路亞，奇妙救主！
5. 那時新歌一同唱，哈利路亞，奇妙救主！
1 Ru - ined sin - ners to re - claim! Hal - le - lu - jah, what a Sav - ior!
2 *Sealed my par - don with His blood; Hal - le - lu - jah, what a Sav - ior!*
3 Full a - tone - ment! Can it be? Hal - le - lu - jah, what a Sav - ior!
4 *Now in heaven ex - alt - ed high, Hal - le - lu - jah, what a Sav - ior!*
5 Then a - new this song we'll sing, Hal - le - lu - jah, what a Sav - ior!

169

高唱和散那

Hosanna, Loud Hosanna

Blessed is He that cometh in the name of the Lord; Hosanna in the highest.
— Matthew 21:9

Based on Matthew 21:15, 16
Jennette Threlfall
Jeff Redd, stanza 2

ELLACOMBE
Gesangbuch der Herzogl, Wirtemberg

1. 和散那，讚美上主，衆孩童高聲唱，
2. 群衆擁戴我救主，歡呼聲達雲霄，
3. "和散那，歸至高神，"昔日詩歌再唱，
1 Ho-san-na, loud ho-san-na, The lit-tle chil-dren sang;
2 From Ol-i-vet they fol-lowed, A hap-py, joy-ous crowd,
3 "Ho-san-na in the high-est!" That an-cient song we sing,
1. 和諧聲直達天庭，歌聲美妙悠揚；
2. 手持棕樹枝揮搖，歌聲清脆美妙；
3. 基督是我的救主，是天地的君王；
1 Through pil-lared court and tem-ple The love-ly an-them rang:
2 Their large palm branch-es wav-ing, And sing-ing clear and loud;
3 For Christ is our Re-deem-er, The Lord of heaven our King;
1. 耶穌愛賜福小孩，常以慈愛環抱，
2. 救主謙卑騎小驢，歡然欣喜進城，
3. 口唱心和齊讚美，永遠稱頌我主，
1 To Je-sus, who had blessed them Close fold-ed to His breast,
2 The Lord of men and an-gels Rode on in sim-ple joy,
3 O may we ev-er praise Him With heart and life and voice,
1. 孩童揚聲讚美主，歌聲單純崇高。
2. 男女幼童齊聚集，迎接救主我神。
3. 直到天家見主面，永遠歡欣同住！
1 The chil-dren sang their prais-es, The sim-plest and the best.
2 And wel-comed all the chil-dren: Each lit-tle girl and boy.
3 And in His ho-ly pres-ence E-ter-nal-ly re-joice!

無量讚美榮光

All Glory, Laud and Honor

Hosanna; Blessed is the King of Israel that cometh in the name of the Lord.
— John 12 :13
Theodulph of Orleans
Tr. by John M. Neale
ST. THEODULPH
Melchior Teschner
1. 無 量 讚 美 和 榮 光，全 歸 救 世 君 王，
2. 天 使 天 軍 無 量 數，在 天 頌 讚 主 名，
3. 主 在 受 難 捨 生 前，已 受 歌 頌 讚 美；
1 All glo - ry, laud, and hon - or To Thee, Re-deem - er, King,
2 *The com - pa - ny of an - gels Are prais - ing Thee on high,*
3 To Thee, be - fore Thy pas - sion, They sang their hymns of praise;
1. 高 高 在 上 和 散 那，當 年 孩 童 歌 唱：
2. 受 造 萬 物 與 萬 民，在 地 高 聲 響 應：
3. 如 今 主 已 升 高 天，我 衆 更 當 讚 美：
1 To whom the lips of chil - dren Made sweet ho - san - nas ring:
2 *And mor - tal men and all things Cre - at - ed make re - ply:*
3 To Thee, now high ex - alt - ed, Our mel - o - dy we raise:
1. 大 衛 王 室 之 後 裔，以 色 列 人 君 王，
2. 昔 日 選 民 來 見 主，手 拂 棕 枝 相 迎；
3. 求 主 今 向 我 施 恩，悅 納 讚 美 敬 拜，
1 Thou art the King of Is - ra - el, Thou Da - vid's roy - al Son,
2 *The peo - ple of the He - brews With palms be - fore Thee went;*
3 Thou didst ac - cept their prais - es— Ac - cept the praise we bring,
1. 奉 父 聖 名 來 世 界，當 受 萬 民 頌 揚！
2. 如 今 我 衆 當 奉 獻，祈 禱 讚 美 歌 聲。
3. 主 是 至 善 至 美 主，當 受 稱 頌 敬 佩！阿 們。
1 Who in the Lord's name com - est, The King and bless - ed one!
2 *Our praise and prayer and an - thems Be - fore Thee we pre - sent.*
3 Who in all good de - light - est, Thou good and gra - cious King! A - men.

171

衆城門哪，抬起頭來

Lift Up Your Heads, Ye Mighty Gates

Based on Psalm 24:7
Georg Weissel
Tr. by Catherine Winkworth
Give unto the Lord the glory due His name.
— I Chronicles 16:29
TRURO
Psalmodia Evangelica
1. 衆 城 門 哪，抬 起 頭 來，請 看，榮 耀 王
2. 美 麗 大 地，蒙 福 之 城，耶 穌 基 督 掌
3. 敞 開 你 心，向 主 奉 獻，分 別 為 聖 成
4. 親 愛 救 主，我 願 祢 來，今 將 心 門 完
5. 至 尊 上 主，求 入 我 心，使 我 得 美 好
1 Lift up your heads, ye might-y gates: Be-hold, the King of
2 O blest the land, the cit-y blest, Where Christ the rul-er
3 Fling wide the por-tals of your heart: Make it a tem-ple,
4 Re-deem-er, come! I o-pen wide My heart to Thee: here,
5 So come, my Sov-ereign, en-ter in! Let new and no-bler
1. 要 進 來！萬 王 之 王 將 要 臨
2. 權 執 政！家 家 戶 戶 何 等 歡
3. 為 聖 殿！祈 禱 頌 讚 為 主 而
4. 全 打 開，求 主 進 入 我 心 居
5. 新 生 命！聖 靈 引 我 直 到 天
1 glo-ry waits! The King of kings is draw-ing
2 is con-fessed! O hap-py hearts and hap-py
3 set a-part From earth-ly use for heaven's em-
4 Lord, a-bide! Let me Thy in-ner pres-ence
5 life be-gin! Thy Ho-ly Spir-it guide us
1. 近，世 人 的 救 主 已 降 臨。
2. 欣，得 勝 君 王 今 已 來 臨！
3. 活，以 愛 敬 拜 何 等 快 樂。
4. 住，彰 顯 祢 恩 祢 愛 豐 富。
5. 上，榮 耀 冠 冕 為 我 獎 賞。
1 near, The Sav-ior of the world is here.
2 homes To whom this King of tri-umph comes!
3 ploy, A-dorned with prayer and love and joy.
4 feel: Thy grace and love in me re-veal.
5 on, Un-til the glo-rious crown be won. A-men.

哦！至聖之首受創傷

O Sacred Head, Now Wounded

Latin: 12th Century
German: Paul Gerhardt
Tr. by James W. Alexander, alt.

When they had platted a crown of thorns they put it upon His head.
— Matthew 27:29

PASSION CHORALE
Hans Leo Hassler
Harmonized by J. S. Bach

1. 哦，至聖之首低垂，滿了憂痛創傷，
2. 我主祢受盡苦楚，罪人得蒙恩典，
3. 我用何辭來感謝，如此親愛朋友？

1 O sa-cred Head, now wound-ed, With grief and shame weighed down,
2 *What Thou, my Lord, hast suf-fered Was all for sin-ners' gain;*
3 What lan-guage shall I bor-row To thank Thee, dear-est friend,

1. 遭凌辱荊棘刺遍，作成冠冕戴上；
2. 祢受創痛至死亡，是因我的罪愆；
3. 因祢捨命極傷痛，慈愛存到永久；

1 Now scorn-ful-ly sur-round-ed With thorns, Thy on-ly crown,
2 *Mine, mine was the trans-gres-sion, But Thine the dead-ly pain.*
3 For this Thy dy-ing sor-row, Thy pit-y with-out end?

1. 哦，至聖之首本有天上一切榮光！
2. 思念苦刑我當受，俯伏我主脚邊；
3. 哦使我永遠屬祢，雖至體力衰朽；

1 How art Thou pale with an-guish, With sore a-buse and scorn!
2 *Lo, here I fall, my Sav-ior! 'Tis I de-serve Thy place;*
3 O make me Thine for-ev-er; And, should I faint-ing be,

1. 雖被棄嫌並血染，我樂歸附祢旁！
2. 懇求繼續賜恩典，願常瞻仰聖顏。
3. 求使我一心愛主，永遠忠誠信守！阿門。

1 How does that vis-age lan-guish Which once was bright as morn!
2 *Look on me with Thy fa-vor, Vouch-safe to me Thy grace.*
3 Lord, let me nev-er, nev-er Out-live my love for Thee! A-men.

173

羔羊是配得榮耀
Worthy Is The Lamb

. . . Surely I come quickly; even so, come, Lord Jesus.
— Revelation 22: 20
Based on Revelation 5:12
Don Wyrtzen
被殺的羔羊是配得，被殺的羔羊是配
Wor - thy is the Lamb that was slain, Wor - thy is the Lamb that was
得，被殺的羔羊是配得，去接受：
slain, Wor - thy is the Lamb that was slain, to re - ceive:
權柄與豐富，智慧與能力，尊貴與榮耀和
Pow - er and rich - es and wis - dom and strength, Hon - or and glo - ry and
頌讚！被殺的羔羊，是配得榮耀，
bless - ing! Wor - thy is the Lamb. Wor - thy is the Lamb,
被殺的羔羊是配得——尊貴與榮耀！
Wor - thy is the Lamb that was slain, Wor - thy is the Lamb!

我曾捨命為你

I Gave My Life

And that He might reconcile unto God . . . by the cross . . .

– Ephesians 2:16

Frances R. Havergal

Philip P. Bliss

1. 我曾捨命為你，我血為你流出，
2. 我曾抛父家庭，並我榮光寶座，
3. 我曾受大苦難，非人口舌能説，
4. 我曾将父救恩，從我天上攜來，
1. I gave My life for thee, My pre-cious blood I shed,
2. My fa-ther's house of light, My glo - ry cir-cled throne,
3. I suf-fered much for thee, More than thy tongue can tell,
4. And I have brought to thee, Down from My home a-bove,
1. 救你從死復起，使你由死得贖；
2. 凄涼孤身獨行，在此暗世經過；
3. 臨刑身同囚犯，救你地獄得脱；
4. 此恩充滿你身，即我寬容仁愛；
1. That thou might'st ran-somed be, And quick-ened from the dead;
2. I left, for earth-ly night, For wan-d'rings sad and lone;
3. Of bit - t'rest ag - o - ny, To res - cue thee from hell;
4. Sal - va-tion full and free, My par-don and My love;
1. 為你，為你我命曾捨，你捨何事為我？
2. 為你，為你天家曾捨，你抛何福為我？
3. 為你，為你我身曾捨，你捨何事為我？
4. 為你，為你大恩曾施，你将何物獻我？
1. I gave, I gave My life for thee-What hast thou giv'n for Me?
2. I left, I left it all for thee-Hast thou left aught for Me?
3. I've borne, I've borne it all for thee-What hast thou borne for Me?
4. I bring, I bring rich gifts to thee-What hast thou brought to Me?

175

尊貴，榮耀，都歸被殺羔羊

Worthy the Lamb

Gloria Gaither
William J. Gaither
Thou art worthy, O Lord, to receive glory, and honor, and power. . . .
— Revelation 4:11
WORTHY
William J. Gaither
1. 聽 哪，被 罪 惡 捆 綁 者，發 出 呼 喊 救
2. 哀 哭 之 聲 今 已 停 止，歡 樂 歌 聲 響
3. 天 上 千 萬 歷 代 聖 徒，會 同 衆 天 使
1 Hear the cries of the shack-led from the on-set of
2 Then the cry-ing is stilled as the cho-rus rings
3 Then all the arch-an-gels, the saints of all
1. 聲，無 一 鑰 匙 能 打 開 衆 鎖 鏈；看 哪，
2. 起，罪 惡 鎖 鍊 被 囚 者 得 釋 放；千 萬
3. 長，手 持 冠 冕 極 榮 耀 與 光 亮，屈 膝
1 time– For the chains of de-feat there's no key; See the
2 out– The shack-led re-leased from their chains; And
3 time, Hold-ing their crowns in their hands,
1. 傷 心 流 淚 者，為 奴 的 呼 喊—"竟 然
2. 蒙 恩 的 靈 魂，高 聲 齊 頌 揚—"尊 貴
3. 跪 在 祂 脚 前，同 聲 唱 新 歌—"尊 貴
1 tears of the bro-ken, the cries of the slaves– "Is there
2 thou-sands of voic-es are swell-ing the song–
3 Fall down be-fore Him, join-ing the song–
1. 無 人 能 將 我 罪 赦 免？"
2. 榮 耀 都 歸 被 殺 羔 羊。" 尊 貴，
3. 榮 耀 都 歸 被 殺 羔 羊。" Worth-y,
1 no one worth-y to set us free?"
2 "Worth-y the Lamb that was slain."
3 "Worth-y, worth-y the Lamb."

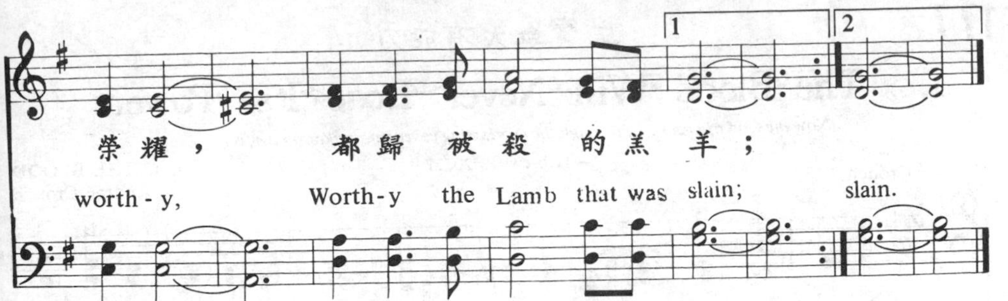
1
2
榮耀， 都歸被殺的羔羊；
worth - y, Worth - y the Lamb that was slain; slain.

耶穌，耶穌 176

Jesus, Jesus

The darkness and the light are the same to Thee.

Psalm 139:12

Traditional

Traditional

Unison

1. 耶 穌，耶 穌，清晨耶穌 同在，午間耶穌

1. Je - sus, Je - sus, Je - sus in the morn - ing, Je - sus in the

1. 同在 耶 穌，耶 穌，直到日落仍同 在。

1. noon - time; Je - sus, Je - sus, Je - sus when the sun goes down!

2. 讚美，讚美，清晨讚美耶穌，午間讚美耶穌
直到日落仍讚美。

3. 愛祂，愛祂，清晨我愛耶穌，午間我愛耶穌
直到日落仍愛祂。

4. 事奉，事奉，清晨事奉耶穌，午間事奉耶穌
直到日落仍事奉。

5. 耶穌，耶穌，清晨耶穌同在，午間耶穌同在
直到日落仍同在。

2. *Praise Him . . .* 3. Love Him . . . 4. *Serve Him . . .* 5. Jesus . . .

177 主寶血大有能力

The Blood Will Never Lose Its Power

Now the God of peace . . . through the everlasting covenant, make you perfect . . . .

— Hebrews 13:20, 21

Andraé Crouch

THE BLOOD
Andraé Crouch

1 加略山上救主流血，是為我衆罪孽，主寶血使我每日得力量，主寶血大有能力。
2 寶血能使我除憂驚，使我心得安寧，主寶血使我每日得力量，主寶血大有能力。
1 The blood that Je - sus shed for me, Way back on Cal - va - ry, The blood that gives me strength from day to day, It will nev - er lose its power.
2 *It soothes my doubts and calms my fears, And it dries all my tears; The blood that gives me strength from day to day, It will nev - er lose its power.*
寶血的能力大過高山。寶血能力
It reach-es to the high - est moun-tain. It flows to the

深 及幽 谷， 主 寶血使我 每 日
low - est val - ley The blood that gives me strength from
得 力 量， 主寶 血 大 有 能力。
day to day, It will nev - er lose its power.

A Confession of Faith

I believe in God, who is for me spirit, love, the principle of all things.

I believe that God is in me, as I am in Him.

I believe that the true welfare of man consists in fulfilling the will of God.

I believe that from the fulfillment of the will of God there can follow nothing but that which is good for me and for all men.

I believe that the will of God is that every man should love his fellow men, and should act toward others as he desires that they should act toward him.

I believe that the reason of life is for each of us simply to grow in love.

I believe that this growth in love will contribute more than any other force to establish the Kingdom of God on earth.

–Leo Tolstoy

178

耶穌，真神兒子

Jesus, the Son of God

Believe me that I am in the Father, and the Father in me. — John 14:11

G. T. Haywood

SWEET WONDER
G. T. Haywood

1. 你曾　認識祂麼，耶穌　我的救主，　耶穌，真
2. 神賜　祂作贖價，拯救　我的靈魂，　耶穌，真
3. 你能　拒絕祂麼，輕看　我的救主，　耶穌，真
4. 你若　願意接受，相信　依靠救主，　耶穌，真
5. 不久　祂要再臨，駕雲　大有榮耀，　耶穌，真
1 Do you know Je-sus, Our Lord, our Sav-ior, Je-sus, the
2 God gave Him, a ran-som, Our souls to re-cov-er; Je-sus, the
3 O who would re-ject Him, De-spise, or for-sake Him, Je-sus, the
4 If you will ac-cept Him And trust and be-lieve Him, Je-sus, the
5 Then some-day from heav-en, On clouds of bright glo-ry, Je-sus, the

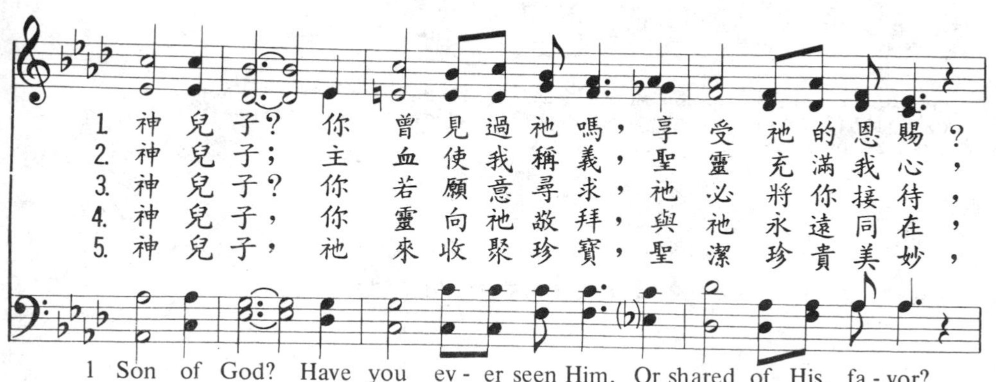
1. 神兒子？　你曾見過祂嗎，享受祂的恩賜？
2. 神兒子；　主血使我稱義，聖靈充滿我心，
3. 神兒子？　你若願意尋求，祂必將你接待，
4. 神兒子，　你靈向祂敬拜，與祂永遠同在，
5. 神兒子，　祂來收聚珍寶，聖潔珍貴美妙，
1 Son of God? Have you ev-er seen Him, Or shared of His fa-vor?
2 Son of God; His blood made us wor-thy His Spir-it to hov-er:
3 Son of God? O who ev-er sought Him, And He would not take him?
4 Son of God. Your soul will ex-alt Him, And nev-er will leave Him;
5 Son of God, Will come for His jew-els, Most pre-cious and ho-ly,

耶穌　真神兒子。　何等美妙！何等　美妙！
Je-sus, the Son of God. O sweet Won-der! O sweet Won-der!

耶穌 真 神 兒 子； 我 何等敬 祢 ！
Je - sus, the Son of God; How I a - dore Thee!

我 何 等 愛 祢 ！ 耶 穌 真 神 兒 子。
O how I love Thee! Je - sus, the Son of God.

178-1

天父我相信祢
Father, I Believe You

True worshipers will worship the Father in spirit and truth. John 4:23

Sally Anderson — Sally Anderson

Unison
天父，我 相 信 祢， 耶 穌 我 接 受 祢， 懇 求
Fa ther, I be lieve you, Je - sus, I re - ceive you, Ho - ly
聖 靈，自 由 運 行， 使 我 靈 得 更 新。
Spir it, I now free you. Cre - ate in me new life.

179

我深信在那各各他山頂

I Believe in a Hill Called Mount Calvary

Dale Oldham
Gloria Gaither
William J. Gaither
And when they came to the place called Calvary, they crucified Him
Luke 23:33
MOUNT CALVARY
William J. Gaither
1. 人一生在世如客旅轉眼逝去，
2. 我深信基督旣為人受死十架，
3. 我深信人生雖然如。謎難測透，
1 There are things as we trav - el this earth's shift - ing sands
2 I be - lieve that the Christ who was slain on that cross
3 I be - lieve that this life with its great mys - ter - ies
1. 世上並無一處能久留；
2. 今日能使你生命改變；
3. 有一天這一切將結束；
1 That trans - cend all the rea - son of man;
2 Has the pow - er to change lives to - day;
3 Sure - ly some - day will come to an end;
1. 雖然有名利財寶一生在追求，
2. 因為祂曾改變我，賜我新生命，
3. 但因信我能得勝死亡與黑暗，
1 But the things that mat - ter the most in this world,
2 For He changed me com - plete - ly, a new life is mine,
3 But faith will con - quer the dark - ness and death
1. 但不能使我永遠擁有。
2. 我今願靠近十架身邊。
3. 到天家與我良友同住。
1 They can nev - er be held in our hand.
2 That is why by the cross I will stay.
3 And will lead me at last to my friend.

我深信在那各各他山頂——我救主曾
I be - lieve in a hill called Mount Cal-vary – I'll be - lieve what -
為我被掛；當歲月漸漸消失，世
ev - er the cost; And when time has sur - ren - dered and
界成過去，我仍願倚靠古舊十架。
earth is no more, I'll still cling to that old rug - ged cross.

I shall pass
through this world
but once.
Anything good therefore
that I can do
or any kindness
that I can show
to any human being.
let me do it now.
Let me not
defer or neglect it,
for I shall not pass
this way again.

— Anonymous

180

慈愛的救主

Blessed Redeemer

And the Redeemed shall come to Zion,
and unto them that turn from transgression . . . — Isaiah 59:20

Avis B. Christiansen

REDEEMER
Harry Dixon Loes

1. 各各他山上，凄涼清晨，耶穌我救主，
2. 主在十架上，熱血縱流，仍然不忘記，
3. 我深愛救主，祂是我友！我願讚美主，

1 Up Calvary's mountain, one dreadful morn, Walked Christ my Savior,
2 *"Father, forgive them!" thus did He pray, E'en while His life-blood*
3 O how I love Him, Savior and Friend! How can my praises

1. 辛苦獨行；為世上罪人，釘死十架，
2. 為罪人求 "父啊我求祢，赦免他們，"
3. 祂聽我求！願在世年日，常述主恩，

1 weary and worn; Facing for sinners death on the cross,
2 *flowed fast away; Praying for sinners while in such woe—*
3 ever find end! Thru years unnumbered on heaven's shore,

1. 為要救他們免永沉淪。
2. 無人像耶穌以愛拯救。
3. 常讚美救主直到永久。

1 That He might save them from endless loss.
2 *No one but Jesus ever loved so.*
3 My tongue shall praise Him forevermore.

慈愛的救主，尊貴的救主！我彷彿見祂身懸掛十架，受創傷

Blessed Redeemer, precious Redeemer! Seems now I see Him on Calvary's tree Wounded and

流血，為罪人 代求，憂痛被 釘死，作我贖 價！
bleed-ing, for sin-ners plead-ing—Blind and un-heed-ing—dy-ing for me!

耶穌獨自行走

Jesus Walked This Lonesome Valley

181

He was in all points tempted as we are, yet without sin. — Hebrews 4:15

Traditional
Erna Moorman, 2nd stanza

LONESOME VALLEY
Traditional Spiritual

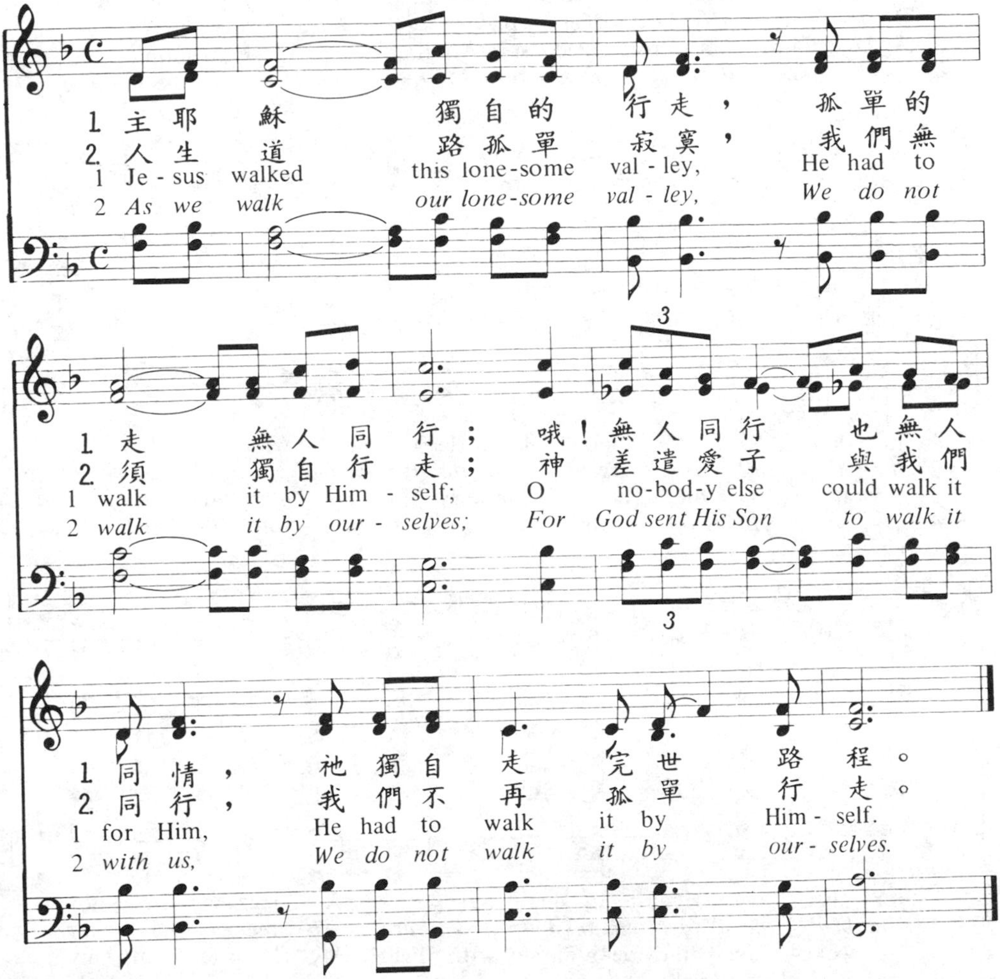

1. 主耶穌獨自的行走，孤單的走無人同行；哦！無人同行也無人同情，祂獨自走完世路程。
2. 人生道路孤單寂寞，我們無須獨自行走；神差遣愛子與我們同行，我們不再孤單行走。

1 Jesus walked this lonesome valley, He had to walk it by Himself; O nobody else could walk it for Him, He had to walk it by Himself.

2 *As we walk our lonesome valley, We do not walk it by ourselves; For God sent His Son to walk it with us, We do not walk it by ourselves.*

怎能如此

And Can It Be That I Should Gain?

For God hath not appointed us to wrath, but . . . salvation, by our Lord Jesus Christ.
— I Thessalonians 5:9

Charles Wesley

SAGINA
Thomas Campbell

1. 怎能如此，像我這樣罪人，也能蒙
2. 主竟拋棄，天上榮耀寶座，白白恩
3. 我的心靈，多年被囚捆綁，被罪包
4. 不再定罪，今我不再畏懼，耶穌與
1 And can it be that I should gain An in - terest
2 He left His Fa - ther's throne a - bove, So free, so
3 Long my im - pris - oned spir - it lay Fast bound in
4 No con - dem - na - tion now I dread: Je - sus, and
1. 主寶血救贖？因我罪過使祂受苦，
2. 典何等無限！捨去己身成全大愛，
3. 圍幽暗無光；主眼發出復活榮光，
4. 祂所有屬我！我活在永活元首裡，
1 in the Sav - ior's blood? Died He for me, who caused His pain?
2 in - fi - nite His grace! Emp - tied Him - self of all but love,
3 sin and na - ture's night. Thine eye dif - fused a quick - ening ray;
4 all in Him, is mine! A - live in Him, my liv - ing Head,
1. 因我罪過使祂受死；奇異的愛！何
2. 救贖可憐亞當後代！恩典憐憫，何
3. 使我覺醒光滿牢房！鎖鏈斷落，心
4. 穿起公義聖潔白衣，坦然進到神
1 For me, who Him to death pur - sued? A - maz - ing love! how
2 And bled for A - dam's help - less race! 'Tis mer - cy all, im -
3 I woke— the dun - geon flamed with light! My chains fell off, my
4 And clothed in right - eous - ness di - vine, Bold I ap - proach th'e -

1. 能 如 此， 我 主 我 神 竟 為 我 死？
2. 等 無 限， 我 主 我 神 将 我 尋 回。
3. 得 釋 放， 我 起 來 跟 隨 主 前 往。
4. 寶 座 前， 因 我 救 主， 我 得 榮 冕。
1 can it be That Thou, my God, shouldst die for me?
2 mense and free, For, O my God, it found out me.
3 heart was free, I rose, went forth, and fol - lowed Thee.
4 ter - nal throne, And claim the crown, through Christ my own.

奇 異 的 愛！ 何 能 如 此，
A - maz - ing love! how can it be
奇 異 的 愛！何 能 如 此，
A - maz - ing love! how can it be

我 主，我 神，竟 為 我 死。阿 門。
That Thou, my God, shouldst die for me! A - men.

183

美哉主耶穌

Fairest Lord Jesus

Thou art fairer than the children of men.
— Psalm 45:2

From *Münster Gesangbuch*

CRUSADERS' HYMN
Silesian Folk Melody

1. 美哉主耶穌，宇宙萬物主宰，
2. 美哉芳草地，原野更是美麗，
3. 陽光多美麗，月光更覺清新，
4. 美哉主耶穌，統轄萬國萬民！

1 Fair - est Lord Je - sus, Rul - er of all na - ture,
2 *Fair are the mead - ows, Fair - er still the wood - lands,*
3 Fair is the sun - shine, Fair - er still the moon - light,
4 *Beau - ti - ful Sav - ior! Lord of the na - tions!*

1. 祂是真神降世為人：我心所景仰，
2. 大地披上彩色春衣：耶穌更美麗，
3. 繁星點點燦爛閃耀：耶穌更光明，
4. 世人救主天上真神！尊貴與光榮，

1 O Thou of God and man the Son: Thee will I cher - ish,
2 *Robed in the bloom - ing garb of spring: Je - sus is fair - er,*
3 And all the twin - kling star - ry host: Je - sus shines bright - er,
4 *Son of God and Son of Man! Glo - ry and hon - or,*

1. 我靈所崇敬，是我榮耀冠冕歡欣。
2. 耶穌更清潔，使憂傷心發出歌聲。
3. 耶穌更皎潔，天使榮光不足比較。
4. 讚美與敬崇，都歸主耶穌到無窮！阿們。

1 Thee will I hon - or, Thou my soul's glo - ry, joy, and crown.
2 *Je - sus is pur - er, Who makes the woe - ful heart to sing.*
3 Je - sus shines pur - er Than all the an - gels heaven can boast.
4 *Praise, ad - o - ra - tion, Now and for - ev - er - more be Thine!* A - men.

耶穌愛我，我知道
Jesus Loves Me, This I Know

I love them that love Me, and those who seek Me early shall find Me.
— Proverbs 8:17
JESUS LOVES ME
William B. Bradbury
Anna B. Warner
1. 耶 穌 愛 我 我 知 道， 因 有 聖 書 告 訴 我；
2. 耶 穌 愛 我 捨 性 命， 將 我 罪 惡 洗 乾 淨；
3. 耶 穌 愛 我 愛 到 底， 愛 我 罪 人 真 希 奇；
1 Je - sus loves me! this I know, For the Bi - ble tells me so;
2 Je - sus loves me! He who died Heav-en's gate to o - pen wide;
3 Je - sus, take this heart of mine, Make it pure and whol - ly Thine;
1. 凡 小 孩 子 主 牧 養， 我 雖 軟 弱 主 剛 強 。
2. 天 上 榮 門 為 我 開， 把 祂 小 羊 引 進 來 。
3. 我 若 生 前 愛 救 主， 日 後 必 到 天 家 住 。
1 Lit - tle ones to Him be - long, They are weak but He is strong.
2 He will wash a - way my sin, Let His lit - tle child come in.
3 On the cross You died for me, I will try to live for Thee.
主 耶 穌 愛 我 ！ 主 耶 穌 愛 我 ！
Yes, Je - sus loves me! Yes, Je - sus loves me!
主 耶 穌 愛 我 ！ 有 聖 書 告 訴 我 。
Yes, Je - sus loves me! The Bi - ble tells me so.

185

在十架上

Down at the Cross

I am crucified with Christ; Nevertheless I live . . .
— Galatians 2:20

Elisha A. Hoffman

GLORY TO HIS NAME
John H. Stockton

1. 在十架上我救主捨命，靠主十架我罪得洗淨，除我重擔安慰我傷心；
2. 我今靠主脫離罪權柄，有主時常住在我內心，我真不配蒙救主宏恩；
3. 主寶貝血將我全釋放，靠主恩典我心甚快樂，讚美我主時常潔淨我；
4. 罪人，請來俯伏主脚前，同得奇妙贖罪大恩典，救主寶血洗淨你罪愆；
1 Down at the cross where my Sav - ior died, Down where for cleans-ing from sin I cried, There to my heart was the blood ap - plied;
2 I am so won-drous-ly saved from sin, Je - sus so sweet-ly a - bides with - in; There at the cross where He took me in;
3 O, pre-cious foun-tain that saves from sin, I am so glad I have en - tered in; There Je - sus saves me and keeps me clean;
4 Come to this foun-tain so rich and sweet; Cast your poor soul at the Sav - ior's feet; Plunge in to - day, and be made com - plete;
榮耀歸主名。榮耀歸主名，榮耀歸主名！
Glo - ry to His name. Glo - ry to His name, Glo - ry to His name!
主寶貝血將我罪洗淨；榮耀歸主名。
There to my heart was the blood ap - plied; Glo - ry to His name.

為我受傷
Wounded for Me

But He was wounded for our transgressions . . . . — Isaiah 53:5

FOR ME
W. G. Ovens, stanza 1
W. G. Ovens
Gladys Westcott Roberts, stanzas 2-5
1. 為我受傷，為我受傷，在十字架
2. 為我受死，為我受死，在十字架
3. 為我復活，為我復活，由墳墓裡
4. 為我活着，為我活着，在高天上
5. 為我再來，為我再來，必有一天
1 Wound-ed for me, wound-ed for me, There on the cross
2 Dy - ing for me, dy-ing for me, There on the cross
3 Ris - en for me, ris-en for me, Up from the grave
4 Liv - ing for me, liv-ing for me, Up in the skies
5 Com - ing for me, com-ing for me, One day to earth
1. 耶穌為我受傷；罪蒙赦免我今得着釋
2. 耶穌為我受死；因祂受死我得救贖福
3. 主已為我復活；死亡毒鈎今後不能害
4. 耶穌為我活着；救主晝夜禱告祈求為
5. 主要為我再來；見主愛臉何等喜樂暢
1 He was wound-ed for me; Gone my trans-gres-sions, and now I am
2 He was dy - ing for me; Now in His death my re - demp-tion I
3 He has ris - en for me; Now ev - er-more from death's sting I am
4 He is liv - ing for me; Dai - ly He's plead-ing and pray-ing for
5 He is com-ing for me; Then with what joy His dear face I shall
1. 放，都因救主耶穌為我受傷。
2. 氣，都因救主耶穌為我受死。
3. 我，都因救主耶穌為我復活。
4. 我，都因救主耶穌為我活着。
5. 快，滿心讚美主，祂為我再來！
1 free, All be-cause Je - sus was wound - ed for me.
2 see, All be-cause Je - sus was dy - ing for me.
3 free, All be-cause Je - sus has ris - en for me.
4 me, O how I praise Him, He's liv - ing for me.
5 see, O how I praise Him— He's com - ing for me!

187

古舊十架

The Old Rugged Cross

Who for the joy that was set before Him endured the cross . . . .
— Hebrews 12:2

George Bennard

RUGGED CROSS
George Bennard

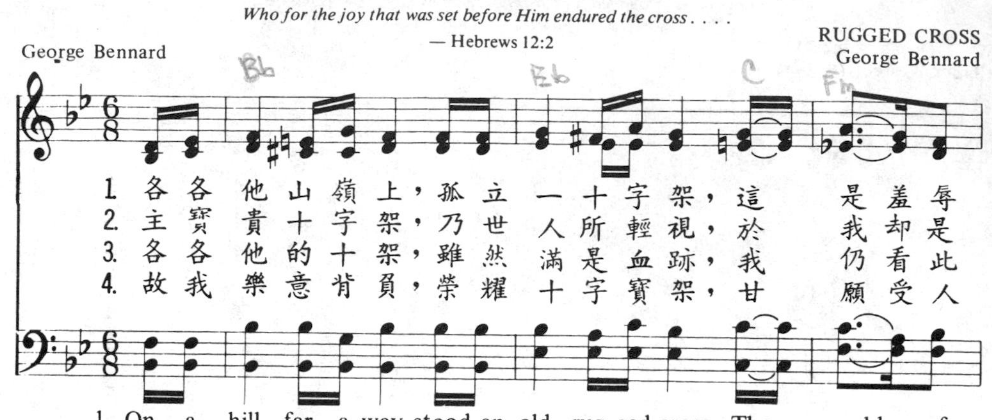
1. 各各他山嶺上，孤立一十字架，這是羞辱
2. 主寶貴十字架，乃世人所輕視，於我却是
3. 各各他的十架，雖然滿是血跡，我仍看此
4. 故我樂意背負，榮耀十字寶架，甘願受人
1 On a hill far a-way stood an old rug-ged cross, The em-blem of
2 *O that old rug-ged cross, so de-spised by the world, Has a won-drous at-*
3 In the old rug-ged cross, stained with blood so di-vine, A won - drous
4 *To the old rug-ged cross I will ev - er be true, Its shame and re -*

1. 痛苦記號；神愛子主耶穌，為世人被釘死，
2. 真神仁慈；神愛子主耶穌，離天堂衆榮華，
3. 十架為美；因在此寶架上，救主為我捨命，
4. 輕視辱罵；他日救主再臨，迎接我升天庭，
1 suf-fering and shame; And I love that old cross where the dear-est and best
2 *trac- tion for me; For the dear Lamb of God left His glo - ry a-bove*
3 beau - ty I see; For 'twas on that old cross Je-sus suf-fered and died
4 *proach glad-ly bear; Then He'll call me some day to my home far a-way,*

1. 這十架為我最愛珍寶。
2. 甘願為世人背此十架。
3. 潔淨我赦免我的衆罪。
4. 將永遠享受榮耀天家。
故我愛高舉十字寶
So I'll cher-ish the old rug-ged
1 For a world of lost sin-ners was slain.
2 *To bear it to dark Cal-va - ry.*
3 To par-don and sanc-ti-fy me.
4 *Where His glo - ry for-ev - er I'll share.*

Bb
Eb
Bb
架，直到在主台前見主面；我一生要背
cross, 'Til my tro-phies at last I lay down; I will cling to the
Eb
Bb
Fm
Bb
負十字架，此十架可換公義冠冕。
old rug-ged cross, And ex-change it some day for a crown.

他本有神的形像，不以自己與神同等為強奪的，反倒虛己，取了奴僕的形像，成為人的樣式，既有人的樣子，就自己卑微，存心順服，以至於死，且死在十字架上。

腓立比書二章
6－7節

Who, being in very nature of God, did not consider equality with God something to be grasped, but made himself nothing, taking the very nature of a servant, being made in human likeness.

And being found in appearance as a man, he humbled himself and became obedient to death — even death on a cross!

— (Philippians 2:6-8, NIV)

我每思念十字寶架

When I Survey the Wondrous Cross

What things were gain to me, those I counted loss for Christ.
— Philippians 3:7

Isaac Watts

HAMBURG
Based on Gregorian Chant
Arr. by Lowell Mason

1. 我每思念十字寶架，並主如
2. 願主禁我別有所誇，除了基
3. 看從祂頭，祂腳，祂手，憂情慈
4. 假若宇宙都歸我有，盡獻於
1 When I sur - vey the won - drous cross On which the
2 For - bid it, Lord, that I should boast, Save in the
3 See, from His head, His hands, His feet, Sor - row and
4 Were the whole realm of na - ture mine, That were a

1. 何在上懸掛；我就不禁渾
2. 督的十字架；前所珍愛虛
3. 愛和血而流；那有愛憂如
4. 主仍覺不夠；愛既如此奇
1 Prince of glo - ry died, My rich - est gain I
2 death of Christ my God; All the vain things that
3 love flow min - gled down: Did e'er such love and
4 pres - ent far too small; Love so a - maz - ing,

1. 忘身家，鄙視從前所有驕傲。
2. 空榮華，今為祂血情願丟下。
3. 此相遘，荊棘編成如此冕旒？
4. 妙深厚，當得我心，我命，所有。阿門。
1 count but loss, And pour con - tempt on all my pride.
2 charm me most, I sac - ri - fice them to His blood.
3 sor - row meet, Or thorns com - pose so rich a crown?
4 so di - vine, De - mands my soul, my life, my all. A-men.

有一活泉，充滿寶血

There Is a Fountain Filled with Blood
For in Thee is the fountain of life: in Thy light shall we see light – Psalm 36:9
William Cowper
BELMONT
William Gardiner
1. 有一活泉充滿寶血，從主肋旁流下；罪人只要在此一洗，必能潔淨無瑕。
2. 臨死一賊得見此泉，心喜求主紀念；我罪雖然比祂更深，主能洗我完全。
3. 被殺羔羊血何奇妙，蘊藏除罪能力；洗淨教會聖潔榮美，何等奇妙能力。
4. 自我因信看見此泉，能力湧我心間；我心讚美主愛完全，一生必要傳揚。阿門。
1 There is a fountain filled with blood Drawn from Emmanuel's veins; And sinners, plunged beneath that flood, Lose all their guilty stains.
2 The dying thief rejoiced to see That fountain in his day; And there may I, though sinful, too, Wash all my sins away.
3 Dear dying Lamb, Thy precious blood Shall never lose its power, 'Til all the ransomed Church of God Be saved, to sin no more.
4 And since, by faith, I saw the stream Thy flowing wounds supply, Redeeming love has been my theme, And shall be 'til I die. A - men.

靠血洗淨

Are You Washed in the Blood?

But if we walk in the light . . . the blood of Jesus Christ cleanses us . . .

— I John 1:7

Elisha A. Hoffman

WASHED IN THE BLOOD
Elisha A. Hoffman

1. 請問可曾信主倚寶血洗淨，可曾
2. 你願順從救主行這危險路，可曾
3. 當新郎回來時你要穿何衣？總要
4. 往日污穢衣裳今須全丟盡，總要

1 Have you been to Je-sus for the cleans-ing power? Are you
2 *Are you walk-ing dai-ly by the Sav-ior's side? Are you*
3 When the Bride-groom com-eth, will your robes be white, Pure and
4 *Lay a-side the gar-ments that are stained with sin And be*

1. 倚聖羔血洗乾淨？可曾倚靠救主得着
2. 倚聖羔血洗乾淨？可曾望主引導倚靠
3. 倚聖羔血洗乾淨，聖徒被接升天你願
4. 倚聖羔血洗乾淨，曾有十架寶血為你

1 washed in the blood of the Lamb? Are you ful-ly trust-ing in His
2 *washed in the blood of the Lamb? Do you rest each mo-ment in the*
3 white in the blood of the Lamb? Will your souls be read-y for the
4 *washed in the blood of the Lamb? There's a foun-tain flow-ing for the*

新生命，可曾倚聖羔血洗乾淨？
主保護，可曾倚聖羔血洗乾淨？ 你總
否同進？總要倚聖羔血洗乾淨。 Are you
白白流，總要倚聖羔血洗乾淨

1 grace this hour? Are you washed in the blood of the Lamb?
2 *Cru-ci-fied? Are you washed in the blood of the Lamb?*
3 man-sions bright And be washed in the blood of the Lamb?
4 *soul un-clean; O be washed in the blood of the Lamb?*

要 倚寶血，倚寶 血你方能 洗乾淨！你的
washed in the blood, In the soul-cleans-ing blood of the Lamb? Are your
衣裳是否洗淨白 如雪，你可曾倚寶血洗乾淨？
garments spotless? Are they white as snow? Are you washed in the blood of the Lamb?

Christ Is Crucified Anew

Not only once, and long ago,
There on Golgotha's side,
Has Christ, the Lord, been crucified
Because He loved a lost world so.
But hourly souls, sin-satisfied,
Mock His great love, flout His commands.
And I drive nails deep in His hands,
You thrust the spear within His side.

—John Richard Moreland

191

主，祢犧牲的愛

Savior, Thy Dying Love
S. Dryden Phelps, alt.
It was the third hour and they crucified Him
– Mark 15:25
SOMETHING FOR JESUS
Robert Lowry
1. 主 祢 犧 牲 的 愛， 已 賜 給 我，
2. 賜 我 忠 誠 之 心， 像 祢 真 誠，
3. 此 生 所 有 一 切， 皆 祢 所 賜，
1 Sav - ior, Thy dy - ing love Thou gav - est me,
2 Give me a faith - ful heart, Guid - ed by Thee,
3 All that I am and have, Thy gifts so free,
1. 主 我 不 願 為 己， 留 下 什 麼；
2. 時 光 飛 逝 而 去， 求 主 鑒 定；
3. 祇 要 為 我 恩 主， 苦 樂 不 辭；
1 Noth - ing should I with - hold, Dear Lord, from Thee;
2 That each de - part - ing day Hence - forth may see
3 Ev - er in joy or grief, My Lord, for Thee;
1. 我 在 愛 中 景 仰， 將 我 心 願 還 償，
2. 使 我 殷 勤 工 作， 喜 愛 行 善 扶 弱，
3. 將 來 見 祢 榮 面， 靠 祢 救 贖 恩 典，
1 In love my soul would bow, My heart ful - fill its vow,
2 Some work of love be - gun, Some deed of kind - ness done,
3 And when Thy face I see, My ran - somed soul shall be,
1. 今 將 供 物 獻 上， 奉 獻 與 祢。
2. 領 人 進 入 天 國， 奉 獻 與 祢。
3. 直 到 永 永 遠 遠， 奉 獻 與 祢。 阿 門。
1 Some of - fering bring Thee now, Some - thing for Thee.
2 Some wan - derer sought and won, Some - thing for Thee.
3 Through all e - ter - ni - ty, Some - thing for Thee. A - men.

寶架清影
Beneath the Cross of Jesus

Now there stood by the cross of Jesus . . . .
— John 19:25

Elizabeth C. Clephane

ST. CHRISTOPHER
Frederick C. Maker

1. 在主寶架清影中，歡然立定脚跟，
2. 神聖莊嚴的十架，我常抬頭仰望，
3. 願在寶架清影中，事主愛人行道，
1 Be-neath the cross of Je-sus I glad-ly take my stand:
2 Up-on that cross of Je-sus My eyes at times can see
3 I take, O cross, thy shad-ow For my a-bid-ing place;
1. 好像盛暑遠行辛苦，投進磐石蔭影；
2. 雙眼如見寶血流下，為我捨身景象；
3. 我不尋求旭日光華，因有慈光引照；
1 The shad-ow of a might-y rock With-in a wea-ry land,
2 The ver-y dy-ing form of One Who suf-fered there for me;
3 I ask no oth-er sun-shine than The sun-shine of His face,
1. 又像曠野欣逢居處，長途喜見涼亭，
2. 熱淚滿眶寸心將裂，仔細反覆思量，
3. 世界虛榮無可貪圖，得失無關重要，
1 A home with-in the wil-der-ness, A rest up-on the way,
2 And from my smit-ten heart, with tears, Two won-ders I con-fess—
3 Con-tent to let the world go by, To know no gain or loss,
1. 到此得息肩頭重負，養力奔赴前程。
2. 思量我本不配蒙恩，思量主愛非常。
3. 但將罪惡看為羞辱，寶架看為榮耀。
1 From the burn-ing of the noon-tide heat And the bur-den of the day.
2 The won-ders of His glo-rious love And my un-wor-thi-ness.
3 My sin-ful self my on-ly shame, My glo-ry all the cross.

193

主替我捨身

Jesus Paid It All

Ye are bought with a price; be ye not servants of men.
— I Corinthians 7: 23
Elvina M. Hall
ALL TO CHRIST
John T. Grape
1. 我聽救主説道：“你的力量微小！
2. 我無嘉言善行，可藉此得救恩，
3. 将來身體得贖，榮耀站主面前，
1 I hear the Sav-ior say, “Thy strength in-deed is small!
2 For noth-ing good have I Where-by Thy grace to claim—
3 And when be-fore the throne I stand in Him com-plete,
1. 應當儆醒祈禱，因我作你中保。”
2. 唯主所流寶血，能洗一切罪痕。
3. 我口仍要頌揚—“主賜救恩完全”。
1 Child of weak-ness watch and pray, Find in me thine all in all.”
2 I will wash my gar-ments white. In the blood of Cal-vary's Lamb.
3 “Je-sus died my soul to save,” My lips shall still re-peat.
主替我捨身，罪債全還清；
Je-sus paid it all, All to Him I owe;
無數罪孽污穢心，主洗比雪白淨。
Sin had left a crim-son stain— He washed it white as snow.

哀哉！主流寶血為我

Alas! and Did My Savior Bleed

He was bruised for our iniquities. — Isaiah 53:5
MARTYRDOM
Isaac Watts
Hugh Wilson
1. 哀 哉！ 我 主 寶 血 流 出， 甘
2. 實 在 因 我 所 犯 的 罪， 使
3. 大 地 昏 暗 紅 日 消 失， 隱
4. 我 今 念 主 死 於 十 架， 心
5. 我 的 眼 淚 縱 然 流 盡， 不
1 A - las! and did my Sav - ior bleed And
2 Was it for sins that I have done He
3 Well might the sun in dark - ness hide And
4 Thus might I hide my blush - ing face While
5 But drops of grief can ne'er re - pay The
1. 心 替 我 受 苦！ 貴 重 身 體 為
2. 主 十 架 懸 掛， 無 限 慈 悲 無
3. 藏 一 切 榮 光， 正 當 基 督 救
4. 裡 無 限 羞 慚， 我 剛 硬 心 漸
5. 能 報 答 主 心， 願 將 身 心 完
1 did my sov - ereign die? Would He de - vote that
2 suf - fered on the tree? A - maz - ing pit - y!
3 shut his glo - ries in, When Christ, the great Re -
4 His dear cross ap - pears, Dis - solve my heart in
5 debt of love I owe: Here, Lord, I give my
1. 我 釘 死， 愛 我 罪 人 如 此！
2. 量 恩 惠！ 如 山 如 海 廣 大！
3. 主 耶 穌， 為 人 擔 罪 死 亡。
4. 被 改 變， 不 覺 淚 流 滿 面。
5. 全 奉 獻， 滿 足 祂 的 愛 情。 阿 門。
1 sa - cred Head For sin - ners such as I?
2 grace un - known! And love be - yond de - gree!
3 deem - er, died For man the crea - ture's sin.
4 thank - ful - ness, And melt mine eyes to tears.
5 self a - way— 'Tis all that I can do. A - men.

195

你在那裡？

Were You There?

American Folk Hymn
He is . . . a man of sorrows and acquainted with grief; and we hid as it were our faces from Him. — Isaiah 53:3
WERE YOU THERE
American Folk Melody
1. 主捨命十架時你在那裡？主捨命十架時你在那裡？
2. 當救主被釘時你在那裡？當救主被釘時你在那裡？啊
3. 主被葬墳墓時你在那裡？主被葬墳墓時你在那裡？O!
4. 當救主復活時你在那裡？當救主復活時你在那裡？
1 Were you there when they cru - ci - fied my Lord? Were you there when they cru - ci - fied my Lord?
2 Were you there when they nailed Him to the tree? Were you there when they nailed Him to the tree?
3 Were you there when they laid Him in the tomb? Were you there when they laid Him in the tomb?
4 Were you there when He rose up from the grave? Were you there when He rose up from the grave?
有時我一想到就戰抖，戰抖，戰抖。
Some-times it caus - es me to trem-ble, trem-ble, trem-ble.
1. 主捨命十架時你在那裡？
2. 當救主被釘時你在那裡？
3. 主被葬墳墓時你在那裡？
4. 當救主復活時你在那裡？
1 Were you there when they cru - ci - fied my Lord?
2 Were you there when they nailed Him to the tree?
3 Were you there when they laid Him in the tomb?
4 Were you there when He rose up from the grave?

196

城外青山

There Is a Green Hill Far Away

Wherefore . . . Jesus also suffered outside the gate . . .
– Hebrews 13:12

GREEN HILL
George C. Stebbins
Arranged by A. Royce Eckhardt

Cecil Frances Alexander

1. 離此遥遠有一座城，城外有一青山，
2. 誰能想像誰能描述，祂受痛苦何深！
3. 祂死為使我罪得赦，流血為贖我們，
4. 世間沒有這樣義人，能還我們罪債，

1 There is a green hill far a-way, Out-side a cit-y wall,
2 *We may not know, we can-not tell What pains He had to bear,*
3 He died that we might be for-given, He died to make us good,
4 *There was no oth-er good e-nough To pay the price of sin;*

1. 在那山上救主被釘，為救我們捨身。
2. 但我確信救主受苦，是為我這罪人。
3. 好叫我們脫離罪惡，得蒙祂的救恩。
4. 惟祂受死流血功成，能贖我們回來。

1 Where the dear Lord was cru-ci-fied, Who died to save us all.
2 *But we be-lieve it was for us He hung and suf-fered there.*
3 That we might go at last to heaven, Saved by His pre-cious blood.
4 *He on-ly could un-lock the gate Of heaven and let us in.*

救主這樣為你受害，恩愛何等深重，
O dear-ly, dear-ly has He loved, And we must love Him too,

我願信靠祂的大愛，盡心做祂聖工。
And trust in His re-deem-ing blood, And try His works to do.

197

千萬天使

Ten Thousand Angels

Being justified . . . through the redemption that is in Christ Jesus.
— Romans 3:24

Ray Overholt　　　　Ray Overholt

1. 救主在禱告的園裡，他們捆綁主的手，帶
2. 在救主尊貴的頭上，被戴上荊棘冠冕，戲
3. 祂向忿怒羣衆忍辱，祂並未乞憐呼喊，甘

1. They bound the hands of Je-sus in the gar-den where He prayed; They
2. *Up - on His pre-cious head they placed a crown of thorns; They*
3. To the howl-ing mob He yield-ed; He did not for mer-cy cry. The

1. 祂遊行備受唾罵；聖潔無罪的救主，
2. 笑祂說"看哪！這王；"被他們鞭打辱罵，
3. 願背負羞辱十架；當祂大聲說"成了，"

1. led Him thro' the streets in shame. They spat up-on the Sav-iour
2. *laughed and said, "Be-hold the king." They struck Him and they cursed Him*
3. Cross of shame He took a-lone. And when He cried, "It's fin-ished,"

1. 竟被他們吐唾沫，說祂有罪要釘祂十架。
2. 又被嘲笑祂的名，祂獨自忍受一切頂撞。
3. 祂就捨了祂生命，奇妙救贖計劃已完成。

1. so pure and free from sin; They said, "Cru-ci-fy Him; He's to blame."
2. *and mocked His ho-ly name. All a - lone He suf-fered ev-'ry thing.*
3. He gave him-self to die; Sal - va-tion's won-drous plan was done.

f
祂可求父 差千萬天 使，毀滅這世
He could have called ten thou-sand an - gels To de-stroy the
界， 將祂釋放； 祂可求父
world and set Him free. He could have called
差千萬天 使，祂竟願受死， 為你為我。
ten thou-sand an - gels, But He died a - lone for you and me.

我要歌唱慈愛和公平，耶和華阿，我要向你歌頌。

詩篇一百零一篇
1節

198

十字架
Near the Cross

I will open rivers in high places, and fountains . . .

– Isaiah 41:18

Fanny J. Crosby

NEAR THE CROSS
William H. Doane

1. 求 主 使 我 靠 十 架，在 彼 有 生 命 水；
2. 我 來 到 主 十 架 前，蒙 救 主 的 愛 憐；
3. 求 主 使 我 依 十 架，思 念 昔 日 情 景；
4. 儆 醒 等 候 十 架 前，盼 望 信 心 加 增；
1 Je - sus, keep me near the cross– There a pre - cious foun - tain,
2 At the cross I stood one day. Love and mer - cy found me;
3 Near the cross! O Lamb of God, Bring its scenes be - fore me;
4 Near the cross I'll watch and wait, Hop - ing, trust - ing ev - er,
1. 寶 血 由 十 架 流 下，白 白 賜 人 洗 罪。
2. 祂 賜 我 聖 靈 亮 光，照 亮 我 的 心 田。
3. 常 在 十 架 蔭 庇 下，緊 緊 跟 主 前 行。
4. 直 到 走 完 世 路 程，天 家 永 享 安 穩。
1 Free to all, a heal - ing stream, Flows from Cal - vary's moun - tain.
2 There the bright and morn - ing star Shed its beams a - round me.
3 Help me walk from day to day With its shad - ow o'er me.
4 'Til I reach the gold - en strand Just be-yond the riv - er.
十 字 架，十 字 架，永 是 我 的 榮 耀，
In the cross, in the cross, Be my glo - ry ev - er,
我 衆 罪 都 洗 清 潔，唯 靠 耶 穌 寶 血。阿 門。
'Til my rap-tured soul shall find Rest be-yond the riv - er. A-men.

顯明的基督
The Unveiled Christ

And Jesus . . . gave up the ghost.
And the veil of the temple was rent from the top to the bottom.
— Mark 15:37, 38

N. B. Herrell

UNVEILED CHRIST
N. B. Herrell

1 從前我榮美的基督，隱藏着人看不見；
2 祂現在正為你禱告，與父神一同在天；
3 地上萬民要讚美祂，天使伏在祂脚前；

1 Once our bless-ed Christ of beau-ty Was veiled off from hu-man view;
2 *Yes, He is with God, the Fa-ther, In-ter-ced-ing there for you;*
3 Ho-ly an-gels bow be-fore Him, Men of earth give prais-es due;

1 但祂曾經憂傷死亡，幔子已裂成兩片。
2 祂是神喜悅的愛子，祂使幔裂成兩片。
3 因祂是大能的主宰，祂使幔裂成兩片。

1 But through suf-fering, death, and sor-row He has rent the veil in two.
2 *For He is the Well-be-lov-ed Since He rent the veil in two.*
3 For He is the might-y Con-queror Since He rent the veil in two.

看，常經憂患的人子！看，祂已清楚顯現！
O be-hold the Man of Sor-rows! O be-hold Him in plain view!

看！祂是大能的主宰，幔子已裂成兩片。
Lo! He is the might-y Con-queror Since He rent the veil in two;

看！祂是大能的主宰，幔子已裂成兩片。
Lo! He is the might-y Con-queror Since He rent the veil in two.

200

哈利路亞歸十架

Hallelujah for The Cross

God hath fulfilled the same unto us . . . in that He hath raised up Jesus again. — Acts 13: 33

Horatius Bonar, Arr.
James McGranahan
1. 十 架 永 遠 堅 定，哈 利 路 亞！哈利 路 亞！得 勝 魔
2. 十 架 歷 久 常 存，哈 利 路 亞！哈利 路 亞！頌 讚 十
1. The cross it stand-eth fast, Hel-le-lu-jah, hal-le-lu-jah! De fy-ing
2. It , is the old cross still, Hal-le-lu-jah, hal-le-lu-jah! Its tri-umph
1. 鬼 權 柄，哈 利 路 亞！哈 利 路 亞！陰 府 權 勢 雖 勁，世
2. 架 得 勝，哈 利 路 亞！哈 利 路 亞！天 父 賜 下 救 恩，差
1. ev - 'ry blast, Hal-le-lu-jah, hal-le-lu-jah! The winds of hell have blown, The
2. let us tell, Hal-le-lu-jah, hal-le-lu-jah! The grace of God here shone Thro'
1. 界 攻 擊 不 停，十 架 仍 然 堅 定，哈 利 路 亞 歸 十 架！
2. 遣 愛 子 降 生，十 字 架 上 捨 身，哈 利 路 亞 歸 十 架！
1. world its hate hath shown, Yet it is not o-ver thrown, Hal-le-lu-jah for the cross!
2. Christ the bless-ed Son, Who did for sin a - tone, Hal-le-lu-jah for the cross!
哈 利 路 亞！哈 利 路 亞！哈 利 路 亞 歸 十 架！
Hal - le - lu - jah, hal - le - lu - jah, hal-le-lu-jah for the cross!

哈利 路亞！哈利 路亞！十字寶架永得 勝。
Hal - le - lu - jah, hal - le - lu - jah, It shall nev - er suf-fer loss

201

哈利路亞(2)

Hallelujah

Unknown

Unison

哈利路，哈利路，哈利路，哈利路亞；讚 美 上 主！哈利
Hal-le-lu, hal-le-lu, hal-le-lu, hal-le-lu-jah; Praise ye the Lord! Hal-le-

路，哈利路，哈利路，哈利路亞；讚美上主！ 讚 美 上 主！哈利路亞；
lu, hal-le-lu, hal-le-lu, hal-le-lu-jah; Praise ye the Lord! Praise ye the Lord! Hal-le-lu-jah;

讚 美 上 主，哈利路亞， 讚 美 上 主，哈利 路亞， 讚 美 上 主！
Praise ye the Lord, Hal-le-lu-jah, Praise ye the Lord, Hal-le-lu-jah, Praise ye the Lord!

202

惟靠主耶穌的寶血

Nothing but the Blood

Christ died for us, much more then,
being now justified by His blood, we shall be saved.
— Romans 5:8, 9

Robert Lowry

PLAINFIELD
Robert Lowry

1. 我罪怎能得洗淨？惟靠主耶穌的寶血；
2. 我的刑罰怎得除？惟靠主耶穌的寶血；
3. 我無功勞補罪過－惟靠主耶穌的寶血；
4. 靠主寶血享平安－惟靠主耶穌的寶血；
1 What can wash a - way my sin? Noth-ing but the blood of Je - sus;
2 For my par- don this I see– Noth-ing but the blood of Je - sus;
3 Noth-ing can for sin a - tone– Noth-ing but the blood of Je - sus;
4 This is all my hope and peace– Noth-ing but the blood of Je - sus;
1. 我心怎能得完全？惟靠主耶穌的寶血。
2. 得救是否靠得住？惟靠主耶穌的寶血。
3. 一生言語都有錯－惟靠主耶穌的寶血。
4. 洗去困苦並愁煩－惟靠主耶穌的寶血。
1 What can make me whole a - gain? Noth-ing but the blood of Je - sus.
2 For my cleans-ing this my plea– Noth-ing but the blood of Je - sus.
3 Naught of good that I have done– Noth-ing but the blood of Je - sus.
4 This is all my right- eous-ness– Noth-ing but the blood of Je - sus.
主寶血當頌揚，洗我罪免死亡；
O! pre - cious is the flow That makes me white as snow;
此、活泉世無雙，惟有主耶穌的寶血。
No oth - er fount I know, Noth-ing but the blood of Je - sus.

耶穌的寶血和公義

Jesus, Thy Blood and Righteousness

. . . our Lord Jesus Christ, by whom we have now received the atonement.

— Romans 5:11

Nicolaus L. von Zinzendorf
Tr. by John Wesley

GERMANY
William Gardiner's *Sacred Melodies*

1. 耶 穌 的 寶 血 和 公 義 ， 作 我 榮
2. 審 判 之 日 我 無 所 懼 ， 誰 能 指
3. 主 祢 寶 血 我 深 相 信 ， 在 祢 施
4. 主 我 相 信 罪 人 雖 多 ， 如 海 邊
1 Je - sus, Thy blood and right - eous - ness My beau - ty
2 Bold shall I stand in that great day, For who aught
3 Lord, I be - lieve Thy pre - cious blood, Which, at the
4 Lord, I be - lieve were sin - ners more Than sands up -
1. 美 聖 潔 之 衣 ； 如 此 裝 飾 有 何 能
2. 控 我 為 不 義 ？ 寶 血 洗 淨 我 的 罪
3. 恩 寶 座 之 前 ， 祢 為 罪 人 長 遠 代
4. 散 沙 之 深 厚 ， 但 祢 已 付 救 贖 代
1 are, my glo - rious dress; 'Midst flam - ing worlds, in these ar -
2 to my charge shall lay? Ful - ly ab - solved through these I
3 mer - cy seat of God, For - ev - er doth for sin - ners
4 on the o - cean shore, Thou hast for all a ran - som
1. 比 ， 昂 首 前 行 我 心 歡 喜 。
2. 情 ， 使 我 脫 離 一 切 罪 刑 。
3. 求 ， 靠 祢 寶 血 我 靈 得 救 。
4. 價 ， 完 備 救 恩 功 效 無 涯 。 阿 們 。
1 rayed, With joy shall I lift up my head.
2 am, From sin and fear, from guilt and shame.
3 plead, For me, e'en for my soul was shed.
4 paid, For all a full a - tone - ment made. A - men.

204

主恩更多

His Grace Aboundeth More

Give and it shall be given unto you; good measure, . . . and running over . . .

— Luke 6:38

Kate Ulmer

William J. Kirkpatrick

1. 何等希奇一位救主，我所尋着乃主耶穌，
2. 主尋我時我是罪人，毫無善行在我內心，
3. 我靠自己毫無功勞，惟獨救主為我義袍，
4. 救主尊名我要讚美，我靈情願歌頌歡喜，
1. Oh, what a won-der-ful Sav-iour In Je-sus, my Lord, I have found!
2. When a poor sin-ner He found me, No good-ness to of-fer had I;
3. Nothing of mer-it pos-sess-ing, All help-less be-fore Him I lay;
4. How can I keep from re-joic-ing? I'll sing of the joy in my soul.

1. 雖然我曾犯罪受苦，主賜恩典真真無數。
2. 我犯誡命日久月恒，應該受着地獄死刑。
3. 所流寶血出於羊羔，能使罪跡不剩絲毫。
4. 讚美主愛極大無比，世世代代永無改變。
1. Tho' I had sins without num-ber, His grace un-to me did a-bound.
2. Of-ten His law I had brok-en, And mer-it-ed naught but to die.
3. But in the pre-cious blood flow-ing He wash'd all my sin-stains a-way.
4. Prais-ing the love of my Sav-iour, While years of e-ter-ni-ty roll.

主恩實在更多，主恩實在更多，
His grace a-bound-eth more. His grace a-bound-eth more.
我罪雖多主血塗抹，主恩實在更多。
Tho' sin a-bound-ed in my heart, His grace a-bound-eth more.

耶穌聖名

The Name of Jesus

. . . And of His kingdom there shall be no end.
— Luke 1:33

W. C. Martin — Edmund S. Lorenz

1. 耶 穌 聖 名 何 等 甘 甜，美 似 音 樂 我 愛 誦 念，
2. 耶 穌 聖 名 我 最 心 愛，祂 知 我 苦 分 擔 我 災，
3. 耶 穌 聖 名 我 最 愛 聽，美 似 音 樂 暢 快 我 心，
4. 千 言 萬 語 難 以 說 明，我 心 如 何 愛 主 聖 名，

1. The name of Je - sus is so sweet, I love its mu- sic to re-peat;
2. *I love the name of Him whose heart Knows all my griefs and bears a part;*
3. That name I fond-ly love to hear, It nev- er fails my heart to cheer;
4. *No word of man can ev- er tell How sweet the name I love so well;*

1. 能 使 我 心 快 樂 無 邊，耶 穌 聖 名 真 甘 甜。
2. 一 切 憂 驚 為 我 挪 開，耶 穌 聖 名 我 最 愛。
3. 止 我 眼 淚 慰 我 苦 情，我 要 高 舉 主 聖 名。
4. 願 主 聖 名 永 受 頌 揚，我 要 讚 美 主 聖 名。

1. It makes my joys full and com-plete, The precious name of Je - sus!
2. *Who bids all anx-ious fears de-part— I love the name of Je - sus!*
3. Its mu-sic dries the fall-ing tear— Ex-alt the name of Je - sus!
4. *O let its prais-es ev - er swell, O praise the name of Je - sus!*

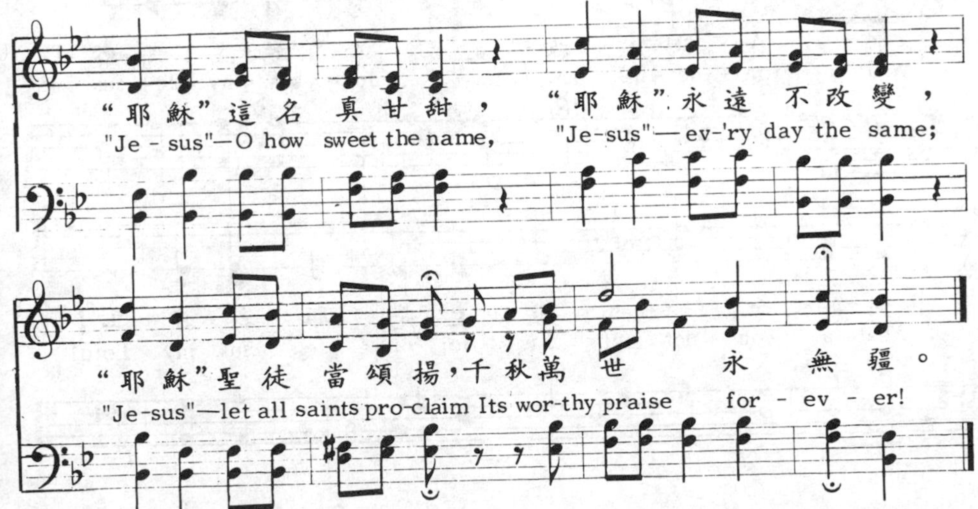
"耶 穌" 這 名 真 甘 甜，"耶 穌" 永 遠 不 改 變，
"Je - sus"—O how sweet the name, "Je-sus"—ev-'ry day the same;
"耶 穌" 聖 徒 當 頌 揚，千 秋 萬 世 永 無 疆。
"Je-sus"—let all saints pro-claim Its wor-thy praise for - ev - er!

206

何等奇妙的救主

What a Wonderful Savior

. . . by the righteousness of One the free Gift came upon all men unto justification of life.
— Romans 5:18

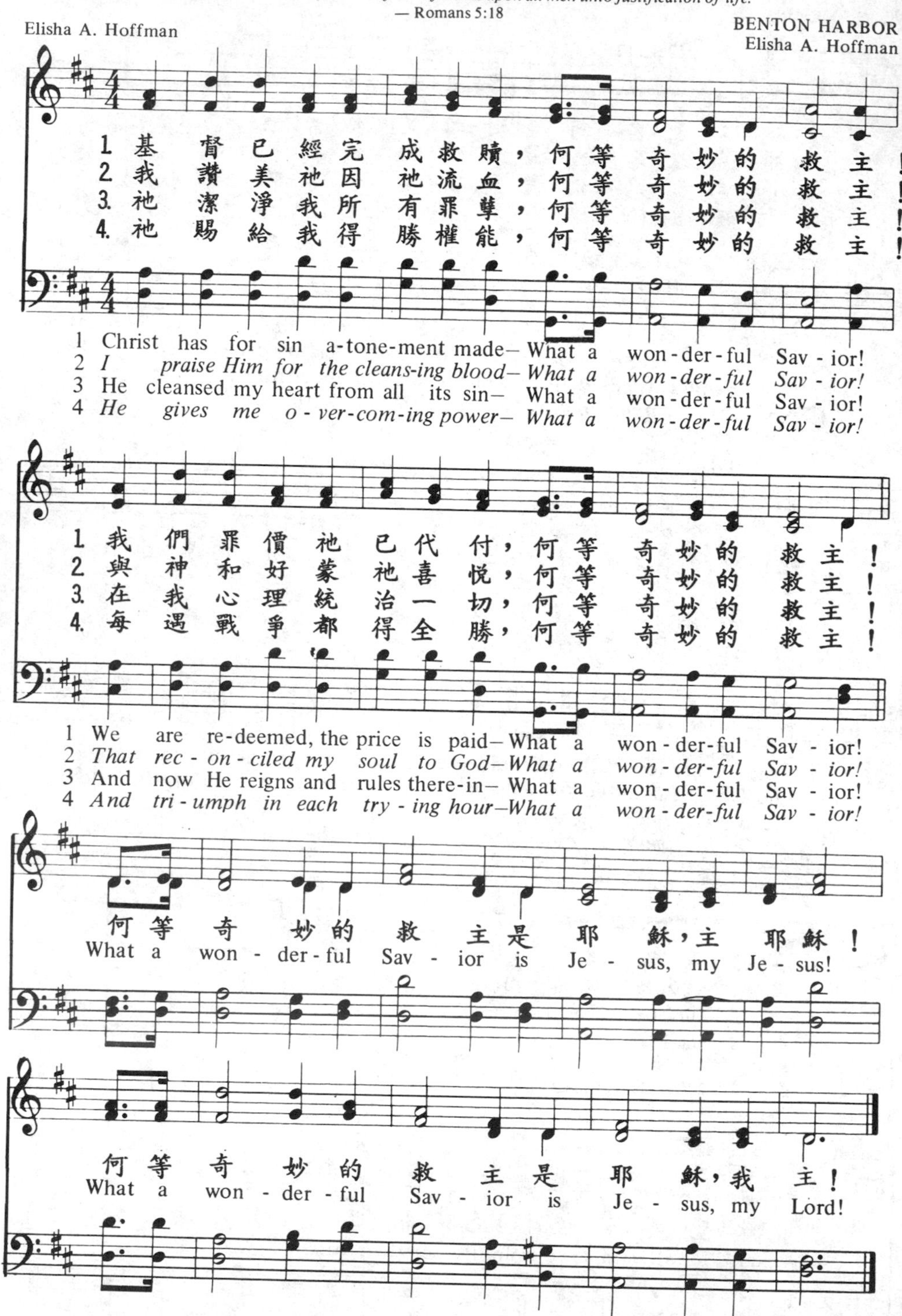

Elisha A. Hoffman
BENTON HARBOR
Elisha A. Hoffman
1. 基督已經完成救贖，何等奇妙的救主！
2. 我讚美祂因祂流血，何等奇妙的救主！
3. 祂潔淨我所有罪孽，何等奇妙的救主！
4. 祂賜給我得勝權能，何等奇妙的救主！
1 Christ has for sin a-tone-ment made– What a won-der-ful Sav - ior!
2 I praise Him for the cleans-ing blood– What a won-der-ful Sav - ior!
3 He cleansed my heart from all its sin– What a won-der-ful Sav - ior!
4 He gives me o - ver-com-ing power– What a won-der-ful Sav - ior!
1. 我們罪價祂已代付，何等奇妙的救主！
2. 與神和好蒙祂喜悅，何等奇妙的救主！
3. 在我心理統治一切，何等奇妙的救主！
4. 每遇戰爭都得全勝，何等奇妙的救主！
1 We are re-deemed, the price is paid– What a won-der-ful Sav - ior!
2 That rec - on - ciled my soul to God– What a won-der-ful Sav - ior!
3 And now He reigns and rules there-in– What a won-der-ful Sav - ior!
4 And tri - umph in each try - ing hour–What a won-der-ful Sav - ior!
何等奇妙的救主是耶穌，主耶穌！
What a won - der - ful Sav - ior is Je - sus, my Je - sus!
何等奇妙的救主是耶穌，我主！
What a won - der - ful Sav - ior is Je - sus, my Lord!

207

基督荣耀满天庭

Christ Whose Glory Fills the Skies

The sun of righteousness shall rise with healing in His wings. — Malachi 4:2

LUX PRIMA
Charles Gounod

Charles Wesley

1. 基督　荣耀　满天庭，　基督　惟一　真光明；
2. 未得　我主　為伴侶，　清晨　陰晦　少歡欣；
3. 願主　眷顧　我心靈，　照透　罪惡　散陰翳；

1 Christ, whose glo-ry fills the skies, Christ, the true, the on-ly Light,
2 *Dark and cheer-less is the morn Un-ac-com-pa-nied by Thee;*
3 Vis-it, then, this soul of mine; Pierce the gloom of sin and grief;

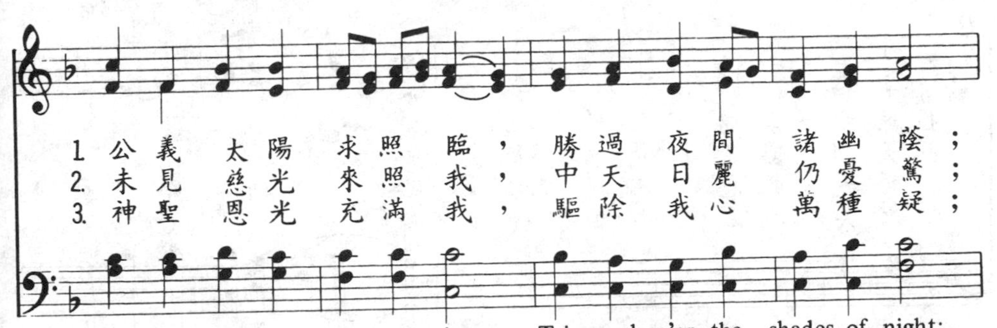

1. 公義　太陽　求照臨，　勝過　夜間　諸幽陰；
2. 未見　慈光　來照我，　中天　日麗　仍憂驚；
3. 神聖　恩光　充滿我，　驅除　我心　萬種疑；

1 Sun of Right-eous-ness, a-rise, Tri-umph o'er the shades of night;
2 *Joy-less is the day's re-turn Till Thy mer-cy's beams I see;*
3 Fill me, Ra-dian-cy Di-vine; Scat-ter all my un-be-lief;

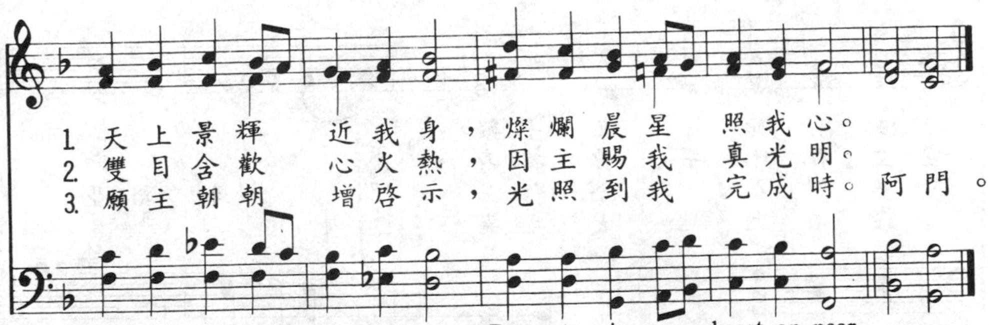

1. 天上　景輝　近我身，燦爛　晨星　照我心。
2. 雙目　含歡　心火熱，因主　賜我　真光明。
3. 願主　朝朝　增啓示，光照　到我　完成時。阿門。

1 Day-spring from on high, be near; Day-star, in my heart ap-pear.
2 *Till they in-ward light im-part, Cheer my eyes and warm my heart.*
3 More and more Thy-self dis-play, Shin-ing to the per-fect day. A-men.

208

基督耶穌今復活

Jesus Christ Is Risen Today

Praise ye the Lord, Sing unto the Lord a new song.
— Psalm 149:1

Latin: 14th Century
English translation, *New Version*
Charles Wesley, stanza 4

LLANFAIR
Robert Williams
Harmonized by John Roberts

1. 基督耶穌今復活，
2. 齊來稱頌讚美主，
3. 因主已為我受苦，
4. 齊來歌頌同敬拜，
哈利路亞！
1 Je - sus Christ is risen to - day,
2 Hymns of praise then let us sing,
3 But the pains which He en - dured,
4 Sing we to our God a - bove,
Al - le - lu - ia!
1. 死亡黑暗已勝過，
2. 天國君王是基督，
3. 賜我救恩永遠福，
4. 讚美我主永恒愛，
哈利路亞！
1 Our tri - um - phant ho - ly day,
2 Un - to Christ, our heaven - ly King,
3 Our sal - va - tion have pro - cured;
4 Praise e - ter - nal as His love;
Al - le - lu - ia!
1. 主曾捨身在十架，
2. 主在十架曾捨身，
3. 基督在天今作王，
4. 讚美天地大主宰，
哈利路亞！
1 Who did once up - on the cross,
2 Who en - dured the cross and grave,
3 Now a - bove the sky He's King,
4 Praise Him, all ye heaven - ly host,
Al - le - lu - ia!

1. 為救我罪恩何大。
2. 為要拯救世上人。
3. 天使永遠高聲唱。
4. 父,子,聖靈永同在。
哈利路亞!阿門。
1 Suf - fer to re - deem our loss.
2 *Sin - ners to re - deem and save.*
3 Where the an-gels ev - er sing.
4 *Fa - ther, Son and Ho - ly Ghost.*
Al - le - lu - ia!
A-men.

萬民哪,你們當稱頌我們的神,使人得讚美祂的聲音。

詩篇六十六篇
8節

209

祂是神
He Is Lord

And that every tongue should confess that Jesus Christ is Lord. — Philippians 2:11

HE IS LORD
Traditional

Based on Philippians 2:11

祂是神,祂是神!基督已從死裡復活祂是神!
He is Lord, He is Lord! He is ris-en from the dead and He is Lord!
萬膝當跪拜,萬口當承認,基督耶穌是神。
Ev-ery knee shall bow, ev-ery tongue con - fess That Je - sus Christ is Lord.

主復活
Christ Arose

Thou hast led captivity captive . . .

Robert Lowry
CHRIST AROSE
Robert Lowry
1. 主 在墳 墓安睡，耶 穌，我 救 主！等 待 復
2. 兵 丁守 墓無用，耶 穌，我 救 主！封 石 也
3. 死 權不 能困主，耶 穌，我 救 主！因 已 被
1 Low in the grave He lay, Je - sus, my Sav - ior! Wait - ing the
2 Vain - ly they watched His bed, Je - sus, my Sav - ior! Vain - ly they
3 Death could not keep his prey, Je - sus, my Sav - ior! He tore the
1. 活日來，耶 穌，我 主！
2. 歸虛空，耶 穌，我 主！
3. 主得勝，耶 穌，我 主！
主從墳墓裡復活，
Up from the grave He a - rose,
主復活，
He a-rose,
1 com-ing day, Je - sus, my Lord!
2 sealed the dead, Je - sus, my Lord!
3 bars a - way, Je - sus, my Lord!
得勝一切仇敵與罪惡；
With a might-y tri-umph o'er His foes;
主復活；
He a-rose;
主耶穌復活，得勝黑
He a - rose a vic-tor from the
暗君王，從此永遠與聖徒一同做王；主復
dark do-main, And He lives for - ev - er with His saints to reign; He a -

活！ 主復活！ 哈利 路亞！主 復 活！
rose! He a - rose! Hal - le - lu - jah! Christ a - rose!
主復活！ 主復活！
He a - rose! He a - rose!

211

萬民都要拍掌
Clap Your Hands

Let the sea roar, let the floods clap their hands,
let the hills be joyful together. — Psalm 98:7,8

Psalm 47:1

Jimmy Owens

Unison

萬民哪！都要拍掌，向神用誇勝的聲音呼喊，
Clap your hands all you peo - ple, Shout un-to God with a voice of tri-umph!

萬民哪！都要拍掌，向神呼喊高聲讚美祂。
Clap your hands! all you peo - ple, Shout un-to God with a voice of praise!

和散哪！和散哪！向神用誇勝的聲音呼喊，
Ho - san - na! Ho - san - na! Shout un-to God with a voice of tri - umph!

讚美，讚美，向神呼喊高聲讚美祂
Praise Him! Praise Him! Shout un-to God with a voice of praise!

212 基督我主今復活

Christ the Lord Is Risen Today

Ye seek Jesus of Nazareth who was crucified; He is risen . . .

— Mark 16:6

Charles Wesley

EASTER HYMN
"Lyra Davidica"

1. 基督我主今復活，
2. 榮耀君王今復活，
3. "愛"之救贖已完成，
4. 高唱讚美天上神，
哈利路亞！
1 Christ the Lord is risen to-day,
2 Lives a-gain our glo-rious King,
3 Love's re-deem-ing work is done,
4 Sing we to our God a-bove,
Al - le - lu - ia!
1. 天人一致同歡欣：
2. 祂曾捨命為救我，
3. 與敵爭戰主得勝，
4. 頌祂慈愛到永恒；
哈利路亞！
1 Sons of men and an-gels say:
2 Where, O death, is now thy sting?
3 Fought the fight, the bat-tle won,
4 Praise e-ter-nal as His love;
Al - le - lu - ia!
1. 高聲歌頌讚主名，
2. 死亡毒鈎今何在？
3. 墓石守兵均徒然，
4. 讚美至高天上君，
哈利路亞！
1 Raise your joys and tri-umphs high,
2 Dy-ing once, He all doth save,
3 Death in vain for-bids Him rise,
4 Praise Him, all ye heaven-ly host,
Al - le - lu - ia!

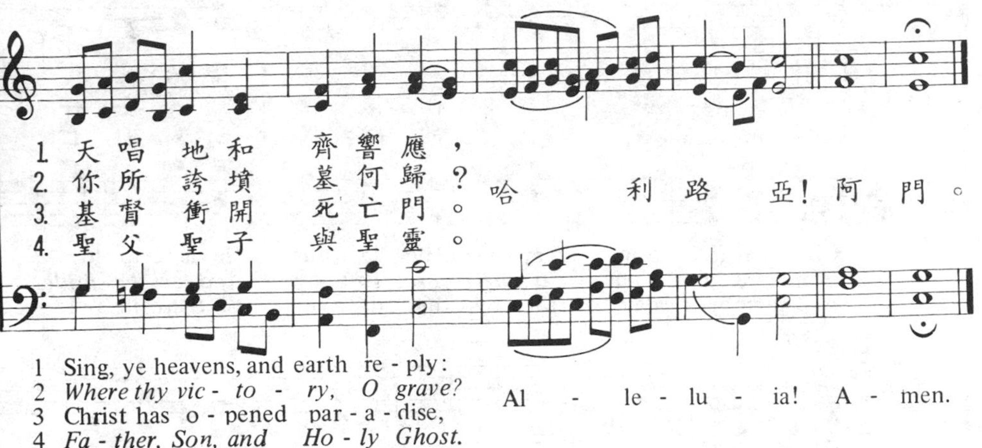

1. 天唱地和齊響應，
2. 你所誇墳墓何歸？
3. 基督衝開死亡門。
4. 聖父聖子與聖靈。
哈利路亞！阿門。
1 Sing, ye heavens, and earth re - ply:
2 Where thy vic - to - ry, O grave?
3 Christ has o - pened par - a - dise,
4 Fa - ther, Son, and Ho - ly Ghost.
Al - le - lu - ia! A - men.

*Fourth verse to be sung more broadly, and in unison.

212-1 God Is Light

Minister: God is light, and in Him there is no darkness.

PEOPLE: GREAT IS THE LORD, AND GREATLY TO BE PRAISED.

Minister: God is love, and in Him we can all be fulfilled.

PEOPLE: GREAT IS THE LORD, AND GREATLY TO BE PRAISED.

Minister: God is truth, and in His Son we see something of what He is like and something of what we can become.

PEOPLE: GREAT IS THE LORD, AND GREATLY TO BE PRAISED.

Minister: God is holy, and through His generosity we can please Him with a borrowed goodness.

PEOPLE: GREAT IS THE LORD, AND GREATLY TO BE PRAISED.

Minister: Here is the wonder, that we are recipients of grace, and grace is God giving us for free that which none of us can afford.

PEOPLE: GREAT IS THE LORD, AND GREATLY TO BE PRAISED.

–Bryan Jeffery Leech
based on I John 1:5-7

213

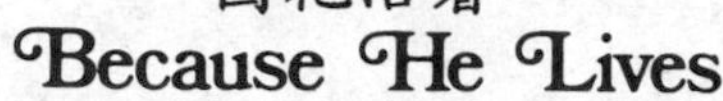

因祂活着
Because He Lives

Gloria Gaither
William J. Gaither

Because I live, ye shall live also. — John 14:19

RESURRECTION
William J. Gaither

1. 神子耶穌，降生到世界，醫治拯救
2. 新生嬰孩，被抱在懷裡，何等安祥
3. 當我走完，人生的路程，面對死亡
1 God sent His Son, they called Him Je - sus, He came to love,
2 How sweet to hold a new-born ba - by, And feel the pride,
3 And then one day I'll cross the riv - er, I'll fight life's fi -

1. 世上罪人；為贖我罪主釘死
2. 令你欣喜；但你確信這幼小
3. 痛苦爭戰；救主為我戰勝了
1 heal, and for - give; He lived and died to buy my
2 and joy He gives; But great - er still the calm as -
3 nal war with pain; And then as death gives way to

1. 十架，空的墳墓却證明救主仍活着。
2. 生命，却能面對着明天因救主活着。
3. 死權，在榮光中我見救主祂是活着。
1 par-don, An emp - ty grave is there to prove my Sav - ior lives.
2 sur-ance, This child can face un - cer-tain days be-cause He lives.
3 vic-tory, I'll see the lights of glo - ry and I'll know He lives.

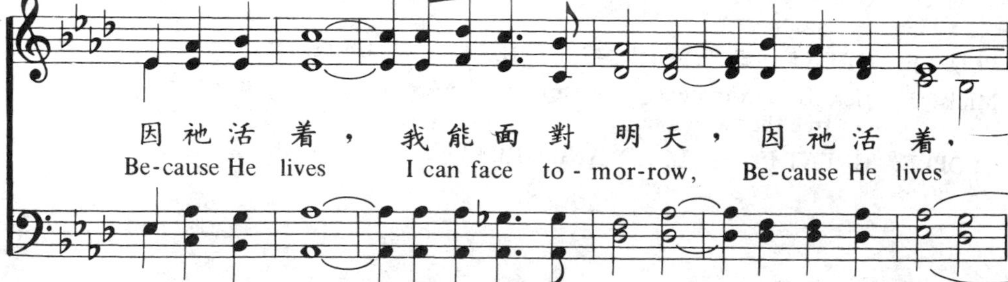

因祂活着，我能面對明天，因祂活着，
Be-cause He lives I can face to - mor-row, Be-cause He lives

不再懼怕；我深知道　祂掌握
all fear is gone; Be-cause I know He holds the
明天，生命充滿了希望，只因祂活着。
fu-ture. And life is worth the liv-ing just be-cause He lives.

我當日所領受又傳給你們的，第一、就是基督照聖經所說，為我們的罪死了，而且埋葬了，又照聖經所說，第三天復活了。若基督沒有復活，我們所傳的便是枉然，你們所信的也是枉然。

哥林多前書十五章
3 — 4
14，

主活着

He Lives

Go quickly and tell . . . His disciples that He is risen from the dead.
— Matthew 28:7

Alfred H. Ackley

ACKLEY
Alfred H. Ackley

1. 我 奉 一 位 復 活 主，他 今 在 世 活 着，
2. 在 我 所 處 環 境 中，主 愛 常 在 我 旁，
3. 衆 聖 徒 歡 欣 喜 樂，都 當 揚 聲 歌 唱，
1 I serve a ris - en Sav - ior, He's in the world to - day;
2 *In all the world a - round me I see His lov - ing care,*
3 Re - joice, re - joice, O Chris - tian, lift up your voice and sing

1. 我 知 道 他 確 活 着，不 管 人 怎 麼 説；
2. 雖 然 有 時 心 煩 惱，但 我 決 不 失 望；
3. 當 歌 唱 哈 利 路 亞，永 歸 基 督 君 王！
1 I know that He is liv - ing, what - ev - er men may say;
2 *And though my heart grows wea - ry I nev - er will de - spair;*
3 E - ter - nal hal - le - lu - jahs to Je - sus Christ the King!

1. 我 見 他 手 施 憐 憫，我 聞 他 安 慰 聲，
2. 我 知 救 主 引 領 我，衝 破 狂 風 怒 潮，
3. 祂 是 尋 者 的 盼 望，又 是 求 者 力 量，
1 I see His hand of mer - cy, I hear His voice of cheer,
2 *I know that He is lead - ing through all the storm - y blast,*
3 The Hope of all who seek Him, the Help of all who find,

1. 每 次 當我 需 求 祂， 總 必 答 應。
2. 一 日 我主 必 再來， 大 顯 榮 耀。
3. 無 一 人像 他 可愛， 仁 慈 善 良。
1 And just the time I need Him He's al - ways near.
2 The day of His ap - pear - ing will come at last.
3 None oth - er is so lov - ing, so good and kind.
基 督， 耶 穌， 今 天 仍然 活 着！
He lives, 基 督，He lives, 耶 穌，Christ Je - sus lives to - day!
He lives, He lives,
祂 與 我 談，祂 伴 我 走，生 命 窄 路 同 過。
He walks with me and talks with me a - long life's nar - row way.
我 要 傳 揚， 救 恩 臨 到 萬 民！
He lives, 我 要 He lives, 傳 揚， sal - va - tion to im - part!
He lives, He lives,
你 問 我 怎 知 主 活 着？ 因 主 活 在 我 心。
You ask me how I know He lives? He lives with - in my heart.

215

祂是我靈的救主
He's the Savior of My Soul

. . . My soul shall be joyful in my God . . .

— Isaiah 61:10

Adapted

SAVIOR OF MY SOUL
Spanish Melody

祂是我靈的救主，主耶穌，主耶穌，祂是我靈的救主，祂是我靈的救主。耶穌，耶穌，耶穌，耶穌。祂是我靈的救主，祂是我靈的救主。
He's the Savior of my soul, My Jesus, My Jesus, He's the Savior of my soul, He's the Savior of my soul. Jesus, Jesus, Jesus, Jesus. He's the Savior of my soul, He's the Savior of my soul.

救主降臨

Lo! He Comes with Clouds Descending

Charles Wesley
Martin Madan
Based on John Cennick
Jeff Redd, alt.

This same Jesus, . . . shall come in like manner as ye have seen Him go into Heaven.
— Acts 1:11

REGENT SQUARE
Henry T. Smart

1. 仰看救主昔曾捨命，今自天乘雲降臨；
2. 千萬百姓舉目瞻仰，救主赫赫大威嚴；
3. 長年所望身靈得贖，浩大恩典今實現；
4. 誠心所願向主敬拜，神有威信到永遠；

1 Lo, He comes with clouds de-scend-ing, Once for fa-vored sin-ners slain;
2 *Ev - ery eye shall now be-hold Him, Robed in awe-some maj - es - ty;*
3 Now re-demp-tion, long ex-pect-ed, See in sol-emn pomp ap-pear:
4 *Yes, A-men! let all a-dore Thee, High on the e - ter-nal throne;*

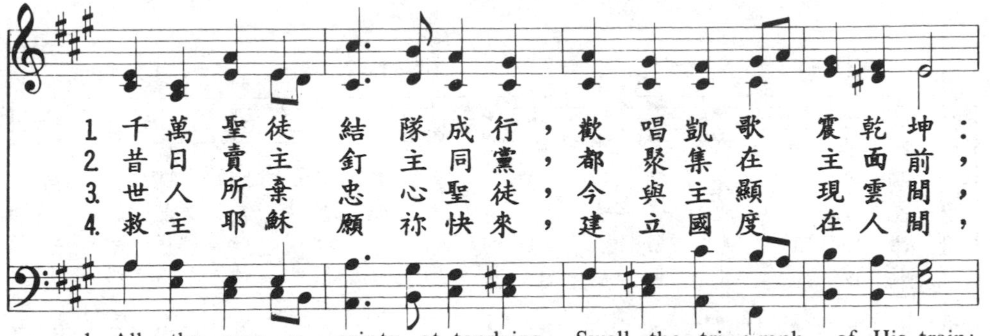
1. 千萬聖徒結隊成行，歡唱凱歌震乾坤：
2. 昔日賣主釘主同黨，都聚集在主面前，
3. 世人所棄忠心聖徒，今與主顯現雲間，
4. 救主耶穌願祢快來，建立國度在人間，

1 All the man - y saints at-tend-ing Swell the tri - umph of His train:
2 *Those who once de - nied and killed Him, Pierced and nailed Him to the tree,*
3 All His saints, by man re-ject - ed, Now shall meet Him in the air:
4 *Sav - ior, take the power and glo - ry, Claim the king - dom for Your own:*

1. 哈利路亞！哈利路亞！基督君王今降臨。
2. 悲哀痛哭，悲哀痛哭，今見真彌賽亞面。
3. 哈利路亞！哈利路亞！榮耀日見主顯現。
4. 哈利路亞！哈利路亞！惟主基督掌王權！阿門。

1 Al - le - lu - ia! Al - le - lu - ia! God ap-pears on earth to reign.
2 *Deep-ly wail-ing, deep-ly wail-ing, Shall the true Mes - si - ah see.*
3 Al - le - lu - ia! Al - le - lu - ia! See the day of God ap-pear.
4 *Al - le - lu - ia! Al - le - lu - ia! Christ shall reign and Christ a - lone!* A-men.

217

基督再來

Christ Returneth!

. . . be ye also ready; for in such an hour as ye think not the Son of man cometh.

— Matthew 24:44

H. L. Turner

CHRIST RETURNETH
James McGranahan

1. 或在黎明時，正當朝陽初昇起，當
2. 或在正午時，或在日暮黃昏時，或
3. 歌聲由天降，高聲歡唱和散那，榮
4. 何等的喜樂，若活着就被主接，無
1 It may be at morn, when the day is a wak-ing, When
2 It may be at mid-day, it may be at twi-light, It
3 While hosts cry "Ho-san-na," from heav-en de-scend-ing, With
4 O joy! O de-light! Should we go with-out dy-ing, No

1. 明亮晨光，趨散黑暗陰影時，耶穌要再
2. 在半夜裡，當一切最幽暗時，忽然有大
3. 耀中的聖徒與天使也參加，慈祥與光
4. 疾病憂傷，也無哀哭與胆怯，被提到雲
1 sun-light through dark-ness and shad-ow is break-ing, That Je-sus will
2 may be, per-chance, that the black-ness of mid-night Will burst in-to
3 glo-ri-fied saints and the an-gels at-tend-ing, With grace on His
4 sick-ness, no sad-ness, no dread and no cry-ing, Caught up through the

1. 來，在極大的榮耀中，迎接世上屬祂子民。
2. 光，主降臨在榮耀中，主來迎接屬祂子民。
3. 輝，充滿主在榮耀中，主要迎接屬祂子民。
4. 裡，與主同進榮耀中，主來迎接屬祂子民。
1 come in the full-ness of glo-ry, To re-ceive from the world His own.
2 light in the blaze of His glo-ry, When Je-sus re-ceives His own.
3 brow, like a ha-lo of glo-ry, Will Je-sus re-ceive His own.
4 clouds with our Lord in-to glo-ry, When Je-sus re-ceives His own.

哦，主 耶穌，是 何 時 候 能 高 唱 歡 樂 歌，基 督
O, Lord Je-sus, how long, how long 'Til we shout the glad song Christ re-
再 來！哈 利 路 亞！哈 利 路 亞！阿 門，哈 利 路 亞！阿 門。
turn-eth! Hal-le - lu-jah! hal-le - lu-jah! A-men, Hal-le - lu-jah! A-men.

弟兄們，論到時候日期，……你們自己明明曉得主的日子來到，好像夜間的賊一樣。

我們不要睡覺，像別人一樣，總要儆醒謹守

帖撒羅尼迦前書五章
1、2、6

Now, brothers, about times and dates we do not need to write to you, for you know very well that the day of the Lord will come like a thief in the night.

So then, let us not be like others, who are asleep, but let us be alert and self-controlled.

— I Thessalonians 5:1, 6. NIV

218

主耶穌必再來

Jesus Is Coming Again

Watch, therefore, for ye know neither the day nor the hour. . . . — Matthew 25:13

John W. Peterson

COMING AGAIN
John W. Peterson

1. 傳揚這奇異信息，歌唱這榮耀詩歌，聖經有奇妙應許：主耶穌必要再來！
2. 叢林和花朵發聲，山嶺和田野響應，天上和全地宣揚：主耶穌必要再來！
3. 那日要站在主前，試煉與苦難已過，將冠冕獻主腳前：主耶穌必要再來！
1 Marvelous message we bring, Glorious carol we sing, Wonderful word of the King: Jesus is coming again!
2 *Forest and flower exclaim, Mountain and meadow the same, All earth and heaven proclaim: Jesus is coming again!*
3 Standing before Him at last, Trial and trouble all past, Crowns at His feet we will cast: Jesus is coming again!
主必再來，主必再來；或在早晨，或正午，或在晚上或在瞬間！
Coming again, coming again; May-be morning, may-be noon, may-be evening and may-be soon!

主 必 再 來， 主 必 再 來； 那 日 将
Com - ing a - gain, com - ing a - gain; O, what a
是何等 奇 妙 光 彩， 主 耶 穌 必 要 再 來！
won - der - ful day it will be— Je - sus is com - ing a - gain!

金色的黎明

219

Some Golden Daybreak

Ye shall see the Son of man . . . coming in the clouds of Heaven
— Mark 14:62

Carl Blackmore

DAYBREAK
Carl Blackmore

金 色 的 黎 明， 主 要 再 來.
Some gold - en day - break, Je - sus will come;

金 色 的 黎 明， 何 等 光 彩。 勝 利 呼 喊 聲，
Some gold - en day - break, bat - tles all won, He'll shout the vic - tory,

衝 破 雲 河。 金 色 的 黎 明， 為 你、為 我。
break through the blue— Some gold - en day - break, for me, for you.

220

主或許今日來？

Is It the Crowning Day?

Looking for and hasting unto the coming of the Day of God.
— I John 3:12

George Walker Whitcomb

GLAD DAY
Charles H. Marsh

1. 主若今日來臨，何等歡欣！我與恩
2. 我今若回天庭，何等歡欣！天上似
3. 我今向主忠心，何等歡欣！盡情向
1 Je - sus may come to - day, Glad day! Glad day! And I would
2 I may go home to - day, Glad day! Glad day! Seems like I
3 Faith - ful I'll be to - day, Glad day! Glad day! And I will
1. 友相見，不再有愁煩危險，救
2. 有歌聲，寶座前歡呼高升！我
3. 人傳述：為何我要愛救主，我
1 see my Friend; Dan - gers and trou - bles would end If
2 hear their song; Hail to the ra - di - ant throng! If
3 free - ly tell Why I should love Him so well, For
1. 主今日必來臨。
2. 願今日回天庭。
3. 今願奉獻身心。
何等歡欣！主必快要來
Glad day! Glad day! Is it the crown - ing
1 Je - sus should come to - day.
2 I should go home to - day.
3 He is my all to - day.
臨。我今為主活，不再愁煩，救主耶穌與
day? I'll live for to - day, nor anx - ious be, Je - sus, my Lord, I

我相見，何 等 歡欣！主必快要 來臨！
soon shall see; Glad day! Glad day! Is it the crown-ing day?
Copyright 1910 by Praise Publishing Co. © Renewed 1938 (extended), The Rodeheaver Co., owner. Used by permission.
221
感謝耶穌
Thank You, Jesus
Anne Ortlund
Anne Ortlund
Arr. by Norman Johnson
Unison
感謝 耶穌，祢將自己 完全給我們，
Thank You, Je-sus, Thanks for Your-self, Thanks for the Bod-y,
感謝祢賜豐富生命！哦！主，我們
Thanks for the rich-ness of liv-ing! Lord, Lord, We
向祢舉手 感謝 祢賜福，感謝祢賜我們
lift up our hands, Thanks for Your Spir-it, Thanks for the bless-ings You're
聖 靈 。
giv- ing.

222

主若今日來如何？

What If It Were Today?

"Jesus has gone away to Heaven, and some day, just as He went, He will return." — Acts 1:11b

WHAT IF IT WERE TODAY?

Lelia N. Morris | Lelia N. Morris

1. 主耶穌不久要 再降臨，若今日來如何？
2. 撒但操權時日 快過去，但願今日就來！
3. 我們是否誠實 又忠心，主今日來如何？
1 Je - sus is com-ing to earth a-gain, What if it were to - day?
2 Sa - tan's do-min-ion will then be o'er, O that it were to - day!
3 Faith-ful and true would He find us here If He should come to-day?

1. 以威嚴和慈愛掌王權，若今日來如何？
2. 那時再沒有悲傷嘆息，但願今日就來！
3. 歡樂的等候坦然無懼，主今日來如何？
1 Com - ing in pow-er and love to reign, What if it were to - day?
2 Sor - row and sigh-ing shall be no more, O that it were to - day!
3 Watch-ing in glad-ness and not in fear, If He should come to-day?

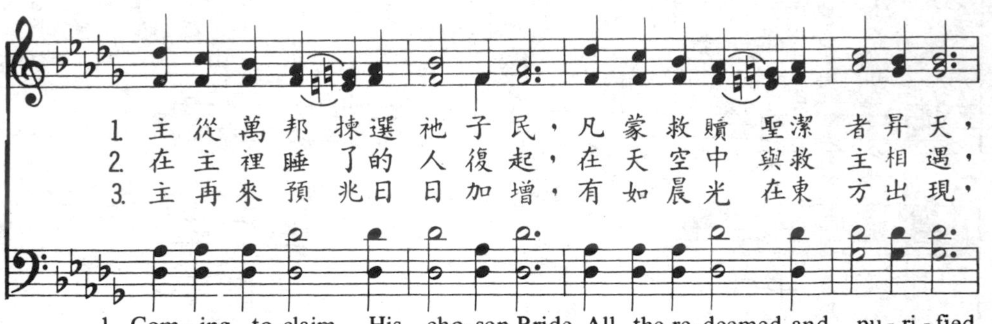
1. 主從萬邦揀選祂子民，凡蒙救贖聖潔者昇天，
2. 在主裡睡了的人復起，在天空中與救主相遇，
3. 主再來預兆日日加增，有如晨光在東方出現，
1 Com-ing to claim His cho-sen Bride, All the re-deemed and pu - ri - fied,
2 Then shall the dead in Christ a-rise, Caught up to meet Him in the skies,
3 Signs of His com - ing mul - ti - ply, Morning light breaks in east-ern sky,

1. 與 主 同 在 直 到 永 遠 ， 若 今日 來 如 何 ？
2. 何 時 眼 見 此 榮 耀 日 ？ 但 願 今 日 就 來 。
3. 儆 醒 等 候 時 日 快 臨 ， 主 今日 來 如 何 ？
1 O - ver this whole earth scat-tered wide, What if it were to - day?
2 When shall these glo - ries meet our eyes? What if it were to - day?
3 Watch, for the time is draw - ing nigh, What if it were to - day?
榮 耀 ， 榮 耀 ！ 我 要 歡 樂 歌 唱 ； 榮 耀
Glo - ry, glo - ry! Joy to my heart 'twill bring; Glo - ry,
榮 耀 ！ 擁 戴 我 主 為 王 ； 榮 耀 ， 榮 耀 ！
glo - ry! When we shall crown Him King; Glo - ry, glo - ry!
快 快 預 備 主 道 ； 榮 耀 ， 榮 耀 ！ 願 主 早 日 臨 到 。
Haste to pre-pare the way; Glo-ry, glo - ry! Je-sus will come some-day.

223

主要來臨

The King Is Coming

Gloria Gaither, stanzas 1, 2, 3
William J. Gaither, stanzas 1, 2, 3
Charles Millhuff, stanza 3

Behold, the Lord cometh with ten thousands of His saints. — Jude 1:14

KING IS COMING
William J. Gaither

1. 市場上空曠無人影，街道上交通稀落，匠人
2. 蒙恩被救贖的子民，歡樂聚集在盼望，淪落
3. 隆隆聲天使乘車來，壯烈隊伍向前進，神的
1 The mar-ket place is emp-ty, No more traf-fic in the streets, All the
2 Hap-py fac-es line the hall-ways, Those whose lives have been redeemed, Broken
3 I can hear the char-iots rum-ble, I can see the march-ing throng, The

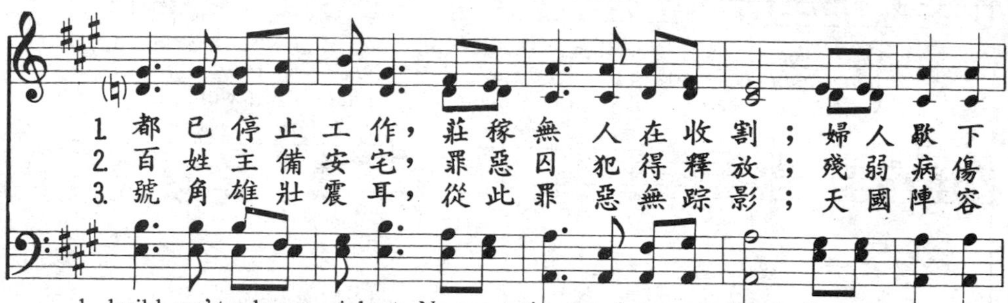

1. 都已停止工作，莊稼無人在收割；婦人歇下
2. 百姓主備安宅，罪惡囚犯得釋放；殘弱病傷
3. 號角雄壯震耳，從此罪惡無踪影；天國陣容
1 build-ers' tools are si-lent, No more time to har-vest wheat; Bus-y house-wives
2 homes that He has mend-ed, Those from pris-on He has freed; Lit-tle chil-dren
3 flur-ry of God's trum-pets Spells the end of sin and wrong; Re-gal robes are

1. 日夜辛勞，法庭案件都停止，世上生活都要
2. 都得醫治，身穿白衣極光明，男女老幼攜手
3. 聲勢浩大，紫袍有待聖者穿，天韻歌聲已高
1 cease their la-bors, In the court room no de-bate, Work on earth is all sus-
2 and the a-ged Hand in hand stand all a-glow, Who were crippled, broken,
3 now un-fold-ing, Heav-en's grandstands all in place, Heav-en's choir is now as-

1. 終止，因為我的王來臨。
2. 相迎，欣喜盼望主來臨。 我的王要來臨，我
3. 聲唱，頌讚神"奇妙恩典！" O the King is com-ing, the
1 pend-ed As the King comes thru the gate.
2 ru-ined, Clad in gar-ments white as snow.
3 sem-bled, Start to sing "A-maz-ing Grace!"

王 要來臨！我已聽 見號角聲音，我将見主容形；
King is com-ing! I just heard the trumpets sounding, And now His face I see;
我的王 要來臨，我 王 要來臨，為我，祂
O the King is com-ing, the King is com-ing! Praise God, He's
必要來 臨！
com-ing for me!

我觀看，見天開了，有一匹白馬，騎在馬上的，稱為誠信真實，他審判爭戰都按着公義。他的眼睛如火焰，他頭上戴着許多冠冕，又有寫着的名字，除了他自己沒有人知道。他穿着濺了血的衣服，他的名稱為神之道。天上的衆軍，……跟隨他。在他的衣服和大腿上，有名寫着說〝萬王之王，萬主之主〞。

啓示錄十九章
11 — 16

Then I saw Heaven wide open, and before my eyes appeared a white horse, whose rider is called faithful and true, for his judgment and his warfare are just. His eyes are a flame of fire and there are many diadems upon his head. There is a name written upon him, known only to himself. He is dressed in a cloak dipped in blood, and the name by which he is known is the Word of God.

The armies of Heaven follow him, riding upon white horses and clad in white and spotless linen. Out of his mouth there comes a sharp sword with which to strike the nations. He will shepherd them "with a rod of iron," and alone he will tread the winepress of the furious wrath of God the Almighty. Written upon his cloak and upon his thigh is the name, KING OF KINGS AND LORD OF LORDS.

— Revelation 19:11-16

何等榮耀日

What a Day That Will Be

And the Lord will wipe all tears from their eyes;
. . . for the former things are passed away. — Revelation 21:4

Jim Hill

WHAT A DAY
Jim Hill

1 有一日要來臨，無憂傷無眼淚，
2 有一地無憂慮，無重擔無畏懼，
1 There is com - ing a day when no heart - aches shall come,
2 *There'll be no sor - row there, no more bur - dens to bear,*

1 無黑雲遮蓋天，無艱難也無試煉；永與
2 無病痛無呻吟，再無痛苦與分離；救主
1 No more clouds in the sky, no more tears to dim the eye; All is
2 *No more sick - ness, no pain, no more part - ing o - ver there; And for -*

1 主安居在天，在那金色的岸邊，到那日，
2 曾為我被釘，我願與主永相親，到那日，
1 peace for ev - er - more on that hap - py gold - en shore— What a day,
2 *ev - er I will be with the One who died for me— What a day,*

1 何等快樂榮耀日。
2 何等快樂榮耀日。 到那日見主面，何等
1 glo - ri - ous day, that will be.
2 *glo - ri - ous day, that will be.* What a day that will be when my

快 樂 榮 耀 日，我 將 與 主 面 對 面，我 蒙 救
Je - sus I shall see, And I look up - on His face— the One who
贖 靠 主 恩 典；我 行 走 主 手 牽 我，到 應 許
saved me by His grace; When He takes me by the hand, and leads me
地 永 享 福 樂，到 那 日，何 等 快 樂 榮 耀 日。
through the Prom-ised Land, What a day, glo - ri - ous day, that will be.

I Timothy 3: 16b

He appeared in a body,
was vindicated by the Spirit,
was seen by angels,
was preached among the nations,
was believed on in the world,
was taken up in glory.

–(NIV)

225

齊來讚美主

Let's Just Praise the Lord

The Lord Jehovah is my strength and my song . . .
— Isaiah 12:2

Gloria Gaither
William J. Gaither

LET'S JUST PRAISE THE LORD
William J. Gaither

齊來讚美主！讚美主！讓我們向諸天頌揚，讚美我主；齊來讚美主！讚美主！讓我們向諸天頌揚，讚美我主！
Let's just praise the Lord! Praise the Lord! Let's just lift our hearts to heav-en and praise the Lord; Let's just praise the Lord! Praise the Lord! Let's just lift our hearts to heav-en and praise the Lord!
Fine

1. 我們同來向你感謝，感謝祢的慈
2. 主耶穌這寶貴的名，配得讚美頌
1 O we thank You for Your kind - ness, we thank You for Your
2 Just the pre - cious name of Je - sus is worth - y of our
1. 愛，我們在地如同在天，因為有祢同
2. 揚，我們屈膝在祂面前，舉手向天歡
1 love, We have been in heaven-ly plac - es, felt bless-ings from a -
2 praise, Let us bow our knees be - fore Him, our hands to heav - en
1. 在；讓我們一同來分享，主恩何等豐
2. 唱；當祂榮耀駕雲降臨，祂必永遠為
1 bove; We've been shar - ing all the good things, the fam - ily can af -
2 raise; When He comes in clouds of glo - ry, with Him to ev - er
D.C.
1. 富，讓我們向諸天頌揚，來讚美主。
2. 王，讓我們高聲的頌揚，來讚美主。
1 ford, Let's just turn our praise toward heav - en and praise the Lord.
2 reign, Let's just lift our hap - py voic - es, and praise His name.

226

萬福恩源

Come, Thou Fount of Every Blessing

In that day shall a fountain be opened . . . for sin and uncleaness.

— Zechariah 13:1

Robert Robinson
Jeff Redd, 2nd stanza, alt.

NETTLETON
John Wyeth

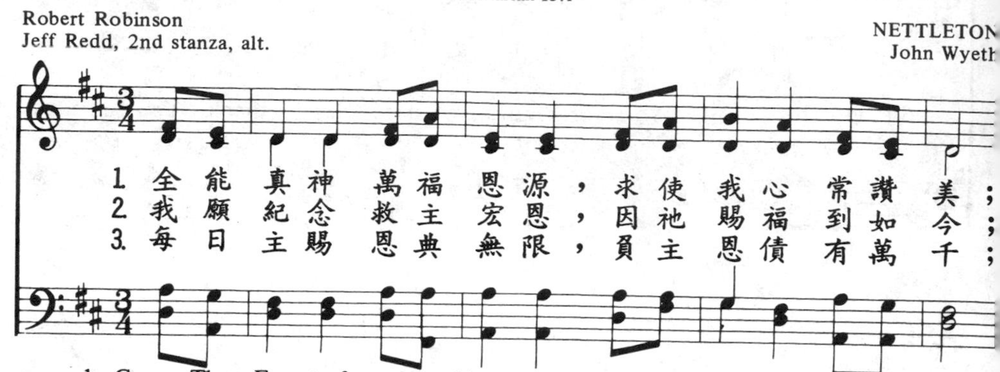

1. 全能真神萬福恩源，求使我心常讚美；
2. 我願紀念救主宏恩，因祂賜福到如今；
3. 每日主賜恩典無限，負主恩債有萬千；
1 Come, Thou Fount of ev-ery bless-ing, Tune my heart to sing Thy grace;
2 *This my glad com-mem-o-ra-tion That 'til now I've safe-ly come;*
3 O to grace how great a debt-or Dai-ly I'm con-strained to be!

1. 主賜恩典湧流不斷，應當頌揚主恩惠。
2. 更求恩主引我前程，使我安然到天庭。
3. 願主恩典如鍊牽連，繫我心在主身邊。
1 Streams of mer-cy, nev-er ceas-ing, Call for songs of loud-est praise.
2 *And I hope, by Thy good pleas-ure, Safe-ly to ar-rive at home.*
3 Let Thy good-ness, like a fet-ter, Bind my wan-dering heart to Thee:

1. 求主教我歌唱不停，如天使歌頌在天，主的
2. 我曾漂流迷失正路，主用大愛尋找我，為救
3. 我深知道我心易變，常離主愛行己路，今將

1 Teach me some me-lo-dious son-net, Sung by flaming tongues a-bove; Praise the
2 *Je-sus sought me when a strang-er, Wan-dering from the fold of God; He, to*
3 Prone to wan-der, Lord, I feel it, Prone to leave the God I love: Here's my

1. 恩典無窮無盡，永遠穩定永不變。
2. 我命寶血流出，賜我平安與快樂。
3. 身心完全奉獻，從今以後永屬主。 阿們。

1 mount! I'm fixed up-on it, Mount of Thy redeeming love.
2 *res - cue me from dan-ger, Interposed His pre-cious blood.*
3 heart, O take and seal it, Seal it for Thy courts a - bove. A - men.

我口發出，天韻歌聲 227

Begin, My Tongue, Some Heavenly Theme

. . . Every hill shall be brought low, and the crooked shall be made straight, and the rough ways shall be made smooth.
— Luke 3:5

Isaac Watts

MANOAH
Henry W. Greatorex's *Collection*

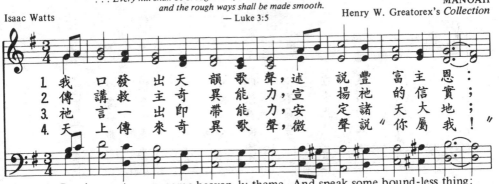

1. 我口發出天韻歌聲，述說豐富主恩：
2. 傳講救主奇異能力，宣揚祂的信實；
3. 祂言一出卽帶能力，安定諸天大地；
4. 天上傳來奇異歌聲，微聲說“你屬我！”

1 Be-gin, my tongue, some heaven-ly theme And speak some bound-less thing:
2 *Tell of His won-drous faith-ful-ness And sound His power a-broad;*
3 His ver - y word of grace is strong As that which built the skies;
4 *O might I hear the heaven-ly tongue But whis - per, "Thou art mine!"*

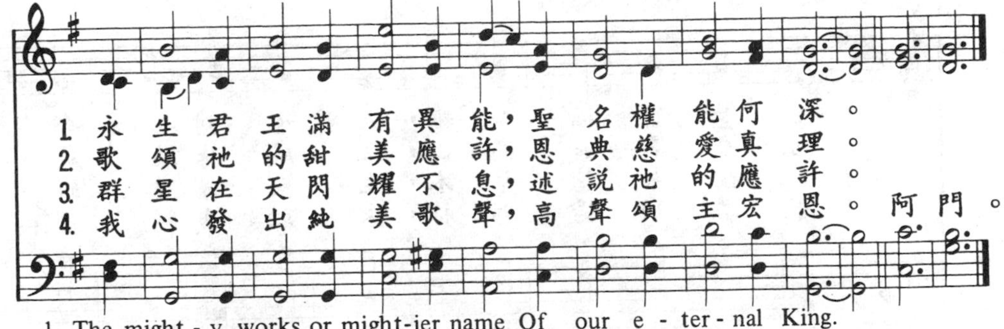

1. 永生君王滿有異能，聖名權能何深。
2. 歌頌祂的甜美應許，恩典慈愛真理。
3. 群星在天閃耀不息，述說祂的應許。
4. 我心發出純美歌聲，高聲頌主宏恩。 阿門。

1 The might - y works or might-ier name Of our e - ter - nal King.
2 *Sing the sweet prom-ise of His grace, The love and truth of God.*
3 The voice that rolls the stars a - long Speaks all the prom - is - es.
4 *Those gen - tle words shall raise my song To notes al - most di - vine.* A-men.

永生神是靈，智慧無限

Immortal, Invisible, God Only Wise

He that keepeth thee shall not slumber . . . or sleep.
— Psalm 121: 3,4

Walter Chalmers Smith

ST. DENIO
Welsh Melody

1. 永生真神是靈，祂智慧無限，
2. 永生神不急躁，安靜如光照，
3. 宇宙大小生命，皆由主而來，
4. 極榮耀極光明，偉大聖天父，
1 Im - mor - tal, in - vis - i - ble, God on - ly wise,
2 Un - rest - ing, un - hast - ing, and si - lent as light,
3 To all, life Thou giv - est, to both great and small;
4 Great Fa - ther of glo - ry, pure Fa - ther of light,
1. 隱藏在光明中，人眼不能見；
2. 無所求不浪廢，萬有掌管好；
3. 祢使生命存活，是生命主宰；
4. 眾天使皆掩目，圍繞敬拜主；
1 In light in - ac - ces - si - ble hid from our eyes,
2 Nor want - ing, nor wast - ing, Thou rul - est in might;
3 In all life Thou liv - est, the true life of all;
4 Thine an - gels a - dore Thee, all veil - ing their sight;
1. 極豐富極榮耀，亙古到如今，
2. 祂公義如高山，極威赫莊嚴，
3. 人生如花草木，生長僅瞬間，
4. 讚美頌揚歸祢，求助我瞻望—
1 Most bless - ed, most glo - rious, the An - cient of Days,
2 Thy jus - tice like moun - tains high soar - ing a - bove
3 We blos - som and flour - ish as leaves on the tree,
4 All praise we would ren - der: O help us to see

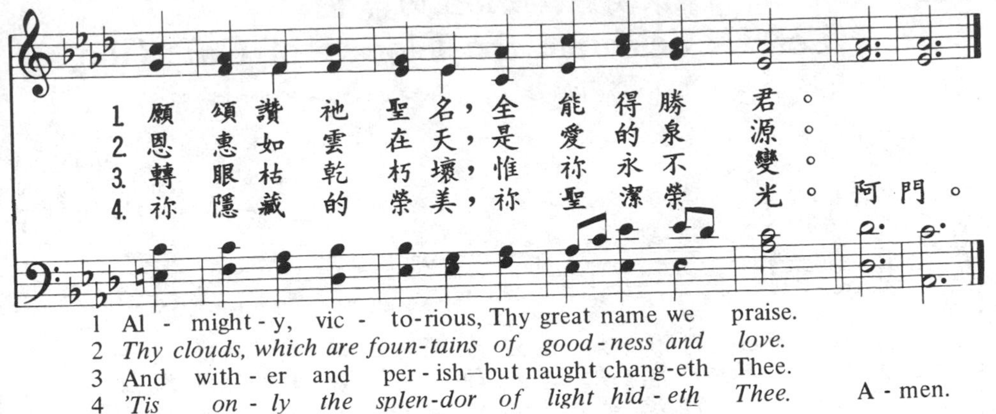

1. 願　頌　讚　祂　聖　名，全　能　得　勝　君。
2. 恩　惠　如　雲　在　天，是　愛　的　泉　源。
3. 轉　眼　枯　乾　朽　壞，惟　祢　永　不　變。
4. 祢　隱　藏　的　榮　美，祢　聖　潔　榮　光。阿　門。
1 Al - might - y, vic - to-rious, Thy great name we praise.
2 Thy clouds, which are foun-tains of good-ness and love.
3 And with - er and per - ish—but naught chang-eth Thee.
4 'Tis on - ly the splen-dor of light hid - eth Thee. A - men.

229

信徒應當奮起

Rise Up, O Men of God

. . . love the Lord, your God and serve Him . . .
— Deuteronomy 11:13

William P. Merrill

FESTAL SONG
William H. Walter

1. 信　徒　應　當　奮　起，撇　開　世　事　纏　身；
2. 信　徒　應　當　奮　起，神　國　不　久　降　臨；
3. 信　徒　應　當　奮　起，教　會　正　待　復　興；
4. 高　舉　基　督　十　架，跟　隨　主　腳　步　行；

1 Rise up, O men of God! Have done with less - er things;
2 *Rise up, O men of God! His king - dom tar - ries long;*
3 Rise up, O men of God! The Church for you doth wait,
4 *Lift high the cross of Christ, Tread where His feet have trod;*

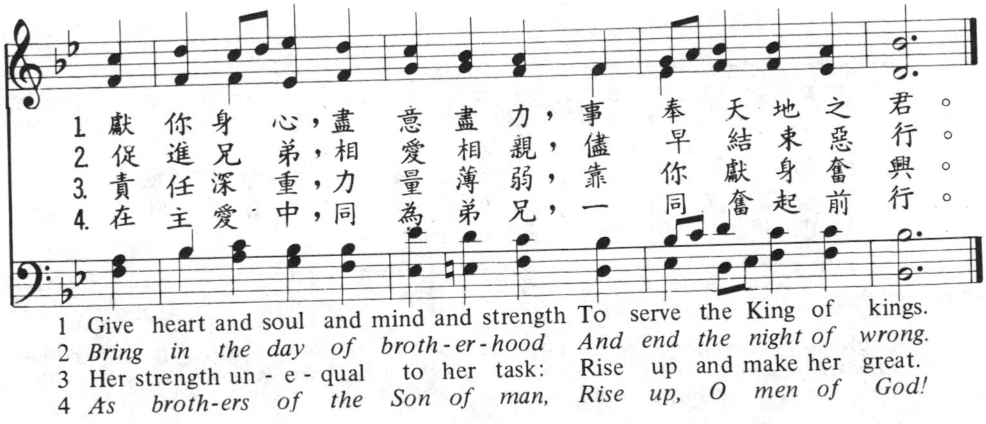

1. 獻　你　身　心，盡　意　盡　力，事　奉　天　地　之　君。
2. 促　進　兄　弟，相　愛　相　親，儘　早　結　束　惡　行。
3. 責　任　深　重，力　量　薄　弱，靠　你　獻　身　奮　興。
4. 在　主　愛　中，同　為　弟　兄，一　同　奮　起　前　行。

1 Give heart and soul and mind and strength To serve the King of kings.
2 *Bring in the day of broth-er-hood And end the night of wrong.*
3 Her strength un - e - qual to her task: Rise up and make her great.
4 *As broth-ers of the Son of man, Rise up, O men of God!*

讓我們稱頌上主的榮耀
Let Us Celebrate the Glories of Our God

Now unto God and our Father be glory forever and ever. — Philippians 4:20

Bryan Jeffery Leech

BELLAMY
Jean Joseph Mouret
Arranged by Fred Bock

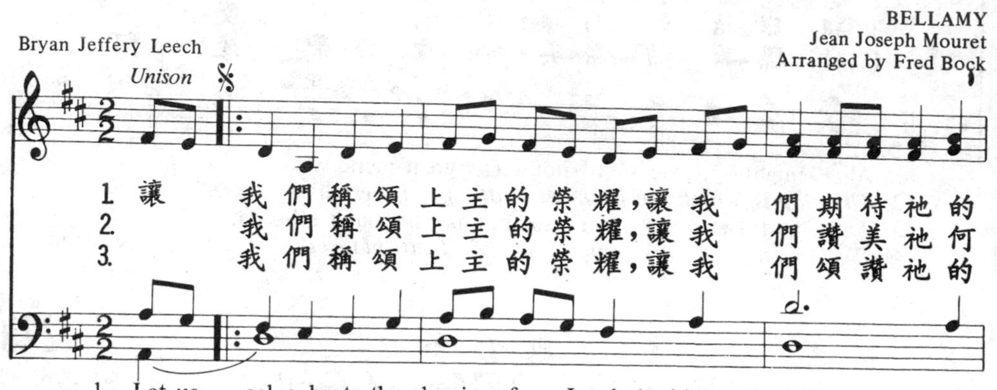
Unison
1. 讓 我們稱頌上主的榮耀，讓我 們期待祂的
2. 我們稱頌上主的榮耀，讓我 們讚美祂何
3. 我們稱頌上主的榮耀，讓我 們頌讚祂的
1 Let us cel-e-brate the glo-ries of our Lord, And let us look for His swift re-
2 (Let us) cel-e-brate the glo-ries of our Lord, And let us tell Him how good and
3 (Let us) cel-e-brate the glo-ries of our Lord, And let us men-tion His great a-

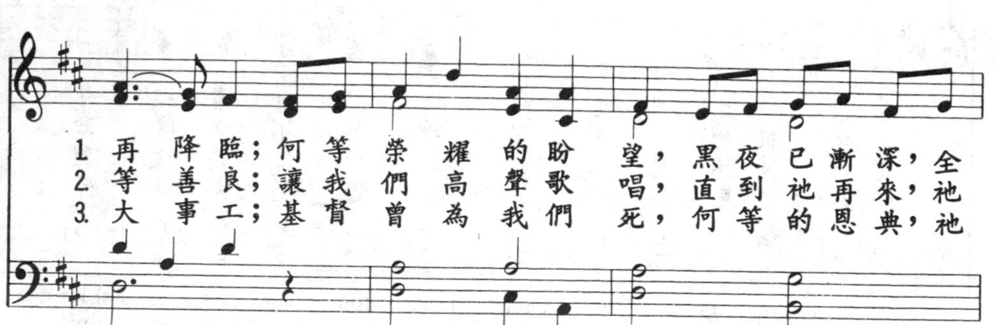
1. 再降臨；何等榮耀的盼望，黑夜已漸深，全
2. 等善良；讓我們高聲歌唱，直到祂再來，祂
3. 大事工；基督曾為我們死，何等的恩典，祂
1 turn - ing; What a glo-rious hope we have in the dark-est hour To
2 great He is; Let's re-hearse the songs we'll sing when He comes to reign, And
3 chieve - ments; For we can - not tell too much how He went to die And

Fine

1. 能的主必快來臨。1 當我們等待祂顯現，
2. 來要治理這地方。2 耶穌基督已經得勝，
3. 今已復活升高天。

1 know He's com-ing soon with power. 1 As we look for His ap - pear - ing,
2 *take His right-ful place a - gain.* 2 *Je - sus Christ is now the vic - tor,*
3 how our God has raised Him high.

1 快去将好信息傳給世上的人。當這時辰快要
2 深知祂必同在我們有何憂驚？遠處鼓聲已可
1 We must share the good news with ev-ery man on earth. As we see this mo-ment
2 Know-ing that He's with us, what cause is there to fear? There's a sound of dis-tant

D.S.
1 臨近，應當熱心事奉，将生命獻給神，2. 讓
2 聽聞，祂應許必再來，這時辰已來臨，3. 讓
1 near-ing, We must live to serve Him for all that we are worth! 2 Let us
2 drum-ming, For His prom-ised com-ing is ver-y, ver-y near! 3 Let us

全地都當向神歡呼。
歌頌祂名的榮耀，用讚美的言語，将祂的榮耀發明。
當對神説，祢的作為何等可畏，因祢的大能仇敵要投降祢。
全地要敬拜祢、歌頌祢，要歌頌祢的名。

詩篇六十六篇
1 — 4

Shout with joy to God, all the earth!
Sing to the glory of his name;
offer him glory and praise!
Say to God, "How awesome are your deeds!
So great is your power
that your enemies cringe before you.
All the earth bows down to you;
they sing praise to you,
they sing praise to your name."

Psalm 66 : 1-4. NIV

231

讚美上主，全能真神

Praise to the Lord, the Almighty

For then shalt thou have delight in the Almighty.
— Job 22:26

Joachim Neander
Tr. by Catherine Winkworth

LOBE DEN HERREN
"Stralsund Gesangbuch"

1. 讚美上主，全能真神，宇宙萬有君王！
2. 讚美上主，奇妙真神，統治世間萬方，
3. 讚美上主，時常保護，賜你工作順利，
4. 讚美上主，我願衷心敬拜讚揚祢名！
1 Praise to the Lord, the Al - might - y, the King of cre - a - tion!
2 Praise to the Lord, who o'er all things so won-drous-ly reign - eth,
3 Praise to the Lord, who doth pros-per thy work and de - fend thee;
4 Praise to the Lord! O let all that is in me a - dore Him!

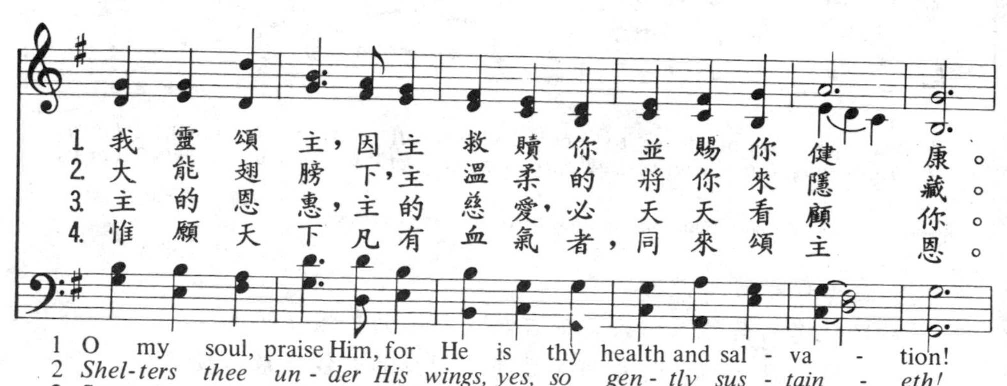
1. 我靈頌主，因主救贖你並賜你健康。
2. 大能翅膀下，主溫柔的將你來隱藏。
3. 主的恩惠，主的慈愛，必天天看顧你。
4. 惟願天下凡有血氣者，同來頌主恩。
1 O my soul, praise Him, for He is thy health and sal - va - tion!
2 Shel-ters thee un - der His wings, yes, so gen - tly sus - tain - eth!
3 Sure - ly His good-ness and mer - cy here dai - ly at - tend thee.
4 All that hath life and breath, come now with prais - es be - fore Him.

1. 萬民敬聽，齊來就近主聖殿；
2. 可曾知道，你心所渴望所想，
3. 你當思想，全能的主愛深長，
4. 屬主的民，歡然到主前敬拜；
1 All ye who hear, Now to His tem - ple draw near;
2 Hast thou not seen How all thy long - ings have been
3 Pon - der a - new What the Al - might - y can do,
4 Let the A - men Sound from His peo - ple a - gain:

1. 歡然向主敬拜讚揚！
2. 按祂旨求必定得償
3. 祂是你友何等福氣。
4. 重新齊聲的說阿門" 阿門
1 Join me in glad ad - o - ra - tion!
2 Grant-ed in what He or - dain - eth?
3 If with His love He be - friend thee.
4 Glad-ly for aye we a - dore Him. A - men.

A Call to Worship

Minister: Let all who love Him come rejoicing.
People: *God is in His heaven.*
Minister: To the Almighty praises voicing!
People: *God is in His heaven!*
Minister: All nature does to Him belong,
Yet we, His children, own the song
That age to age has made us strong.
People: *God is in His heaven.*

Minister: There dawns no day but by His blessing.
People: *God is in His heaven!*
Minister: No night without the stars confessing.
People: *God is in His heaven!*
Minister: Within His hand He does contain
All pow'r of sun, moon, wind and rain,
And watchful to His vast domain:
People: *God is in His heaven.*

Minister: Through all the years that are before us:
People: *God is in His heaven!*
Minister: His love forever reigning o'er us:
People: *God is in His heaven!*
Minister: Each season in its turn shall be
A glimpse of His eternity,
As God has been, so God shall be!
People: *God is in His heaven!*

–Jacqueline Hanna McNair

232

朝陽初昇

When Morning Gilds the Skies

Unto Him be glory in the church by Jesus Christ throughout all ages world without end.
— Ephesians 3:21

From the German
Tr. by Edward Caswall

LAUDES DOMINI
Joseph Barnby

1. 燦爛朝陽初昇，我心發出歌
2. 我若煩悶憂愁，安慰何處尋
3. 黑夜變為白晝—當我心稱頌
4. 世上萬國萬邦，主裡同心歌
5. 當我仍活在世，願仍唱此聖

1 When morn - ing gilds the skies, My heart a - wak - ing
2 *Does sad - ness fill my mind? A sol - ace here I*
3 The night be - comes as day When from the heart we
4 *Ye na - tions of man - kind In this your one - ness*
5 Be this, while life is mine, My can - ti - cle di -

1. 聲，讚美耶穌基督！不
2. 求？讚美耶穌基督！人
3. 主：讚美耶穌基督！黑
4. 唱：讚美耶穌基督！惟
5. 詩：讚美耶穌基督！但

1 cries, May Je - sus Christ be praised! A -
2 *find, May Je - sus Christ be praised! Or*
3 say, May Je - sus Christ be praised! The
4 *find, May Je - sus Christ be praised! Let*
5 vine, May Je - sus Christ be praised! Be

1. 論祈禱作工，常與耶穌交
2. 生幸福幾何？安慰仍是這
3. 暗權勢消失，當我向主唱
4. 願地上萬族，齊向我主歡
5. 願此歌悠久，存到萬古千

1 like at work and prayer To Je - sus I re -
2 *fades my earth - ly bliss? My com - fort still is*
3 powers of dark - ness fear When this sweet chant they
4 *all the earth a - round Ring joy - ous with the*
5 this th'e - ter - nal song Through all the a - ges

1. 通，讚美耶穌基督！
2. 歌：讚美耶穌基督！
3. 詩：讚美耶穌基督！
4. 呼：讚美耶穌基督！
5. 秋：讚美耶穌基督！阿們。
1 pair, May Je - sus Christ be praised!
2 *this, May Je - sus Christ be praised!*
3 hear, May Je - sus Christ be praised!
4 *sound, May Je - sus Christ be praised!*
5 long, May Je - sus Christ be praised! A - men.

諸天述說神的榮耀，穹蒼傳揚祂的手段。
這日到那日發出言語，這夜到那夜傳出知識。
無言無語，也無聲音可聽。
他的量帶通遍天下，他的言語傳到地極。神在其間為太陽安設帳幕
太陽如同新郎出洞房，又如勇士歡然奔路。
他從天這邊出來，繞到天那邊，沒有一物被隱藏不得祂的熱氣。

詩篇十九篇
1 — 6

The heavens are telling the glory of God;
　and the firmament proclaims his handiwork.
Day to day pours forth speech,
　and night to night declares knowledge.
There is no speech, nor are there words;
　their voice is not heard;
yet their voice goes out through all the earth,
　and their words to the end of the world.
In them he has set a tent for the sun,
　which comes forth like a bridegroom
　leaving his chamber,
and like a strong man runs its course with joy.
Its rising is from the end of the heavens,
　and its circuit to the end of them;
　and there is nothing hid from its heat.

— Psalm 19:1-6. RSV

233

聖哉！聖哉！聖哉！全能大主宰

Holy! Holy! Holy! Lord God Almighty

Holy, holy, holy, Lord God Almighty; who was, and is, and is to come. — Revelation 4:8

Reginald Heber
NICAEA
John B. Dykes
Arranged by David McK. Williams
1. 聖哉，聖哉，聖哉！全能的大主宰！
2. 聖哉，聖哉，聖哉！聖徒虔誠敬拜，
3. 聖哉，聖哉，聖哉！主藏在雲彩裡，
4. 聖哉，聖哉，聖哉！全能的大主宰！
1 Ho-ly, ho-ly, ho-ly! Lord God Al-might-y!
2 Ho-ly, ho-ly, ho-ly! all the saints a-dore Thee,
3 Ho-ly, ho-ly, ho-ly! though the dark-ness hide Thee,
4 Ho-ly, ho-ly, ho-ly! Lord God Al-might-y!
1. 清晨歡悅歌詠，高聲頌主聖恩；
2. 各以華麗金冠，奉獻寶座之前；
3. 罪人焉得瞻望，真主威嚴榮光；
4. 天上地下海中，萬物頌主聖名；
1 Ear-ly in the morn-ing our song shall rise to Thee;
2 Cast-ing down their gold-en crowns a-round the glass-y sea;
3 Though the eye of sin-ful man Thy glo-ry may not see;
4 All Thy works shall praise Thy name in earth and sky and sea;
1. 聖哉，聖哉，聖哉！恩慈永不更改！
2. 千萬天使天軍，謙敬崇拜上主，
3. 惟耶和華至聖，誰堪與主相比？
4. 聖哉，聖哉，聖哉！恩慈永不更改！
1 Ho-ly, ho-ly, ho-ly! mer-ci-ful and might-y!
2 Cher-u-bim and ser-a-phim fall-ing down be-fore Thee,
3 On-ly Thou art ho-ly— there is none be-side Thee
4 Ho-ly, ho-ly, ho-ly! mer-ci-ful and might-y!

1. 榮耀與讚美，歸三一真神！
2. 昔在而今在，永在萬萬年。
3. 力、仁、聖、完備，大哉天地王。
4. 榮耀與讚美，歸三一真神！阿門。
1 God in three per - sons, bless - ed Trin - i - ty!
2 Who wert, and art, and ev - er - more shalt be.
3 Per - fect in power, in love and pu - ri - ty.
4 God in three per - sons, bless - ed Trin - i - ty! A-men.

234

讚美救主

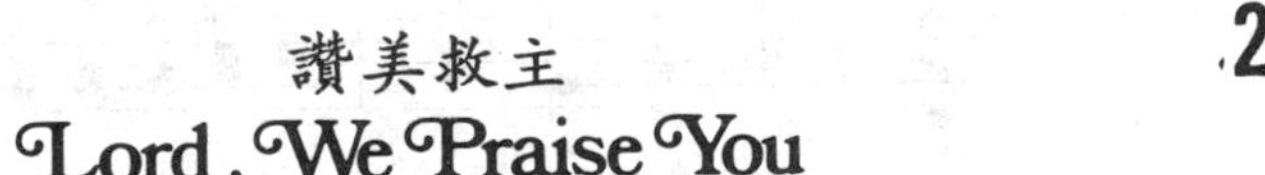

Lord, We Praise You

Sing unto Him, sing unto him;
talk ye of all His wondrous works . . . . — Psalm 105:2

Otis Skillings

LORD, WE PRAISE YOU
Otis Skillings

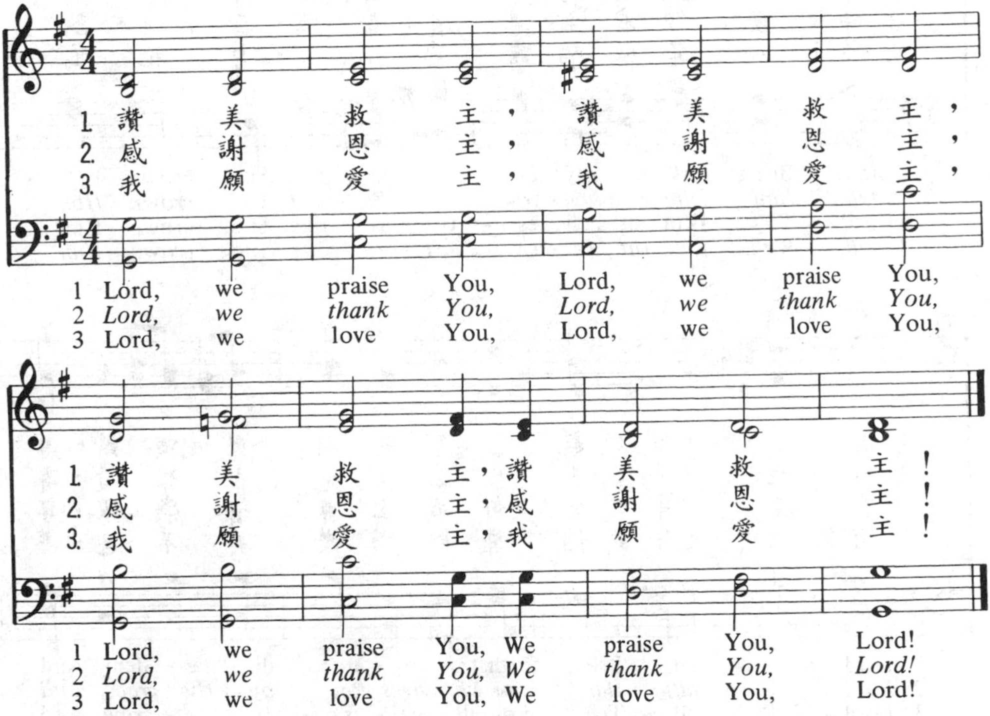

1. 讚美救主，讚美救主，讚美救主，讚美救主！
2. 感謝恩主，感謝恩主，感謝恩主，感謝恩主！
3. 我願愛主，我願愛主，我願愛主，我願愛主！

1 Lord, we praise You, Lord, we praise You, Lord, we praise You, We praise You, Lord!
2 *Lord, we thank You, Lord, we thank You, Lord, we thank You, We thank You, Lord!*
3 Lord, we love You, Lord, we love You, Lord, we love You, We love You, Lord!

235

大哉，聖哉，耶穌尊名(1)

All Hail the Power of Jesus' Name

Edward Perronet
John Rippon, alt.
Great is the Lord and greatly to be praised. — Psalm 145:3
CORONATION
Oliver Holden
(FIRST TUNE)
1. 大哉聖哉耶穌尊名，天使俯伏敬拜，奉獻冠冕同聲頌讚，尊祂萬有主宰；奉獻冠冕同聲頌讚，尊
2. 蒙恩救贖真神選民，齊當感謝敬拜，靠主宏恩免我罪債，尊祂萬有主宰；靠主宏恩免我罪債，尊
3. 普天之下萬民萬邦，齊來擁戴敬拜，瞻仰我主尊貴榮耀，尊祂萬有主宰；瞻仰我主尊貴榮耀，尊
4. 願與衆聖徒在天上，屈膝向主敬拜！同聲歡唱讚美不息，尊祂萬有主宰；同聲歡唱讚美不息，尊
1 All hail the power of Je - sus' name! Let an - gels pros - trate fall; Bring forth the roy - al di - a - dem, And crown Him Lord of all; Bring forth the roy - al di - a - dem, And
2 Ye cho - sen seed of Is - rael's race, Ye ran-somed from the fall, Hail Him who saves you by His grace, And crown Him Lord of all; Hail Him who saves you by His grace, And
3 Let ev - ery kin - dred, ev - ery tribe, On this ter - res - trial ball, To Him all maj - es - ty as - cribe, And crown Him Lord of all; To Him all maj - es - ty as - cribe, And
4 O that with yon - der sa - cred throng We at His feet may fall! We'll join the ev - er - last - ing song, And crown Him Lord of all; We'll join the ev - er - last - ing song, And

1. 祂 萬 有 主 宰！
2. 祂 萬 有 主 宰！
3. 祂 萬 有 主 宰！
4. 祂 萬 有 主 宰！ 阿 門。
1 crown Him Lord of all!
2 crown Him Lord of all!
3 crown Him Lord of all!
4 crown Him Lord of all! A - men.

使徒信經

我信　神，全能的父，創造天地的主。

我信我主耶穌基督，神獨生的兒子；因聖靈感孕，由童貞女馬利亞所生；在本丟彼拉多手下受難，被釘於十字架，受死，埋葬；降在陰間，第三天從死人中復活；升天，坐在全能父　神的右邊；將來必從那裏降臨，審判活人死人。

我信聖靈；我信聖而公之教會；我信聖徒相通；我信罪得赦免；我信身體復活；我信永生。　阿們。

The Apostles' Creed

I believe in God the Father Almighty, maker of heaven and earth:

And in Jesus Christ His only Son, our Lord; Who was conceived by the Holy Spirit, born of the Virgin Mary, suffered under Pontius Pilate, was crucified, dead, and buried; He descended into hades; the third day He rose again from the dead; He ascended into heaven, and sitteth on the right hand of God, the Father Almighty; from thence He shall come to judge the quick and the dead.

I believe in the Holy Spirit, the holy Christian church, the communion of saints, the forgiveness of sins, the resurrection of the body, and the life everlasting.

Amen.

236

大哉，聖哉，耶穌尊名(2)

All Hail the Power of Jesus' Name

Thou art worthy, O Lord, to receive glory, and honor, and power: — Revelation 4:11

Edward Perronet
John Rippon, alt.

(SECOND TUNE)

DIADEM
James Ellor

1. 大哉聖哉耶穌尊名！天上萬軍頌揚，天上萬軍頌揚；奉獻冠冕極其光榮，
2. 真神選民蒙救贖恩，應當感謝敬拜，應當感謝敬拜；靠主宏恩免我罪債，慶賀
3. 天上地下聞主尊名，應該敬畏頌揚，應該敬畏頌揚；萬膝跪拜萬口稱頌，
4. 尊貴榮耀智慧能力，都歸被殺羔羊，都歸被殺羔羊！聖徒天使讚美不息，慶賀祂，賀祂，
1 All hail the power of Je - sus' name! Let an - gels pros-trate fall, Let an - gels pros - trate fall; Bring forth the roy - al di - a - dem,
2 Ye cho - sen seed of Is - rael's race, Ye ran-somed from the fall, Ye ran - somed from the fall; Hail Him who saves you by His grace, And crown
3 Let ev - ery kin - dred, ev - ery tribe, On this ter - res - trial ball, On this ter - res - trial ball, To Him all maj - es - ty as - cribe,
4 O that with yon - der sa - cred throng We at His feet may fall, We at His feet may fall! We'll join the ev - er - last - ing song, And crown Him, crown Him,

祂，　賀　祂，　賀　祂，
Him, crown Him, crown Him,
賀　祂，　賀　祂，　賀　祂，　賀　祂，
crown Him, crown Him, crown Him, crown Him,
賀
crown
賀　祂，慶　賀　祂　為　君　王。阿　門。
crown Him, And crown Him Lord of all. A - men.
祂，
Him,

來敬拜主

O Worship the Lord 236-1

Worship the Lord in the splendor of His holiness. Ps. 96:9

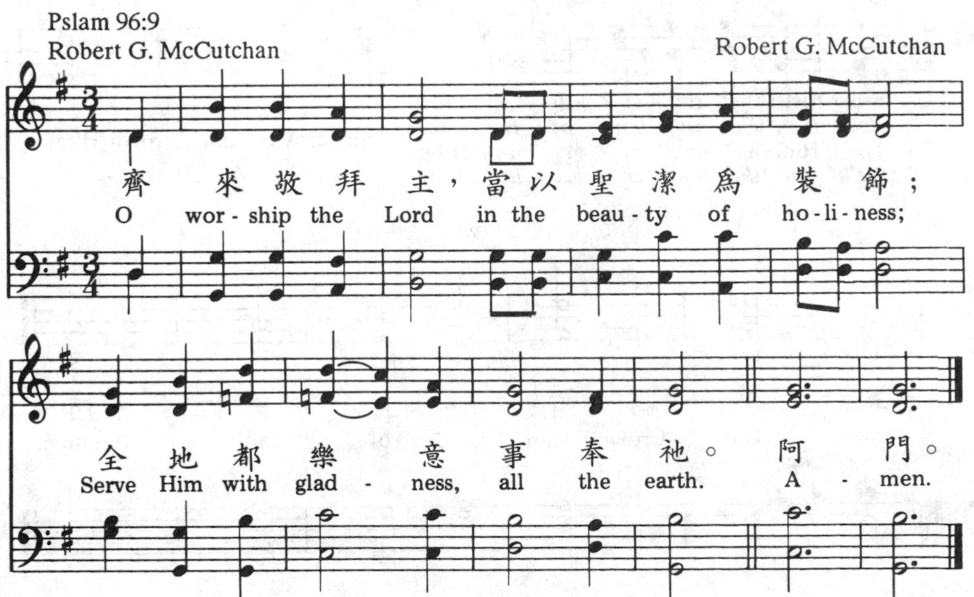

Pslam 96:9
Robert G. McCutchan
Robert G. McCutchan
齊　來　敬　拜　主，當以聖　潔　爲　裝　飾；
O wor - ship the Lord in the beau - ty of ho - li - ness;
全　地　都　樂　意　事　奉　祂。阿　門。
Serve Him with glad - ness, all the earth. A - men.

237

大哉，聖哉，耶穌尊名(3)

All Hail the Power of Jesus' Name

We made known unto you the power, and coming of our Lord Jesus Christ;
. . . were eyewitness of His majesty. — II Peter 1:16

Edward Perronet
John Rippon, alt.

(THIRD TUNE)

MILES LANE
William Shrubsole

1. 大 哉 聖 哉 耶 穌 尊 名！天 使 俯 伏 敬 拜，
2. 蒙 恩 救 贖 真 神 選 民，齊 當 感 謝 敬 拜，
3. 普 天 之 下 萬 民 萬 邦，齊 來 擁 戴 敬 拜，
4. 願 與 衆 聖 徒 在 天 上，屈 膝 向 主 敬 拜！

1 All hail the power of Je - sus' name! Let an - gels pros - trate fall;
2 *Ye cho - sen seed of Is - rael's race, Ye ran-somed from the fall,*
3 Let ev - ery kin - dred, ev - ery tribe, On this ter - res - trial ball,
4 *O that with yon - der sa - cred throng We at His feet may fall!*

1. 奉 獻 冠 冕 同 聲 頌 讚，
2. 靠 主 宏 恩 免 我 罪 債，
3. 瞻 仰 我 主 尊 貴 榮 耀，當 尊 祂，尊 祂，
4. 同 聲 歡 唱 讚 美 不 息，

1 Bring forth the roy - al di - a - dem,
2 *Hail Him who saves you by His grace,*
3 To Him all maj - es - ty as - cribe, And crown Him, crown Him,
4 *We'll join the ev - er - last - ing song,*

尊 祂，萬 有 大 主 宰！ 阿 門。
crown Him, Crown Him Lord of all! A - men.

亞伯拉罕的神

The God of Abraham Praise!

238

The eternal God is thy refuge, and underneath are the everlasting arms.
— Deuteronomy 33:27

Revised version of the *Yigdal*
Daniel ben Judah
Tr. by Newton Mann
and Max Landsberg

LEONI
Hebrew Melody
Adapted by Meyer Lyon

1. 亞伯拉罕的神，祢名當得稱頌；
2. 聖靈自由運行，如潮水之衝力；
3. 祂有永遠生命，白白賜給世人；
1 The God of A-braham praise, All prais-ed be His name,
2 *His spir-it flow-eth free, High surg-ing where it will;*
3 He hath e-ter-nal life Im-plant-ed in the soul;
1. 昔在今在自始至終，永遠相同！
2. 昔日神藉先知預言，今仍啓示，
3. 世世代代以愛相助，何等宏恩，
1 Who was, and is, and is to be, Al-ways the same!
2 *In proph-et's word He spoke of old, He speak-eth still.*
3 His love shall be our strength-en-ing While a-ges roll.
1. 永恒獨一真神，自有永有清新；
2. 親自建立主道，永遠不變長存，
3. 讚美永活真神！祢名當得稱頌，
1 The one e-ter-nal God, Whose time-less-ness is clear;
2 *Es-tab-lished is His law, And change-less it shall stand,*
3 Praise to the liv-ing God! All prais-ed be His name,
1. 是初是終莫測高深，永世無盡！
2. 主道遍滿海洋大陸，更印我心。
3. 昔在今在自始至終，永遠相同！阿門。
1 The First, the Last: be-yond all thought, Through-out the years!
2 *Now writ-ten deep up-on the heart, On sea or land.*
3 Who was, and is, and is to be, Al-ways the same! A-men.

諸天當讚美主

Praise the Lord! Ye Heavens Adore Him

Praise ye Him sun and moon; praise Him all ye stars. — Psalm 148:3

From Psalm 148
Foundling Hospital Collection, Stanzas 1, 2
Edward Osler, Stanza 3

FABEN
John H. Willcox

1. 諸天啊！皆當讚美主，衆天使同心敬拜；
2. 讚美主！因祂大榮耀，祂應許永不落空；
3. 衆信徒同心來奉獻，敬拜主恩典無限；

1 Praise the Lord! ye heavens, a-dore Him, Praise Him, an-gels in the height;
2 *Praise the Lord! for He is glo-rious, Nev-er shall His prom-ise fail;*
3 Wor-ship, hon-or, glo-ry, bless-ing, Lord, we of-fer un-to Thee;

1. 日和月歡欣同事奉，衆星宿快來擁戴。
2. 神喜悅聖徒皆得勝，罪與死驅除無蹤。
3. 長和幼齊聲同頌讚，同跪拜在主台前。

1 Sun and moon, re-joice be-fore Him, Praise Him, all ye stars of light.
2 *God hath made His saints vic-to-rious, Sin and death shall not pre-vail.*
3 Young and old, Thy praise ex-press-ing, In glad hom-age bend the knee.

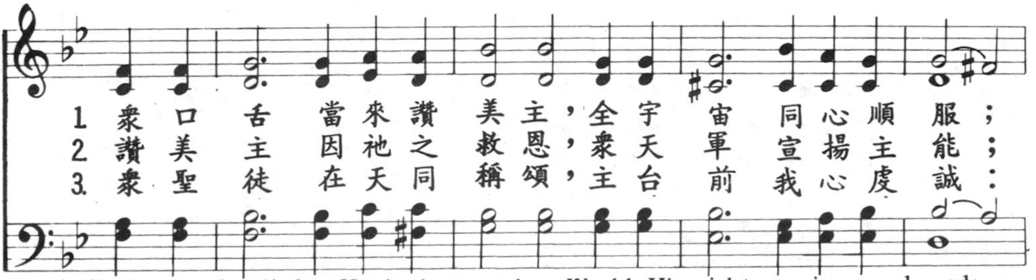
1. 衆口舌當來讚美主，全宇宙同心順服；
2. 讚美主因祂之救恩，衆天軍宣揚主能；
3. 衆聖徒在天同稱頌，主台前我心虔誠：

1 Praise the Lord! for He hath spo-ken, Worlds His might-y voice o-beyed:
2 *Praise the God of our sal-va-tion, Hosts on high, His power pro-claim;*
3 All the saints in heaven a-dore Thee, We would bow be-fore Thy throne:

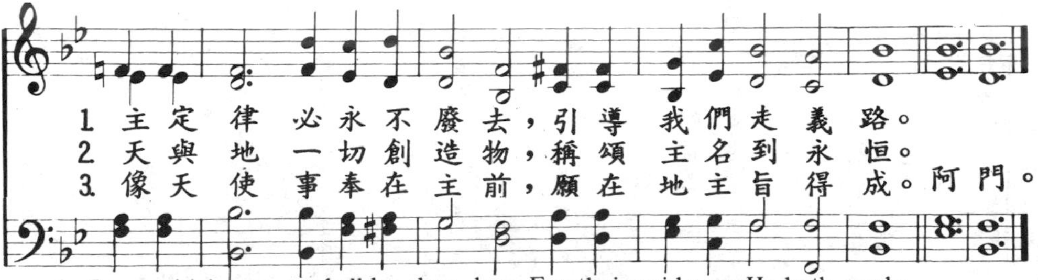
1. 主定律必永不廢去，引導我們走義路。
2. 天與地一切創造物，稱頌主名到永恒。
3. 像天使事奉在主前，願在地主旨得成。阿們。

1 Laws which nev-er shall be bro-ken For their guid-ance He hath made.
2 *Heaven and earth and all cre-a-tion Laud and mag-ni-fy His name.*
3 As Thine an-gels serve be-fore Thee, So on earth Thy will be done. A-men.

240

讚美救主真神

We Praise Thee, O God, Our Redeemer

As for our Redeemer, the Lord of hosts is His name. — Isaiah 47:4

Julia C. Cory

KREMSER
Netherlands Folk Song
Arranged by Edward Kremser

1 讚美我救主，創造一切的真神，
2 虔誠的敬拜，稱頌我們的父神，
3 齊向天上神，衆口同心的讚美，

1 We praise Thee, O God, our Re-deem-er, Cre-a-tor,
2 *We wor-ship Thee, God of our fa-thers, we bless Thee;*
3 With voic-es u-ni-ted our prais-es we of-fer,

1 衷心感激，熱忱的向祢獻呈；
2 蒙祢引導，經過風暴的人生；
3 誠實敬拜，歡樂歌聲達天庭；

1 In grate-ful de-vo-tion our trib-ute we bring.
2 *Through life's storm and tem-pest our guide hast Thou been.*
3 And glad-ly our songs of true wor-ship we raise.

1 願将一切奉獻，屈膝在祢面前，
2 當危險來侵襲，主永不把我棄，
3 主在身旁護我，大能膀臂助我，

1 We lay it be-fore Thee, we kneel and a-dore Thee,
2 *When per-ils o'er-take us, Thou wilt not for-sake us,*
3 Thy strong arm will guide us, our God is be-side us,

1 我願歡欣稱頌，以祢名為聖。
2 祢以大能幫助，使我永得勝。
3 讚美我的救主，讚美永不停。阿門。

1 We bless Thy ho-ly name, glad prais-es we sing.
2 *And with Thy help, O Lord, life's bat-tles we win.*
3 To Thee, our great Re-deem-er, for-ev-er be praise. A-men.

241

齊來同敬拜
O Worship the King

The true worshipper shall worship the Father in spirit and in truth. — John 4:23

Robert Grant
LYONS
Adapted from Johann Michael Haydn
1. 齊 來 同 敬 拜， 至 高 大 主 宰， 我
2. 齊 來 同 歌 唱， 主 全 能 大 愛， 光
3. 口 舌 何 能 述， 我 主 關 切 心？ 主
4. 無 量 的 權 能， 無 窮 的 慈 愛， 天
1 O wor - ship the King all glo - rious a - bove, And
2 O tell of His might and sing of His grace, Whose
3 Thy boun - ti - ful care what tongue can re - cite? It
4 Frail chil - dren of dust, and fee - ble as frail, In
1. 深 願 讚 美， 祂 奇 妙 大 愛； 祂 護 我 如
2. 輝 是 主 袍， 穹 蒼 是 主 幔； 黑 雲 内 藏
3. 使 風 吹 拂， 主 使 光 生 明， 主 使 泉 源
4. 軍 都 樂 意， 讚 美 而 敬 拜； 我 卑 微 受
1 grate - ful - ly sing His won - der - ful love; Our Shield and De -
2 robe is the light, whose can - o - py space; His char - iots of
3 breathes in the air, it shines in the light, It streams from the
4 Thee do we trust, nor find Thee to fail; Thy mer - cies how
1. 盾 牌， 祂 亙 古 常 在， 榮 耀 籠 罩
2. 雷 電， 主 當 華 車 乘， 狂 風 追 逐
3. 自 高 山 下 注 平 原， 主 降 甘 霖
4. 造 物， 歌 聲 雖 柔 弱， 卻 真 心 來
1 fend - er, the An - cient of Days, Pa - vil - ioned in
2 wrath the deep thun - der - clouds form, And dark is His
3 hills, it de - scends to the plain, And sweet - ly dis -
4 ten - der, how firm to the end, Our Mak - er, De -

1. 明 宮，頌 聲 環 如 帶。
2. 暴 雨，主 當 道 路 行。
3. 時 雨，使 地 得 滋 潤。
4. 俯 伏，唱 聖 詩 歡 樂。 阿 門。
1 splen - dor and gird - ed with praise.
2 path on the wings of the storm.
3 tills in the dew and the rain.
4 fend - er, Re - deem - er and Friend. A - men.

242

我的心哪，當稱頌主

Bless The Lord, O My Soul

He delivereth me . . . therefore shall I give thanks. — Psalm 18:48,49

Psalm 103:1

Unknown

我的 心 哪，當 稱 頌 主；我的 心 哪，當 稱 頌
Bless the Lord. Oh my soul; Bless the Lord, Oh my
主；凡在 我 裡 面 的 也 要 稱 頌 祂 聖 名。
soul; And all that is with - in me bless His ho - ly name.

243

榮耀歸於天父

To God Be the Glory

That ye may with one mind and one mouth glorify God . . . .
— Romans 15:6

TO GOD BE THE GLORY
William H. Doane

Fanny J. Crosby

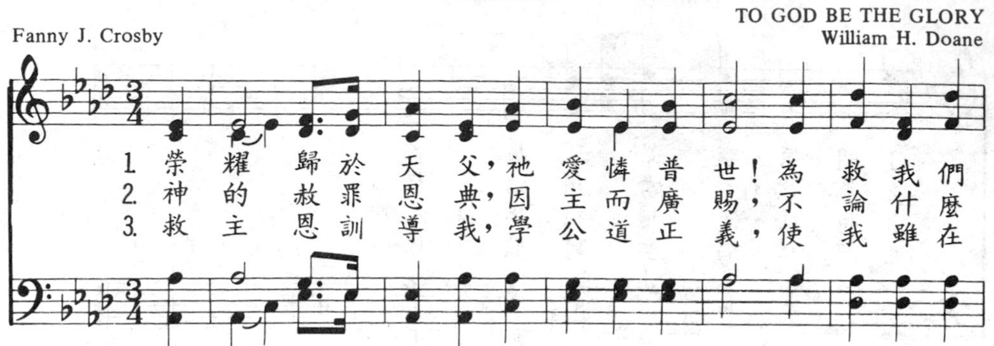

1. 榮 耀 歸 於 天 父，祂 愛 憐 普 世！為 救 我 們
2. 神 的 赦 罪 恩 典，因 主 而 廣 賜，不 論 什 麼
3. 救 主 恩 訓 導 我，學 公 道 正 義，使 我 雖 在

1 To God be the glo - ry—great things He hath done! So loved He the
2 *O per - fect re - demp - tion, the pur - chase of blood, To ev - ery be -*
3 Great things He hath taught us, great things He hath done, And great our re -

1. 罪 人 賜 下 獨 生 子；主 也 甘 心 情 願 為
2. 罪 人 靠 主 都 得 贖；你 罪 惡 雖 極 重 若
3. 世 上 安 樂 如 在 天；直 等 我 的 眼 睛 得

1 world that He gave us His Son, Who yield - ed His life an a -
2 *liev - er the prom - ise of God; The vil - est of - fen - der who*
3 joic - ing through Je - sus the Son; But pur - er, and high - er, and

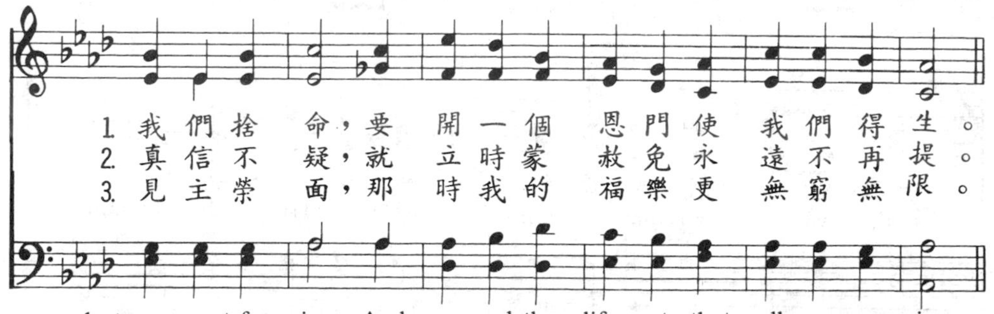

1. 我 們 捨 命，要 開 一 個 恩 門 使 我 們 得 生。
2. 真 信 不 疑，就 立 時 蒙 赦 免 永 遠 不 再 提。
3. 見 主 榮 面，那 時 我 的 福 樂 更 無 窮 無 限。

1 tone - ment for sin, And o - pened the life - gate that all may go in.
2 *tru - ly be - lieves, That mo - ment from Je - sus a par - don re - ceives.*
3 great - er will be Our won - der, our trans - port, when Je - sus we see.

讚美主，讚美主，全地當尊祂名！讚美
Praise the Lord, praise the Lord, Let the earth hear His voice! Praise the
主，讚美主，萬民都當歡欣！藉着聖子耶穌可
Lord, praise the Lord, Let the peo-ple re-joice! O come to the Fa-ther thru
親近天父，祂已成功救贖，榮耀歸天父！
Je-sus the Son, And give Him the glo-ry—great things He hath done!

神阿，願你崇高，過於諸天，願你的榮耀，高過全地。

詩篇五十七篇
5節

244

讚美我主極大權能

We Sing the Greatness of Our God

Isaac Watts
Jeff Redd, alt.

Great is our Lord, and of great power; His understanding is infinite.
— Psalm 147:5

ELLACOMBE
"Gesangbuch der Herzogl," Wirtemberg

1. 讚美我主極大權能，祂使群山屹立，
2. 讚美恩主滿有憐恤，使地生出五穀，
3. 天下所有花草樹木，無不彰顯主榮，
1 We sing the great-ness of our God That made the moun-tains rise,
2 *We sing the good-ness of the Lord That filled the earth with food;*
3 There's not a plant or flower be-low But makes Thy glo-ries known;

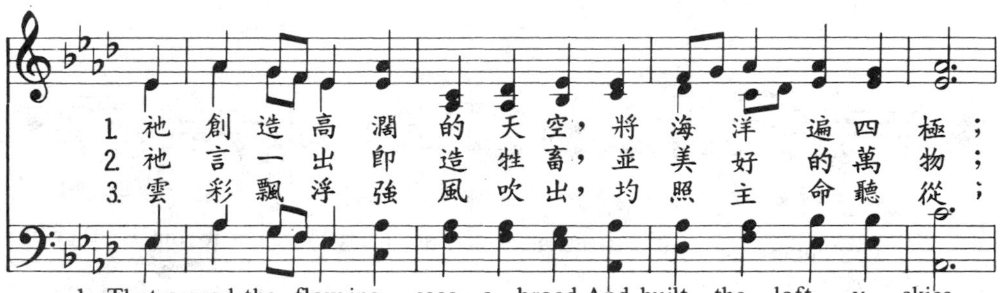
1. 祂創造高濶的天空，将海洋遍四極；
2. 祂言一出卽造牲畜，並美好的萬物；
3. 雲彩飄浮強風吹出，均照主命聽從；
1 That spread the flow-ing seas a-broad And built the loft-y skies.
2 *He formed the crea-tures with His word And then pro-nounced them good.*
3 And clouds a-rise and tem-pests blow By or-der from Thy throne,

1. 祂設日光治理白晝，祂的智慧無窮；
2. 主祢所陳設的萬象，都呈現在眼前；
3. 衆生都從主得氣息，蒙主眷顧愛寵；
1 We sing the wis-dom that or-dained The sun to rule the day;
2 *Lord, how Thy won-ders are dis-played Wher-e'er we turn our eyes:*
3 While all that bor-rows life from Thee Is ev-er in Thy care,

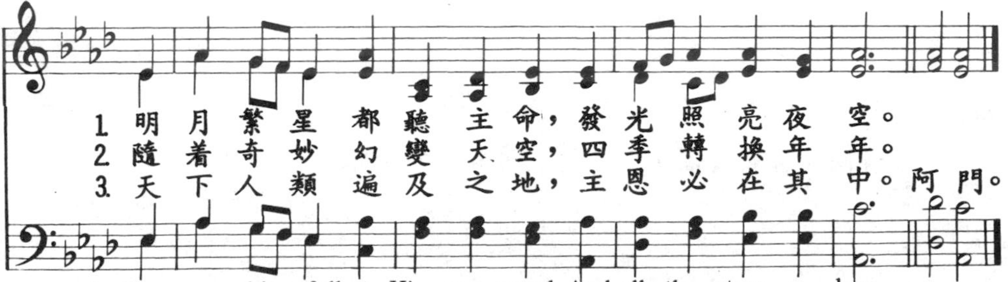
1. 明月繁星都聽主命，發光照亮夜空。
2. 隨着奇妙幻變天空，四季轉換年年。
3. 天下人類遍及之地，主恩必在其中。阿門。
1 The moon shines full at His com-mand, And all the stars o-bey.
2 *In ev-ery sea-son of the year, And through the changing skies.*
3 And ev-ery-where that man can be, Thou, God, art pres-ent there. A-men.

聖徒齊來歌唱
Come, Christians, Join to Sing

For . . . we have a building of God, a house not made with hands, eternal in the heavens.
— II Corinthians 5:1

Christian Henry Bateman

MADRID
Traditional

1. 聖徒齊來歌唱：哈利路亞！阿門！
2. 齊來向主仰望：哈利路亞！阿門！
3. 再來讚美基督：哈利路亞！阿門！
1 Come, Chris - tians, join to sing Al - le - lu - ia! A - men!
2 Come, lift your hearts on high; Al - le - lu - ia! A - men!
3 Praise yet our Christ a - gain; Al - le - lu - ia! A - men!
1. 讚美基督我王；哈利路亞！阿門！
2. 頌讚聲滿天上；哈利路亞！阿門！
3. 生命喜樂滿足；哈利路亞！阿門！
1 Loud praise to Christ our King; Al - le - lu - ia! A - men!
2 Let prais - es fill the sky; Al - le - lu - ia! A - men!
3 Life shall not end the strain; Al - le - lu - ia! A - men!
1. 大家一心頌揚，在寶座前歡唱；主必喜
2. 祂是牧者良友，降卑代贖罪尤；祂的慈
3. 在天福樂美境，主前崇拜奉敬；歌唱永
1 Let all, with heart and voice, Be - fore His throne re - joice; Praise is His
2 He is our Guide and Friend; To us He'll con - de - scend; His love shall
3 On heav-en's bliss - ful shore His good - ness we'll a - dore, Sing - ing for-
1. 悅欣賞：哈利路亞！阿門！
2. 愛永久：哈利路亞！阿門！
3. 遠不停：哈利路亞！阿門！阿門！
1 gra-cious choice: Al - le - lu - ia! A - men!
2 nev - er end: Al - le - lu - ia! A - men!
3 ev - er-more, "Al - le - lu - ia! A - men!" A - men.

246

主手所造

All Creatures of Our God and King

Francis of Assisi
Tr. by William H. Draper
Bryan Jeffery Leech, stanza 5

Sing unto the Lord a new song, and praise Him in the congregation.
— Psalm 149:1

LASST UNS ERFREUEN
Geistliche Kirchengesäng

Unison
1. 主 手 所 造 萬 象 生 靈， 同 發 聲 音 讚 美 真
2. 清 清 河 水 長 流 不 歇， 熊 熊 烈 火 供 人 光
3. 仁 心 世 人 遵 守 主 命， 饒 恕 弟 兄 榮 神 益
4. 萬 物 讚 美 造 物 主 宰， 都 當 謙 卑 向 主 敬
1 All crea-tures of our God and King, Lift up your voice and with us
2 Thou rush-ing wind that art so strong, Ye clouds that sail in heaven a-
3 Thou flow-ing wa-ter, pure and clear, Make mu-sic for thy Lord to
4 Let all things their Cre-a-tor bless, And wor-ship Him in hum-ble-
Harmony
Unison
1. 神， 哈 利 路 亞！哈 利 路 亞！溫 柔 明 月，光
2. 熱， 哈 利 路 亞！哈 利 路 亞！大 地 高 山 無
3. 人， 哈 利 路 亞！哈 利 路 亞！世 人 飽 受 痛
4. 拜， 哈 利 路 亞！哈 利 路 亞！讚 美 聖 父，聖
1 sing, Al-le-lu-ia! Al-le-lu-ia! Thou burn-ing sun with
2 long, O praise Him! Al-le-lu-ia! Thou ris-ing morn, in
3 hear, Al-le-lu-ia! Al-le-lu-ia! Thou fire so mas-ter-
4 ness. O praise Him! Al-le-lu-ia! Praise, praise the Fa-ther,
1. 耀 日 輪， 狂 風 密 雲 清 晨 黃 昏， 讚 美 真 神！
2. 盡 寶 藏， 滋 生 萬 物 花 草 芬 芳， 讚 美 真 神！
3. 苦 憂 驚， 速 將 憂 慮 卸 給 真 神， 讚 美 真 神！
4. 子，聖 靈， 同 聲 讚 美 三 一 真 神， 讚 美 真 神！
1 gold-en beam, Thou sil-ver moon with soft-er gleam, O praise Him!
2 praise re-joice, Ye lights of eve-ning, find a voice! O praise Him!
3 ful and bright, That giv-est man both warmth and light, O praise Him!
4 praise the Son, And praise the Spir-it, Three in One! O praise Him!

讚美真 神!哈利路 亞!哈利路 亞!哈利路 亞!
O praise Him! Al-le-lu-ia! Al-le-lu-ia! Al-le-lu-ia!

247

耶穌呼召

Jesus Calls Us o'er the Tumult

Lord, if it be Thou, bid me come . . And He said, Come.
— Matthew 14:28,29

Cecil Frances Alexander
Jeff Redd, alt.

GALILEE
William H. Jude

1. 人生 海上 波濤 洶湧，主耶 穌向 我呼 召，
2. 加利 利海 主曾 呼召，衆門 徒捨 網投 靠，
3. 或是 喜樂 或是 憂傷，或辛 勞或 享安 樂，
4. 耶穌 召我 滿有 恩慈，求使 我聽 主呼 召，

1 Je - sus calls us o'er the tu-mult Of our life's wild, rest-less sea;
2 *As, of old, dis - ci - ples heard it By the Gal - i - le - an lake,*
3 In our joys and in our sor-rows, Days of toil and hours of ease,
4 *Je - sus calls us: by Thy mer-cies, Sav-ior, may we hear Thy call,*

1. 主聲 溫柔 天天 呼召，"跟隨 我必 免飄 搖。"
2. 家庭 親友 工作 嗜好，今為 愛主 甘願 拋。
3. 主仍 關懷 向我 呼召，"你要 愛我 更加 多。"
4. 獻我 身心 遵行 主道，事主 愛主 不動 搖。阿門。

1 Day by day I hear Him say-ing, "Chris-tian, come and fol-low me."
2 *Turned from home and work and lei-sure, Leav-ing all for His dear sake:*
3 Still He calls in cares and pleas-ures, "Chris-tian, love me more than these."
4 *Give our hearts to Thine o-be-dience, Serve and love Thee best of all.* A-men.

248

來擁戴主為王

Crown Him with Many Crowns

And on His head were many crowns.
— Revelation 19:12

Matthew Bridges
Godfrey Thring

DIADEMATA
George J. Elvey

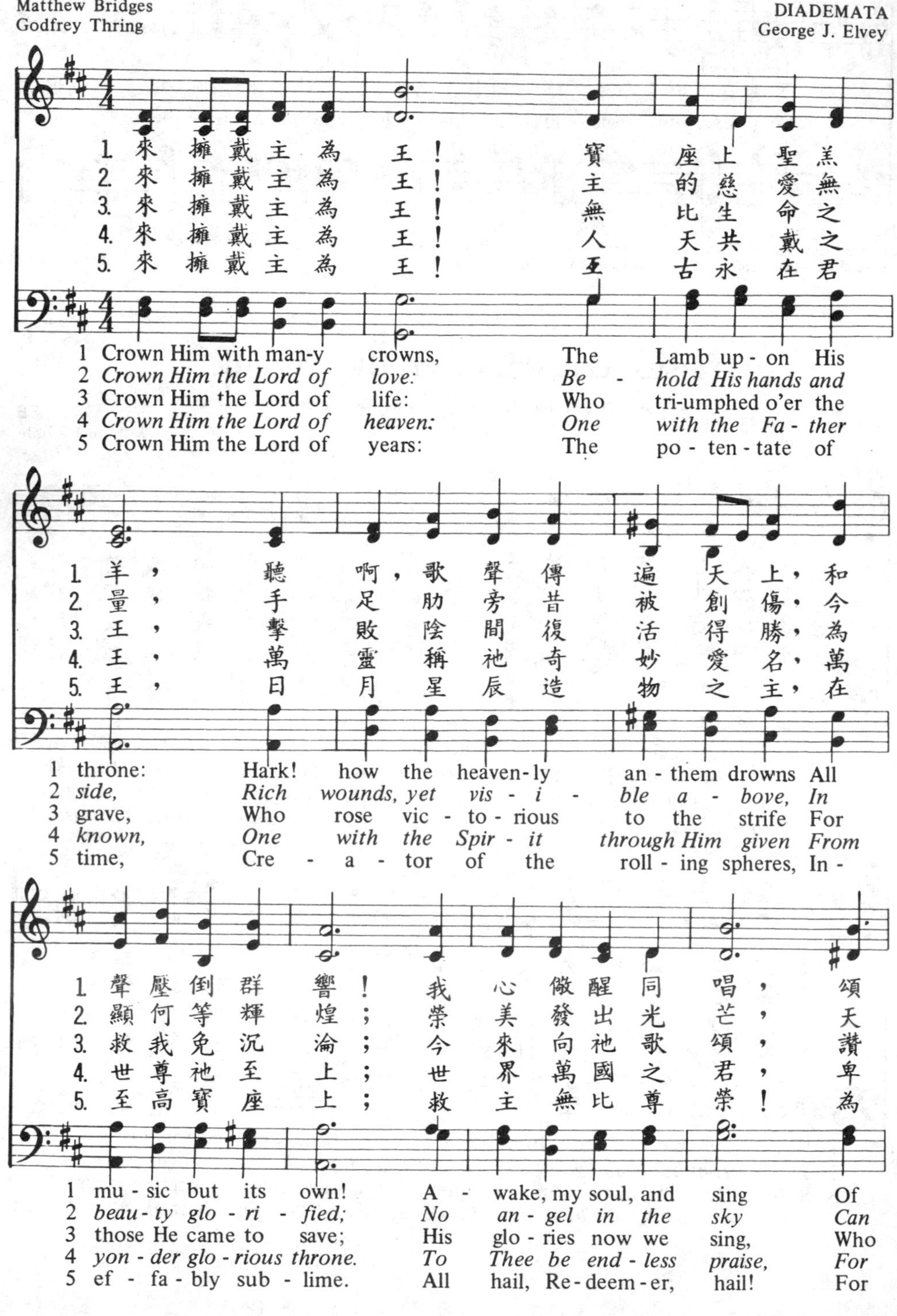

1. 來 擁 戴 主 為 王！寶 座 上 聖 羔
2. 來 擁 戴 主 為 王！主 的 慈 愛 無
3. 來 擁 戴 主 為 王！無 比 生 命 之
4. 來 擁 戴 主 為 王！人 天 共 戴 之
5. 來 擁 戴 主 為 王！亙 古 永 在 君
1 Crown Him with man-y crowns, The Lamb up-on His
2 Crown Him the Lord of love: Be-hold His hands and
3 Crown Him the Lord of life: Who tri-umphed o'er the
4 Crown Him the Lord of heaven: One with the Fa-ther
5 Crown Him the Lord of years: The po-ten-tate of
1. 羊，聽 啊，歌 聲 傳 遍 天 上，和
2. 量，手 足 肋 旁 昔 被 創 傷，今
3. 王，擊 敗 陰 間 復 活 得 勝，為
4. 王，萬 靈 稱 祂 奇 妙 愛 名，萬
5. 王，日 月 星 辰 造 物 之 主，在
1 throne: Hark! how the heaven-ly an-them drowns All
2 side, Rich wounds, yet vis-i-ble a-bove, In
3 grave, Who rose vic-to-rious to the strife For
4 known, One with the Spir-it through Him given From
5 time, Cre-a-tor of the roll-ing spheres, In-
1. 聲 壓 倒 群 響！我 心 儆 醒 同 唱，頌
2. 顯 何 等 輝 煌；榮 美 發 出 光 芒，天
3. 救 我 免 沉 淪；今 來 向 祂 歌 頌，讚
4. 世 尊 祂 至 上；世 界 萬 國 之 君，卑
5. 至 高 寶 座 上；救 主 無 比 尊 榮！為
1 mu-sic but its own! A-wake, my soul, and sing Of
2 beau-ty glo-ri-fied; No an-gel in the sky Can
3 those He came to save; His glo-ries now we sing, Who
4 yon-der glo-rious throne. To Thee be end-less praise, For
5 ef-fa-bly sub-lime. All hail, Re-deem-er, hail! For

1. 主救恩浩蕩，歡呼為我受
2. 使敬拜頌揚，諦視驚喜讚
3. 美我主宏恩，因祂為罪替
4. 伏覲見至尊，齊摘華冠敬
5. 我竟捨己命，讚美尊貴榮
1 Him who died for thee; And hail Him as thy
2 *ful - ly bear that sight, But down - ward bends His*
3 died and rose on high, Who died e - ter - nal
4 *Thou for us hast died; Be Thou, O Lord, through*
5 Thou hast died for me; Thy praise and glo - ry
1. 死之主，千秋萬歲無疆。
2. 其超奇，奧祕不可測想。
3. 我受死，為我帶來永生。
4. 伏座前，稱頌我主奇恩。
5. 耀救主，到永遠無窮盡。 阿門。
1 match - less King Through all e - ter - ni - ty.
2 *won - dering eye At mys - ter - ies so bright.*
3 life to bring, And lives that death may die.
4 *end - less days A - dored and mag - ni - fied.*
5 shall not fail Through - out e - ter - ni - ty. A - men.

Praise to God

Leader: We lift up our hearts,
and bring You our worship and praise!

People: We lift up our voices
and sing You our worship and praise!

Leader and People: Praise and honor, glory and might,
to Him who sits on the throne,
and to the Lamb for ever and ever! Amen!!

249 我靈讚美天上君王
Praise My Soul, the King of Heaven

'Til we all come to the unity and knowledge of the Son of God. — Ephesians 4:13
Henry F. Lyte
LAUDA ANIMA
Mark Andrews
Unison
1. 我靈讚美天上君王，在主前將心獻上；蒙恩拯救醫治創傷，應當永遠高聲唱；哈利路亞，
2. 應當讚美上主宏恩，曾救先祖免沉淪；從古至今主恩不變，不輕責罰仍施恩；哈利路亞，
3. 脆弱生命瞬卽消失，但主慈愛仍看顧；體恤憐憫恩手扶持，永遠不變常保護；哈利路亞，
4. 天上天使虔誠敬拜，注目瞻仰主榮面；得勝聖徒屈膝跪拜，萬民同伏在主前；哈利路亞，
1 Praise, my soul, the King of heaven, To His feet thy tribute bring; Ransomed, healed, restored, forgiven, Evermore His praises sing; Alleluia!
2 Praise Him for His grace and favor To our fathers in distress; Praise Him, still the same as ever, Slow to chide and swift to bless; Alleluia!
3 Frail as summer's flower we flourish, Blows the wind and it is gone; But, while mortals rise and perish, God endures unchanging on: Alleluia!
4 Angels in the height, adore Him; Ye behold Him face to face; Saints triumphant, bow before Him, Gathered in from every race; Alleluia!

1. 哈 利 路 亞！高聲 讚美 永 生 王。
2. 哈 利 路 亞！主的 信實 何 等深。
3. 哈 利 路 亞！讚美 至高 救 世主。
4. 哈 利 路 亞！同聲 頌讚 主 恩 典。 阿 們。
1 Al - le - lu - ia! Praise the ev - er - last - ing King.
2 Al - le - lu - ia! Glo - rious in His faith - ful - ness.
3 Al - le - lu - ia! Praise the high e - ter - nal one.
4 Al - le - lu - ia! Praise with us the God of grace. A - men.
我知一活泉
I Know a Fount
250
I KNOW A FOUNT
O. Cooke
In that day there shall be a fountain opened . . . for sin and for uncleanness.
— Zechariah 13:1
O. Cooke
我 知 一 活 泉 能 洗 衆 罪 孽，
I know a fount where sins are washed a - way,
我 知 有 一 地 不 再 有 黑 夜；
I know a place where night is turned to day;
重 擔 得 脱 落， 瞎 眼 能 看 見， 寶 血
Bur - dens are lift - ed, blind eyes made to see; There's a
能 力 有 功 效， 全 靠 加 略 山 恩 典。
won - der work - ing power in the blood of Cal - va - ry.

251

有時 "哈利路亞"

Sometimes "Alleluia"

Blessed is His glorious name forever; let the whole earth be filled with His glory.

— Psalm 72:19

Chuck Girard
SOMETIMES ALLELUIA
Chuck Girard
有時"哈利路亞," 有時"讚美主;"
Some-times "Al-le-lu-ia," Some-times "Praise the Lord;"
有時柔聲輕唱,同心齊聲頌揚。
Some-times gent-ly sing-ing, Our hearts in one ac-cord.
1. 讓我們齊聲同唱,向天舉目高聲頌揚;
2. 讓我們盡情歡欣,自由自在的高聲唱;
3. 當主與我們同在,歡呼歌聲到處悠揚;
4. 讓聖靈自由運行,充滿我們的全身體;
1 O let us lift our voic-es, Look toward the sky and start to sing;
2 O let our joy be un-con-fined, Let us sing with free-dom un-re-strained;
3 O let us feel His pres-ence, Let the sound of prais-es fill the air;
4 O let the Spir-it o-ver-flow, As we are filled from head to toe;

1. 哦，讓我們報答主的恩愛，齊來向主高聲歌唱。
2. 讓我們撇開愁苦與煩惱，流露出快樂與歡暢。
3. 哦，讓我們歌頌救主慈愛，願主慈愛遍及各方。
4. 聖父，聖子，聖靈，我願愛祢，願世人都能認識祢。
1 O, let us now re - turn His love— Just let our voic - es ring.
2 Let's take this feel - ing that we're feel - ing now Out - side these walls and let it rain.
3 O, let us sing the song of Je - sus' love To peo - ple ev - ery - where.
4 We love You Fa - ther, Son and Ho - ly Ghost, And we want this world to know.
1, 2, 3
D.C.
4
有時"哈利路亞，"有時"讚美主；"
Some - times "Al - le - lu - ia," Some - times "Praise the Lord;"
有時柔聲輕唱，同心齊聲頌揚。
Some - times gent - ly sing - ing, Our hearts in one ac - cord.

我心獻曲
My Tribute

Not unto us, O Lord, but unto Thy name give glory. — Psalm 115:1

Andraé Crouch

MY TRIBUTE
Andraé Crouch

當 如何訴 說 祢為 我 成就 的 事情？
How can I say thanks for the things You have done for me?

我 何等不配，但祢 却 用愛向 我顯明；雖
Things so un-de-served, Yet You gave to prove Your love for me; The

然有千萬天使歌頌，仍難表 達 我的感恩。
voic-es of a mil-lion an-gels could not ex-press my gra-ti-tude.

我今願 意將一切所有的， 完全都歸於 祢。
All that I am, and ev-er hope to be; I owe it all to Thee.

榮 耀 歸於 真 神，榮 耀 歸於 真 神，
To God be the glo - ry, To God be the glo - ry,
榮 耀 歸於 真 神，因 祂 成 就 大 事。
To God be the glo - ry For the things He has done.
祂 流 血，救 我 性 命；祂 能 力，使 我 復 興；
With His blood He has saved me; With His power He has raised me;
Fine
榮 耀 歸 於 真 神，因 祂 成 就 大 事。
To God be the glo - ry for the things He has done.
願 我 活 着 生 命 — 討 主 的 喜 悅，聽 主 令；
Just let me live my life — Let it be pleas-ing, Lord, to Thee;
D.S. al Fine
一 切 榮 耀 和 讚 美，都 歸 於 加 略 山 頂，祂 流
And if I gain an-y praise, Let it go to Cal - va - ry. With His

榮耀是主聖名

Glorious Is Thy Name

But in every nation He that feareth Him,
and worketh righteousness is accepted by Him. — Acts 10:35

B. B. McKinney

B. B. McKinney

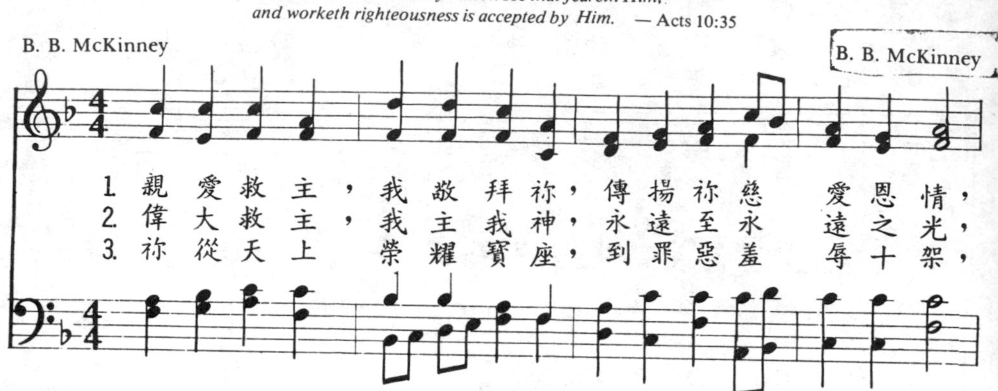
1. 親 愛 救 主，我 敬 拜 祢，傳 揚 祢 慈 愛 恩 情，
2. 偉 大 救 主，我 主 我 神，永 遠 至 永 遠 之 光，
3. 祢 從 天 上 榮 耀 寶 座，到 罪 惡 羞 辱 十 架，

1. Bless-ed Sav-iour, we a-dore Thee, We Thy love and grace pro-claim;
2. *Great re-deem-er, Lord and Mas-ter, Light of all e - ter - nal days;*
3. From the throne of heav-en's glo - ry To the cross of sin and shame,

1. 祢 有 能 力，祢 是 聖 潔，榮 耀 是 祢 無 比 名。
2. 讓 普 天 下 萬 衆 聖 徒，頌 讚 公 義 永 生 王。
3. 為 要 救 贖 世 人 靈 魂，甘 願 死 在 各 各 他。

1. Thou art might-y, Thou art ho - ly, Glo-rious is Thy match-less name!
2. *Let the saints of ev - 'ry na - tion Sing thy just and end - less praise!*
3. Thou didst come to die a ran - som Guilt - y sin - ners to re - claim.

真 ……………… 榮 耀，真 ……………… 榮 耀，
Glo - - - - - ri-ous, Glo - - - - - ri - ous,

榮 耀 是 救 主 聖 名！榮 耀 是 救 主 聖 名！
Glo - rious is Thy name, O Lord! Glo - rious is Thy name, O Lord!

榮耀是救 主聖 名！真…………… 榮耀，
Glo-rious is Thy name, O Lord! Glo - - - - ri-ous,
榮耀是救 主聖名！
Glo-rious is Thy name,O Lord!
真………… 榮耀，榮耀是救主聖 名！
Glo - - - - ri-ous, Glo-rous is Thy name, O Lord!
榮耀是救 主聖名！
Glo-rious is Thy name, O Lord!

神阿，願你崇高，過於諸天，願你的榮耀，高過全地。
神阿，我心堅定，我心堅定，我要唱詩，我要歌頌。
我的靈阿，你當醒起，琴瑟阿，你們當醒起，我自己要極早醒起。
主阿，我要在萬民中稱謝你，在列邦中歌頌你。
因為你的慈愛高及諸天，你的誠實達到穹蒼。
神阿，願你崇高，過於諸天，願你的榮耀，高過全地。

詩篇五十七篇
5，7—11節

讚美！讚美！
Praise Him! Praise Him!

The Kingdom of God is . . . righteousness and peace, and joy in the Holy Spirit.
— Romans 14:17

Fanny J. Crosby

Chester G. Allen

1. 讚美！讚美！讚美耶穌慈愛救主，全地
2. 讚美！讚美！讚美耶穌慈愛救主，為我
3. 讚美！讚美！讚美耶穌慈愛救主，天上
1. Praise Him! praise Him! Je - sus, our bless-ed Re - deem - er! Sing, O
2. Praise Him! praise Him! Je - sus, our bless-ed Re - deem - er! For our
3. Praise Him! praise Him! Je - sus, our bless-ed Re - deem - er! Heav'n-ly

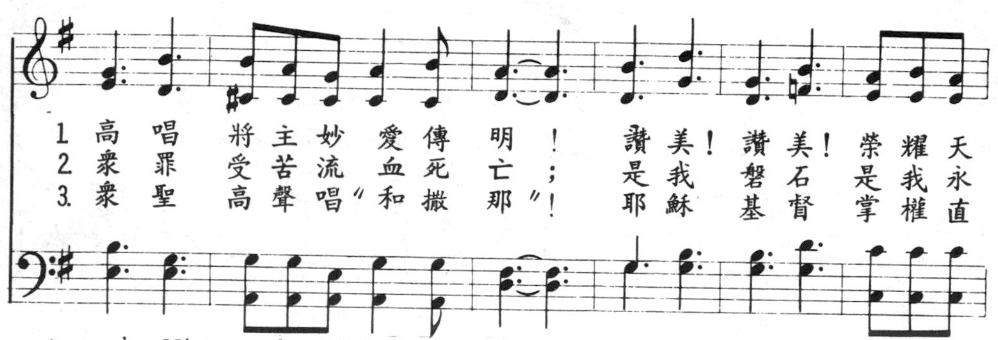
1. 高唱將主妙愛傳明！讚美！讚美！榮耀天
2. 衆罪受苦流血死亡；是我磐石是我永
3. 衆聖高聲唱“和撒那”！耶穌基督掌權直
1. earth—His won-der-ful love pro - claim! Hail Him! hail Him! high-est arch-
2. sins He suf-fered and bled and died; He our Rock, our hope of e -
3. por - tals loud with ho-san - nas ring! Je - sus, Sav - ior, reign-eth for

1. 使俯伏歌唱，榮耀，尊貴，都歸救主聖名！
2. 遠救恩盼望，讚美！讚美！耶穌被釘君王！
3. 到永永遠遠，冠祂！冠祂！先知祭司君王！
1. an - gels in glo - ry, Strength and hon - or give to His ho - ly name!
2. ter - nal sal - va - tion, Hail Him! hail Him! Je - sus the Cru - ci - fied.
3. ev - er and ev - er, Crown Him! crown Him! Proph-et and Priest and King!

1. 如同牧人耶穌保護祂小羊，用祂膀臂
2. 高聲讚美耶穌担當我憂傷，無比大愛
3. 基督來臨戰勝罪惡與死亡，榮耀權能
1. Like a shep - herd Je-sus will guard His chil - dren— In His arms He
2. Sound His prais - es— Je-sus who bore our sor - rows— Love un - bound-ed,
3. Christ is com - ing, O - ver the world vic - to - rious— Pow'r and glo - ry
1. 終日懷抱撫養：
2. 奇妙深厚堅強：
3. 都歸耶穌我王：
讚美！讚美！述說祂無比的
Praise Him! praise Him! tell of His ex-cel-lent
1. car - ries them all day long:
2. won- der- ful, deep and strong:
3. un - to the Lord be - long:
大愛！讚美！讚美！歡呼直到萬代！
great - ness! Praise Him! praise Him! ev - er in joy - ful song!

255

懇求聖父來臨

Come, Thou Almighty King

Until the Ancient of Days came . . . and . . . the saints possessed the Kingdom.
— Daniel 7:22

Anonymous
ITALIAN HYMN
Felice de Giardini
1. 懇 求 聖 父 來 臨，助 我 讚 美 主 名，敬 獻 心 聲：惟 主 無 上 尊 榮，惟 主 完 全 得 勝，求 主 統
2. 懇 求 聖 子 來 臨，彰 顯 威 嚴 大 能，垂 聽 呼 聲：施 恩 與 衆 子 民，使 主 聖 道 振 興；求 主 聖
3. 懇 求 聖 靈 來 臨，顯 出 神 聖 見 證，感 化 衆 人：惟 主 全 能 至 尊，懇 求 統 治 衆 心，永 不 離
4. 聖 父 聖 子 聖 靈，當 受 萬 民 稱 頌，世 世 無 盡！領 我 進 入 光 榮，見 你 威 嚴 慈 容，獻 上 虔
1 Come, Thou Al - might - y King, Help us Thy name to sing, Help us to praise: Fa - ther, all - glo - ri - ous, O'er all vic - to - ri - ous, Come, and reign
2 Come, Thou In - car - nate Word, Gird on Thy might - y sword, Our prayer at - tend: Come, and Thy peo - ple bless, And give Thy word suc - cess; Spir - it of
3 Come, Ho - ly Com - fort - er, Thy sa - cred wit - ness bear In this glad hour: Thou who al - might - y art, Now rule in ev - ery heart, Nev - er from
4 To Thee, great One in Three, The high - est prais - es be, Hence ev - er - more! Thy sov - ereign maj - es - ty May we in glo - ry see, And to e -

1. 治我們，萬古之神。
2. 潔之靈，臨到我們。
3. 開我們，大能聖靈。
4. 誠敬崇，永遠無窮。阿門。
1 o - ver us, An - cient of Days.
2 ho - li - ness, On us de - scend.
3 us de - part, Spir - it of power.
4 ter - ni - ty Love and a - dore. A - men.

三一頌（1） 256

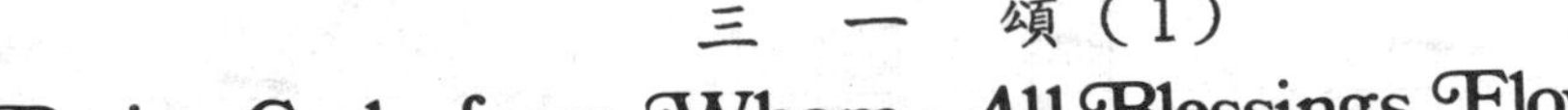
Praise God, from Whom All Blessings Flow

. . . *Who hath blessed us with all spiritual blessings.* — Ephesians 1:3

OLD 100th
Attributed to Louis Bourgeois
Genevan Psalter

Thomas Ken

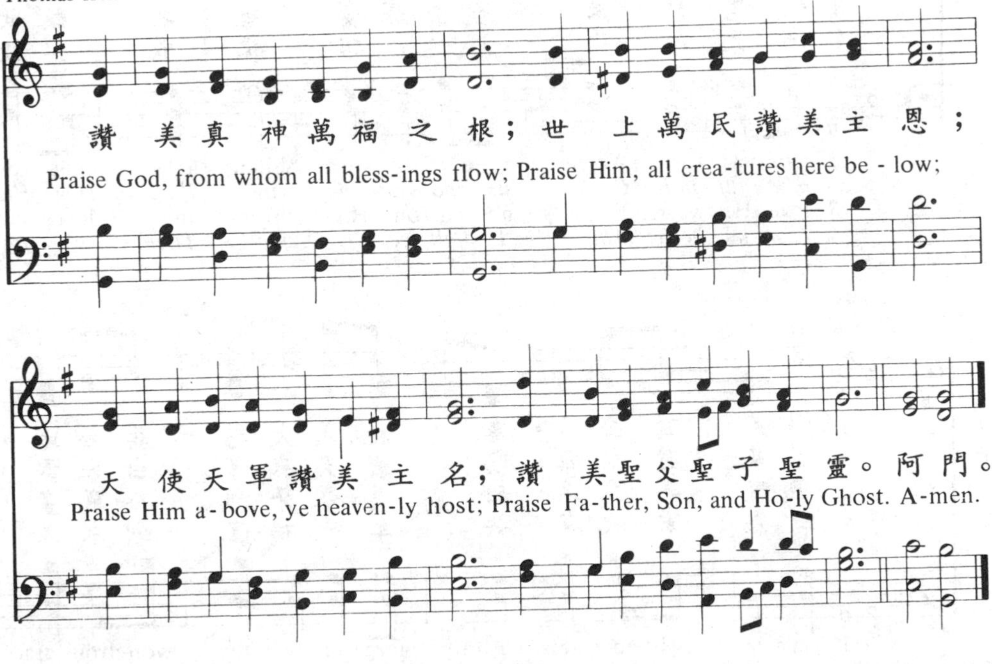

讚美真神萬福之根；世上萬民讚美主恩；
Praise God, from whom all bless-ings flow; Praise Him, all crea-tures here be - low;

天使天軍讚美主名；讚美聖父聖子聖靈。阿門。
Praise Him a-bove, ye heaven-ly host; Praise Fa-ther, Son, and Ho-ly Ghost. A-men.

257

述說恩主功德無量

O Could I Speak the Matchless Worth

This is the Lord's doing, and it is marvelous in our eyes.
— Psalm 118:23
ARIEL
Wolfgang A. Mozart
Adapted by Lowell Mason
Samuel Medley
1. 述 說 恩 主 功 德 無 量，向 神 發 出 讚
2. 歌 頌 救 主 所 流 寶 血，賜 我 救 贖 除
3. 歌 頌 救 主 豐 功 偉 蹟，救 主 滿 有 憐
4. 快 樂 之 日 將 要 來 臨，救 主 接 我 回
1 O could I speak the match - less worth, O could I sound the
2 I'd sing the pre - cious blood He spilt, My ran-som from the
3 I'd sing the char - ac - ter He bears, And all the forms of
4 Soon the de - light - ful day will come When my dear Lord will
1. 美 聲 響，救 主 的 大 榮 光！我 願 高
2. 我 罪 孽，使 我 得 着 盼 望；我 願 高
3. 憫 恩 慈，高 居 榮 耀 寶 座；我 願 歌
4. 到 天 庭，與 主 永 遠 相 親；我 與 救
1 glo-ries forth Which in my Sav - ior shine! I'd sing His
2 dread-ful guilt Of sin, and wrath di - vine; I'd sing His
3 love He wears, Ex - alt - ed on His throne; In loft - iest
4 bring me home, And I shall see His face; Then with my
1. 唱 基 督 公 義，尊 祂 為 大 恩 典 無 比，
2. 唱 基 督 聖 潔，賜 我 天 衣 潔 白 如 雪，
3. 頌 讚 美 主 名，甜 美 歌 聲 到 無 窮 盡，
4. 主 與 衆 親 友，共 享 天 福 直 到 永 久，
1 per - fect right-eous-ness, And mag - ni - fy the won-drous grace
2 glo - rious ho - li - ness, In which all-per - fect, heaven-ly dress
3 songs of sweet - est praise, I would to ev - er - last - ing days
4 Sav - ior, broth - er, friend, A blest e - ter - ni - ty I'll spend,

1. 救恩使我歡暢，救恩使我歡暢。
2. 我靈永遠發光，我靈永遠發光。
3. 榮耀歸祂寶座，榮耀歸祂寶座。
4. 在祂恩中歡慶，在祂恩中歡慶。
1 Which made sal - va - tion mine, Which made sal - va - tion mine.
2 *My soul shall ev - er shine, My soul shall ev - er shine.*
3 Make all His glo - ries known, Make all His glo - ries known.
4 *Tri - um - phant in His grace, Tri - um-phant in His grace.*

258

我願全心讚美
I Will Praise Thee

Let all the people praise thee, O God . . . — Psalm 67:3

Psalm 9:1.2

Dana Rhodes

我願全心讚美我主我神，我願彰顯祢奇妙大工；我願意在祢裡面歡樂高聲唱，讚美祢至高聖名。

I will praise Thee, O Lord with all my heart, I will show forth Thy mar - vel - ous works. I will be glad and re - joice in Thee I will sing praise to Thy name, O most high.

259

頌讚主聖名

Blessed Be the Name

For He must reign until He hath put all enemies under His feet.

I Corinthians 15: 25

BLESSED BE THE NAME
W. H. Clark
Refrain added by Ralph E. Hudson
Ralph E. Hudson
Harmonized by William J. Kirkpatrick
1 頌讚歸與耶穌聖名，至高至聖至尊，天上地下歌頌主名，歌聲晝夜不停！
2 耶穌聖名滿有權能，使魔鬼都逃遁，能使罪人出死入生，得到天堂福份。
3 主名稱為奇妙策士，全能和平之君，萬膝跪拜萬口承認，榮耀永歸主名。
4 主名何等佳美馨香，普遍宇宙穹蒼，主名超乎萬名之上，配受一切頌揚。
1 All praise to Him who reigns a-bove In maj-es-ty su-preme, Who gave His Son for man to die, That He might man re-deem!
2 His name a-bove all names shall stand, Ex-alt-ed more and more, At God the Fa-ther's own right hand, Where an-gel-hosts a-dore.
3 Re-deem-er, Sav-ior, friend of man Once ru-ined by the fall, Thou hast de-vised sal-va-tion's plan, For Thou hast died for all.
4 His name shall be the Coun-sel-or, The might-y Prince of Peace, Of all earth's king-doms con-quer-or, Whose reign shall nev-er cease.
頌讚主聖名！頌讚主聖名！頌讚榮耀歸主聖名！
Bless-ed be the name! Bless-ed be the name! Bless-ed be the name of the Lord!
頌讚主聖名！頌讚主聖名！頌讚榮耀歸主聖名！
Bless-ed be the name! Bless-ed be the name! Bless-ed be the name of the Lord!

讚美耶穌
I Will Praise Him!

And they overcame Him by the blood of the Lamb.
— Revelation 12:11

Margaret J. Harris

I WILL PRAISE HIM
Margaret J. Harris

1. 當我見那寶貴血泉，要洗我一切罪愆；
2. 頌讚永歸耶穌聖名，因主歡喜救罪人；
3. 前所懷抱追求盼望，今都算足下灰塵；
4. 榮耀榮耀歸於聖父！榮耀榮耀歸聖子！
1 When I saw the cleans-ing foun-tain, O - pen wide for all my sin,
2 Tho the way seems straight and nar-row, All I claimed was swept a - way;
3 Bless - ed be the name of Je - sus! I'm so glad He took me in;
4 Glo - ry, glo - ry to the Fa-ther! Glo - ry, glo - ry to the Son!
1. 心中隱聞聖靈微聲，問說"你願否潔淨？"
2. 白白赦我一切罪惡，洗淨我的污穢心。
3. 路雖崎嶇敵雖凶猛，靠主十架全得勝。
4. 榮耀榮耀歸於聖靈！榮耀歸於三一主！
1 I o-beyed the Spir - it's call - ing When He said, "Wilt thou be clean?"
2 My am - bi - tions, plans and wish - es At my feet in dis - ar - ray.
3 He's for-giv - en my trans - gres-sions, He has cleansed by heart from sin.
4 Glo - ry, glo - ry to the Spir - it! Glo - ry to the Three in One!
讚美耶穌！讚美耶穌！讚美主為罪人死；
I will praise Him! I will praise Him! Praise the Lamb for sin-ners slain;
萬民當將榮耀歸主，因主血能洗淨衆罪污。
Give Him glo-ry, all ye peo-ple, For His blood can wash a-way each stain.

願有讚美主之心
O for a Heart to Praise My God

God forbid that I glory, save in the cross of our Lord Jesus Christ . . . .
— Galatians 6:14

Charles Wesley

RICHMOND
Thomas Haweis

1. 願 我 常 有 讚 主 之 心，此 心 蒙
2. 願 有 謙 卑 溫 和 之 心，篤 信、誠
3. 願 将 我 心 舊 態 換 新，換 作 我
4. 懇 求 恩 主 将 祢 性 情，自 天 上
1 O for a heart to praise my God, A heart from
2 A hum-ble, low - ly, con - trite heart, Be - liev - ing,
3 A heart in ev - ery thought re - newed, And full of
4 Thy na-ture, gra - cious Lord, im - part– Come quick - ly

1. 主、釋 放，此 心 常 覺 救 主 為
2. 實、清 潔，或 生 或 死 與 主 相
3. 主 容 形，意 念 更 新 純 潔 純
4. 降 下 來，在 我 心 中 刻 主 新
1 sin set free, A heart that al - ways feels Thy
2 true and clean, Which neith - er life nor death can
3 love di - vine; Per fect and right and pure and
4 from a - bove; Write Thy new name up - on my

1. 我 把 血 灑 在 其 上！
2. 親，永 不 與 主 離 別。
3. 善，能 與 主 心 相 印！
4. 名，此 名 即 是 仁 愛。阿 門。
1 blood So free - ly shed for me!
2 part From Him that dwells with - in.
3 good, A cop - y, Lord, of Thine!
4 heart, Thy new best name of Love. A - men.

262

主，我們願敬愛祢

Christ, We Do All Adore Thee

Thou art worthy, O Lord, to receive glory and honor, and power . . . .

— Revelation 4:11

Adoramus Te
English version by Theodore Baker

ADORE THEE
From "The Seven Last Words of Christ"
Theodore Dubois

主，我們願敬愛祢，讚美祢一直到永遠；
Christ, we do all a - dore Thee, and we do praise Thee for - ev - er;

主，我們願敬愛祢，讚美祢一直到永遠，
Christ, we do all a - dore Thee, and we do praise Thee for - ev - er,

為救贖世上罪人，祢曾在十架上捨身。
For on the ho - ly cross hast Thou the world from sin re - deem - ed.

主，我們願敬愛祢，讚美祢一直到永遠。
Christ, we do all a - dore Thee, and we do praise Thee for - ev - er.

*Organ

主，我們願敬愛祢！
Christ, we do all a - dore Thee!

我奇妙的救主
My Wonderful Lord

His name shall be called wonderful . . . — Isaiah 9:6

Haldor Lillenas

WONDERFUL LORD
Haldor Lillenas

1. 我心深處有平安非人所能知，我有喜樂非
2. 我願将我的生命交托主管理，我心志完全
3. 我願将所有才幹奉獻祢腳前，蒙祢悅納既
4. 世上一切的美好中祢最美好，祢是全能者

1 I have found a deep peace that I nev-er had known, And a joy this world
2 *I de-sire that my life shall be or-dered by Thee, That my will be in*
3 All the tal-ents I have I have laid at Thy feet, Thy ap-prov-al shall
4 *Thou art fair-er to me than the fair-est of earth, Thou om-nip-o-tent,*

1. 人所能給，自我将我身心，完全奉獻與主，
2. 歸向救主，惟願救主旨意，成全在我身上，
3. 是我賞賜，所有或多或少，我願完全獻上，
4. 生命之道，從亙古到永久，配得榮耀讚美，

1 could not af-ford, Since I yield-ed con-trol of my bod-y and soul
2 *per-fect ac-cord With Thine own sov-ereign will, Thy de-sires to ful-fill,*
3 be my re-ward; Be my store great or small, I sur-ren-der it all
4 *life-giv-ing Word O Thou An-cient of Days, Thou art wor-thy all praise,*

1. 獻給奇妙，奇妙救主。
2. 我奇妙的，奇妙救主。
3. 獻給奇妙，奇妙救主。
4. 我奇妙的，奇妙救主。
我奇妙救主，我
My won-der-ful Lord, my

1 To my won-der-ful, won-der-ful Lord.
2 *My won-der-ful, won-der-ful Lord.*
3 To my won-der-ful, won-der-ful Lord.
4 *My won-der-ful, won-der-ful Lord.*

奇 妙 救 主，在 天 上 衆 天 使 在 歌 唱 讚 美！我
won-der-ful Lord, By an-gels and ser-aphs in heav-en a-dored! I
俯 伏 敬 拜，我 救 贖 恩 主，我 奇 妙 的，奇 妙 救 主。
bow at Thy shrine, my Sav-ior di-vine, My won-der-ful, won-der-ful Lord.

我的心哪，你要稱頌耶和華。凡在我裏面的，也要稱頌他的聖名。
我的心哪你要稱頌耶和華，不可忘記他的一切恩惠。
他用美物，使你所願的得以知足，以致你如鷹反老還童。
他救贖你的命脱離死亡，以仁愛和慈悲為你的冠冕。
他赦免你的一切罪孽，醫治你的一切疾病。

詩篇一〇三篇
1 — 5

Bless the Lod, O my soul; and all that is within me, bless his holy name!
Bless the Lord, O my soul, and forget not all his benefits,
who forgives all your iniquity, who heals all your diseases,
who redeems your life from the pit, who crowns you with steadfast love and mercy,
who satisfies you with good as long as you live so that your youth is renewed like the eagle's.

— (Psalms 103:1-5, RSV)

快樂歡欣向主敬拜

Joyful, Joyful, We Adore Thee

But unto you . . . the sun of righteousness shall arise with healing in His wings. — Malachi 4:2

Henry van Dyke

HYMN TO JOY
Ludwig van Beethoven
Adapted by Edward Hodges

1. 快 樂 歡 欣 向 主 敬 拜，榮 耀 真 神 大 慈 愛；
2. 天 地 萬 有 宇 宙 穹 蒼，欣 然 彰 顯 主 榮 光；
3. 萬 福 之 主 極 愛 施 捨，赦 罪 賜 福 到 永 遠；
4. 晨 星 發 出 讚 美 歌 聲，地 上 萬 民 齊 響 應；
1 Joy - ful, joy - ful, we a - dore Thee, God of glo - ry, Lord of love;
2 *All Thy works with joy sur-round Thee, Earth and heaven re - flect Thy rays,*
3 Thou art giv - ing and for - giv - ing, Ev - er bless - ing, ev - er blest,
4 *Mor - tals, join the hap - py cho - rus With the morn - ing stars be - gan;*

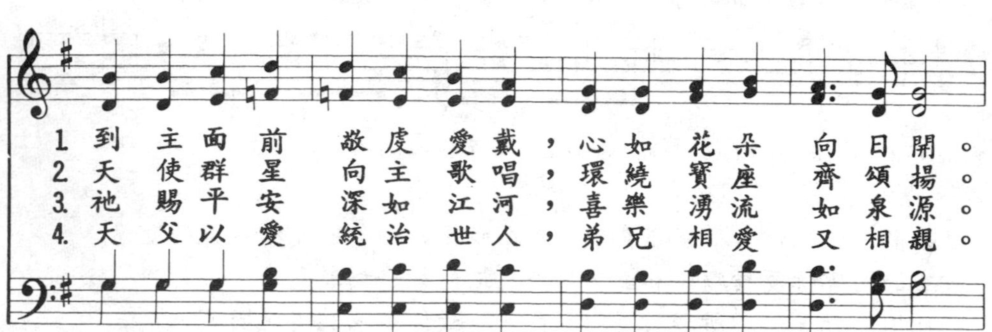
1. 到 主 面 前 敬 虔 愛 戴，心 如 花 朵 向 日 開。
2. 天 使 群 星 向 主 歌 唱，環 繞 寶 座 齊 頌 揚。
3. 祂 賜 平 安 深 如 江 河，喜 樂 湧 流 如 泉 源。
4. 天 父 以 愛 統 治 世 人，弟 兄 相 愛 又 相 親。
1 Hearts un - fold like flowers be - fore Thee, Open - ing to the sun a - bove.
2 *Stars and an - gels sing a - round Thee, Cen - ter of un - bro - ken praise.*
3 Well - spring of the joy of liv - ing, O - cean depth of hap - py rest!
4 *Fa - ther love is reign - ing o'er us, Broth - er love binds man to man.*

1. 愁 霧 疑 雲 罪 惡 憂 驚，懇 求 救 主 全 除 盡；
2. 田 野 森 林 高 山 幽 谷，青 翠 草 原 及 海 洋；
3. 屬 主 子 民 愛 中 生 活，基 督 是 主 是 弟 兄；
4. 齊 向 前 進 歌 唱 不 停，奮 勇 爭 戰 齊 得 勝；
1 Melt the clouds of sin and sad - ness, Drive the dark of doubt a - way;
2 *Field and for - est, vale and moun - tain, Flow - ery mead - ow, flash - ing sea,*
3 Thou our Fa - ther, Christ our Broth - er– All who live in love are Thine;
4 *Ev - er sing - ing, march we on - ward, Vic - tors in the midst of strife,*

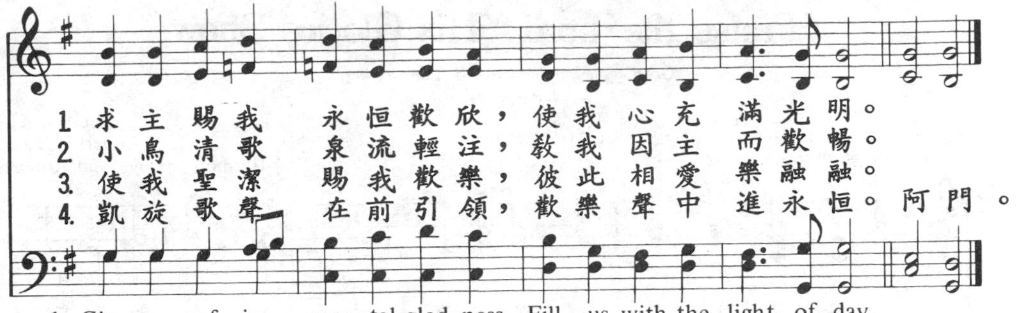
1. 求主賜我 永恒歡欣，使我心充 滿光明。
2. 小鳥清歌 泉流輕注，教我因主 而歡暢。
3. 使我聖潔 賜我歡樂，彼此相愛 樂融融。
4. 凱旋歌聲 在前引領，歡樂聲中 進永恒。阿門。

1 Giv - er of im - mor - tal glad - ness, Fill us with the light of day.
2 *Chant - ing bird and flow - ing foun - tain, Call us to re - joice in Thee.*
3 Teach us how to love each oth - er, Lift us to the joy di - vine.
4 *Joy - ful mu - sic leads us sun - ward In the tri - umph song of life.* A - men.

265

讚美祂聖名
Bless His Holy Name

O Bless our God, ye people, and make the voice of His praise to be heard. — Psalm 66:8

Psalm 103
Andraé Crouch

BLESS THE LORD
Andraé Crouch

我的心 稱頌神，在我 裡面的 都要稱頌
Bless the Lord, O my soul, and all that is with - in me, Bless His

Fine

祂 聖 名。 祂成就大事， 祂成就大
ho - ly Name. He has done great things, He has done great

D.C. al Fine

事， 祂 成就 大 事，讚美 祂 聖 名。
things, He has done great things, Bless His ho - ly Name.

讚美上主大榮耀

Praise the Lord, His Glories Show

Great is the Lord and greatly to be praised.

— Psalm 145:3

Based on Psalm 150
Henry Francis Lyte

LLANFAIR
Robert Williams
Harmonized by John Roberts

1. 讚 美 上 主 大 榮 耀，哈 利 路 亞！
2. 讚 美 聲 天 地 迴 響，哈 利 路 亞！
3. 讚 美 上 主 慈 愛 深，哈 利 路 亞！
1 Praise the Lord, His glo - ries show, Al - le - lu - ia!
2 *Earth to heaven and heaven to earth, Al - le - lu - ia!*
3 Praise the Lord, His mer - cies trace, Al - le - lu - ia!

1. 聖 徒 齊 向 主 禱 告，哈 利 路 亞！
2. 高 聲 頌 主 齊 讚 揚，哈 利 路 亞！
3. 讚 美 救 主 奇 妙 恩，哈 利 路 亞！
1 Saints with - in His courts be - low, Al - le - lu - ia!
2 *Tell His won - ders, sing His worth, Al - le - lu - ia!*
3 Praise His prov - i - dence and grace, Al - le - lu - ia!

1. 衆 天 使 圍 繞 寶 座，哈 利 路 亞！
2. 世 世 代 代 到 永 久，哈 利 路 亞！
3. 神 差 愛 子 成 肉 身，哈 利 路 亞！
1 An - gels round His throne a - bove, A - le - lu - ia!
2 *Age to age and shore to shore, A - le - lu - ia!*
3 All that He for man hath done, A - le - lu - ia!

1. 同 享 主 愛 同 歡 樂，哈 利 路 亞！
2. 讚 美 歌 聲 永 不 休，哈 利 路 亞！
3. 救 贖 大 工 今 完 成，哈 利 路 亞！
1 All that see and share His love. A - le - lu - ia!
2 *Praise Him, praise Him ev - er - more! A - le - lu - ia!*
3 All He sends us through His Son. A - le - lu - ia!

267

聖徒齊當讚美救主

Praise the Savior, Ye Who Know Him

Blessing, and honor, and glory, and power be unto Him,
— Revelation 5:13

Thomas Kelly
Byran Jeffery Leech, alt. stanza 4

ACCLAIM
German Melody

1. 聖 徒 齊 當 讚 美 救 主，因 蒙 主 恩 無 法 記 數；
2. 耶 穌 聖 名 何 其 美 好，敵 人 不 能 對 我 侵 擾；
3. 聖 徒 應 當 堅 信 不 移，主 是 信 實 始 終 如 一；
4. 求 主 施 恩 保 守 我 們，或 生 或 死 總 是 相 信；

1 Praise the Sav - ior, ye who know Him! Who can tell how much we owe Him?
2 *Je - sus is the name that charms us, He for con-flict fits and arms us;*
3 Trust in Him, ye saints, for - ev - er, He is faith - ful, chang-ing nev - er;
4 *Keep us, Lord, on Thee re - ly - ing Wheth-er liv - ing, wheth-er dy - ing;*

1. 當 將 一 生 一 切 所 有 甘 心 獻 給 主。
2. 因 為 相 信 依 靠 救 主 我 必 不 動 搖。
3. 世 上 一 切 不 能 使 我 與 主 愛 隔 離。
4. 將 來 天 上 永 遠 讚 美 與 主 永 相 親。阿 門。

1 Glad - ly let us ren - der to Him All we are and have.
2 *Noth-ing moves and noth-ing harms us While we trust in Him.*
3 Nei - ther force nor guile can sev - er Those He loves from Him.
4 *Let no bit - ter - ness or sigh - ing Mar our trust and praise.* A - men.

感謝神

Thanks to God for My Redeemer

Thanks be to God for His unspeakable gift. — II Corinthians 9:15

August Ludwig Storm
Tr. by Carl E. Backstrom

TACK O GUD
J. A. Hultman

1. 感謝神賜我救贖主，感謝神豐富預備！
2. 感謝神禱告蒙應允，感謝神禱告不聽！
3. 感謝神賜路旁玫瑰，感謝神玫瑰有刺！

1 Thanks to God for my Re - deem - er, Thanks for all Thou dost pro - vide!
2 *Thanks for prayers that Thou hast answered, Thanks for what Thou dost de - ny!*
3 Thanks for ros - es by the way - side, Thanks for thorns their stems contain!

1. 感謝神常與我同在，感謝神一切恩惠！
2. 感謝神我曾經風暴，感謝神豐富供應！
3. 感謝神賜家庭溫暖，感謝神賜我福氣！

1 Thanks for times now but a mem - ory, Thanks for Je - sus by my side!
2 *Thanks for storms that I have weath - ered, Thanks for all Thou dost sup - ply!*
3 Thanks for home and thanks for fire - side, Thanks for hope, that sweet re - frain!

1. 感謝神賜溫暖春天，感謝神凄涼秋景！
2. 感謝神賜我苦與樂，感謝神賜我安慰！
3. 感謝神賜喜樂憂愁，感謝神賜我平安！

1 Thanks for pleas - ant, balm - y spring - time, Thanks for dark and drear - y fall!
2 *Thanks for pain and thanks for pleas - ure, Thanks for com - fort in de - spair!*
3 Thanks for joy and thanks for sor - row, Thanks for heav'n - ly peace with Thee!

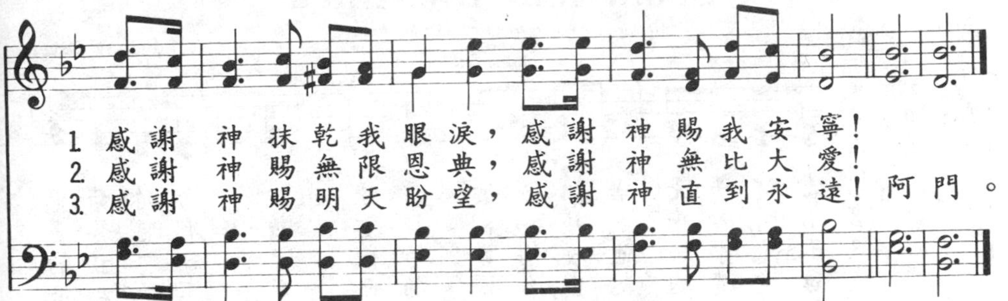
1. 感謝 神抹乾我眼淚，感謝 神賜我安寧！
2. 感謝 神賜無限恩典，感謝 神無比大愛！
3. 感謝 神賜明天盼望，感謝 神直到永遠！阿門。

1 Thanks for tears by now for- got- ten, Thanks for peace within my soul!
2 *Thanks for grace that none can measure, Thanks for love beyond compare!*
3 Thanks for hope in the to-mor-row, Thanks thru all e - ter - ni - ty! A- men.

Hear Our Prayer, O Lord

Hear our prayer, O Lord;
Incline Thine ear to us
And grant us Thy peace. Amen.

–Traditional

三一頌 (2)

Doxology

269

I will greatly praise the Lord with my mouth; yea, I will praise Him among the multitudes. — Psalm 109:30

OLD 100th (original)
Attributed to Louis Bourgeois
Genevan Psalter

Thomas Ken

讚美真神萬福之根，世上萬民讚美主恩；
Praise God, from whom all bless-ings flow; Praise Him, all crea- tures here be - low;

天使天軍讚美主名，讚美聖父聖子聖靈。阿門。
Praise Him a-bove, ye heaven-ly host; Praise Fa-ther, Son, and Ho-ly Ghost. A- men.

270

數主恩典
Count Your Blessings

Johnson Oatman, Jr.

All things are delivered to Me of My Father.
— Luke 10:22

Edwin O. Excell

1. 當你遇見苦難如波浪沖撞，當你憂愁
2. 有時心中掛慮如同挑重擔，有時背負
3. 不必貪戀他人物質的豐富，若想主的
4. 每逢遭遇心靈各樣的戰爭，不要為此

1. When up-on life's bil-lows you are tem-pest-tossed, When you are dis-
2. *Are you ev-er bur-dened with a load of care? Does the cross seem*
3. When you look at oth-ers with their lands and gold, Think that Christ has
4. *So a-mid the con-flict, wheth-er great or small, Do not be dis-*

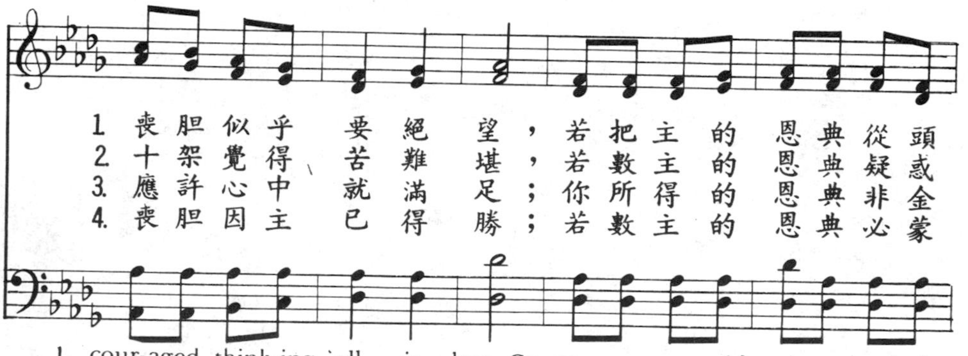

1. 喪胆似乎要絕望，若把主的恩典從頭
2. 十架覺得苦難堪，若數主的恩典疑惑
3. 應許心中就滿足；你所得的恩典非金
4. 喪胆因主已得勝；若數主的恩典必蒙

1. cour-aged, think-ing all is lost, Count your man-y bless-ings—name them
2. *heav-y you are called to bear? Count your man-y bless-ings— ev-'ry*
3. prom-ised you His wealth un-told; Count your man-y bless-ings—mon-ey
4. *cour-aged— God is o-ver all; Count your man-y bless-ings— an-gels*

1. 數一數，必能叫你希奇感謝而歡呼。
2. 便消除，必能叫你快樂立時讚美主。
3. 錢能買；活在父親家裡得蒙祂眷愛。
4. 主幫助，安慰引導我們直到見天父。

1. one by one, And it will sur-prise you what the Lord hath done.
2. *doubt will fly, And you will be sing-ing as the days go by.*
3. can-not buy, Your re-ward in heav-en nor your home on high.
4. *will at-tend, Help and com-fort give you to your jour-ney's end.*

主 的 恩典 樣樣 都 要 數；主 的
Count your bless - ings—name them one by one; Count your
恩典 都 要 記 清 楚；主 的 恩 典 樣 樣 都 要
bless-ings—see what God hath done; Count your bless-ings—name them one by
數，必 能 叫 你 希 奇 感 謝 而 歡 呼。
one; Count your man-y bless-ings—see what God hath done.

270–1 Thanksgiving and Praise

Thanksgiving and praise are to be the major elements in our singing. It is possible to give thanks and praise God individually but if any congregation took time to let everyone do that, it would take all day. . . . Singing is something we can do together. So through the ages the believers in God both of the Old and New Testament have sung their praises and thanksgiving. . . . It is the reason we should be careful not to sing in a desultory manner. There is nothing more conducive to dullness in a service than half-hearted singing. So the exhortation here is most appropriate. "O, come, let us sing to the Lord: let us make a joyful noise to the rock of our salvation."

—Ray Stedman

271

我們同心聚集
We Gather Together

KREMSER

Netherlands Folk Song
Tr. by Theodore Baker

If God be for us who can be against us?
— Romans 8:31

Netherlands Folk Song
Harmonized by Edward Kremser

1. 我 們 同 心 聚 集，祈 求 主 賜 福 氣，主
2. 主 是 我 們 前 導，常 與 我 們 同 行，主
3. 我 們 同 心 尊 主，做 勝 利 的 元 帥，誠
1 We gath - er to - geth - er to ask the Lord's bless - ing– He
2 Be - side us to guide us, our God with us join - ing, Or -
3 We all do ex - tol Thee, Thou lead - er tri - um - phant, And
1. 用 各 樣 方 法 將 旨 意 顯 明；罪
2. 任 命 使 祂 聖 潔 國 度 永 存；爭
3. 心 的 祈 求 主 仍 將 我 護 佑；願
1 chas - tens and has - tens His will to make known; The
2 dain - ing, main - tain - ing His king - dom di - vine; So
3 pray that Thou still our de - fend - er wilt be; Let
1. 勢 不 再 壓 制，痛 苦 憂 傷 停 止，歌
2. 戰 之 始 已 知，勝 利 屬 於 我 們，有
3. 主 施 行 拯 救，使 我 免 受 災 害，永
1 wick - ed op - press - ing now cease from dis - tress - ing: Sing
2 from the be - gin - ning the fight we were win - ning: Thou,
3 Thy con-gre - ga - tion es - cape trib - u - la - tion: Thy
1. 頌 讚 美 主 名，主 不 忘 祂 子 民。
2. 主 親 自 同 在，榮 耀 歸 至 高 神！
3. 遠 讚 美 主 名，主 使 我 得 自 由。阿 門。
1 prais - es to His name– He for - gets not His own.
2 Lord, wast at our side– all glo - ry be Thine.
3 name be ev - er praised! O Lord, make us free! A - men.

讚美真神

Holy God, We Praise Thy Name

I dwell in the high and holy place with him that is of a humble spirit. —Isaiah 57:15

Attr. to Ignaz Franz
Tr. by Clarence A. Walworth

GROSSER GOTT
"Allgemeines Katholisches Gesangbuch"

1. 讚美真神萬有主，屈膝敬拜
2. 歡樂讚美聲悠揚，天上天使
3. 讚美聖父與聖子，讚美聖靈

1 Ho - ly God, we praise Thy name; Lord of all, we
2 *Hark, the glad ce - les - tial hymn An - gel choirs a -*
3 Ho - ly Fa - ther, ho - ly Son, Ho - ly Spir - it:

1. 稱頌主名；全地都向主歡呼，
2. 向主高唱；衆天使與天使長，
3. 三一真神；父子聖靈本屬一，

1 bow be - fore Thee; All on earth Thy scep - ter claim,
2 *bove are rais - ing; Cher - u - bim and ser - a - phim,*
3 three we name Thee, Though in es - sence on - ly one;

1. 諸天萬物齊聲響應：讚美主極
2. 永無止盡高聲讚揚；天韻歌聲
3. 永不分開獨一真神；屈膝向主

1 All in heaven a - bove a - dore Thee: In - fi - nite Thy
2 *In un - ceas - ing cho - rus prais - ing; Fill the heavens with*
3 Un - di - vid - ed God we claim Thee, And a - dor - ing,

1. 大權能，掌王權直到永恒。
2. 齊傳開，聖哉聖哉大主宰。
3. 來跪拜，奇哉奧祕的主宰。阿門。

1 vast do - main, Ev - er - last - ing is Thy reign.
2 *sweet ac - cord: Ho - ly, ho - ly, ho - ly Lord.*
3 bend the knee, While we own the mys - ter - y. A - men.

願你心靈充滿歡欣

O Let Your Soul Now Be Filled with Gladness

Therefore God hath anointed thee with the oil of gladness . . . .
— Hebrews 1:9

Peter Jönsson Aschan
Tr. by Karl A. Olsson

RANSOMED SOUL
Swedish Folk Melody
Harmonized by A. Royce Eckhardt

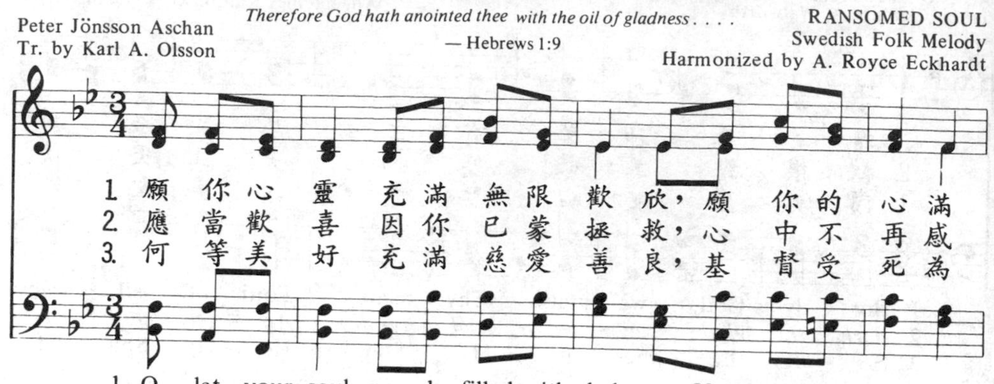
1. 願你心靈充滿無限歡欣，願你的心滿
2. 應當歡喜因你已蒙拯救，心中不再感
3. 何等美好充滿慈愛善良，基督受死為

1 O let your soul now be filled with glad-ness, Your heart re-deemed, re-
2 *If you seem emp-ty of an-y feel-ing, Re-joice—you are His*
3 It is a good, ev-ery good tran-scend-ing, That Christ has died for

1. 有喜樂！除去心中一切悲傷憂情，因
2. 覺空虛！雖然有時黑暗滿佈四周，朋
3. 你為我！永無止盡無限快樂歡暢，主

1 joice in-deed! O may the thought ban-ish all your sad-ness That
2 *ran-somed bride! If those you cher-ish seem not to love you, And*
3 you and me! It is a glad-ness that has no end-ing There-

1. 主寶血遮掩罪過；父神的大愛永不變，
2. 友似乎離你遠去；但神的應許永不變，
3. 愛奇妙無法揣摩！讚美耶穌聖潔羔羊，

1 in His blood you have been freed, That God's un-fail-ing love is yours,
2 *dark as-sails from ev-ery side, Still yours the prom-ise, come what may,*
3 in God's won-drous love to see! Praise be to Him, the spot-less Lamb,

1. 将 祂 獨 生 愛 子 賜 給 世 人，痛 苦 受
2. 不 論 是 得 失 歡 笑 或 悲 傷，貧 窮 或
3. 祂 帶 我 靈 魂 經 過 荒 漠 地，到 天 上
1 That you the on - ly Son were giv - en, That by His
2 *In loss and tri - umph, in laugh - ter, cry - ing, In want and*
3 Who through the des - ert my soul is lead - ing To that fair

1. 死 為 你 打 開 天 門，使 你 能 蒙 恩 得 救 贖。
2. 富 足 或 生 或 死 亡，你 已 蒙 主 恩 得 救 贖。
3. 聖 城 歡 樂 美 福 地，因 我 已 蒙 恩 得 救 贖。
1 death He has o - pened heav - en, That you are ran - somed as you are.
2 *rich - es, in liv - ing, dy - ing, That you are pur - chased as you are.*
3 cit - y of joy ex - ceed - ing, For which He bought me as I am.

Look around and be
distressed.
Look inside and be
depressed.
Look at Jesus and be at
rest.

— Corrie ten Boom

收成樂歌

Come, Ye Thankful People, Come

Then shall the righteous shine forth as the sun in the Kingdom . . .

— Matthew 13:43

Henry Alford

ST. GEORGE'S WINDSOR

George J. Elvey

1. 齊來感謝主恩多，同來唱收成樂歌；
2. 普世皆是主禾田，當結果實獻主前；
3. 主將來必再降臨，將穀收入天庫中；
4. 我深願主早來臨，將嘉穀末次收清；

1 Come, ye thank-ful peo-ple, come, Raise the song of har-vest-home;
2 *All the world is God's own field, Fruit un-to His praise to yield;*
3 For the Lord our God shall come And shall take His har-vest-home;
4 *E-ven so, Lord, quick-ly come To Thy fi-nal har-vest-home;*

1. 今美穀已入倉中，及此時尚非嚴冬；
2. 稗與麥同撒田裡，長出時有憂有喜；
3. 到那日主必掃淨，田中污穢全除清；
4. 召齊祢民同聚會，再無憂愁再無罪；

1 All is safe-ly gath-ered in, Ere the win-ter storms be-gin:
2 *Wheat and tares to-geth-er sown, Un-to joy or sor-rows grown:*
3 From His field shall in that day All of-fens-es purge a-way,
4 *Gath-er Thou Thy peo-ple in, Free from sor-row, free from sin:*

1. 造物主預備豐富，足夠我用何等福；
2. 先發幼苗後吐穗，終必顯良苗可貴；
3. 祂必命令衆天使，用火燒滅惡稗子；
4. 使他永遠得清潔，在主面前得基業；

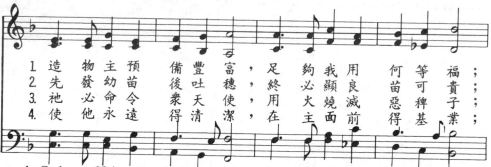

1 God, our Mak-er, doth pro-vide For our wants to be sup-plied;
2 *First the blade, and then the ear, Then the full corn shall ap-pear;*
3 Give His an-gels charge at last In the fire the tares to cast,
4 *There for-ev-er pu-ri-fied, In Thy pres-ence to a-bide;*

1. 同聚集主聖殿中，收成歌齊聲高頌。
2. 收割主求賜我福，使我作潔淨佳穀。
3. 惟嘉穀是主所愛，存入天庫永不壞。
4. 求主與天使同來，同頌主恩同敬拜。阿們。

1 Come to God's own tem-ple, come, Raise the song of har-vest-home.
2 *Lord of har-vest, grant that we Whole-some grain and pure may be.*
3 But the fruit-ful ears to store In His gar-ner ev-er-more.
4 *Come, with all Thine an-gels, come, Raise the glo-rious har-vest-home.* A-men.

感恩歌

Thank You, Lord

275

This is the Lord's doing, and it is marvelous in our eyes.

— Psalm 118:23

Seth Sykes

Mr. & Mrs. Seth Sykes

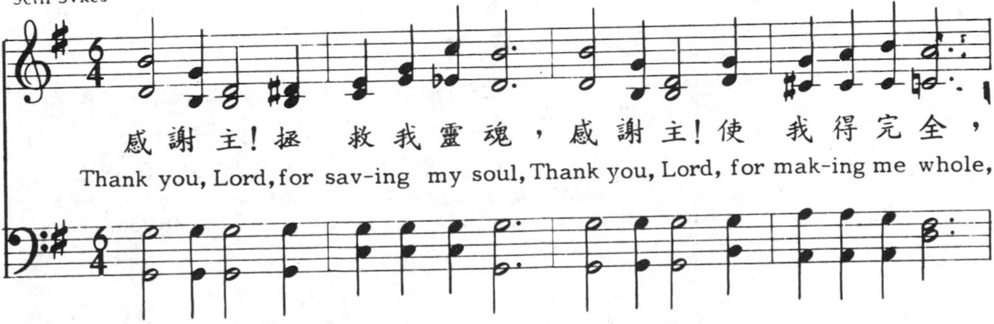

感謝主！拯救我靈魂，感謝主！使我得完全，

Thank you, Lord, for sav-ing my soul, Thank you, Lord, for mak-ing me whole,

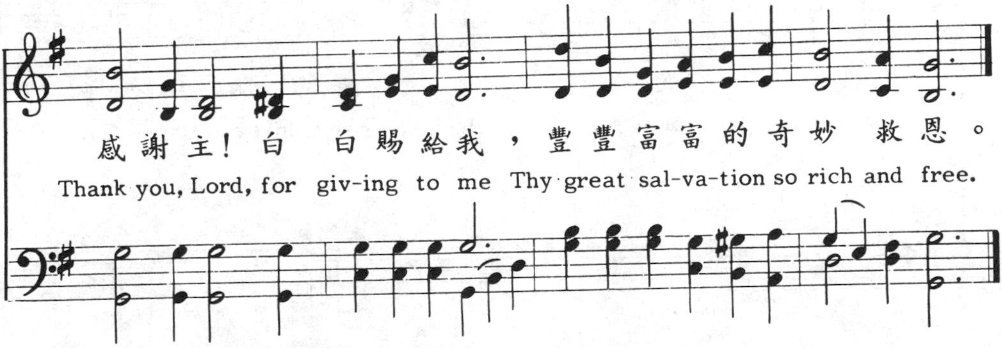

感謝主！白白賜給我，豐豐富富的奇妙救恩。

Thank you, Lord, for giv-ing to me Thy great sal-va-tion so rich and free.

歡欣感謝

Rejoice, Ye Pure in Heart

We will rejoice in Thy salvation and in the name of our God . . . . — Psalm 20:5

Edward H. Plumptre

MARION
Arthur H. Messiter

1. 心 中 清 潔的 人，應 當 感 謝 歡 唱；
2. 奔 走 人 生 道 路，一 路 歌 唱 不 停；
3. 心 中 清 潔的 人，應 當 感 謝 歡 唱；
1 Re - joice, ye pure in heart, Re - joice, give thanks and sing;
2 Go on through life's long path, Still chant-ing as ye go;
3 Then on, ye pure in heart, Re - joice, give thanks and sing;

1. 基 督 十 架 是 你 聖 旗，高 舉 隨 風 飄 揚：
2. 自 幼 至 老 晝 夜 頌 讚，歌 聲 優 美 輕 盈：
3. 十 架 是 你 榮 耀 聖 旗，高 舉 歡 呼 同 唱：
1 Your fes - tive ban - ner wave on high, The cross of Christ your King:
2 From youth to age, by night and day, In glad - ness and in woe:
3 Your glo - rious ban - ner wave on high, The cross of Christ your King:

歡欣，歡欣，歡欣，感謝歌唱。阿門。
Re - joice, re - joice, Re - joice, give thanks and sing. A - men.
歡欣，歡欣，
Re - joice, re - joice,

歡欣，主為君王

277

Rejoice, the Lord Is King!

Based on Philippians 4:4
Charles Wesley

Rejoice in the Lord always; and again I say, Rejoice.
— Philippians 4:4

DARWALL'S 148th
John Darwall

1. 歡 欣，主 為 君 王 ！ 你 當 崇 拜 景 仰 ！
2. 救 主，君 王 掌 權 ， 真 神 慈 愛 無 限 ；
3. 基 督 耶 穌 為 主 ， 國 度 存 到 永 遠 ；
4. 何 等 榮 耀 盼 望 ， 救 主 必 再 來 臨 ；
1 Re - joice, the Lord is King! Your Lord and King a - dore!
2 The Lord, our Sav - ior, reigns, The God of truth and love;
3 His king - dom can - not fail, He rules o'er earth and heaven;
4 Re - joice in glo - rious hope! Our Lord the judge shall come
1. 高 聲 稱 謝 讚 揚 ， 永 遠 得 勝 為
2. 洗 淨 我 罪 完 全 ， 榮 昇 寶 座 在
3. 得 勝 陰 府 死 亡 ， 天 地 屬 祂 掌
4. 迎 接 忠 心 僕 人 ， 同 回 天 上 家
1 Re - joice, give thanks, and sing, And tri - umph ev - er -
2 When He had purged our stains, He took His seat a -
3 The keys of death and hell Are to our Je - sus
4 And take His serv - ants up To their e - ter - nal
1. 王 :
2. 天 :
3. 管 :
4. 庭 :
振 作 你 心 ， 揚 聲 高 唱！歡
Lift up your heart, lift up your voice! Re -
1 more:
2 bove:
3 given:
4 home:
欣，歡 欣，應 當 歡 欣 ！ 阿 門。
joice, a - gain I say, re - joice! A - men.

278

農人耕田忙

We Plow the Fields and Scatter the Good Seed

Mathias Claudius
Tr. by Jane M. Campbell

The field is the world; the good seed are the children of the Kingdom.
— Matthew 13:38

WIR PFLÜGEN
Johann A. P. Schulz

1. 農 人 辛 苦 耕 田 忙，好 種 土 中 撒 放，
2. 主 是 惟 一 造 物 神，造 成 萬 類 群 生，
3. 天 父，我 衆 來 感 謝，萬 物 美 好 光 明，

1 We plow the fields and scat - ter The good seed on the land,
2 *He on - ly is the mak - er Of all things near and far,*
3 We thank Thee, then, O Fa - ther, For all things bright and good—

1. 却 賴 神 手 勤 澆 灌，甘 露 依 時 下 降；
2. 點 綴 路 旁 的 花 草，燃 起 黑 夜 繁 星；
3. 來 感 謝 撒 種 收 成，飲 食 健 康 生 命；
1 But it is fed and wa - tered By God's al-might - y hand;
2 He paints the way-side flow - er, He lights the eve - ning star;
3 The seed-time and the har - vest, Our life, our health, our food;

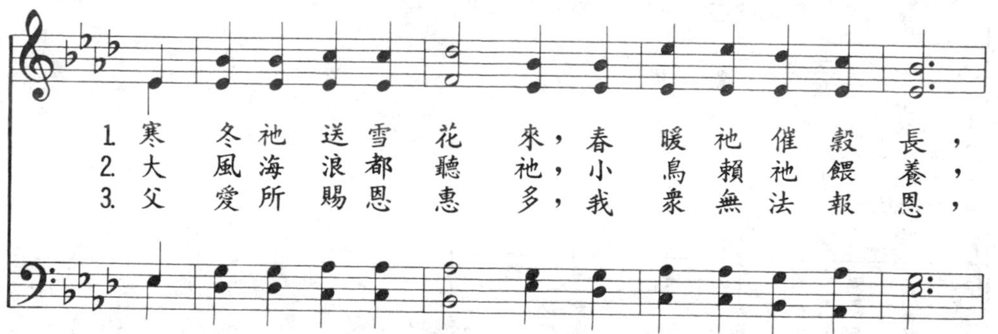
1. 寒 冬 祂 送 雪 花 來，春 暖 祂 催 穀 長，
2. 大 風 海 浪 都 聽 祂，小 鳥 賴 祂 餵 養，
3. 父 愛 所 賜 恩 惠 多，我 衆 無 法 報 恩，
1 He sends the snow in win - ter, The warmth to swell the grain,
2 The winds and waves o - bey Him, By Him the birds are fed:
3 Ac - cept the gifts we of - fer For all Thy love im - parts,

1. 又 賜和風與麗日，好雨助成興旺。
2. 我衆是祂的子女，天天祂賜飯糧。
3. 祇獻主心所悅納，謙虛感謝之心。

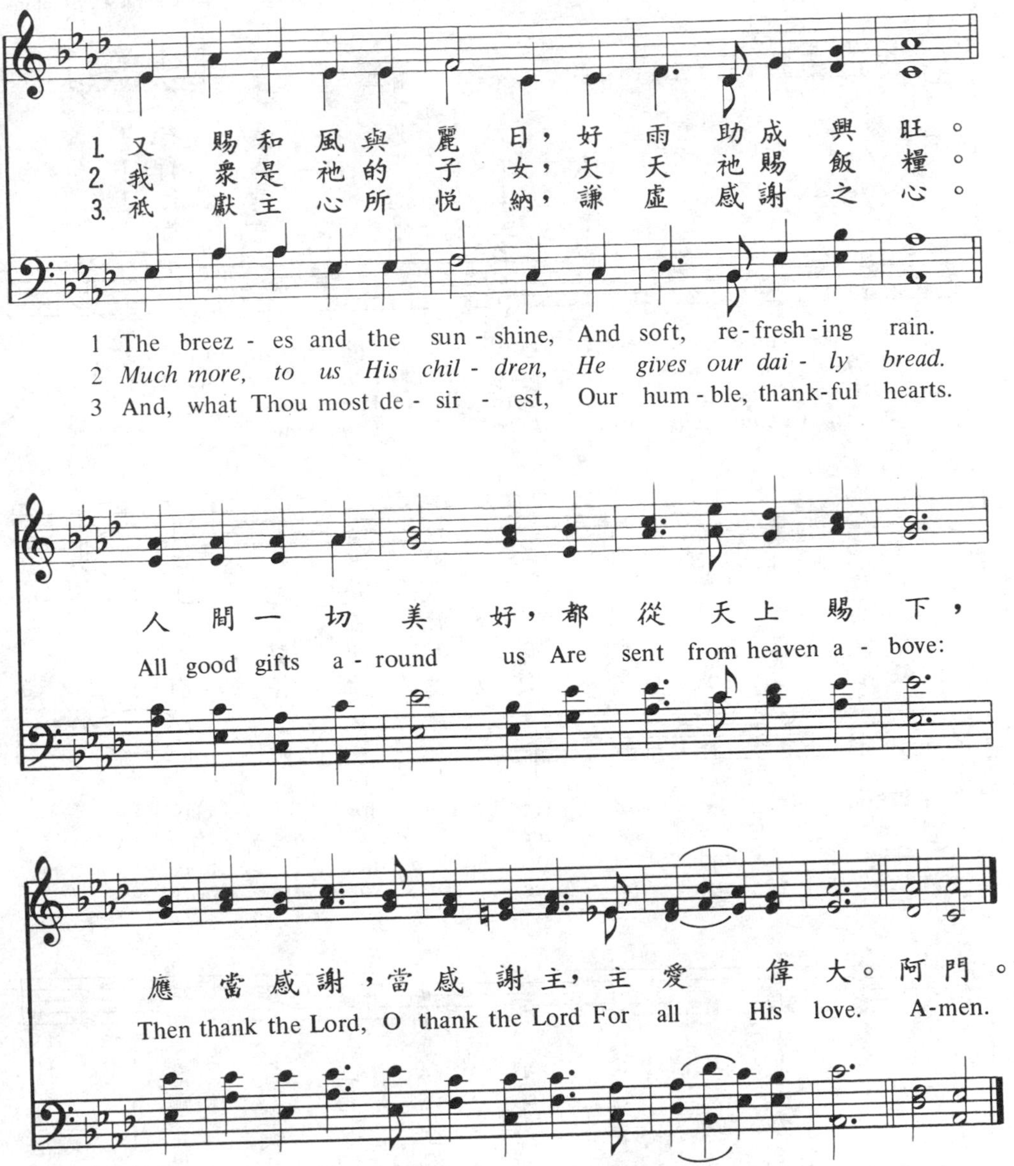

1 The breez - es and the sun - shine, And soft, re - fresh - ing rain.
2 *Much more, to us His chil - dren, He gives our dai - ly bread.*
3 And, what Thou most de - sir - est, Our hum - ble, thank - ful hearts.

人間一切美好，都從天上賜下，
All good gifts a - round us Are sent from heaven a - bove:

應當感謝，當感謝主，主愛偉大。阿門。
Then thank the Lord, O thank the Lord For all His love. A - men.

你們要讚美耶和華，向耶和華唱新歌，在聖民的會中讚美祂

詩篇一百四十九篇
1 節

279

憑祢意行，主！

Have Thine Own Way, Lord!

Give me understanding and I shall keep thy Law . . . I shall observe it with all my heart.

— Psalm 119:34

Adelaide A. Pollard
ADELAIDE
George C. Stebbins
1. 憑祢意行，主！憑祢意行！
2. 憑祢意行，主！憑祢意行！
3. 憑祢意行，主！憑祢意行！
4. 憑祢意行，主！憑祢意行！
1 Have Thine own way, Lord! Have Thine own way!
2 Have Thine own way, Lord! Have Thine own way!
3 Have Thine own way, Lord! Have Thine own way!
4 Have Thine own way, Lord! Have Thine own way!
1. 主祢是陶匠，我是泥土；
2. 鑒察試驗我，就在今天；
3. 憂傷與疲倦，求主幫助；
4. 管理我動作，憑主指引；
1 Thou art the pot - ter, I am the clay!
2 Search me and try me, Mas - ter, to - day!
3 Wound - ed and wea - ry, Help me, I pray!
4 Hold o'er my be - ing Ab - so - lute sway!
1. 陶我與造我，照主旨意，
2. 求主洗淨我，潔白如雪，
3. 能力與權柄，全屬我主！
4. 聖靈充滿我，顯明主恩，
1 Mold me and make me Aft - er Thy will,
2 Whit - er than snow, Lord, Wash me just now,
3 Pow - er— all pow - er— Sure - ly is Thine!
4 Fill with Thy Spir - it 'Til all shall see

1. 我 在 此 等 待，虔 誠 候 主。
2. 我 謙 卑 跪 下，在 主 脚 前。
3. 醫 治 與 拯 救，惟 靠 救 主！
4. 惟 求 主 耶 穌，永 住 我 心！
阿 們。
1 While I am wait - ing, Yield - ed and still.
2 *As in Thy pres - ence Hum - bly I bow.*
3 Touch me and heal me, Sav - ior di - vine!
4 *Christ on - ly, al - ways, Liv - ing in me!*
A - men.

280

求賜我愛靈魂的心

Lord, Lay Some Soul upon My Heart

All power is given unto me in heaven and in earth.
— Matthew 28:18

David H. Johnson — David H. Johnson

求 賜 我 愛 靈 魂 的 心，藉 我 關 懷 別 人，
Lord, lay some soul upon my heart And love that soul thru me;

我 願 忠 心 盡 力 作 工，領 人 歸 向 真 神。
And may I nob - ly do my part To win that soul for thee.

281

耶穌我來

Jesus, I Come

The Lord . . . hath sent me to bind the broken hearted . . . .
— Isaiah 61:1

William T. Sleeper
Jeff Redd, alt.

JESUS, I COME
George C. Stebbins

1. 脱離捆綁憂愁與黑影，耶穌我來，耶穌我來；
2. 脱離失敗羞恥的結果，耶穌我來，耶穌我來；
3. 脱離狂傲不平的血氣，耶穌我來，耶穌我來；
4. 脱離幽暗陰府的可怕，耶穌我來，耶穌我來；
1 Out of my bond-age, sor-row and night, Je-sus, I come, Je-sus, I come;
2 Out of my shame-ful fail-ure and loss, Je-sus, I come, Je-sus, I come;
3 Out of un-rest and ar-ro-gant pride, Je-sus, I come, Je-sus, I come;
4 Out of the fear and dread of the tomb, Je-sus, I come, Je-sus, I come;

1. 進入自由喜樂與光明，耶穌，我來就祢。
2. 進入十架榮耀的恩典，耶穌，我來就祢。
3. 進入完全有福的旨意，耶穌，我來就祢。
4. 進入歡樂光明的父家，耶穌，我來就祢。
1 In-to Thy free-dom, glad-ness and light, Je-sus, I come to Thee.
2 In-to the glo-rious gain of Thy cross, Je-sus, I come to Thee.
3 In-to Thy bless-ed will to a-bide, Je-sus, I come to Thee.
4 In-to the joy and light of Thy home, Je-sus, I come to Thee.

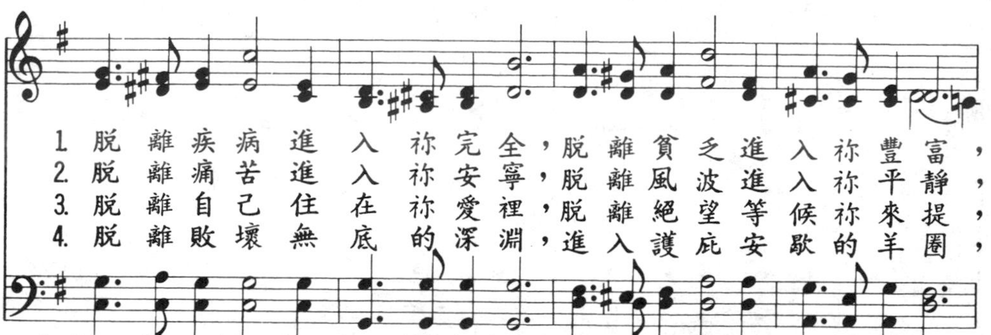

1. 脱離疾病進入祢完全，脱離貧乏進入祢豐富，
2. 脱離痛苦進入祢安寧，脱離風波進入祢平靜，
3. 脱離自己住在祢愛裡，脱離絕望等候祢來提，
4. 脱離敗壞無底的深淵，進入護庇安歇的羊圈，
1 Out of my sick-ness in-to Thy health, Out of my need and in-to Thy wealth,
2 Out of earth's sor-rows in-to Thy balm, Out of life's storms and in-to Thy calm,
3 Out of my-self to dwell in Thy love, Out of de-spair to rap-tures a-bove,
4 Out of the depths of ru-in un-told, In-to Thy peace-ful, shel-ter-ing fold,

1. 脱 離 罪 惡，得 見 祢 聖 顔 ，耶 穌，我 來 就 祢 。
2. 脱 離 怨 嘆，進 入 祢 稱 讚 ，耶 穌，我 來 就 祢 。
3. 離 地 上 騰，如 鷹 展 雙 翼 ，耶 穌，我 來 就 祢 。
4. 永 永 遠 遠，瞻 仰 祢 容 顔 ，耶 穌，我 來 就 祢 。
1 Out of my sin and in - to Thy-self, Je - sus, I come to Thee.
2 Out of dis-tress to ju - bi-lant psalm, Je - sus, I come to Thee.
3 Up - ward I rise on wings like a dove, Je - sus, I come to Thee.
4 Ev - er Thy glo - rious face to be-hold, Je - sus, I come to Thee.

如鹿切慕溪水

As The Deer

281-1

Come, let us bow down in worship. Ps. 95:6

Martin Nystrom — Martin Nystrom

神啊，我心眞切慕祢，如 鹿切慕溪 水；
As the deer pant-eth for the wa-ter, so my soul long-eth af - ter Thee;

1. *Fine*

惟獨祢是我 心所愛，我渴 慕向祢 敬拜。 拜。
You a-lone are my heart's de-sire, and I long to wor - ship Thee. Thee.

D.S. al Fine

祢是我的力量盾牌，我 靈 單 向祢順 服依 賴。
You a - lone are my strength, my shield, to You a - lone may my spir - it yield;

© 1984 Maranatha! Music P.O. Box 31050, Laguna Hills, CA 92654.
All rights reserved. International copyright secured. Used by permission.

282

耶穌溫柔慈聲

Softly and Tenderly

Come unto Me, all ye who labor and are heavy laden . . . .

— Matthew 11:28

Will L. Thompson

THOMPSON
Will L. Thompson

1. 耶穌溫柔慈聲 懇切呼喚你，祂呼喚
2. 為何你還推却 耶穌的懇請？祂懇請
3. 何等奇妙耶穌 已經應許你，應許赦
1 Soft-ly and ten-der-ly Je-sus is call-ing, Call-ing for
2 Why should we lin-ger when Je-sus is plead-ing, Plead-ing for
3 O for the won-der-ful love He has prom-ised, Prom-ised for
1. 你快歸家；耶穌站在你心門外等候你，
2. 你今歸家；為何你還躭延忽略主救恩？
3. 免你罪惡；只要你肯回頭悔改認你罪，
1 you and for me; Pa-tient and lov-ing, He's wait-ing and watch-ing,
2 you and for me? Why should we wait, then, and heed not His mer-cies,
3 you and for me; Tho' we have sinned He has mer-cy and par-don,
1. 等候你來迎接祂。歸家，歸家，
2. 祂因救你把血灑。歸家 歸家，
3. 祂就賜平安喜樂。
1 Watch-ing for you and for me.
2 Mer-cies for you and for me? Come home, come home,
3 Par-don for you and for me. Come home come home,
傷心愁悶者，歸家；耶穌溫
Ye who are wea-ry, come home; Ear-nest-ly,

柔慈聲，懇切呼喚你，"歸家，懇請你歸家！"
ten-der-ly, Je-sus is call-ing— Call-ing, "O sin-ner, come home!"

任領何往

283 Where He Leads Me

Master, I will follow Thee whithersoever Thou goest.
— Matthew 8:19

E. W. Blandy

NORRIS
John S. Norris

1. 我今明聞救主召呼，我今明聞救主召呼，
2. 我必時時求主幫助，我必時時求主幫助，
3. 我必身心專獻耶穌，我必身心專獻耶穌，
1 I can hear my Sav-ior call-ing, I can hear my Sav-ior call-ing,
2 I'll go with Him thru the judg-ment, I'll go with Him thru the judg-ment,
3 He will give me grace and glo-ry, He will give me grace and glo-ry,
副歌：耶穌領我，我必跟隨，任領何往，我仍跟隨，
Refrain: Where He leads me I will fol-low, Where He leads me I will fol-low,

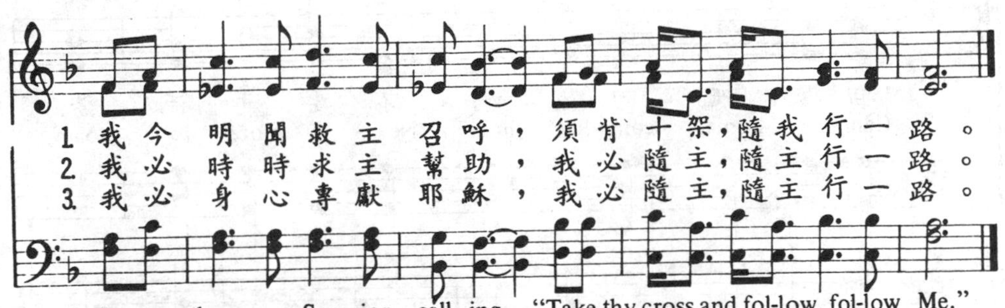

1. 我今明聞救主召呼，須背十架，隨我行一路。
2. 我必時時求主幫助，我必隨主，隨主行一路。
3. 我必身心專獻耶穌，我必隨主，隨主行一路。
1 I can hear my Sav-ior call-ing, "Take thy cross and fol-low, fol-low Me."
2 I'll go with Him thru the judg-ment, I'll go with Him, with Him all the way.
3 He will give me grace and glo-ry, And go with me, with me all the way.
副歌：福也，苦也，終必跟隨，踴躍隨主，隨主行一路。
Refrain: Where He leads me I will fol-low— I'll go with Him, with Him all the way.

284

主，我要回家

Lord, I'm Coming Home

None of his sins which he hath committed shall be mentioned unto him.
— Ezekiel 33:16

William J. Kirkpatrick

COMING HOME
William J. Kirkpatrick

1. 我已流蕩遠離天父，現在要回家；
2. 多年浪費寶貴歲月，現在要回家；
3. 流蕩犯罪我已疲乏，現在要回家；
4. 我魂衰殘我心悲傷，現在要回家；
1 I've wan-dered far a - way from God, Now I'm com-ing home;
2 I've wast - ed man - y pre - cious years, Now I'm com-ing home;
3 I've tired of sin and stray - ing, Lord, Now I'm com-ing home;
4 My soul is sick, my heart is sore, Now I'm com-ing home;
1. 走過悠長罪惡道路，主，我要回家。
2. 今天懊悔流淚悲切，主，我要回家。
3. 投靠祢愛相信祢話，主，我要回家。
4. 加我力量賜我盼望，主，我要回家。
1 The paths of sin too long I've trod, Lord, I'm com-ing home.
2 I now re-pent with bit - ter tears, Lord, I'm com-ing home.
3 I'll trust Thy love, be - lieve Thy word, Lord, I'm com-ing home.
4 My strength re-new, my hope re - store, Lord, I'm com-ing home.
回家吧，回家吧，不要再流蕩，
Com-ing home, com - ing home, Nev - er - more to roam,
慈愛天父伸開雙手，主，我要回家。
O - pen wide Thine arms of love, Lord, I'm com-ing home.

領我到髑髏地

Lead Me to Calvary

And they came to a place which was called Gethsemane . . . .
— Mark 14:32

LEAD ME TO CALVARY

Jennie Evelyn Hussey

William J. Kirkpatrick

1. 生命之主願祢作王，榮耀都歸於祢；
2. 主為我受死葬墳墓，門徒哭泣憂傷；
3. 像馬利亞黎明即起，親至墓旁獻禮；
4. 主啊，我甘心又情願，背十架跟隨祢；

1 King of my life I crown Thee now– Thine shall the glo - ry be;
2 *Show me the tomb where Thou wast laid, Ten - der - ly mourned and wept;*
3 Let me like Ma - ry, through the gloom, Come with a gift to Thee;
4 *May I be will - ing, Lord, to bear Dai - ly my cross for Thee;*

1. 使我莫忘祢荊棘冕，領我到髑髏地。
2. 天使身穿潔白衣袍，看守在主墓旁。
3. 主已復活主墓已空，領我到髑髏地。
4. 救主苦杯我願分嚐，領我到髑髏地。

1 Lest I for-get Thy thorn-crowned brow, Lead me to Cal - va - ry.
2 *An - gels in robes of light ar - rayed Guard-ed Thee whilst Thou slept.*
3 Show to me now the emp - ty tomb– Lead me to Cal - va - ry.
4 *E - ven Thy cup of grief to share– Thou hast borne all for me.*

使我莫忘客西馬尼，莫忘我主痛苦受死，
Lest I for-get Geth - sem - a - ne, Lest I for-get Thine ag - o - ny,

莫忘我主仁愛慈悲，領我到髑髏地。阿門。
Lest I for-get Thy love for me, Lead me to Cal - va - ry. A-men.

286

不忍丟棄我的大愛

O Love That Will Not Let Me Go

The Lord shall be unto thee an everlasting light . . . .

— Isaiah 60:19

George Matheson

ST. MARGARET
Albert L. Peace

1. 不忍丟棄我的大愛，疲倦靈
2. 照我道路生命真光，求將我
3. 救主捨身為拯救我，我怎能
4. 我所仰望恩主十架，實在不
1 O Love that will not let me go, I rest my
2 *O Light that fol-lowest all my way, I yield my*
3 O Joy that seek-est me through pain, I can - not
4 *O Cross that lift-est up my head, I dare not*

1. 魂因祢得安；今將所受生命獻上，
2. 的殘灯剔亮；藉祢無比榮美燦爛，
3. 關閉我心門；我在雨中瞻望彩虹，
4. 敢片刻離棄；今願埋葬此生榮華，
1 wea - ry soul in Thee; I give Thee back the life I owe,
2 *flick-ering torch to Thee; My heart re-stores its bor-rowed ray,*
3 close my heart to Thee; I trace the rain-bow through the rain,
4 *ask to fly from Thee; I lay in dust life's glo - ry dead,*

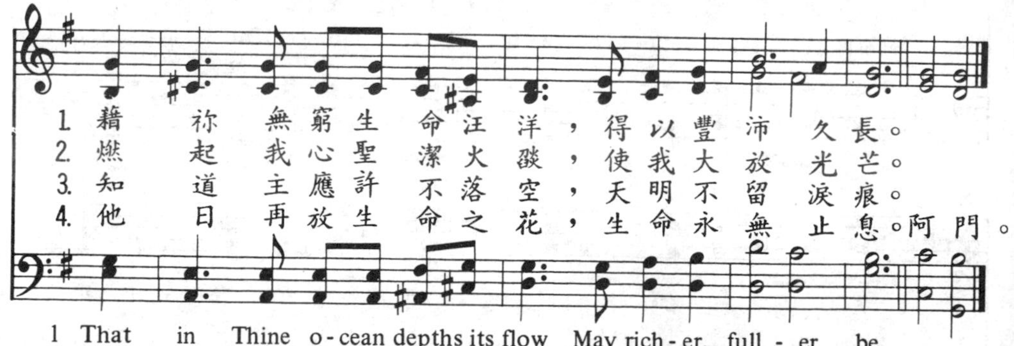

1. 藉祢無窮生命汪洋，得以豐沛久長。
2. 燃起我心聖潔火燄，使我大放光芒。
3. 知道主應許不落空，天明不留淚痕。
4. 他日再放生命之花，生命永無止息。阿門。
1 That in Thine o-cean depths its flow May rich - er, full - er be.
2 *That in Thy sun-shine's blaze its day May bright-er, fair - er be.*
3 And feel the prom-ise is not vain That morn shall tear-less be.
4 *And from the ground there blos-soms red, Life that shall end - less be.* A-men.

我奉獻所有
I Surrender All

He that loveth his life shall lose it; He that hateth his life in this world shall keep it unto life eternal.
— John 12:25
SURRENDER
Judson W. Van de Venter
Winfield S. Weeden
1. 我奉獻所有與耶穌，是甘心樂意奉獻；
2. 我奉獻所有與耶穌，虔誠俯伏主前求；
3. 我奉獻所有與耶穌，整個生命獻與祢；
4. 我奉獻所有與耶穌，將我身心全獻祢；
1 All to Je - sus I sur-ren - der, All to Him I free - ly give;
2 All to Je - sus I sur-ren - der, Hum - bly at His feet I bow,
3 All to Je - sus I sur-ren - der, Make me, Sav - ior, whol - ly Thine.
4 All to Je - sus I sur-ren - der, Lord, I give my - self to Thee;
1. 我願永遠愛主靠主，與主親密到永遠。
2. 撇棄世上所有快樂，主求祢現在收留。
3. 求將聖靈充滿我心，祢已屬我我屬祢。
4. 求主賜我愛心能力，使我從祢得福氣。
1 I will ev - er love and trust Him, In His pres - ence dai - ly live.
2 World - ly plea - sures all for - sak - en; Take me, Je - sus, take me now.
3 Let me feel the Ho - ly Spir - it, Tru - ly know that Thou art mine.
4 Fill me with Thy love and pow - er, Let Thy bless - ing fall on me.
我奉獻所有，
I sur-ren-der all,
我奉獻所有，
I sur-ren-der all,
我奉獻所有，
I sur-ren-der all,
我奉獻所有，
I sur-ren-der all,
完全獻與恩主耶穌，我奉獻所有。
All to Thee, my bless - ed Sav - ior, I sur - ren - der all.

288

主耶穌，我曾應許

O Jesus, I Have Promised

He died for all that they . . . should not henceforth live unto themselves.

— II Corinthians 5:15

John E. Bode

ANGEL'S STORY
Arthur H. Mann

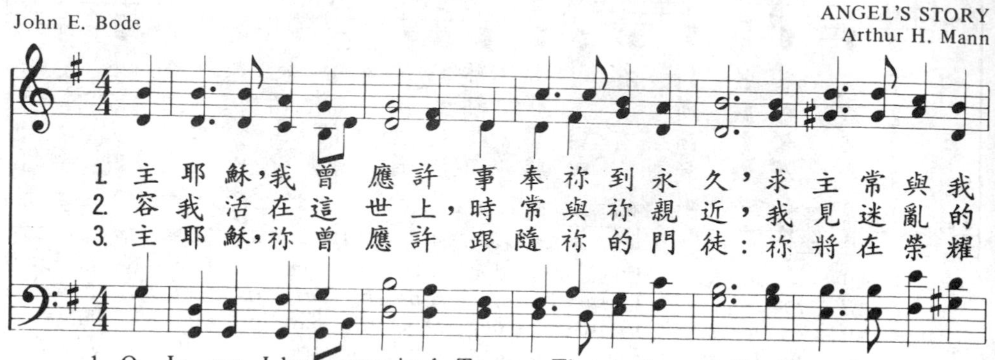

1. 主耶穌，我曾應許事奉祢到永久，求主常與我
2. 容我活在這世上，時常與祢親近，我見迷亂的
3. 主耶穌，祢曾應許跟隨祢的門徒：祢將在榮耀

1 O Je-sus, I have prom-ised To serve Thee to the end; Be Thou for-ev-er
2 *O let me feel Thee near me, The world is ev-er near; I see the sights that*
3 O Je-sus, Thou hast prom-ised To all who fol-low Thee That where Thou art in

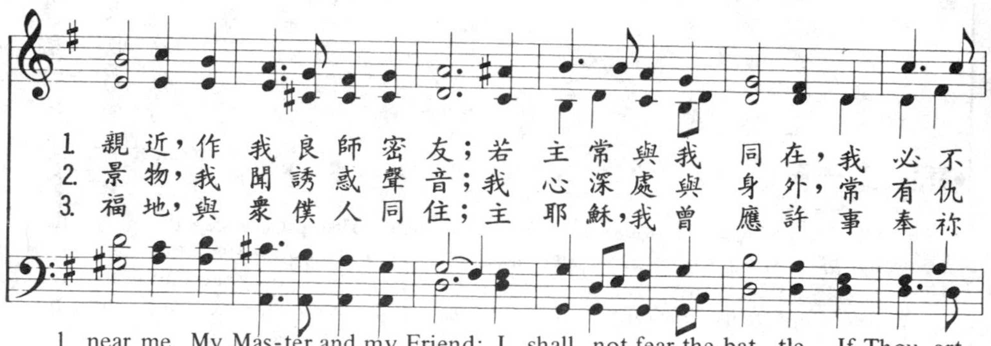

1. 親近，作我良師密友；若主常與我同在，我必不
2. 景物，我聞誘惑聲音；我心深處與身外，常有仇
3. 福地，與眾僕人同住；主耶穌，我曾應許事奉祢

1 near me, My Mas-ter and my Friend; I shall not fear the bat-tle If Thou art
2 *daz-zle, The tempt-ing sounds I hear; My foes are ev-er near me, A-round me*
3 glo-ry There shall Thy ser-vant be; And, Je-sus, I have prom-ised To serve Thee

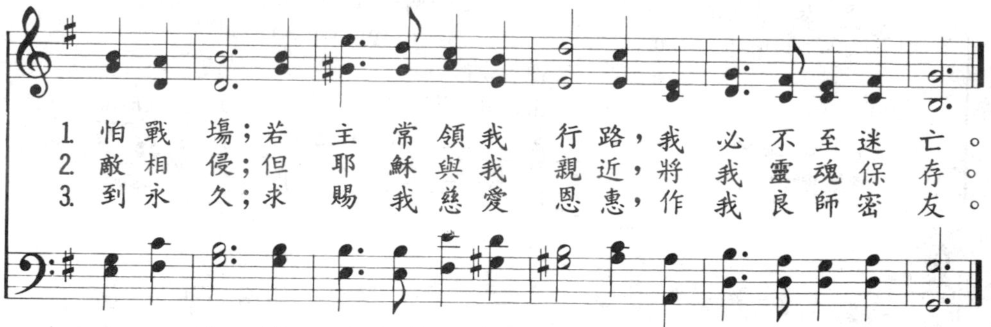

1. 怕戰場；若主常領我行路，我必不至迷亡。
2. 敵相侵；但耶穌與我親近，將我靈魂保存。
3. 到永久；求賜我慈愛恩惠，作我良師密友。

1 by my side, Nor wan-der from the path-way If Thou wilt be my Guide.
2 *and with-in; But, Je-sus, draw Thou near-er, And shield my soul from sin.*
3 to the end; O give me grace to fol-low My Mas-ter and my Friend.

所獻雖少主看為貴重

Little Is Much, When God Is in It

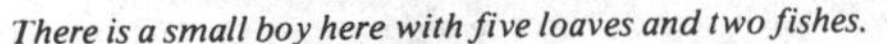

There is a small boy here with five loaves and two fishes.

— John 6:9

Mrs. F. W. Suffield　　　　Mrs. F. W. Suffield

1. 莊稼一片已經成熟，需要工人去作工；
2. 主差你去做工之處，似生疏少有人去；
3. 到那日當爭戰完畢，在世路程已跑盡；

1 In the har-vest field now rip-ened, There's a work for all to do;
2 *Does the place you're called to la-bor Seem so small and lit-tle known?*
3 When the con-flict here is end-ed And our race on earth is run;

1. 請聽主今向你呼召，呼召你為祂作工。
2. 在那地主能重用你，祂不忘屬祂兒女。
3. 忠心僕人主必歡迎，在天家永享安寧。

1 Hark, the voice of God is call-ing, To the har-vest call-ing you.
2 *It is great if God is in it, And He'll not for-get His own.*
3 He will say, if we are faith-ful, "Wel-come home, my child, well done."

所獻雖少，主看為貴重，盡全心名利不求；
Lit-tle is much when God is in it, La-bor not for wealth or fame;

你若肯為祂去作工，榮耀冠冕為你留。
There's a crown and you can win it, If you go in Je-sus' name.

290

都歸耶穌
All for Jesus

Ye are bought with a price; therefore glorify God in your body . . .

— I Corinthians 6:20

Mary D. James

CONSTANCY
Unknown

1. 願我身心才智工夫，都歸耶穌我救主；
2. 願我雙手為主服務，願我雙足跟主行；
3. 自我定睛仰望耶穌，便看萬事如糞土；
4. 何等希奇何等奧妙！榮耀君王是耶穌；
1 All for Je - sus, all for Je - sus! All my be - ing's ran - somed powers:
2 Let my hands per - form His bid - ding, Let my feet run in His ways;
3 Since my eyes were fixed on Je - sus, I've lost sight of all be - side,
4 O what won - der! how a - maz - ing! Je - sus, glo - rious King of kings,

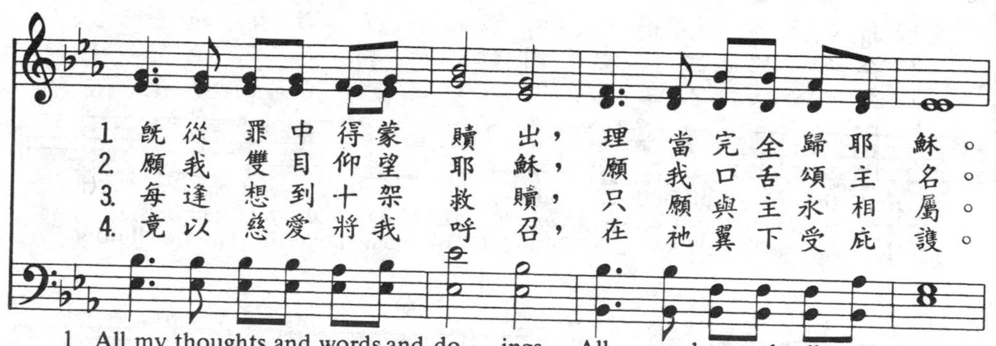
1. 既從罪中得蒙贖出，理當完全歸耶穌。
2. 願我雙目仰望耶穌，願我口舌頌主名。
3. 每逢想到十架救贖，只願與主永相屬。
4. 竟以慈愛將我呼召，在祂翼下受庇護。
1 All my thoughts and words and do - ings, All my days and all my hours:
2 Let my eyes see Je - sus on - ly, Let my lips speak forth His praise:
3 So en - rapt my spir - it's vi - sion, Look - ing at the Cru - ci - fied:
4 Deigns to call me His be - lov - ed, Lets me rest be - neath His wings:

1. 都歸耶穌！都歸耶穌！都歸耶穌我救主；
2. 都歸耶穌！都歸耶穌！都歸耶穌我救主；
3. 都歸耶穌！都歸耶穌！都歸耶穌我救主；
4. 都歸耶穌！都歸耶穌！都歸耶穌我救主；
1 All for Je - sus! all for Je - sus! All my days and all my hours;
2 All for Je - sus! all for Je - sus! Let my lips speak forth His praise;
3 All for Je - sus! all for Je - sus! Look - ing at the Cru - ci - fied;
4 All for Je - sus! all for Je - sus! Rest - ing now be - neath His wings;

1. 都歸耶穌！都歸耶穌！都歸耶穌我救主。
2. 都歸耶穌！都歸耶穌！都歸耶穌我救主。
3. 都歸耶穌！都歸耶穌！都歸耶穌我救主。
4. 都歸耶穌！都歸耶穌！都歸耶穌我救主。
1 All for Je - sus! all for Je - sus! All my days and all my hours.
2 All for Je - sus! all for Je - sus! Let my lips speak forth His praise.
3 All for Je - sus! all for Je - sus! Look-ing at the Cru-ci - fied.
4 All for Je - sus! all for Je - sus! Rest - ing now be-neath His wings.

291

我一生求主管理

Take My Life, and Let It Be Consecrated

HENDON

Present your bodies a living sacrifice.
— Romans 12:1

Frances R. Havergal

Henri A. César Malan

1. 我一生求主管理，願獻身心為活祭；使我手作
2. 使我脚為主行路，步步都聽主吩咐；使我常常
3. 使我口時常頌揚，傳講救主榮耀王；使我金銀
4. 使我愛如火上升，全獻給我主我神；我願獻一

1 Take my life and let it be Con - se-crat-ed, Lord, to Thee; Take my hands and
2 *Take my feet and let them be Swift and beau-ti-ful for Thee; Take my voice and*
3 Take my lips and let them be Filled with mes-sa-ges for Thee; Take my sil - ver
4 *Take my love, my God, I pour At Thy feet its treas - ure store; Take my-self and*

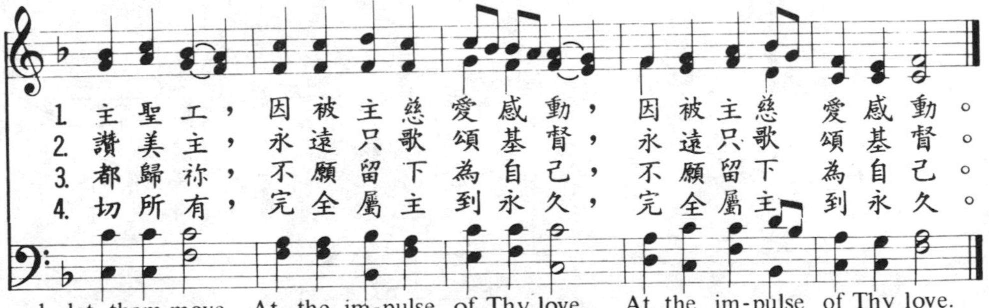
1. 主聖工，因被主慈愛感動，因被主慈愛感動。
2. 讚美主，永遠只歌頌基督，永遠只歌頌基督。
3. 都歸祢，不願留下為自己，不願留下為自己。
4. 切所有，完全屬主到永久，完全屬主到永久。
1 let them move At the im-pulse of Thy love, At the im-pulse of Thy love.
2. let me sing Al-ways, on-ly, for my King, Al-ways, on-ly for my King.
3 and my gold, Not a mite would I with-hold, Not a mite would I with-hold.
4 I will be Ev - er, on - ly, all for Thee, Ev - er, on - ly. all for Thee.

292
将你最好的獻於主
Give of Your Best to the Master

Ye are My friends if ye do whatsoever I command you.

— John 15:14

Howard B. Grose

BARNARD
Charlotte A. Barnard

1. 将 你 最 好 的 獻 於 主，獻 你 年 輕 的 力 量 ；
2. 将 你 最 好 的 獻 於 主，主 在 你 心 居 首 位 ；
3. 将 你 最 好 的 獻 於 主，主 愛 偉 大 無 可 比 ；
1 Give of your best to the Mas - ter, Give of the strength of your youth;
2 *Give of your best to the Mas - ter, Give Him first place in your heart;*
3 Give of your best to the Mas - ter, Naught else is wor - thy His love;

副歌 将 你 最 好 的 獻 於 主；獻 你 年 青 的 力 量 ；
Refrain: Give of your best to the Mas - ter; Give of the strength of your youth;

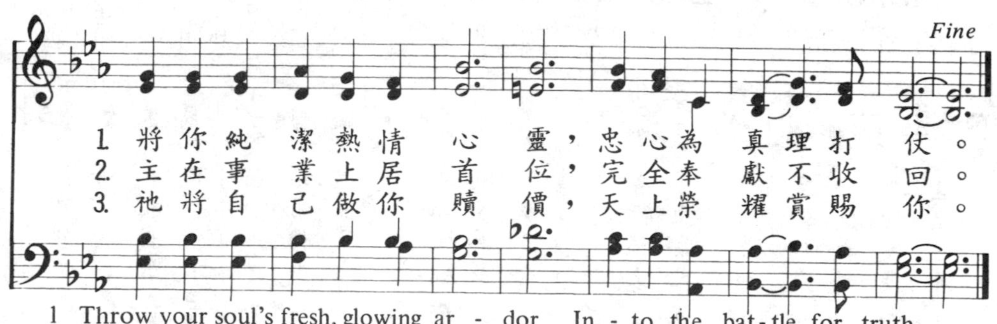
Fine
1. 将 你 純 潔 熱 情 心 靈，忠 心 為 真 理 打 仗 。
2. 主 在 事 業 上 居 首 位，完 全 奉 獻 不 收 回 。
3. 祂 将 自 己 做 你 贖 價，天 上 榮 耀 賞 賜 你 。
1 Throw your soul's fresh, glowing ar - dor In - to the bat-tle for truth.
2 *Give Him first place in your ser - vice; Con-se-crate ev - ery part.*
3 He gave him-self for your ran - som, Gave up His glo - ry a - bove;

副歌 穿 上 救 恩 全 副 軍 裝，忠 心 為 真 理 打 仗 。
Refrain: Clad in sal - va-tion's full ar - mor, Join in the bat-tle for truth.

1. 主 耶 穌 已 做 你 榜 樣，勇 敢 堅 定 不 懼 怕 ；
2. 樂 意 施 捨 必 得 賞 賜，因 神 将 愛 子 賜 下 ；
3. 祂 捨 生 命 毫 無 怨 言，救 你 脱 罪 把 血 洒 ；
1 Je - sus has set the ex - am - ple - Daunt-less was He, young and brave;
2 *Give, and to you shall be giv - en. - God His be - lov - ed Son gave;*
3 Laid down His life with-out mur - mur, You from sin's ru - in to save;

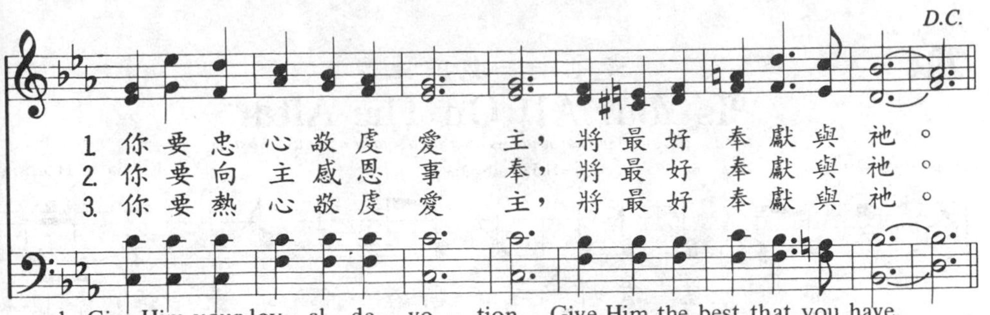
D.C.
1. 你要忠心敬虔愛主，將最好奉獻與祂。
2. 你要向主感恩事奉，將最好奉獻與祂。
3. 你要熱心敬虔愛主，將最好奉獻與祂。

1 Give Him your loy - al de - vo - tion, Give Him the best that you have.
2 *Grate-ful-ly seek-ing to serve Him, Give Him the best that you have.*
3 Give Him your heart's ad-o - ra - tion, Give Him the best that you have.

向主獻呈

293

We Give Thee but Thine Own

Of thine own have we given Thee. — I Chronicles 29:14

SCHUMANN

William W. How

Mason and Webb's *Cantica Laudis*

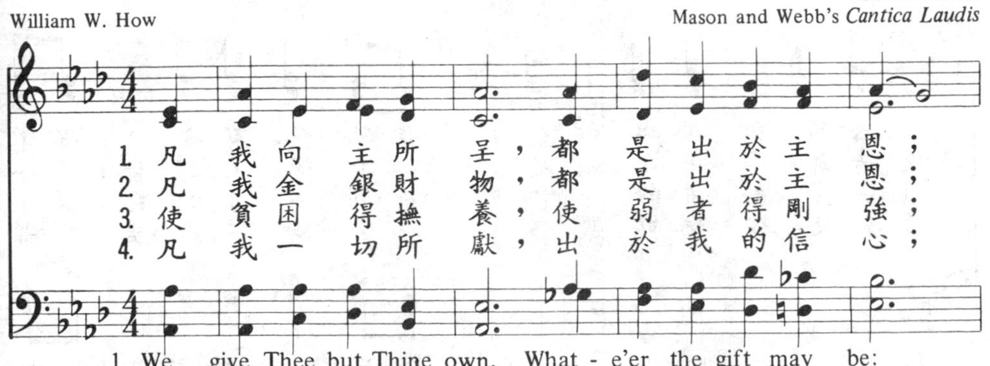
1. 凡我向主所呈，都是出於主恩；
2. 凡我金銀財物，都是出於主恩；
3. 使貧困得撫養，使弱者得剛強；
4. 凡我一切所獻，出於我的信心；

1 We give Thee but Thine own, What - e'er the gift may be:
2 *May we Thy boun-ties thus As stew-ards true re - ceive,*
3 To com-fort and to bless, To find a balm for woe,
4 *And we be-lieve Thy word, Though dim our faith may be:*

1. 凡我所有都屬於主，我是主的僕人。
2. 願將一切初熟果子，樂意向主獻呈。
3. 更將主恩四方傳揚，領回迷路群羊。
4. 願我每日努力所行，都為榮耀主名。阿門。

1 All that we have is Thine a - lone, A trust, O Lord, from Thee.
2 *And glad-ly, as Thou bless-est us, To Thee our first-fruits give.*
3 To tend the lone and fa-ther-less Is our great task be - low.
4 *What - ev - er task we do, O Lord, We do it un - to Thee.* A-men.

是否將一切獻上？

Is Your All On The Altar

Thou therefore endure hardness, as a good soldier of Jesus Christ.
— II Timothy 2:3

Elisha A. Hoffman Elisha A. Hoffman

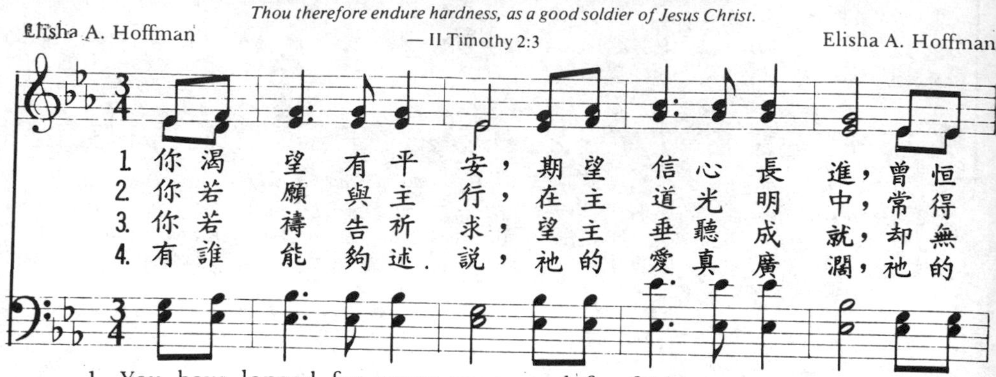
1. 你渴望有平安，期望信心長進，曾恒
2. 你若願與主行，在主道光明中，常得
3. 你若禱告祈求，望主垂聽成就，却無
4. 有誰能夠述說，祂的愛真廣濶，祂的
1. You have longed for sweet peace, and for faith to in-crease, And have
2. *Would you walk with the Lord in the light of His Word, And have*
3. Oh we nev-er can know what the Lord will be-stow Of the
4. *Who can tell all the love He will send from a-bove! Oh, how*

1. 心的祈求與仰望；但不能有安息，得不
2. 着真平安心滿足；必要遵主美旨，將一
3. 法得知主的心意，直到將身心靈，讓主
4. 愛能使我口歌唱！在主脚前靜坐，何等

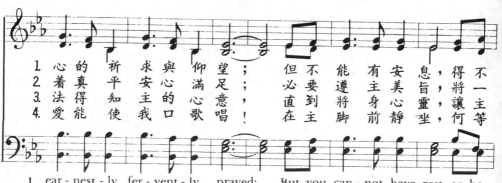

1. ear-nest-ly, fer-vent-ly prayed; But you can-not have rest, or be
2. *peace and con-tent-ment al-way; You must do His sweet will to be*
3. bless-ings for which we have prayed, Till our bod-y and soul He doth
4. *hap-py our hearts will be made! Oh, what fel-low-ship sweet we shall*

1. 着大福祉，除非你將一切全獻上。
2. 切獻壇上，你纔能得脱離衆罪污。
3. 親自管理，獻在壇上不再留為己。
4. 親密交通，當你獻一切在祭壇上。
你所
Is your
1. per-fect-ly blest, Un-til all on the al-tar is laid.
2. *free from all ill; On the al-tar your all you must lay.*
3. ful-ly con-trol, And our all on the al-tar is laid.
4. *share at His feet, When our all on the al-tar is laid!*

有是否作活祭獻在壇上？聖靈是否
all on the al - tar of sac - ri - fice laid? Your heart, does the
管理你心？你若將身、心、靈、交在
Spir - it con - trol? You can on - ly be blest and have
主的手裏必蒙主賜大福享安寧。
peace and sweet rest, As you yield Him your bod - y and soul.

真正的快樂必須依賴與神密切的聯繫，依賴神和服從神。塵世所給你的享受，與由神處每日密切交通而獲得的無價財富與快樂比較起來，就算不得什麼。效法基督的生活必須接近神的心。

295

奉獻上好

Our Best

For me to live is Christ, and to die is gain.

— Philippians 1:21

S. C. Kirk, Grant C. Tullar

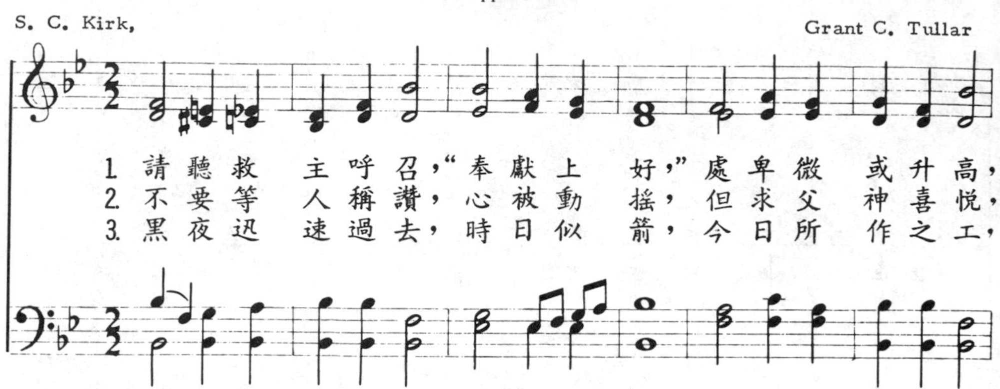

1. 請聽救主呼召，"奉獻上好，"處卑微或升高，
2. 不要等人稱讚，心被動搖，但求父神喜悅，
3. 黑夜迅速過去，時日似箭，今日所作之工，

1. Hear ye the Mas-ter's call, "Give Me thy best!" For, be it great or small,
2. *Wait not for men to laud, Heed not their slight; Win-ning the smile of God*
3. Night soon comes on a-pace, Day has-tens by; Workman and work must face

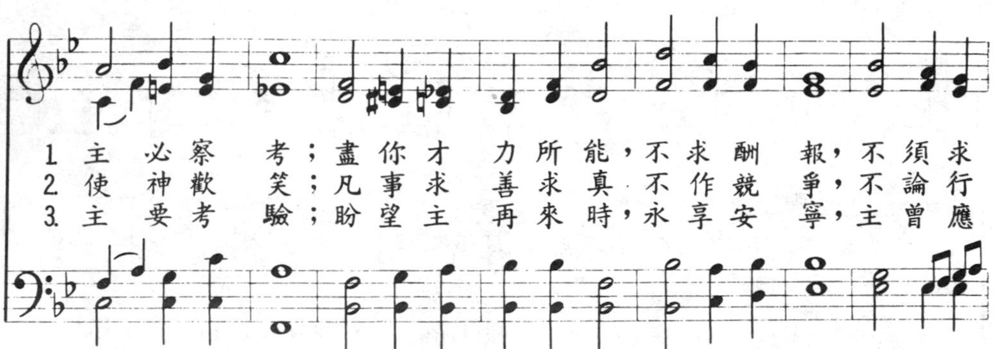

1 主必察考；盡你才力所能，不求酬報，不須求
2 使神歡笑；凡事求善求真不作競爭，不論行
3 主要考驗；盼望主再來時，永享安寧，主曾應

1. That is His test. Do then the best you can, Not for re-ward, Not for the
2. *Brings its de - light! Aid-ing the good and true Ne'er goes un-blest, All that we*
3. Test - ing on high. Oh, may we in that day Find rest, sweet rest, Which God has

1 人稱讚，因主知道。
2 走思想，當盡所能。凡為耶穌所作都蒙福，
3 許賜福盡忠僕人。Ev-ery work for Je-sus will be blest,

1. praise of man, But for the Lord.
2. *think or do, Be it the best.*
3. prom-ised those Who do their best.

恩主要人人全力以赴，我才力雖微小，
But he asks from ev-ery one His best. Our tal-ents may be few,
不足稱道，祇求盡心盡意盡力愛主。
These may be small, But un-to Him is due Our best, our all.

295-1 Prayer of Dedication

Lord, call us into the church.
Call us in often,
  and teach us the old words and old songs
  with their new meanings.
Lord, give us new words
  for the words we wear out.
Give us new songs
  for those that have lost their spirit.
Give us new reasons for coming in
  and for going out,
  into our streets and to our homes.
As the house of the Lord once moved
  like a tent through the wilderness,
  so keep our churches from being rigid.
Make our congregation alive and free.
Give us ideas we never had before,
  so that alleluia and gloria and amen
  are like the experiences we know in daily living.
Alleluia! O Lord, be praised!
In worship and in work, be praised! Amen.

—Herbert Brokering

296

我已經決定要跟隨耶穌
I Have Decided to Follow Jesus

Let us run with patience the race that is set before us.
— Hebrews 12:1

Attributed to an Indian prince
As sung in Garo, Assam

Folk melody from India
Arr. by Norman Johnson

1. 我已經決定，要跟隨耶穌，我已經決定，
2. 雖無人同走，我仍要跟隨，雖無人同走，
3. 十架在前面，世界在背後，十架在前面，
1. I have de-cid-ed to fol-low Je-sus, I have de-cid-ed
2. Tho no one join me, still I will fol-low, Tho no one join me,
3. The world be-hind me, the cross be-fore me, The world be-hind me,

1. 要跟隨耶穌，我已經決定，要跟隨耶穌，
2. 我仍要跟隨，雖無人同走，我仍要跟隨，
3. 世界在背後，十架在前面，世界在背後，
1. to fol-low Je-sus, I have de-cid-ed to fol-low Je-sus—
2. still I will fol-low, Tho no one join me, still I will fol-low—
3. the cross be-fore me, The world be-hind me, the cross be-fore me—

永不回頭，永不回頭！
No turn-ing back, (No turn-ing back,) no turn-ing back!

活着為耶穌，真平安
Living For Jesus, Oh What Peace

I live by the faith of the Son of God who loved me and gave Himself for me.
— Galatians 2:21
C. F. W.
C. F. Weigle
1. 活着為耶穌，真平安！喜樂之江河永不
2. 活着為耶穌，真安息！討我主喜悦福満
3. 活着為耶穌，無不往！一切的重擔主擔
4. 活着為耶穌，見主時進入主榮耀享安
1. Liv - ing for Je - sus, Oh, what peace! Riv-ers of pleas - ure nev - er
2. Liv - ing for Je - sus, Oh, what rest! Pleas-ing my Sav - iour, I am
3. Liv - ing for Je - sus, ev - 'ry - where, All of my bur - dens He doth
4. Liv - ing for Je - sus, till at last In - to His glo - ry I have
1. 乾；試煉雖來臨，我不慌，活着為耶穌，主在旁。
2. 溢；單為主生活，聽主令，直到我走完世路程。
3. 當；朋友雖改變主真實，信靠主帶領，主指示。
4. 息；親眼見主在寶座上，親耳聽説來領獎賞。
1. cease. Tri-als may come, yet I'll not fear. Liv-ing for Je-sus, He is near.
2. blest. On-ly to live for Him a-lone. Do-ing His will till life is done!
3. bear. Friends may for-sake me: He'll be true. Trust-ing in Him, He'll guide me thru.
4. passed; There to be-hold Him on His throne, Hear from His lips, "My child, well done!"
求主助我多事奉祢，求主助我多讚美祢；
Help me to serve Thee more and more, Help me to praise Thee o'er and o'er;
使我活在主慈愛裏，永遠跟隨主不轉離。
Live in Thy pres-ence day by day, Nev-er to turn from Thee a - way.

298

為主而活

Living for Jesus

Present your bodies a living sacrifice, holy, . . . acceptable . . .
— Romans 12:1

Thomas O. Chisholm

LIVING
C. Harold Lowden

1. 我願獻身心，為基督而活，在一切事上討
2. 慈悲主耶穌，受死作中保，使我免罪孽又
3. 無論何境遇，總為主作工，盡我的本份使
4. 在短瞬世間，願為主而活，因我心所愛是

1 Liv-ing for Je-sus a life that is true, Striv-ing to please Him in
2 *Liv-ing for Je-sus who died in my place, Bear-ing on Cal-vary my*
3 Liv-ing for Je-sus wher-ev-er I am, Do-ing each du-ty in
4 *Liv-ing for Je-sus through earth's lit-tle while, My dear-est treas-ure, the*

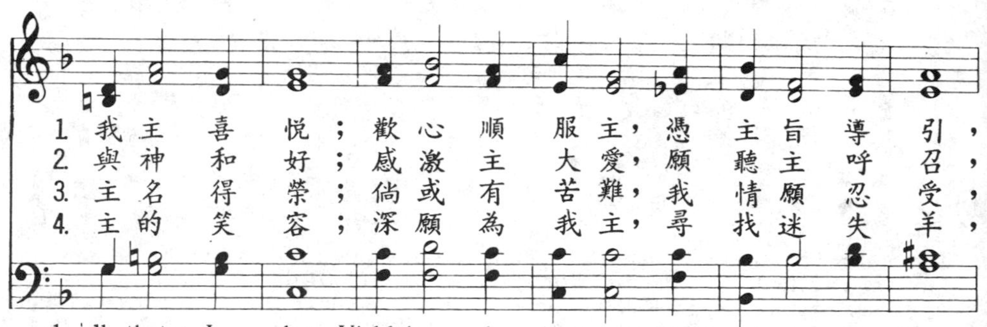

1. 我主喜悦；歡心順服主，憑主旨導引，
2. 與神和好；感激主大愛，願聽主呼召，
3. 主名得榮；倘或有苦難，我情願忍受，
4. 主的笑容；深願為我主，尋找迷失羊，

1 all that I do; Yield-ing al-le-giance, glad-heart-ed and free,
2 *sin and dis-grace; Such love con-strains me to an-swer His call,*
3 His ho-ly name; Will-ing to suf-fer af-flic-tion and loss,
4 *light of His smile; Seek-ing the lost ones He died to re-deem,*

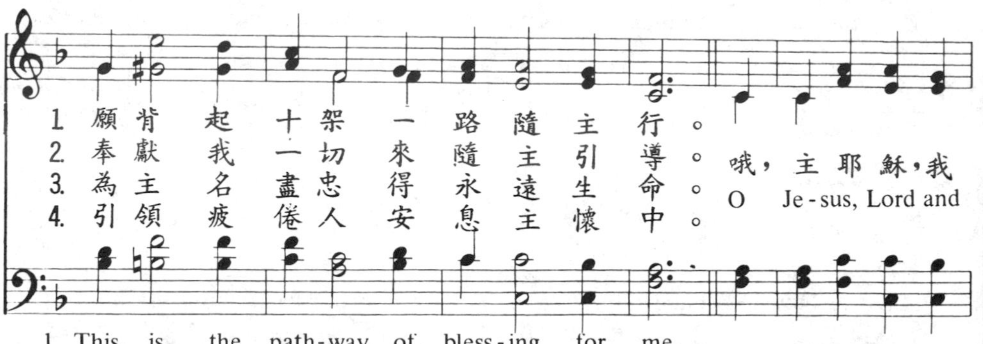

1. 願背起十架一路隨主行。
2. 奉獻我一切來隨主引導。
3. 為主名盡忠得永遠生命。
4. 引領疲倦人安息主懷中。
哦，主耶穌，我
O Je-sus, Lord and

1 This is the path-way of bless-ing for me.
2 *Fol-low His lead-ing and give Him my all.*
3 Tak-ing each trial as a part of my cross.
4 *Bring-ing the wea-ry to find rest in Him.*

救主，我心奉獻給祢，因祢在十字架上，為
Sav-ior, I give my-self to Thee, For Thou, in Thy a-tone-ment, Didst
贖我罪釘死；我要祢作我救主，來住在我心
give Thy-self for me; I own no oth-er Mas-ter, My heart shall be Thy
裡；我一生一世到永遠，哦，主，完全歸祢。
throne; My life I give, hence-forth to live, O Christ, for Thee a - lone.

一個獻身者深切領悟到「主為我死」，他乃是主用重價買贖回來的，他不敢再為自己活；他也深切明白，「為主而活」不是空洞的屬靈口號，乃是一場有血有肉的爭戰，是一條腳踏實地的道路，他不因此而自覺可誇，因為他知道，奉獻就是奉還給主，是基督徒理所當有的正常生活。

299

求主管理我的心意

Take Thou Our Minds, Dear Lord

Let this mind be in you which is also in Christ Jesus.
— Philippians 2:5
William Hiram Foulkes
HALL
Calvin W. Laufer
1. 求主每日管理，我的心意；
2. 今願将我身心，奉獻於祢；
3. 求主完全掌握—我的意志；
4. 我今全身，全體，全意，全心；
1 Take Thou our minds, dear Lord, we hum - bly pray;
2 Take Thou our hearts, O Christ — they are Thine own;
3 Take Thou our wills, dear God! hold Thou full sway;
4 Take Thou our - selves, O Lord, heart, mind, and will;
1. 願以基督的心，為我的心。
2. 我已完全屬祢，求主管理。
3. 使我完全順服，祢的旨意。
4. 完全奉獻於祢，憑祢意行。
1 Give us the mind of Christ through - out each day,
2 Come Thou with - in our souls and claim Thy throne,
3 Have in our in - most souls Thy per - fect way,
4 Through our sur - ren - dered souls Thy plans ful - fill.
1. 教我認識真理，使我自由；
2. 求主用我一生，助我剛強；
3. 成為聖潔像祢，不再自私；
4. 我的一生年日，才幹恩賜；
1 Teach us to know the truth that sets us free;
2 Help us to shed a - broad Thy gen - erous love;
3 Guard Thou each sa - cred hour from self - ish ease;
4 We yield our - selves to Thee— time, tal - ents, all;

1. 我的心思意念，尊主為首。
2. 将祢大愛宣揚，與人分享。
3. 引導我的生命，討祢歡喜。
4. 今願聽主呼召，完全歸祢。
1 Grant us in all our thoughts to hon - or Thee.
2 *Use us to make the earth like heaven a - bove.*
3 Guide Thou our or - dered lives as Thou dost please.
4 *We hear, and hence - forth heed, Thy sov - ereign call.*
A-men.

生命多美好
Something Beautiful

300

There is therefore now no condemnation to them that are in Christ Jesus . . . . — Romans 8:1

Gloria Gaither

SOMETHING BEAUTIFUL
William J. Gaither

生命多奇妙，多美好；
Some - thing beau - ti - ful, some - thing good;

我一切困惑，祂全知道；
All my con - fu - sion He un - der - stood:

我所獻給祂的是憂傷破碎心
All I had to of - fer Him was bro - ken - ness and

靈，但祂賜給我美好的新生命。
strife, But He made some - thing beau - ti - ful of my life.

301 誰順從主耶穌？

Who Is on the Lord's Side?

Who is on the Lord's side?
— Exodus 32:26

Frances R. Havergal

ARMAGEDDON
C. Luise Reichardt

1. 誰 順 從 主 耶 穌？誰 尊 主 為 王？誰 與
2. 並 非 要 得 榮 耀，並 非 要 冠 冕，我 才
3. 主 耶 穌 救 贖 我，並 非 用 金 銀，乃 是
4. 我 既 蒙 主 召 選，為 軍 在 敵 前，當 奮

1 Who is on the Lord's side? Who will serve the King? Who will
2 *Not for weight of glo - ry, Nor for crown and palm, En - ter*
3 Je - sus, Thou hast bought us, Not with gold or gem, But with
4 *Fierce may be the con - flict, Strong may be the foe, But the*

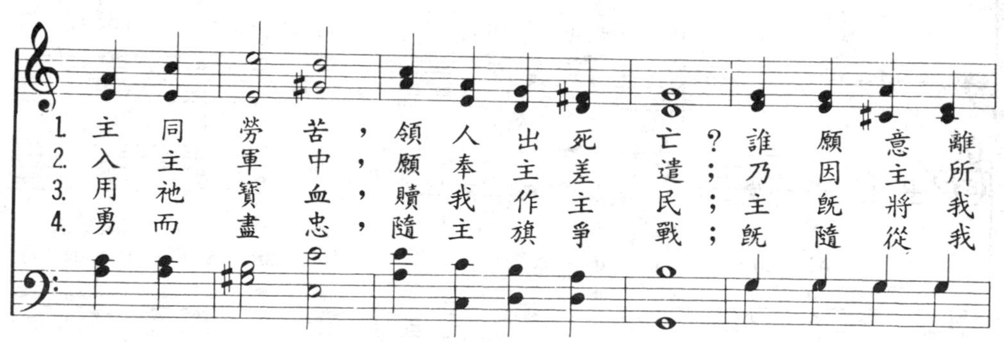
1. 主 同 勞 苦，領 人 出 死 亡？誰 願 意 離
2. 入 主 軍 中，願 奉 主 差 遣；乃 因 主 所
3. 用 祂 寶 血，贖 我 作 主 民；主 既 將 我
4. 勇 而 盡 忠，隨 主 旗 爭 戰；既 隨 從 我

1 be His help - ers, Oth - er lives to bring? Who will leave the
2 *we the ar - my, Raise the war - rior - psalm; But for Love that*
3 Thine own life - blood, For Thy di - a - dem; With Thy bless - ing
4 *King's own ar - my None can o - ver - throw; 'Round His stan - dard*

1. 世 俗？誰 與 惡 抗 拒？ 誰 順 從 主
2. 贖 者，皆 為 主 所 愛， 凡 被 主 所
3. 釋 放，使 我 心 受 感， 來 到 恩 主
4. 君 王，心 何 能 冷 淡， 要 努 力 建

1 world's side? Who will face the foe? Who is on the
2 *claim - eth Lives for whom He died: He whom Je - sus*
3 fill - ing Each who comes to Thee, Thou hast made us
4 *rang - ing, Vic - tory is se - cure, For His truth un -*

1. 耶穌？誰肯為主去？蒙救主呼召我，
2. 召者，必順其元帥。主慈愛激勵我，
3. 面前，恩賜就充滿。主受死我得生，
4. 大工，一時不怠慢。主領我作聖工，
1 Lord's side? Who for Him will go? By Thy call of mer - cy,
2 nam - eth Must be on His side. By Thy love con - strain - ing,
3 will - ing, Thou hast made us free. By Thy grand re - demp - tion,
4 chang - ing Makes the tri - umph sure. Joy - ful - ly en - list - ing,
因主恩無比，我願順從耶穌，主啊，我屬祢！
By Thy grace di - vine, We are on the Lord's side— Sav - ior, we are Thine!

Psalm 144

O God, it is difficult to understand how You can regard man with such high regard and show him so much concern.
His years upon this earth are so few.
He is little more than a wisp of wind in the time and space of Your great universe.
You created him as the object of Your love—only to see him turn from You to play with his foolish toys.
You tried to teach him to love his fellowman—only to see him express his fear and suspicion and hate through cruel acts of violence and war.
You showered upon him Your abundant gifts—only to see him make them his ultimate concern.
Still You continue to love him and seek incessantly to save him from destroying himself and the world You have placed in his hands.
Even while he rejects You, You reach out to draw him back to Yourself.
Even while he suffers the painful consequences of his rank rebelliousness, You offer to him Your healing and demonstrate Your desire to restore him to love and joy.
And when he finally turns to You, he finds You waiting for him, ready to forgive his sins and to reunite him to Your life and purposes once more.
That man who returns to his God is happy indeed!
He will forever be the object of God's love and blessings.

—Leslie Brandt

302

主翅膀下

Under His Wings

Hide me under the shadow of Thy Wing.

— Psalm 17:8

William O. Cushing
HINGHAM
Ira D. Sankey
1. 安穩隱藏在祂大能翅膀下，狂風暴雨攻擊我也不怕；魔鬼雖用計要奪去我靈魂，但我藏主裏他無隙可進。
2. 安穩隱藏在祂大能翅膀下，何等溫暖何等柔和週密！當敵攻擊我無處可得幫助，但在祂蔭庇下必無一失。
3. 安穩隱藏在祂大能翅膀下，直到黑雲過去青天復現；那時祂展翼帶我飛上天庭，見父榮面稱頌主愛無限。
1 Under His wings I am safely abiding, Though the night deepens and tempests are wild; Still I can trust Him— I know He will keep me, He has redeemed me and I am His child.
2 Under His wings, what a refuge in sorrow! How the heart yearningly turns to His rest! Often when earth has no balm for my healing, There I find comfort and there I am blest.
3 Under His wings, O what precious enjoyment! There will I hide 'til life's trials are o'er; Sheltered, protected, no evil can harm me, Resting in Jesus I'm safe evermore.
安穩隱藏主翅膀下，誰能使我脫離主愛？
Under His wings, under His wings, Who from His love can sever?

世界末期雖常有患難，但主翅膀下有平安。
Un-der His wings my soul shall a-bide, Safe-ly a-bide for-ev-er.

天父，我敬拜祢

Father, I Adore You

303

God is a Spirit; and they that worship Him must worship him in spirit and in truth. — John 4:24

MARANATHA
Terrye Coelho

Terrye Coelho

Three-part round (in unison)
1. 天父，我敬拜祢，奉獻身心
2. 耶穌，我敬拜祢，奉獻身心
3. 聖靈，我敬拜祢，奉獻身心
1 Fa-ther, I a-dore You, Lay my life be-
2 Je-sus, I a-dore You, Lay my life be-
3 Spir-it, I a-dore You, Lay my life be-

1. 給祢，我願愛祢。
2. 給祢，我願愛祢。
3. 給祢，我願愛祢。
1 fore You, How I love You.
2 fore You, How I love You.
3 fore You, How I love You.

304
照我本相
Just As I Am, Without One Plea

Ho, everyone who is athirst, come . . . without money . . . and without price.

— Isaiah 55:1

Charlotte Elliott

WOODWORTH
William B. Bradbury

1. 照我本相，無善可陳，惟
2. 照我本相，來到主前，我
3. 照我本相，祢肯收留，賜
4. 照我本相，蒙主大愛，除
1 Just as I am, with - out one plea, But
2 Just as I am, and wait - ing not To
3 Just as I am, Thou wilt re - ceive, Wilt
4 Just as I am, Thy love un - known Hath
1. 祢流血替我受懲，並且召我就
2. 無能力自洗罪愆；惟靠救主寶
3. 我生命赦我愆尤；祢既應許必
4. 我一切罪孽障礙；今願歸主永
1 that Thy blood was shed for me, And that Thou biddest me
2 rid my soul of one dark blot; To Thee, whose blood can
3 wel - come, par - don, cleanse, re - lieve; Be - cause Thy prom - ise
4 bro - ken ev - ery bar - rier down; Now, to be Thine, yes,
1. 祢得生，救主耶穌，我來，我來！
2. 血洗淨，救主耶穌，我來，我來！
3. 定成就，救主耶穌，我來，我來！
4. 遠屬主，救主耶穌，我來，我來！阿門。
1 come to Thee— O Lamb of God, I come, I come!
2 cleanse each spot, O Lamb of God, I come, I come!
3 I be-lieve, O Lamb of God, I come, I come!
4 Thine a - lone, O Lamb of God, I come, I come! A-men.

我時刻需要祢

I Need Thee Every Hour

Your Father knoweth what things ye have need of before ye ask.
— Matthew 6:8

Annie S. Hawks
Robert Lowry

NEED
Robert Lowry

1. 我 時 刻 需 要 祢，救 主 恩 深；
2. 我 時 刻 需 要 祢，與 我 親 近；
3. 我 時 刻 需 要 祢，或 憂 或 樂；
4. 我 時 刻 需 要 祢，賜 我 恩 言；
1 I need Thee ev - ery hour, Most gra - cious Lord;
2 I need Thee ev - ery hour, Stay Thou near by;
3 I need Thee ev - ery hour, In joy or pain;
4 I need Thee ev - ery hour, Teach me Thy will,
1. 誰 有 柔 聲 似 祢，足 慰 我 心。
2. 魔 鬼 若 來 試 探，使 我 得 勝。
3. 主 若 不 來 同 居，我 就 枉 活。
4. 願 主 寶 貴 應 許，於 我 成 全。
1 No ten - der voice like Thine Can peace af - ford.
2 Temp - ta - tions lose their power When Thou art nigh.
3 Come quick - ly, and a - bide, Or life is vain.
4 And Thy rich prom - is - es In me ful - fill.
哦，救 主，我 需 要 祢；每 時 刻 需 要 祢！
I need Thee, O I need Thee; Ev - ery hour I need Thee!
望 主 隨 時 施 恩 惠，我 來 就 祢。阿
O bless me now, my Sav - ior— I come to Thee. A - men.

306

主，我願做祢信徒

Lord, I Want to Be a Christian

And be renewed in the spirit of your mind. — Ephesians 4:23

American Folk Hymn
Unison
I WANT TO BE A CHRISTIAN
American Folk Melody
1. 主啊，我要做祢信徒，在我心，在我心；主啊，我要做祢信徒，在我心。在我心，在我心，
2. 主啊，我要更加愛人，在我心，在我心；主啊，我要更加愛人，在我心。在我心，在我心，
3. 主啊，我要更加聖潔，在我心，在我心；主啊，我要更加聖潔，在我心。在我心，在我心，
4. 主啊，我要學習像祢，在我心，在我心；主啊，我要學習像祢，在我心。在我心，在我心，
1 Lord, I want to be a Christian in my heart, in my heart; Lord, I want to be a Christian in my heart. In my heart, in my heart,
2 Lord, I want to be more loving in my heart, in my heart; Lord, I want to be more loving in my heart. In my heart, in my heart,
3 Lord, I want to be more holy in my heart, in my heart; Lord, I want to be more holy in my heart. In my heart, in my heart,
4 Lord, I want to be like Jesus in my heart, in my heart; Lord, I want to be like Jesus in my heart. In my heart, in my heart,

1. 主啊，我要做祢信徒在我心。
2. 主啊，我要更加愛人在我心。
3. 主啊，我要更加聖潔在我心。
4. 主啊，我要學習像祢在我心。
1 Lord, I want to be a Chris-tian in my heart.
2 Lord, I want to be more lov-ing in my heart.
3 Lord, I want to be more ho-ly in my heart.
4 Lord, I want to be like Je-sus in my heart.

306-1

改造我的心
Change My Heart, Oh God

Those God foreknew, He also predestined to be conformed to the likeness of His Son. Rom. 8:29

Eddie Espinosa — Eddie Espinosa

Unison

改造我的心，永遠的真誠，
Change my heart oh God. make it ev - er true

改造我的心，使我能像祢。
Change my heart oh God, may I be like You.

Fine

主，祢是陶匠，我是泥土，
You are the pot - ter, I am the clay

求祢塑造我，這是我禱告。
mold me and make me, this is what I pray.

D.C. al Fine

307 "你是否肯?" 救主問道

"Are Ye Able," Said the Master

Are ye able to drink of the cup that I shall drink of . . .
— Matthew 20:20

Earl Marlatt

BEACON HILL
Harry S. Mason

1. "你是否肯?"救主問道,"與我釘十架同死?"
2. "你是否肯?"願你記得,同釘十架一罪犯,
3. "你是否肯?"救主問道,主仍.微聲呼召你,
1 "Are ye a - ble," said the Mas - ter, "To be cru - ci - fied with Me?"
2 *"Are ye a - ble" to re - mem - ber, When a thief lifts up his eyes,*
3 "Are ye a - ble?" still the Mas - ter Whis - pers down e - ter - ni - ty,
1. 無知的人堅定回答,"我願跟從祢到底。"
2. 向主舉目求祂赦免,主應許他進樂園。
3. 願拋一切勇敢隨主,如昔日在加利利。
1 "Yea," the stur - dy dream - ers an - swered, "To the death we fol - low Thee:"
2 *That his par - doned soul is wor - thy Of a place in par - a - dise?*
3 And he - ro - ic spir - its an - swer, Now, as then in Gal - i - lee:
"哦,主啊,我肯"–我靈已屬祢;重造我心靈,聖潔像祢,求主賜恩光照耀引導我,使我更愛祢,向祢忠貞到底。
"Lord, we are a - ble"– our spir - its are Thine; Re - mold them– make us like Thee, di - vine. Thy guid - ing ra - diance a - bove us shall be A bea - con to God, to love and loy - al - ty.

只要信祂
Only Trust Him

Trust ye in the Lord forever; for in the Lord . . . is everlasting strength. — Isaiah 26:4

MINERVA

John H. Stockton

John H. Stockton

1. 被罪壓傷衆人快來，救主在此等待；
2. 耶穌為你被釘十架，捨身作你贖價；
3. 主是道路真理生命，領你天家安息；
1 Come, ev - ery soul by sin op-pressed, There's mer-cy with the Lord;
2 For Je - sus shed His pre - cious blood, Rich bless - ings to be - stow;
3 Yes, Je - sus is the Truth, the Way, That leads you in - to rest:
1. 祂要救你安你心懷，只要你肯信賴。
2. 救恩已成功效極大，只要你肯信祂。
3. 不再耽延今日相信，主賜你大福氣。
1 And He will sure - ly give you rest By trust - ing in His word.
2 He of - fers now the crim - son flood To wash us white as snow.
3 Be - lieve in Him with - out de - lay, And you are ful - ly blest.
只要信祂，只要信祂，現在信靠祂；
On - ly trust Him, on - ly trust Him, On - ly trust Him now;
祂必救你，祂必救你，現在拯救你。
He will save you, He will save you, He will save you now.

潔淨我

Cleanse Me

He is faithful and just . . . to cleanse us from all unrighteousness. — I John 1:9

Edwin Orr

MAORI
Maori Melody

1. 懇求救主，來鑒查我心思；求主今
2. 讚美救主，因將我罪洗清；願主的
3. 懇求我主，使我完全歸祢；貧窮的
4. 懇求聖靈，賜下廣大復興；先復興

1 Search me, O God, and know my heart to-day; Try me, O
2 *I praise Thee, Lord, for cleans-ing me from sin; Ful-fill Thy*
3 Lord, take my life, and make it whol-ly Thine; Fill my poor
4 *O Ho-ly Ghost, re-viv-al comes from Thee; Send a re-*

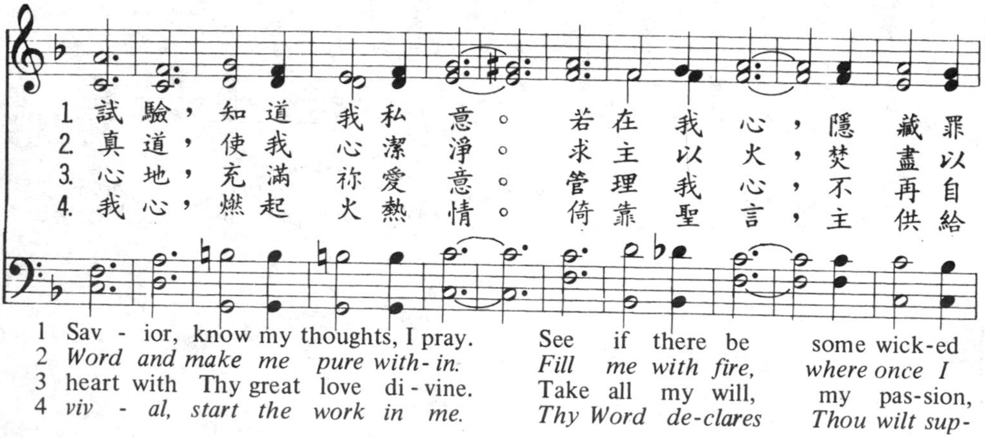

1. 試驗，知道我私意。若在我心，隱藏罪
2. 真道，使我心潔淨。求主以火，焚盡以
3. 心地，充滿祢愛意。管理我心，不再自
4. 我心，燃起火熱情。倚靠聖言，主供給

1 Sav-ior, know my thoughts, I pray. See if there be some wick-ed
2 *Word and make me pure with-in. Fill me with fire, where once I*
3 heart with Thy great love di-vine. Take all my will, my pas-sion,
4 *viv-al, start the work in me. Thy Word de-clares Thou wilt sup-*

1. 惡念頭；洗去諸般不義，使我自由。
2. 往羞情；我今所求所望，榮耀主名。
3. 私驕傲；今願完全聽命，求主引導。
4. 我需要，求主今賜福氣，是我祈禱。
1 way in me; Cleanse me from ev-ery sin, and set me free.
2 burned with shame; Grant my de-sire to mag-ni-fy Thy name.
3 self and pride; I now sur-ren-der, Lord—in me a-bide.
4 ply our need; For bless-ing now, O Lord, I hum-bly plead.

求主垂憐

Pass Me Not, O Gentle Savior

And he sought to see Jesus . . . for He was to pass that way.

— Luke 19: 3-4

PASS ME NOT
William H. Doane
Fanny J. Crosby
1. 懇求救主格外垂憐，請聽我禱告！
2. 讓我在祢恩座台前，永遠不相離；
3. 我只靠祢贖罪救恩，尋求見祢面；
4. 主祢是我平安源頭，比一切寶貴！
1 Pass me not, O gen-tle Sav-ior— Hear my hum-ble cry!
2 Let me at a throne of mer-cy Find a sweet re-lief;
3 Trust-ing on-ly in Thy mer-it, Would I seek Thy face;
4 Thou the spring of all my com-fort, More than life to me!
1. 既有別人被主宣召，莫把我棄掉。
2. 求祢賜我真摯信心，篤信而不疑。
3. 心中憂傷望祢安撫，顯祢大恩典。
4. 天上地下除祢以外，無別名可靠。
1 While on oth-ers Thou art call-ing, Do not pass me by.
2 Kneel-ing there in deep con-tri-tion, Help my un-be-lief.
3 Heal my wound-ed, bro-ken spir-it, Save me by Thy grace.
4 Whom have I on earth be-side Thee? Whom in heaven but Thee?
救主，救主，請聽我禱告！
Sav-ior, Sav-ior, Hear my hum-ble cry!
既有別人被主宣召，莫把我棄掉。阿門。
While on oth-ers Thou art call-ing, Do not pass me by. A-men.

311

我罪全歸耶穌

I Lay My Sins on Jesus

Behold the Lamb of God that taketh away the sins of the world. — John 1:29

Horatius Bonar

CRUCIFIX
Greek Melody

1. 我罪全歸主耶穌，上主聖潔羔羊；
2. 我将需要交給主，祂有豐富憐憫；
3. 我心渴望像耶穌，心存謙柔恩慈；
1 I lay my sins on Jesus, The spotless Lamb of God;
2 *I lay my wants on Jesus– All fullness dwells in Him;*
3 I long to be like Jesus– Pure, loving, lowly, mild;
1. 為我重罪祂受苦，使我得着釋放。
2. 祂能使我得救贖，又能醫我疾病。
3. 我心愛慕主耶穌，祂是天父愛子。
1 He bears them all, and frees us From every guilty load.
2 *He heals all my diseases, He doth my soul redeem.*
3 I long to be like Jesus– The Father's holy child.
1. 我帶罪來就耶穌，求靠祂的寶血，
2. 我将憂患交給主，祂深知我悲傷；
3. 我一生跟隨耶穌，直到天家同住，
1 I bring my guilt to Jesus, To wash my crimson stains
2 *I lay my griefs on Jesus, My burdens and my cares;*
3 I long to be with Jesus, Amid the heavenly throng,
1. 洗去我的衆罪污，使我潔白如雪。
2. 我的重擔祂背負，痛苦祂全承當。
3. 同與天使衆聖徒，歌頌讚美我主。
1 White in His blood most precious, 'Til not a spot remains.
2 *He from them all releases, He all my sorrow shares.*
3 To sing with saints His praises, To learn the angels' song.

貧窮罪人到主前

Come, Ye Sinners, Poor and Needy

BEACH SPRING
"The Sacred Harp"
Harmonized by A. Royce Eckhardt

He that cometh unto Me I will in no wise cast out.
John 6:37

Joseph Hart

1. 心靈痛苦貧窮罪人，可以到主面前來；
2. 莫待你的行為變好，莫想自己能自保；
3. 耶穌為你捨命流血，今已復活升高天；

1 Come, ye sin - ners, poor and need - y, Bruised and bro-ken by the fall;
2 *Let not con-science make you lin - ger, Nor of fit - ness fond-ly dream;*
3 Lo! th'in - car - nate God, as - cend - ed, Pleads the mer - it of His blood;

1. 耶穌愛你樂意救你，只要你願意悔改。
2. 祂要求你回轉向祂，全心相信並依靠。
3. 在父座前為你代求，願你信心永不變。

1 Je - sus read - y stands to save you, Full of par - doning love for all.
2 *All that He re - quires of sin - ners Is to turn and trust in Him.*
3 Ven-ture on Him, ven - ture whol - ly Let no oth - er trust in - trude;

1. 祂能救你，祂能救你，祂肯救你，莫遲疑；
2. 祂要救你，祂要救你，因祂為你曾捨命；
3. 惟有耶穌，惟有耶穌，惟有耶穌，能救你；

1 He is a - ble, He is a - ble, He is will - ing, doubt no more;
2 *He will save you, He will save you, 'Tis the gos - pel's con-stant theme.*
3 None but Je - sus, none but Je - sus Can do help - less sin - ners good.

1. 祂能救你，祂能救你，祂肯救你，莫遲疑。
2. 祂要救你，祂要救你，因祂為你曾捨命。
3. 惟有耶穌，惟有耶穌，惟有耶穌，能救你。

1 He is a - ble, He is a - ble, He is will - ing, doubt no more.
2 *He will save you, He will save you, 'Tis the gos - pel's con-stant theme.*
3 None but Je - sus, none but Je - sus Can do help - less sin - ners good.

求告主耶穌
Reach Out to Jesus

When she had heard of Jesus, came . . . and touched his garment. — Mark 5:27

Ralph Carmichael

REACH OUT TO JESUS
Ralph Carmichael

1 你是否靠自己背負重擔與憂愁？
2 你的人生是否充滿憂愁與失望？
1 Is your bur-den heav-y as you bear it all a-lone?
2 Is the life you're liv-ing filled with sor-row and de-spair?
1 你的人生道路是否覺危險難走？
2 是否為着前途滿心掛慮與惆悵？
1 Does the road you trav-el har-bor dan-ger yet un-known?
2 Does the fu-ture press you with its wor-ry and its care?
1 你是否在掙扎無限疲倦與痛苦？當求告
2 是否困倦孤單幾乎走入了迷途？求告主
1 Are you grow-ing wea-ry in the strug-gle of it all? Je-sus will
2 Are you tired and friend-less, have you al-most lost your way? Je-sus will
1 耶穌，祂必拯救幫助。
2 耶穌，祂必拯救幫助。主與你同在，
1 help you when on His name you call.
2 help you, just come to Him to-day. He is al-ways there,

垂聽你祈求，信實不改；主與你同行，
hear - ing ev - ery prayer, faith - ful and true; Walk - ing by our side,
一直到永遠享受主愛。當你灰心失望，切記
in His love we hide all the day through. When you get dis - cour - aged just re -
求告你恩主，求告主耶穌，祂必拯救幫助。
mem - ber what to do— Reach out to Je - sus, He's reach - ing out to you.

313 1

The prayer preceding all prayers is,
"May it be the real I who speaks.
May it be the real Thou
that I speak to."

— C. S. Lewis

314

耶穌恩召
Jesus Is Calling

Be of good comfort; He calleth thee.
—Matthew 10:49

John 11:28
Fanny J. Crosby

CALLING TODAY
George C. Stebbins

1. 耶穌發慈聲要召你回來， 今日召你，
2. 耶穌今召勞苦者得平安， 今日召你，
3. 耶穌今正等待盼你回來， 祂在等待，
4. 耶穌慈聲懇切求你回來， 今當聽祂，
1 Je - sus is ten - der - ly call - ing you home— Call - ing to - day,
2 Je - sus is call - ing the wea - ry to rest— Call - ing to - day,
3 Je - sus is wait - ing, O come to Him now— Wait - ing to - day,
4 Je - sus is plead - ing, O hear now His voice— Hear Him to - day,
1. 今日召你； 為何到處流浪離開主愛，
2. 今日召你； 可將你重擔交托主承擔，
3. 祂在等待； 將你衆罪俯伏主前悔改，
4. 今當聽祂； 信靠主名必得喜樂暢快，
1 call - ing to - day; Why from the sun - shine of love will you roam
2 call - ing to - day; Bring Him your bur - den and you shall be blest—
3 wait - ing to - day; Come with your sins, at His feet low - ly bow—
4 hear Him to - day; They who be - lieve on His name shall re - joice—
1. 有誰像主能護你？
2. 主必要救你到底。
3. 切莫躭延快回來。
4. 快快起來跟隨祂。
救主召你，
Call - ing to - day,
1 Far - ther and far - ther a - way?
2 He will not turn you a - way.
3 Come, and no long - er de - lay.
4 Quick - ly a - rise and a - way.

今 日 召 你， 耶 穌 今
Call - ing to - day, Je - sus is
召 你，主 今 日 慈 聲 呼 召 你。
call - ing, Is ten - der - ly call - ing to - day.

314-1 Prayer of Acceptance

Minister:

Here is a simple prayer
for those who have decided to receive Jesus:–

People:

Dear Father,
I believe that Jesus Christ is Your only begotten Son,
and that He became a human being,
shed His blood and died on the Cross
to clean away my sin that was separating me from You.
I believe that He rose from the dead,
physically,
to give me new life.

Lord Jesus, I invite You to come into my heart.
I accept You as my Savior and Lord.
I confess my sins, and ask You to wash them away.
I believe that You have come and are living in me right now.
Thank you, Jesus!
Amen.

–Dennis and Rita Bennett

讓耶穌進入你的心
Let Jesus Come Into Your Heart

Behold, now is the accepted time . . . now is the day of salvation.

—II Corinthians 6:2

Lelia N. Morris
McCONNELSVILLE
Lelia N. Morris
1. 你若願意脫離罪的苦情，讓耶穌進
2. 若覺自己罪性不能制服，讓耶穌進
3. 若覺人生風暴無法平靜，讓耶穌進
4. 若願心中充滿快樂歡喜，讓耶穌進
1 If you are tired of the load of your sin, Let Je - sus come
2 If 'tis for pu - ri - ty now that you sigh, Let Je - sus come
3 If there's a tem - pest your voice can - not still, Let Je - sus come
If you would join the glad songs of the blest, Let Je - sus come
1. 入你的心；你若渴慕得着新的生命，
2. 入你的心；主寶血泉源能洗你罪污，
3. 入你的心；若覺世界無法填滿你心，
4. 入你的心；若要全人進入平靜安息，
1 in - to your heart; If you de - sire a new life to be - gin,
2 in - to your heart; Foun-tains for cleans-ing are flow-ing near by,
3 in - to your heart; If there's a void this world nev - er can fill,
4 in - to your heart; If you would en - ter the man-sions of rest,
讓耶穌進入你的心。現在，切
Let Je - sus come in - to your heart. Just now, your
莫再懷疑；現在，切莫再推辭；現在，将
doubt-ings give o'er; Just now, re - ject Him no more; Just now, throw

心門 開啓；讓 耶 穌進入 你的 心。
o - pen the door; Let Je - sus come in - to your heart.

316

天上的榮光

Heavenly Sunshine

We need not fear if the world and the mountains crumble into the sea.

— Psalm 46:2

Charles E. Fuller

Arr. by Charles E. Fuller

天上的 榮 光，天上的 榮 光，天上的

Heav-en-ly sun-shine, heav-en-ly sun-shine, Flood-ing my

榮耀 充滿我 心；天上的 榮 光，天上的

soul with glo-ry di - vine; Heav-en-ly sun-shine, heav-en-ly

榮 光，哈 利 路 亞！耶 穌 屬 我！

sun-shine, Hal - le - lu - jah! Je - sus is mine!

我受死，是為你的眼淚
For Those Tears I Died

Marsha Stevens

But whosoever drinketh of the water that I shall give him shall never thirst. — John 4:14

CHILDREN OF THE DAY
Marsha Stevens

1. 祢曾說祢要來，與我分擔憂傷，祢說祢會同在，解我明天惆悵；我幾乎拒絕，不願讓祢進來，但正如祢應許，祢已經進來，祢與我同在。
2. 主愛何等偉大，我真不能明白，親愛主，我知道，是祢計劃安排；祢與我同在，永遠不會離開，我會得着自由，都因祢的愛，我蒙了大愛。
3. 主耶穌我願意，奉獻我的心靈，我知道離了祢，我無法得潔淨；救主祢為我，已打開了門戶，我願感謝讚美，虔誠敬拜主，我永遠屬主。
1 You said You'd come and share all my sor-rows, You said You'd be there for all my to-mor-rows; I came so close to send-ing You a-way, But just like You prom-ised You came there to stay — I just had to pray.
2 Your good-ness so great I can't un-der-stand, And dear Lord, I know that all this was planned; I know You're here now, and al-ways will be, Your love loosed my chains and in You I'm free — But Je-sus, why me?
3 Je-sus, I give you my heart and my soul, I know that with-out God I'd nev-er be whole; Sav-ior, You o-pened all the right doors, And I thank You, and praise You from earth's hum-ble shores — Take me, I'm Yours.

主 耶 穌 説，"來 到 我 身 旁，飲 我 活
And Je - sus said, "Come to the wa - ter, stand by my
水， 我 知 道 你 乾 渴，請 不 要 拒
side; I know you are thirst - y, you won't be de -
絕， 你 黑 夜 裡 哭 泣，我 也
nied. I felt ev - ery tear - drop when in
為 你 落 淚， 深 願 你 知 我
dark - ness you cried, And I strove to re -
受 死，是 為 你 的 眼 淚。"
mind you that for those tears I died."

318

我要耶穌
I Need Jesus

Bow down Thine ear, O Lord, and hear me; for I am poor and needy . . . — Psalm 86:1

George O. Webster

I NEED JESUS
Charles H. Gabriel

1. 我深 知道，我 真需 要耶 穌，在 憂愁 時，無
2. 我需 一友，有 能力 像耶 穌，在 幽暗 中，祂
3. 自生 至死，我 必需 要耶 穌，無 人像 主，祂
1 I need Je-sus: my need I now con-fess, No Friend like Him in
2 I need Je-sus: I need a Friend like Him, A Friend to guide when
3 I need Je-sus: I need Him to the end, No one like Him – He
1. 朋友 像我 主； 我甚 歡樂，因 我 得到 耶
2. 必引 導保 護； 我靈 與敵 相 攻 時需 要
3. 是罪 人朋 友； 在急 難時，我 更 需要 耶
1 times of deep dis-tress; I need Je-sus; the need I glad-ly
2 paths of life are dim; I need Je-sus; when foes my soul as-
3 is the sin-ners' Friend: I need Je-sus; no oth-er Friend will
1. 穌，雖 有人 願獨 挑重 擔，但 我要 耶穌。
2. 主，我 知靠 自己 必失 敗，故 我要 耶穌。
3. 穌，因 主是 慈愛 和真 實，我 需要 耶穌。
1 own, Though some may bear their load a-lone, Yet I need Je-sus.
2 sail, A-lone, I know I can but fail, So I need Je-sus.
3 do, So con-stant, kind, so strong and true – Yes, I need Je-sus.
我要 耶穌； 我要 耶穌。 我每 日需要耶
I need Je-sus; I need Je-sus. I need Je-sus ev-ery

穌 。 光明 時日我要祂，黑雲滿佈
day. Need Him in the sun-shine hour, need Him when the
我要 祂，每日在 我 生命中，我 需 要 耶穌 。
storm clouds lower, Ev-ery day a-long my way, Yes, I need Je-sus.

Hosea 14:4b-9

I will love them with all my heart,
for my anger has turned from them.
I will fall like dew on Israel.
He shall bloom like the lily,
and thrust out roots like the poplar,
his shoots will spread far;
he will have the beauty of the olive
and the fragrance of Lebanon.
They will come back to live in my shade;
they will grow corn that flourishes,
they will cultivate vines
as renowned as the wine of Helbon.
What has Ephraim to do with idols any more
when it is I who hear his prayer and care for him?
I am like a cypress ever green,
all your fruitfulness comes from me.

Let the wise men understand these words.
Let the intelligent man grasp their meaning.
For the ways of Jehovah are straight,
and virtuous men walk in them,
but sinners stumble.

—(JB)

319

教我禱告
Teach Me To Pray

. . One of His disciples said unto Him, Lord, teach us to pray . . — Luke 11:1

Albert S. Reitz
Albert S. Reitz
1. 親愛的救主，教我禱告，我心向恩主
2. 主求祢賜我，禱告能力—在世界罪惡
3. 我意志薄弱，求主復興，使我能制服
4. 親愛的救主，教我禱告，主是我榜樣
1. Teach me to pray, Lord, teach me to pray— This is my heart-cry
2. Pow-er in prayer, Lord, pow-er in prayer-. Here'mid earth's sin and
3. My weak-ened will, Lord, Thou canst re-new— My sin-ful na-ture
4. Teach me to pray, Lord, teach me to pray— Thou art my pat-tern
1. 發聲求告；願遵主旨意，走主真道，
2. 痛苦之地；無數的靈魂，沉淪迷失，
3. 罪惡本性；賜我新力量，充滿我靈，
4. 是我嚮導；做我的中保，永遠可靠，
1. day un-to day; I long to know Thy will and Thy way—
2. sor-row and care; Men lost and dy-ing, souls in de-spair—
3. Thou canst sub-due; Fill me just now with pow-er a-new—
4. day un-to day; Thou art my sure-ty now and for aye—
1. 親愛的救主，教我禱告。
2. 主求祢賜我，禱告能力！
3. 使我常禱告，聽主命令！
4. 親愛的救主，教我禱告。
主在我心裡，
Liv-ing in Thee, Lord,
1. Teach me to pray, Lord, teach me to pray.
2. O give me pow-er, pow-er in prayer!
3. Pow-er to pray and pow-er to do!
4. Teach me to pray, Lord, teach me to pray.

我在主　裡，我深願　與主常在一　起；使我得
and Thou in　me— Con-stant a - bid - ing,this is my　plea; Grant me Thy
自由，豐富能　力，與神、人、相處，充滿活　力。
pow - er, bound-less and free— Pow-er with　men and pow-er with Thee.

凡敬畏神的人，你們都來聽，我要述說祂為我所行的事。
我曾用口求告祂，我的舌頭，也稱祂為高。
我若心裡注重罪孽，主必不聽。
但神實在聽見了，祂側耳聽了我禱告的聲音。
神是應當稱頌的，祂並沒有推却我的禱告，
也沒有叫祂的慈愛離開我。

詩篇六十六篇
16—20

禱告良辰

Sweet Hour of Prayer

Now Peter and John went up together . . . at the hour of prayer.

— Acts 3:1

William W. Walford

SWEET HOUR

William B. Bradbury

1. 禱 告 良 辰，禱 告 良 辰，使 我 離 開 世 事 操 心，
2. 禱 告 良 辰，禱 告 良 辰，如 有 雙 翼 向 主 飛 昇，
1 Sweet hour of prayer, sweet hour of prayer, That calls me from a world of care,
2 Sweet hour of prayer, sweet hour of prayer, Thy wings shall my pe - ti - tion bear
1. 引 我 到 父 施 恩 座 前，将 我 心 願 向 父 説 明；
2. 将 我 請 求 向 主 禀 陳，主 應 我 求 主 愛 永 恒；
1 And bids me at my Fa - ther's throne Make all my wants and wish-es known:
2 To Him whose truth and faith - ful - ness En - gage the wait - ing soul to bless:
1. 每 逢 痛 苦 憂 愁 之 時，我 靈 在 主 前 得 安 息，
2. 主 既 願 我 常 見 主 面，信 靠 祂 的 真 理 恩 言，
1 In sea - sons of dis - tress and grief My soul has oft - en found re-lief,
2 And since He bids me seek His face, Be - lieve His Word, and trust His grace,
1. 試 探 網 羅 得 以 脱 離，我 惟 靠 此 禱 告 良 辰。
2. 我 便 卸 去 一 切 重 擔，安 靜 等 候 禱 告 良 辰。
1 And oft es - caped the tempt-er's snare By thy re-turn, sweet hour of prayer.
2 I'll cast on Him my ev - ery care, And wait for thee, sweet hour of prayer.

321

幾乎聽勸

Almost Persuaded

I would to God that not only thou, . . . but all . . .
were both almost and altogether such as I am . . . — Acts 26:29

ALMOST
Philip P. Bliss
Philip P. Bliss
1. "幾乎要聽勸"棄絕罪途；"幾乎要聽勸"
2. "幾乎要聽勸"切勿離開；"幾乎要聽勸"
3. "幾乎要聽勸"還誤機會；"幾乎要聽勸"
1 "Al-most per-suad-ed" now to be-lieve; "Al-most per-suad-ed"
2 "Al-most per-suad-ed," come, come to-day; "Al-most per-suad-ed,"
3 "Al-most per-suad-ed," har-vest is past! "Al-most per-suad-ed,"
1. 相信耶穌；有人却在自語，"聖靈，目
2. 今日就來；親人為你祈禱，天使望
3. 難免定罪！"幾乎"甚為不妥，"幾乎"難
1 Christ to re-ceive: Seems now some soul will say, "Go, Spir-it,
2 turn not a-way: Je-sus in-vites you here, An-gels are
3 doom comes at last! "Al-most" can-not a-vail, "Al-most" is
1. 前請去，等有更好機會，我再求祢。"
2. 你趁早，耶穌等你求告，請快回來。
3. 免大錯，"幾乎"只能使你至終滅亡！
1 go Thy way; Some more con-ven-ient day On Thee I'll call."
2 lin-gering near, Prayers rise from hearts so dear, O wan-derer, come.
3 but to fail! Sad, sad, that bit-ter wail, "Al-most," but lost!

322

主禱文
The Lord's Prayer

And when thou hast shut thy door, pray to the Father . . . — Matthew 6:6

MALOTTE
Albert Hay Malotte
Arranged by Fred Bock

Matthew 6:9-13

Unison
哦，天父，大上的真神，願尊祢
Our Fa - ther, which art in heav - en, hal - low - ed
名為聖。祢國降臨，
be Thy name. Thy king-dom come,
旨意行在地上，如同行在
Thy will be done on earth as it is in
天上。賜給我們日用飲
heav - en. Give us this day our dai - ly

食，免我們的債如我們免
bread, and for-give us our debts as we for-give our
人債，不叫我們遇見試探，救我們脫離那
debt-ors. And lead us not in-to temp-ta-tion, but de-liv-er us from
兇惡，因為國度、權柄和榮耀，全是
e-vil, for Thine is the King-dom and the Pow-er and the
父的，到永遠。阿門。
Glo-ry, for-ev-er. A men.

323

凡事必能成就
Nothing Is Impossible

Eugene L. Clark
Teach me Thy Way, O Lord; Lead me in a plain path . . . .
— Psalm 27:11
Eugene L. Clark
凡事必定能成就，只要全心信靠主；
Noth-ing is im - pos - si - ble when you put your trust in God;
凡事必定能成就，只要信靠祂應許。
Noth-ing is im - pos - si - ble when you're trust - ing in His Word.
請聽主的聲音對你説：〃在我何曾
Heark - en to the voice of God to thee: "Is there an - y -
有難成的事？〃你當專心依賴救主，信
thing too hard for Me?" Then put your trust in God a - lone and
靠祂的應許，因為世上所有的事，
rest up - on His Word— For ev - 'ry-thing, O ev - 'ry - thing.

所有的事，祂必定能成就！
Yes, ev - 'ry - thing is pos - si - ble with God!

大山可以挪開 324

The Mountains Shall Depart

. . . In every nation he that feareth Him, and worketh righteousness is accepted by Him.
— Acts 10:35

Isaiah 54:10 John E. Su

大山可以挪開，小山可以遷移，但
The moun tains shall de - part, and the hills be re - moved; but

主的慈愛永不離開你。大山可以挪開小
my kind-ness shall not de-part from thee. The moun-tains shall de-part, and the

山可以遷移但主的慈愛永不離開你。
hills be re - moved; but my kind-ness shall not de-part from thee.

325

告訴耶穌
Tell It to Jesus

He shall cover thee with His feathers, and under His wings shalt thou trust . . .
— Psalm 91:4
Jeremiah E. Rankin
Edmund S. Lorenz
1. 你若疲倦心靈沉悶悲嘆，當告訴耶穌，當告訴耶穌，
2. 你若情不自禁傷心流淚，當告訴耶穌，當告訴耶穌，
3. 你若充滿懼怕愁雲籠罩，當告訴耶穌，當告訴耶穌，
4. 你若心中懼怕死亡痛苦，當告訴耶穌，當告訴耶穌，
1. Are you wea-ry, are you hea-vy heart-ed? Tell it to Je-sus, Tell it to Je-sus;
2. Do the tears flow down your cheeks unbid-den? Tell it to Je-sus, Tell it to Je-sus;
3. Do you fear the gath-ring clouds of sor-row? Tell it to Je-sus, Tell it to Je-sus;
4. Are you troub-led at the thought of dy-ing? Tell it to Je-sus, Tell it to Je-sus;
1. 你若滿懷悲哀喜樂消散，
2. 你若心中隱藏諸般的罪，單要告訴主耶穌。
3. 你若滿心為着明日煩惱，
4. 你若心中盼望主的國度，
1. Are you griev-ing o-ver joys de-part-ed? Tell it to Je - sus a - lone.
2. Have you sins that to men's eyes are hid-den?
3. Are you anx-ious what shall be to-mor-row?
4. For Christ's com-ing King-dom are you sigh-ing?
當告訴耶穌，當告訴耶穌，祂是偉大的良友，
Tell it to Je - sus, tell it to Je - sus, He is a friend that's well known;
無朋友兄弟能像主耶穌，單要告訴主耶穌。
You've no oth - er such a friend or broth-er, Tell it to Je- sus a - lone.

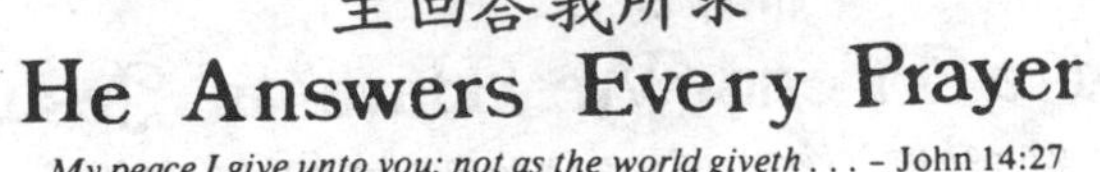
主回答我所求
He Answers Every Prayer

My peace I give unto you: not as the world giveth . . . – John 14:27

C. Austin Miles

C. Austin Miles

1. 不 再疑惑 不 再懼怕，我 知道 神常 在保守，
2. 縱 有黑雲 遮 蓋我頭，却 要成為福 氣傾流，

1. A - way with doubt, a - way with fear, I know that God is al-ways near;
2. *Let storm-clouds roll a-bove my head, they're filled with blessings he will shed;*

1. 各 樣掛慮 我 卸給祂，因祂 回答我所 求。
2. 故 我不用 掛 慮憂愁，因祂 回答我所 求。

1. I lay on Him my ev - 'ry care. For He an-swers ev - 'ry pray'r.
2. *I'll have for these no anx-ious care, For He an-swers ev - 'ry pray'r.*

主回答我所求， 祂 有時説"可"有時説"否"，祂 有時説"去"

He answers ev- 'ry pray'r. To some He says "Yes" to others "No" To some He says "Stay"

有 時説"留"，照 祂旨 意，按 祂時候 主 回答我所 求

to others "Go" In His own time and way, I know He answers ev-'ry pray'r.

327 耶穌恩友

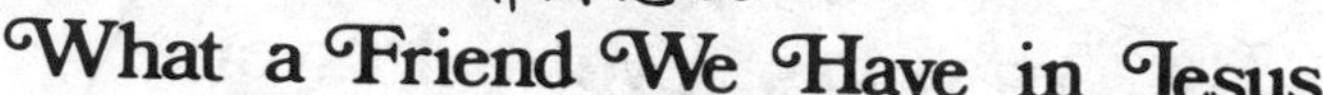
What a Friend We Have in Jesus

. In whom we have boldness and access with confidence by faith in Him.
— Ephesians 3:12
Joseph M. Scriven
ERIE
Charles C. Converse
1. 耶穌是我親愛朋友，擔當我罪與憂愁，
2. 或遇試煉或遇引誘，或有煩惱壓心頭，
3. 是否軟弱勞苦多愁，掛慮重擔壓肩頭？
1 What a friend we have in Je - sus, All our sins and griefs to bear!
2 Have we tri - als and temp - ta - tions? Is there trou-ble an - y - where?
3 Are we weak and heav - y - lad - en, Cum-bered with a load of care?

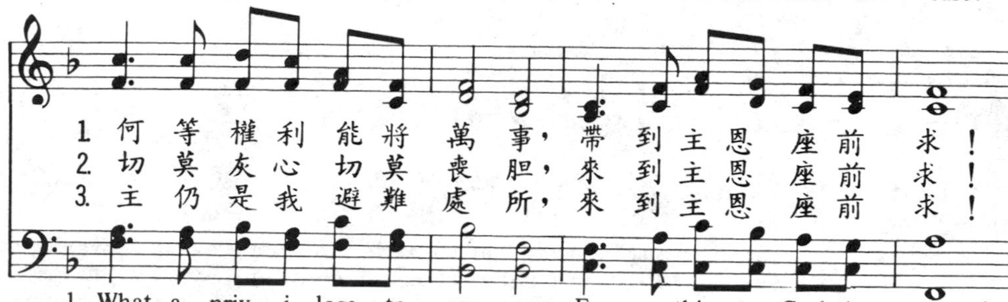
1. 何等權利能將萬事，帶到主恩座前求！
2. 切莫灰心切莫喪胆，來到主恩座前求！
3. 主仍是我避難處所，來到主恩座前求！
1 What a priv - i - lege to car - ry Ev - ery-thing to God in prayer!
2 We should nev - er be dis - cour-aged– Take it to the Lord in prayer!
3 Pre - cious Sav - ior, still our ref - uge– Take it to the Lord in prayer!

1. 多少平安屢屢失去，多少痛苦白白受，
2. 何處得此忠心朋友，分擔一切苦與憂？
3. 親或棄我友或離我，來到主恩座前求！
1 O what peace we oft - en for - feit, O what need-less pain we bear,
2 Can we find a friend so faith - ful, Who will all our sor - rows share?
3 Do thy friends de - spise, for - sake thee? Take it to the Lord in prayer!

1. 皆因未將各樣事情，帶到主恩座前求。
2. 耶穌深知我們軟弱，來到主恩座前求！
3. 在主懷中必蒙護佑，與主同在永無憂。
1 All be - cause we do not car - ry Ev - ery-thing to God in prayer.
2 Je - sus knows our ev - ery weak-ness– Take it to the Lord in prayer!
3 In His arms He'll take and shield thee– Thou wilt find a sol - ace there.

靠主而得的喜樂

The Joy of the Lord

And those things write we unto you that your joy may be full.
— John 1:4

THE JOY OF THE LORD
Alliene G. Vale

Based on Nehemiah 8:10

Unison
1. 靠 主 而 得 的 喜 樂 是 我 的 力 量， 靠
2. 常 常 讚 美 主 我 必 得 喜 樂， 常
3. 祂 賜 我 生 命 活 水 我 必 不 再 渴， 祂
4. 祂 能 使 心 靈 破 碎 者 不 再 憂 傷、 祂
1 The joy of the Lord is my strength, The
2 If you want joy you must praise for it, If
3 He giv - eth liv - ing wa - ter and I thirst no more, He
4 He heals the bro - ken heart-ed and they cry no more, He

1. 主 而 得 的 喜 樂 是 我 的 力 量， 靠 主 而 得 的
2. 常 讚 美 主 我 必 得 喜 樂， 常 常 讚 美
3. 賜 我 生 命 活 水 我 必 不 再 渴， 祂 賜 我 生 命
4. 能 使 心 靈 破 碎 者 不 再 憂 傷， 祂 能 使 心 靈
1 joy of the Lord is my strength, The joy of the
2 you want joy you must praise for it, If you want
3 giv - eth liv - ing wa-ter and I thirst no more, He giv - eth liv - ing
4 heals the bro - ken heart-ed and they cry no more, He heals the bro - ken

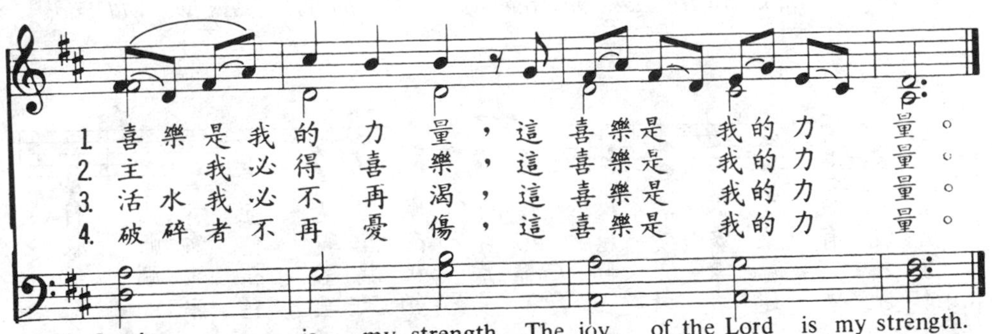
1. 喜 樂 是 我 的 力 量， 這 喜 樂 是 我 的 力 量。
2. 主 我 必 得 喜 樂， 這 喜 樂 是 我 的 力 量。
3. 活 水 我 必 不 再 渴， 這 喜 樂 是 我 的 力 量。
4. 破 碎 者 不 再 憂 傷， 這 喜 樂 是 我 的 力 量。
1 Lord is my strength, The joy of the Lord is my strength.
2 joy you must praise for it — The joy of the Lord is my strength.
3 wa - ter and I thirst no more — The joy of the Lord is my strength.
4 heart-ed and they cry no more — The joy of the Lord is my strength.

329

信靠順服

Trust and Obey

To obey is better than sacrifice . . .

— I Samuel 15:22

James H. Sammis

TRUST AND OBEY
Daniel B. Towner

1. 當我與主同行，在祂話的光中，
2. 沒有一點黑影，沒有一片烏雲，
3. 沒有一個重擔，沒有一點為難，
4. 然後，我才會在祂的腳前敬拜，
1 When we walk with the Lord In the light of His Word,
2 Not a shad - ow can rise, Not a cloud in the skies,
3 Not a bur - den we bear, Not a sor - row we share,
4 Then in fel - low - ship sweet We will sit at His feet,

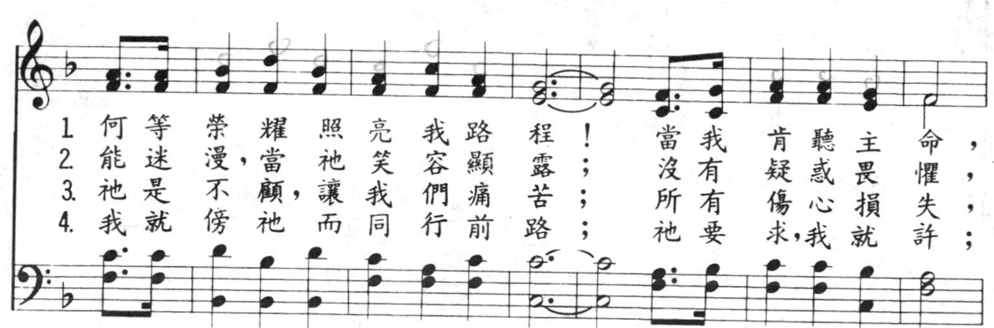
1. 何等榮耀照亮我路程！當我肯聽主命，
2. 能迷漫，當祂笑容顯露；沒有疑惑畏懼，
3. 祂是不顧，讓我們痛苦；所有傷心損失，
4. 我就傍祂而同行前路；祂要求，我就許；
1 What a glo - ry He sheds on our way! While we do His good will,
2 But His smile quick - ly drives it a - way; Not a doubt or a fear,
3 But our toil He doth rich - ly re - pay; Not a grief or a loss,
4 Or we'll walk by His side in the way; What He says we will do,

1. 祂就充滿我心，信靠順服者主肯同行。
2. 沒有流淚憂慮，能存在若我信靠順服。
3. 所有厭棄羞恥，都成祝福若信靠順服。
4. 祂差遣，我就去；不要怕只要信靠順服。
1 He a - bides with us still, And with all who will trust and o - bey.
2 Not a sigh or a tear, Can re - main when we trust and o - bey.
3 Not a frown or a cross, But is blest if we trust and o - bey.
4 Where He sends we will go, Nev - er fear, on - ly trust and o - bey.

信靠順服，因為除此以外，
Trust and o - bey, for there's no oth - er way
不能得耶穌喜愛，惟有信靠順服。
To be hap - py in Je - sus, but to trust and o - bey.

求充滿我
Fill Me Now

329-1

Be filled with the Spirit. Eph. 5:18

Sherry Saunders　　　　Sherry Saunders

充滿我，主聖靈，解我乾渴的靈，
Fill me now, pre - cious Lord, Quench my thirs - ty soul.
充滿我，主聖靈，求使我得完全。
Fill me now, pre-cious Lord, Touch and make me whole.

神的路
God's Way

Lida Shivers Leech

He died for all that they . . . should not henceforth live unto themselves.
— II Corinthians 5:15

Lida Shivers Leech

Duet.
1. 神的路最美善，雖我不明瞭，為何憂愁試煉，
2. 神的路最美善，計劃我前途，我願時常依靠，
3. 神的路我最愛，惟祂能引導，我全心投靠祂，

1. God's way is the best way, Tho' I may not see Why sor-rows and tri-als
2. *God's way is the best way, My path He hath planned, I'll trust in Him al-way*
3. God's way shall be my way, He know-eth the best, And lean-ing up-on Him,

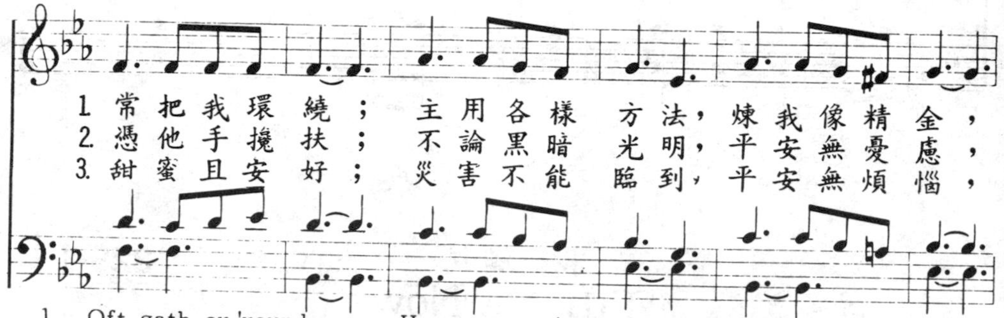
1. 常把我環繞；主用各樣方法，煉我像精金，
2. 憑他手攙扶；不論黑暗光明，平安無憂慮，
3. 甜蜜且安好；災害不能臨到，平安無煩惱，

1. Oft gath-er 'round me; He ev - er is seek - ing My gold to re - fine,
2. *While hold-ing His hand. In shad - ow or sun - shine He ev - er is near,*
3. Sweet, sweet is my rest. No harm can be-fall me, Safe, safe shall I be,

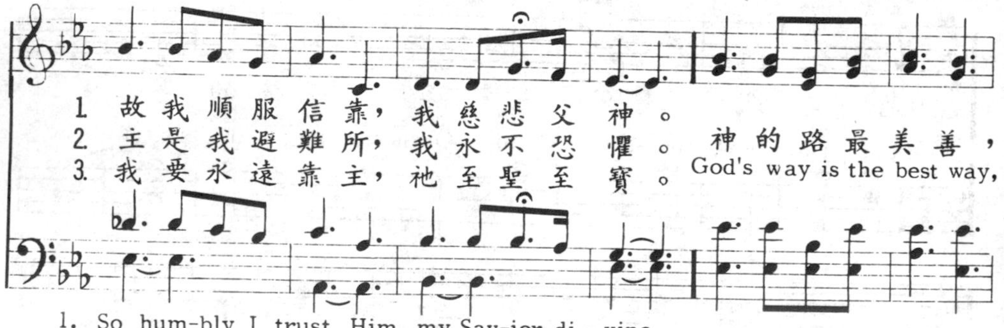
1. 故我順服信靠，我慈悲父神。
2. 主是我避難所，我永不恐懼。神的路最美善，
3. 我要永遠靠主，祂至聖至寶。God's way is the best way,

1. So hum-bly I trust Him, my Sav-ior di - vine.
2. *With Him for my ref-uge, I nev-er need fear.*
3. I'll cling to Him ev - er, So pre-cious is He.

神的路最美好，我願常倚靠祂，惟祂能引導。
God's way is the right way, I'll trust in Him al-way, He know-eth the best.

祂自己

Himself

Acquaint thyself with Him and be at peace.
— Job 22:21

A. B. Simpson A. B. Simpson

1. 前我要得福祉，今要得着主；前我要得感覺，
2. 前我忙於打算，今專心祈求；前我常常掛慮，
1. Once it was the bless-ing, Now it is the Lord; Once it was the feel-ing,
2. Once 'twas bu-sy plan-ning, Now 'tis trust-ful prayer; Once 'twas anxious caring,
1. 今要主言語；前我切慕恩賜，今要賜恩主；
2. 今有主保佑；前我隨己所欲，今聽主言語；
1. Now it is His Word; Once His gift I want-ed, Now, the Giv-er own;
2. Now He has the care; Once 'twas what I want-ed, Now what Je-sus says;
1. 前我尋求醫治，今要主自己。永遠高舉耶穌，
2. 前我不住討求，今常讚美主。
1. Once I sought for heal-ing, Now Him-self a - lone.
2. Once 'twas cons-tant ask-ing, Now Him-self a - lone.
All in all for- ev - er,
讚美主不歇，一切在耶穌裏，耶穌是我一切。
Je-sus will I sing; Ev-'ry thing in Je - sus, And Je-sus ev-'ry thing.

332

主啊！我屬祢

I Am Thine, O Lord

. . . What would Thou have me to do?
— Acts 9:6

I AM THINE
Fanny J. Crosby
William H. Doane
1. 主啊，我屬祢，祢也深知我，祢曾說過
2. 今歸主為聖，終身歸主用，求賜能力
3. 跪禱於神前，與主面對面，如同朋友
4. 何等深厚愛，何等廣慈懷，皆藉主恩
1 I am Thine, O Lord— I have heard Thy voice, And it told Thy
2 Con-se-crate me now to Thy serv-ice, Lord, By the power of
3 O the pure de-light of a sin-gle hour That be-fore Thy
4 There are depths of love that I can-not know 'Til I cross the
1. 祢愛我；今求主賜恩，加增我信心，
2. 作聖工；以信心仰望，以口舌宣講，
3. 之暢談；心裡有平安，得祝福無限，
4. 顯出來；何等快樂哉，有聖靈同在，
1 love to me; But I long to rise in the arms of faith
2 grace di-vine; Let my soul look up with a stead-fast hope
3 throne I spend, When I kneel in prayer and with Thee, my God,
4 nar-row sea; There are heights of joy that I may not reach
1. 我願以信與主親。
2. 心口一致常讚揚。
3. 喜樂陶陶如湧泉。
4. 儆醒預備等主來。
願主吸我，日近十架前，
Draw me near-er, nearer, blessed Lord,
1 And be clos-er drawn to Thee.
2 And my will be lost in Thine.
3 I com-mune as friend with friend.
4 'Til I rest in peace with Thee.

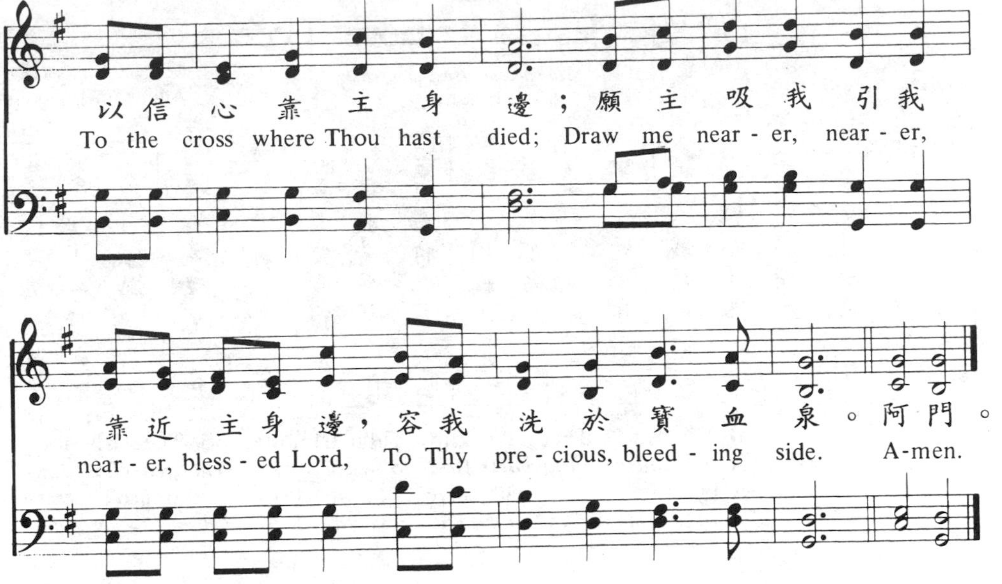
以信心靠主身邊；願主吸我引我
To the cross where Thou hast died; Draw me near - er, near - er,
靠近主身邊，容我洗於寶血泉。阿門。
near - er, bless - ed Lord, To Thy pre - cious, bleed - ing side. A-men.

Psalm 59

Deliver me, O God, from the enemies of my soul.
I am no longer afraid of men who stand in my way, even of those who obstruct Your purposes and who deceive their fellowmen with their arrogant and clever cliches.
They anger me, but they do not frighten me.
My pain and confusion come by way of my own weaknesses and faithlessness.

I strive for success and am fractured by failure.
I reach for ecstacy and am clobbered with depression.
I wait for guidance and Your heavens are gray with silence.
I ask for infilling and am confronted with emptiness.
I seek opportunities and run into stone walls.

I overcome these pernicious demons in the morning—only to face them again when day turns into night.
They refuse to die, these persistent devils.
They plague my days and haunt my nights and rob me of the peace and joy of God-motivated living.

And yet, O Lord, You have surrounded my life like a great fortress.
There is nothing that can touch me save by Your loving permission.

—Leslie Brandt

333

主耶穌我愛祢

My Jesus, I Love Thee

William R. Featherston

We love Him because He first loved us.
— I John 4:19

GORDON
Adoniram J. Gordon

1. 主 耶 穌，我 愛 祢，深 知 我 屬 祢，世 上 諸 般
2. 主 耶 穌，我 愛 祢，因 祢 先 愛 我，為 我 十 架
3. 無 論 生 死 禍 福，我 必 愛 我 主，當 我 一 息
4. 救 主 來 迎 接 我，永 住 榮 耀 中，我 必 時 時
1 My Je - sus, I love Thee, I know Thou art mine; For Thee all the
2 I love Thee be - cause Thou hast first lov - ed me, And pur-chased my
3 I'll love Thee in life, I will love Thee in death, And praise Thee as
4 In man-sions of glo - ry and end - less de - light, I'll ev - er a -
1. 樂 趣，為 祢 全 丟 棄；祢 是 我 的 救 主，為
2. 釘 死，赦 我 衆 罪 過；祢 戴 荊 棘 冠 冕，受
3. 尚 存，仍 要 讚 美 主；臨 終 聲 雖 微 弱，仍
4. 頌 揚 救 主 的 恩 寵；戴 榮 耀 的 冠 冕，與
1 fol - lies of sin I re - sign; My gra - cious Re - deem - er, my
2 par - don on Cal - va - ry's tree; I love Thee for wear - ing the
3 long as Thou lend - est me breath; And say when the death - dew lies
4 dore Thee in heav - en so bright; I'll sing with the glit - ter - ing
1. 我 還 罪 債；若 我 曾 愛 救 主，如 今 更 親 愛。
2. 羞 辱 苦 害；若 我 曾 愛 救 主，如 今 更 親 愛。
3. 向 主 示 愛；若 我 曾 愛 救 主，如 今 更 親 愛。
4. 主 永 同 在；若 我 曾 愛 救 主，如 今 更 親 愛。阿 門。
1 Sav - ior art Thou: If ev - er I loved Thee, my Je - sus, 'tis now.
2 thorns on Thy brow: If ev - er I loved Thee, my Je - sus, 'tis now.
3 cold on my brow: If ev - er I loved Thee, my Je - sus, 'tis now.
4 crown on my brow: If ev - er I loved Thee, my Je - sus, 'tis now. A-men.

我心之樂，我主耶穌

Jesus, Thou Joy of Loving Hearts

334

. . . Ye rejoice with joy unspeakable and full of glory. — I Peter 1:8

Attr. to Bernard of Clairvaux
Tr. by Ray Palmer

QUEBEC
Henry Baker

1. 我心之樂，我主耶穌，生命泉
2. 真理不變主恩依舊，凡求主
3. 生命的糧我曾親嚐，願這靈
4. 我的心靈緊隨救主，無論何
5. 求主耶穌與我同住，使我時

1 Je - sus, Thou joy of lov - ing hearts, Thou fount of
2 *Thy truth un - changed hath ev - er stood, Thou sav - est*
3 We taste Thee, O Thou liv - ing bread, And long to
4 *Our rest - less spir - its yearn for Thee, Wher - e'er our*
5 O Je - sus, ev - er with us stay, Make all our

1. 源真理道路；我願撇下世
2. 名必蒙拯救；尋求主者蒙
3. 糧飽我飢腸；主是活水泉
4. 往跟主腳步；每見主面歡
5. 刻心滿意足；求主除去罪

1 life, Thou light of men, From the best bliss that
2 *those that on Thee call; To them that seek Thee*
3 feast up - on Thee still; We drink of Thee, the
4 *change - ful lot is cast: Glad when Thy gra - cious*
5 mo - ments calm and bright; Chase the dark night of

1. 間幸福，專求我主賜我真福。
2. 主眷愛，從此屬主永遠同在。
3. 源湧流，止我乾渴直到永久。
4. 樂難述，得蒙主恩信心堅固。
5. 惡黑雲，向我顯現聖潔光明。阿門。

1 earth im - parts We turn un - filled to Thee a - gain.
2 *Thou art good, To them that find Thee all in all.*
3 foun-tain - head, And thirst our souls from Thee to fill.
4 *smile we see, Blest when our faith can hold Thee fast.*
5 sin a - way, Shed o'er the world Thy ho - ly light. A - men.

成聖須要工夫

Take Time to Be Holy

Because it is written: Be ye holy for I am holy. — I Peter 1:16

William D. Longstaff

LONGSTAFF
George C. Stebbins

1. 成聖須用工夫，常做醒禱告；常與恩主
2. 成聖須用工夫，世人何忙碌；在密室朝
3. 成聖須用工夫，讓主引你路；一路與主

1 Take time to be ho - ly, Speak oft - en with God; Find rest in Him
2 *Take time to be ho - ly, The world rush - es on; Much time spend in*
3 Take time to be ho - ly, Let Him be Thy guide, And run not be-

1. 交通，常領受主道。與神兒女為友，幫
2. 見主，領受主恩福。注目仰望耶穌，你
3. 同走，主手常扶助。不論是福或苦，仍
1 al - ways, And feed on His Word. Make friends of God's chil - dren, Help
2 se - cret With Je - sus a - lone. By look - ing to Je - sus, Like
3 fore Him, What - ev - er be - tide. In joy or in sor - row, Still

1. 助軟弱人，無論所做何事，莫忘求主恩。
2. 就必像主，親友從你行為，能看見耶穌。
3. 要跟隨主，定睛仰望耶穌，堅信我救主。
1 those who are weak, For - get - ting in noth - ing His bless - ing to seek.
2 Him Thou shalt be; Thy friends in thy con - duct His like - ness shall see.
3 fol - low Thy Lord, And, look - ing to Je - sus, Still trust in His word.

求主容我與祢同行
O Master, Let Me Walk with Thee

He that loseth his life for My sake shall find it. — Matthew 10:39

MARYTON
H. Percy Smith

Washington Gladden

1. 求 主 容 我 與 祢 同 行， 甘 願 自 卑 服 事 他 人； 求 主 示 我 治 事 祕 訣， 教 我 忍 耐 克 服 艱 辛。
2. 求 主 助 我 善 用 愛 心， 常 以 良 言 感 化 鄰 人； 隨 時 隨 地 引 人 離 惡， 歸 依 救 主 行 走 天 程。
3. 求 主 教 我 學 祢 忍 耐， 與 主 相 親 與 主 同 在； 工 作 之 時 加 我 信 心， 使 我 剛 強 將 敵 戰 敗。
4. 求 主 助 我 盼 望 常 存， 展 望 前 途 遠 大 光 明； 無 上 平 安 惟 主 能 賜， 主 啊， 容 我 與 祢 同 行。 阿 門。
1 O Mas - ter, let me walk with Thee In low - ly paths of serv - ice free; Tell me Thy se - cret– help me bear The strain of toil, the fret of care.
2 Help me the slow of heart to move By some clear, win - ning word of love; Teach me the way - ward feet to stay, And guide them in the home - ward way.
3 Teach me Thy pa - tience: still with Thee In clos - er, dear - er com - pa - ny, In work that keeps faith sweet and strong, In trust that tri - umphs o - ver wrong.
4 In hope that sends a shin - ing ray Far down the fu - ture's broad - ening way, In peace that on - ly Thou canst give, With Thee, O Mas - ter, let me live.
A - men.

助我進深
Deeper, Deeper

. . . they drank of the Spiritual Rock . . . and that Rock is Christ.

— I Corinthians 10:4

C. P. Jones C. P. Jones

1. 進深！進深！入主仁愛深淵，每日更進深；
2. 進深！進深！直趨保惠恩師，時刻受啓示；
3. 進深！進深！雖經艱難試煉，還向標竿行；
4. 進深！登高！每日跟主脚步，行走得勝路；
1. Deep-er, deep-er in the love of Je-sus Dai-ly let me go;
2. Deep-er, deep-er! bless-ed Ho-ly Spir-it, Take me deep-er still,
3. Deep-er, deep-er! tho' it cost hard tri-als, Deep-er let me go!
4. Deep-er, high-er, ev-'ry day in Je-sus, Till all con-flict past

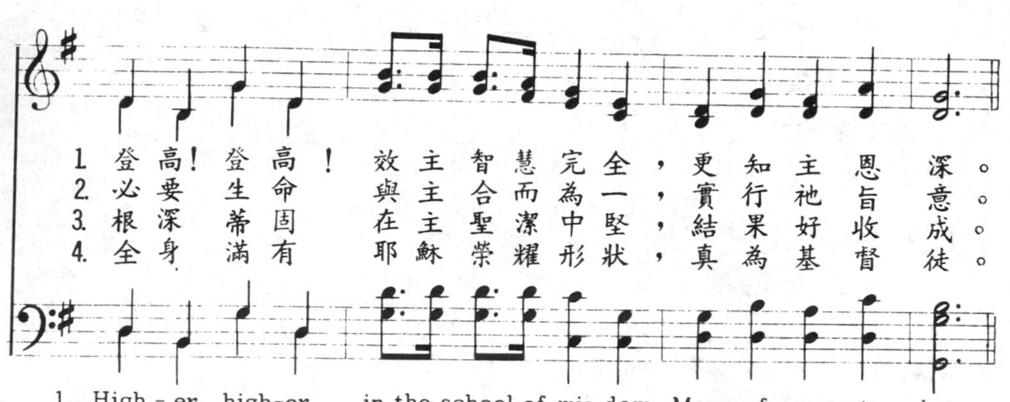
1. 登高！登高！效主智慧完全，更知主恩深。
2. 必要生命與主合而為一，實行祂旨意。
3. 根深蒂固在主聖潔中堅，結果好收成。
4. 全身滿有耶穌榮耀形狀，真為基督徒。
1. High-er, high-er in the school of wis-dom, More of grace to know.
2. Till my life is whol-ly lost in Je-sus And His per-fect will.
3. Root-ed in the ho-ly love of Je-sus, Let me fruit-ful grow.
4. Finds me con-qu'ror, and in His own im-age Per-fect-ed at last.

求主助我進深！我
Oh, deep-er yet, I pray, And

願 登峯造極！ 賜我 悟
high - er ev - 'ry day, And wis - er,

性更新， 領 我 進 入 真 理。
bless-ed Lord, In thy pre-cious, ho - ly Word.

I Corinthians 2:10-16

The Spirit searches all things, even the deep things of God. For who among men knows the thoughts of a man except the man's spirit within him? In the same way no one knows the thoughts of God except the Spirit of God. We have not received the spirit of the world but the Spirit who is from God, that we may understand what God has freely given us. This is what we speak, not in words taught us by human wisdom but in words taught by the Spirit, expressing spiritual truths in spiritual words. The man without the Spirit does not accept the things that come from the Spirit of God, for they are foolishness to him, and he cannot understand them, because they are spiritually discerned. The spiritual man makes judgments about all things, but he himself is not subject to any man's judgment:

"For who has known the mind of the Lord that he may instruct him?"

But we have the mind of Christ.

–(NIV)

我願常見祢
Be Thou My Vision

Leave us not I pray thee . . . . and thou mayest be to us instead of eyes.
— Numbers 10:31

Ancient Irish
Tr. by Mary Byrne
Versified by Eleanor Hull

SLANE
Traditional Irish Melody
Harmonization by David Evans

Unison
1. 我 願 常 見 祢，親 愛 的 救 主，
2. 求 作 我 智 慧，求 作 我 真 道，
3. 我 不 求 財 富，也 不 求 虛 榮，
4. 至 高 天 上 王，我 已 凱 旋 歸，
1 Be Thou my Vi - sion, O Lord of my heart;
2 Be Thou my Wis - dom, and Thou my true Word;
3 Rich - es I heed not, nor man's emp - ty praise,
4 High King of heav - en, my vic - to - ry won,
1. 不 見 任 何 事 務，只 見 耶 穌；
2. 祢 常 與 我 同 在，我 願 投 靠；
3. 祢 是 我 的 產 業，世 代 無 窮；
4. 得 享 天 上 喜 樂，沐 主 光 輝！
1 Nought be all else to me, save that Thou art—
2 I ev - er with Thee and Thou with me, Lord;
3 Thou mine in - her - it - ance, now and al - ways:
4 May I reach heav - en's joys, O bright heaven's Sun!
1. 白 晝 或 黑 夜，我 常 思 念，
2. 偉 大 聖 天 父，我 懇 求 祢，
3. 祢 在 我 心 中，獨 居 首 位，
4. 以 祢 心 為 心，不 論 禍 福，
1 Thou my best thought, by day or by night,
2 Thou my great Fa - ther, I Thy true son;
3 Thou and Thou on - ly, first in my heart,
4 Heart of my own heart, what - ev - er be - fall,

1. 起 來 或 躺 臥，光 照 在 我 前。
2. 常 住 我 裡 面，我 與 袮 合 一。
3. 至 高 天 上 王，是 我 最 寶 貴。
4. 我 願 常 見 袮，天 地 萬 物 主。阿 門。
1 Wak - ing or sleep - ing, Thy pres - ence my light.
2 *Thou in me dwell - ing, and I with Thee one.*
3 High King of heav - en, my Treas - ure Thou art.
4 *Still be my Vi - sion, O Rul - er of all.* A - men.

在主愛裏 In Love

338-1

We love because He first loved us. 1 John 4:19

Georgian Banou

Georgian Banou

Unison

我 敬拜袮，因袮先愛我，惟獨敬拜袮，我 時常敬拜
I wor-ship you, and you love me too, wor-ship on- ly you. I wor-ship you, and I

主我神，惟獨敬拜袮，主 愛，主 愛，與
al - ways do, wor-ship on - ly you In love, in love, oh,

主同在愛 裏，主 愛，主 愛，與 主同在愛 裏。
I'm in love with you, In love, in love, oh, I'm in love with you.

339

向高處行
Higher Ground

Lead me to the Rock that is higher than I. . . .
— Psalm 61:2

Johnson Oatman, Jr.

HIGHER GROUND
Charles H. Gabriel

1. 我今直往高處而行，靈性地位日日高昇；我行天路有時軟弱，求主扶助進入樂境。
2. 世上時有疑慮恐怖，非我安然久居之處；別人或願宮室久住，我惟注目更高之處。
3. 我願跳出世界範圍，魔鬼利劍非我所畏；我今因信常聞天歌，妙音佳樂使我快樂。
4. 我必上升穹蒼極境，進入天堂榮華美景；如今我靈祈禱不停，求主同行直到天庭。
求主扶助使我堅
1 I'm press-ing on the up-ward way, New heights I'm gain - ing ev - ery day; Still pray - ing as I'm on - ward bound, "Lord, plant my feet on high - er ground."
2 My heart has no de-sire to stay Where doubts a - rise and fears dis - may; Though some may dwell where these a - bound, My prayer, my aim is high - er ground.
3 I want to live a-bove the world, Though Sa-tan's darts at me are hurled; For faith has caught the joy - ful sound, The song of saints on high - er ground.
4 I want to scale the ut-most height And catch a gleam of glo - ry bright; But still I'll pray, 'til heaven I've found "Lord, lead me on to high - er ground."
Lord, lift me up and let me

立，因信站在屬靈高地，使我逐
stand By faith on heav - en's ta - ble - land, A high - er
日所處地位，較之往日有進無退。
plane than I have found: Lord, plant my feet on high - er ground.

主阿，你世世代代作我們的居所。
諸山未曾生出，地與世界你未曾造成，從亙古到永遠，你是　神。
你使人歸於塵土，說，你們世人要歸回。
在你看來，千年如已過的昨日，又如夜間的一更。
你叫他們如水沖去，他們如睡一覺。早晨他們如生長的草。
早晨發芽生長，晚上割下枯乾。
我們因你的怒氣而消滅，因你的忿怒而驚惶。
你將我們的罪孽擺在你面前，將我們的隱惡擺在你面光之中。
我們經過的日子，都在你震怒之下，我們度盡的年歲，好像一聲歎息。
我們一生的年日是七十歲，若是強壯可到八十歲，但其中所矜誇的，不過是勞苦愁煩，轉眼成空，我們便如飛而去。
誰曉得你怒氣的權勢，誰按着你該受的敬畏曉得你的忿怒呢。
求你指教我們怎樣數算自己的日子，好叫我們得着智慧的心。

詩篇九十篇
1—12節

求主充滿我杯

Fill My Cup, Lord

I will take the cup of my salvation. . . . —Psalm 116:13

Richard Blanchard
FILL MY CUP
Richard Blanchard
1. 像那井旁的婦人我在尋求，却無一事能滿足我；那時我聽救主對我說："我是活泉能使你永不渴。"
2. 這世界有千萬人正在追求：世上的享受與歡樂；但不能與一珍寶相比，我在主裡這珍寶已得着。
3. 親愛朋友，這世界所能給你，不能除你飢渴難受；但救主能施恩拯救你，若你謙卑跪下向祂祈求。
1 Like the wom-an at the well I was seek-ing For things that could not sat-is-fy; And then I heard my Sav-ior speak-ing: "Draw from My well that nev-er shall run dry."
2 There are mil-lions in this world who are crav-ing The pleas-ure earth-ly things af-ford; But none can match the won-drous treas-ure That I find in Je-sus Christ my Lord.
3 So, my broth-er, if the things this world gave you Leave hun-gers that won't pass a-way, My bless-ed Lord will come and save you, If you kneel to Him and hum-bly pray:
求主充滿，將我杯充滿！滋潤我，除我心靈乾渴；天上靈糧，
Fill my cup, Lord, I lift it up, Lord! Come and quench this thirst-ing of my soul; Bread of heav-en,

求主賜下餵養我，充滿我，使我能福杯滿溢！
feed me 'til I want no more—Fill my cup, fill it up and make me whole!

341

求主充滿我的生命

Fill Thou My Life, O Lord My God

Now the Lord of hope fill you with all joy and peace . . . .
— Romans 15:13

Horatius Bonar

RICHMOND
Thomas Haweis

1. 求主充滿我的生命，使我能讚美祢；我
2. 我心稱頌我口讚揚，不單是心和口—我
3. 不論外出或是家居，每日大小事情；時
4. 主充滿我使我稱頌，讚美祢的偉大；讚
5. 求主接受我的稱頌，救主配得榮耀；使
6. 不分晝夜時時歌頌，讚美歌聲不停；我
1 Fill Thou my life, O Lord my God, In ev - ery part with praise, That
2 *Not for the lip of praise a - lone, Nor for the prais - ing heart – I*
3 Praise in the com - mon things of life, Its go - ings out and in; Praise
4 *Fill ev-ery part of me with praise: Let all my be - ing speak Of*
5 So shalt Thou, Lord, from e - ven me Re - ceive the glo - ry due; And
6 *So shall no part of day or night From sa - cred-ness be free; But*

1. 以身心見證宣揚，祢的聖潔旨意。
2. 懇求祢使我全人，全身都在拜叩。
3. 時歌頌時時讚美，凡事都知謝恩。
4. 美祢的無比慈愛，雖我軟弱貧乏。
5. 我在世永唱新歌，讚美救主聲高。
6. 的一生每一步路，與主相親同行。阿們
1 my whole be - ing may pro-claim Thy be - ing and Thy ways.
2 *ask Thee for a life made up Of praise in ev - ery part:*
3 in each du - ty and each deed, How - ev - er small and mean.
4 *Thee and of Thy love, O Lord, Poor though I be, and weak.*
5 so shall I be - gin on earth The song for - ev - er new.
6 *all my life, in ev - ery step, Be fel - low-ship with Thee.* A - men.

主，我願像祢
O To Be Like Thee

And every man that hath this hope in him purifieth himself, even as He is pure. —I John 3:3

Thomas O. Chisholm

CHRISTLIKE
William J. Kirkpatrick

1. 主我願像祢！榮耀的救主，這是我盼望，
2. 主我願像祢！能滿有憐憫，溫柔和謙卑，
3. 主我願像祢！那樣的忍耐，聖潔的謙卑，
4. 主我願像祢！我今向祢求，我願付代價，
5. 主我願像祢！聽我的祈求，傾下祢的愛，
1 O to be like Thee! Bless - ed Re - deem - er, This is my con - stant
2 O to be like Thee! Full of com - pas - sion, Lov - ing, for - giv - ing,
3 O to be like Thee! Low - ly in spir - it, Ho - ly and harm - less,
4 O to be like Thee! Lord, I am com - ing, Now to re - ceive th'a -
5 O to be like Thee! While I am plead - ing, Pour out Thy Spir - it,
1. 是我禱告；我甘願捨棄，世上的財寶，
2. 慈愛善良；幫助軟弱者，慰痛苦憂傷，
3. 於人無傷；溫和的接受，兇惡與苦害，
4. 跟隨祢行；將我的所是，和我的所有，
5. 充滿我心；使我作聖殿，配給主居住，
1 long - ing and prayer; Glad - ly I'll for - feit all of earth's treas - ures,
2 ten - der and kind, Help - ing the help - less, cheer - ing the faint - ing,
3 pa - tient and brave; Meek - ly en - dur - ing cru - el re - proach - es,
4 noint - ing di - vine; All that I am and have I am bring - ing.
5 fill with Thy love; Make me a tem - ple deemed to re - ceive You:
1. 披戴主基督，守主聖道。
2. 領人歸基督，尋找亡羊。
3. 寧可救別人，自己死亡。
4. 完全獻給祢，不自經營。
5. 使我的生命與祢相印。
主，我願像祢！
O to be like Thee!
1 Je - sus, Thy per - fect like - ness to wear.
2 Seek - ing the wan - dering sin - ner to find!
3 Will - ing to suf - fer oth - ers to save.
4 Lord, from this mo - ment all shall be Thine.
5 Fit me for life and heav - en a - bove.

主，我願像祢，榮耀的救主，潔淨像祢！有主的
O to be like Thee, Bless-ed Re-deem-er, pure as Thou art! Come in Thy
甘甜，有主的豐盛；願主的聖形，深印我心。
sweet-ness, come in Thy full-ness; Stamp Thine own im-age deep on my heart.

我說，你們當順着聖靈而行，就不放縱肉體的情慾了。因為情慾和聖靈相爭，聖靈和情慾相爭，這兩個是彼此相敵，使你們不能作所願意作的。但你們若被聖靈引導，就不在律法以下。情慾的事，都是顯而易見的，就如姦淫、污穢、邪蕩、拜偶像、邪術、仇恨、爭競、忌恨、惱怒、結黨、紛爭、異端、嫉妒、醉酒、荒宴等類，我從前告訴你們，現在又告訴你們，行這樣事的人，必不能承受　神的國。聖靈所結的果子，就是仁愛、喜樂、和平、忍耐、恩慈、良善、信實、溫柔、節制，這樣的事，沒有律法禁止。

加拉太書第五章
16—23節

343

更像我恩主

More Like The Master

And this I pray, that your love may abound more and more . . . .

— Philippians 1:9

Charles H. Gabriel

Charles H. Gabriel

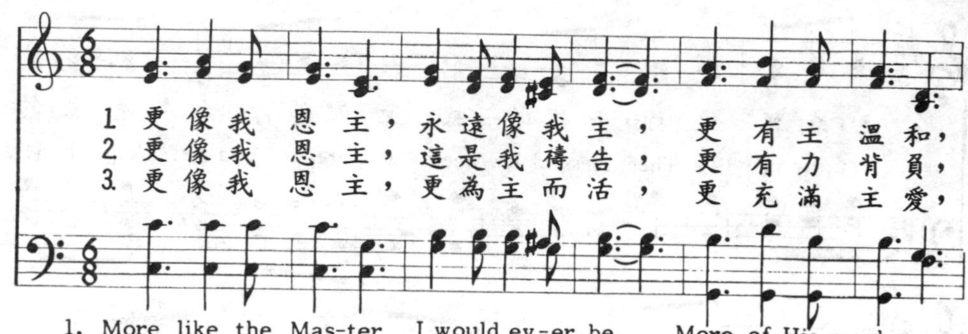

1. 更像我恩主，永遠像我主，更有主溫和，
2. 更像我恩主，這是我禱告，更有力背負，
3. 更像我恩主，更為主而活，更充滿主愛，
1. More like the Mas-ter I would ev-er be, More of His meek-ness,
2. More like the Mas-ter is my dai-ly prayer, More strength to car-ry
3. More like the Mas-ter I would live and grow, More of His love to

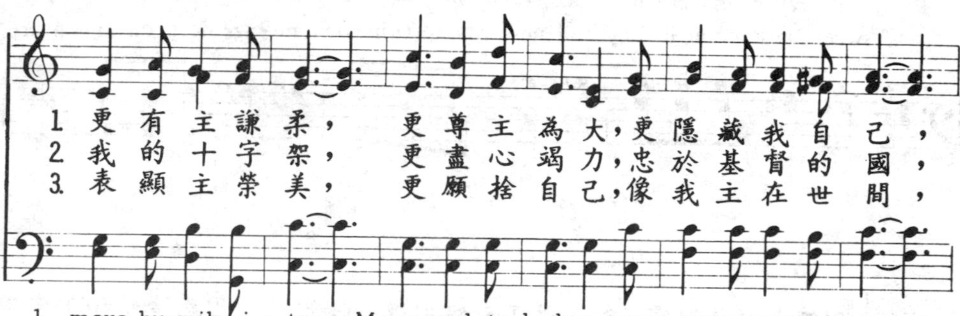

1. 更有主謙柔，更尊主為大，更隱藏我自己，
2. 我的十字架，更盡心竭力，忠於基督的國，
3. 表顯主榮美，更願捨自己，像我主在世間，
1. more hu-mil-i-ty; More zeal to la-bor, more cour-age to be true,
2. cross-es I must bear; More ear-nest ef-fort to bring His king-dom in,
3. oth-ers I would show; More self-de-ni-al, like His in Gal-i-lee,

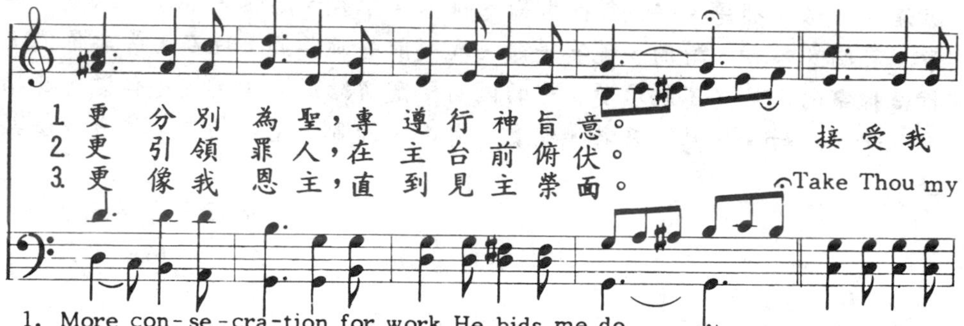

1. 更分別為聖，專遵行神旨意。
2. 更引領罪人，在主台前俯伏。
3. 更像我恩主，直到見主榮面。
接受我
Take Thou my
1. More con-se-cra-tion for work He bids me do.
2. More of His Spir-it, the wan-der-er to win.
3. More like the Mas-ter I long to ev-er be.

心，我願單單屬主。接受我心，願
heart, I would be Thine a - lone; Take Thou my heart and
完全屬我主，使我潔淨。主啊，我今懇
make it all Thine own. Purge me from sin, O Lord, I now im-
求！洗淨保守我，永屬祢所有。
plore, Wash me and keep me Thine for - ev - er - more.

所以你們既是　神的選民，聖潔蒙愛的人，就要存憐憫、恩慈、謙虛、溫柔、忍耐的心。倘若這人與那人有嫌隙，總要彼此包容，彼此饒恕，主怎樣饒恕了你們，你們也要怎樣饒恕人。在這一切之外，要存着愛心，愛心就是聯絡全德的。

歌羅西書第三章
12—14節

344

耶穌，我們要感謝祢

Jesus, We Just Want to Thank You

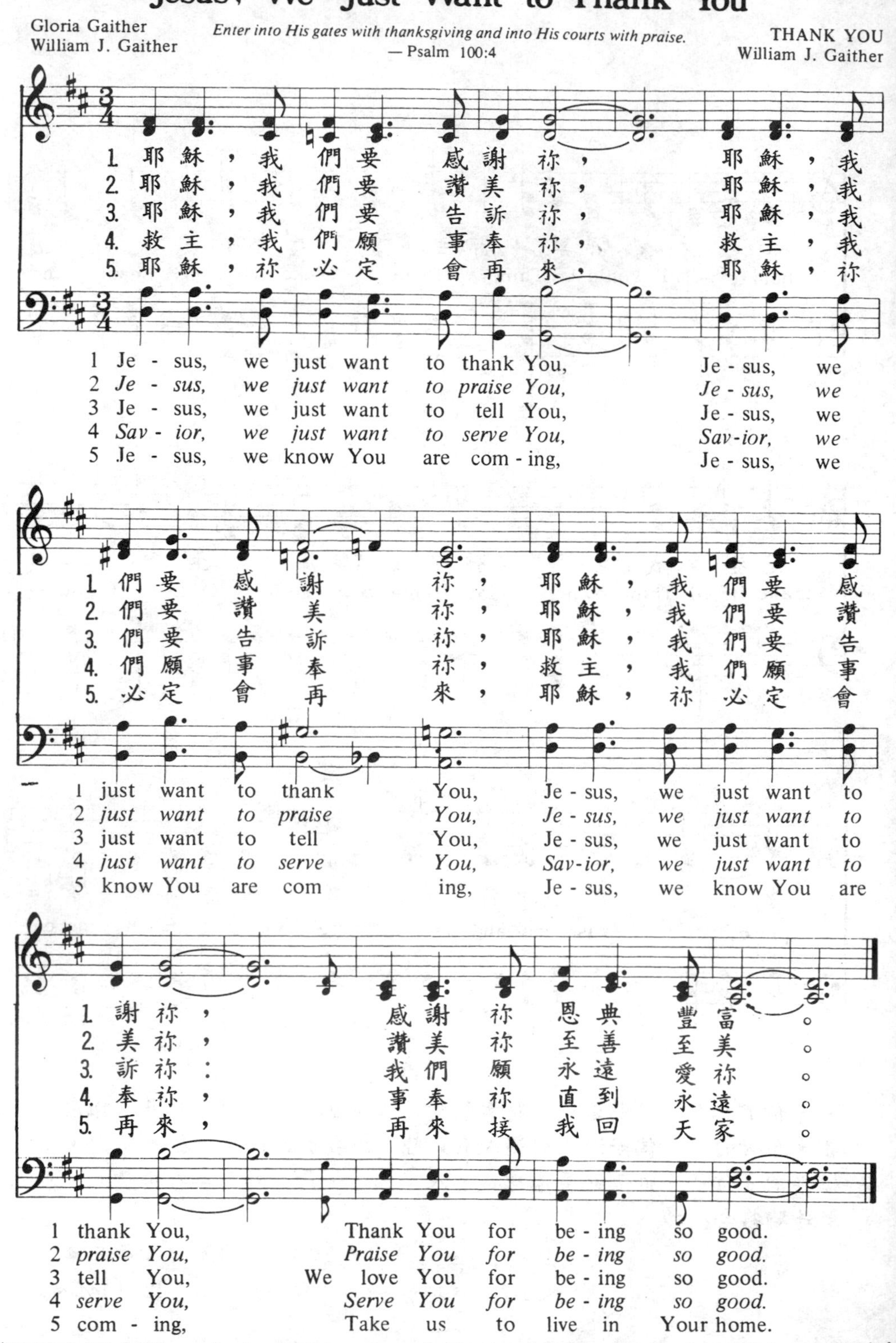

Gloria Gaither
William J. Gaither
Enter into His gates with thanksgiving and into His courts with praise.
— Psalm 100:4
THANK YOU
William J. Gaither
1. 耶穌，我們要感謝祢，耶穌，我們要感謝祢，耶穌，我們要感謝祢，感謝祢恩典豐富。
2. 耶穌，我們要讚美祢，耶穌，我們要讚美祢，耶穌，我們要讚美祢，讚美祢至善至美。
3. 耶穌，我們要告訴祢，耶穌我們要告訴祢，耶穌，我們要告訴祢：我們願永遠愛祢。
4. 救主，我們願事奉祢，救主，我們願事奉祢，救主，我們願事奉祢，事奉祢直到永遠。
5. 耶穌，祢必定會再來，耶穌，祢必定會再來，耶穌，祢必定會再來，再來接我回天家。
1 Je - sus, we just want to thank You, Je - sus, we just want to thank You, Je - sus, we just want to thank You, Thank You for be - ing so good.
2 Je - sus, we just want to praise You, Je - sus, we just want to praise You, Je - sus, we just want to praise You, Praise You for be - ing so good.
3 Je - sus, we just want to tell You, Je - sus, we just want to tell You, Je - sus, we just want to tell You, We love You for be - ing so good.
4 Sav - ior, we just want to serve You, Sav - ior, we just want to serve You, Sav - ior, we just want to serve You, Serve You for be - ing so good.
5 Je - sus, we know You are com - ing, Je - sus, we know You are com ing, Je - sus, we know You are com - ing, Take us to live in Your home.

我願事奉祢
I Will Serve Thee

If any man serve Me let him follow Me . . . .
— John 12:26
Gloria Gaither
William J. Gaither
SERVING
William J. Gaither
我願愛祢，全心事奉祢，祢已將生
I will serve Thee because I love Thee, You have giv - en
命賜我；我無所有，祢將我尋回，
life to me: I was noth-ing be-fore You found me,
將生命白白賜我。憂傷，破碎
You have giv - en life to me. Heart-aches, bro - ken
心靈，使祢為我在各各他受死；慈愛
piec - es, Ru-ined lives are why You died on Cal-vary; Your touch
滿足我需求，又將生命賜給我。
was what I longed for, You have giv - en life to me.

346 多多認識耶穌

More About Jesus Would I Know

But grow in grace in the knowledge of our Lord Jesus Christ
– 11 Peter 3:18

Eliza E Hewitt | SWENEY
John R. Sweney

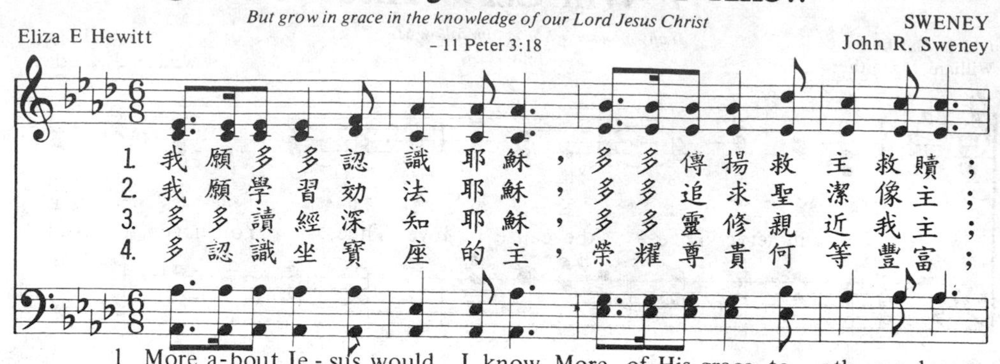
1. 我願多多認識耶穌，多多傳揚救主救贖；
2. 我願學習効法耶穌，多多追求聖潔像主；
3. 多多讀經深知耶穌，多多靈修親近我主；
4. 多認識坐寶座的主，榮耀尊貴何等豐富；
1 More a-bout Je-sus would I know, More of His grace to oth-ers show;
2 More a-bout Je-sus let me learn, More of His ho-ly will dis-cern;
3 More a-bout Je-sus; in His word, Hold-ing com-mun-ion with my Lord;
4 More a-bout Je-sus on His throne, Rich-es in glo-ry all His own;

1. 多多見主救恩豐富，多多認識愛我的主。
2. 懇求聖靈我的導師，教我從主多得啓示。
3. 從聖經中聽主聲音，主的應許滿足我心。
4. 多多擴大主的國度，和平之君我主基督。
1 More of His sav-ing full-ness see, More of His love who died for me.
2 Spir-it of God, my teach-er be, Show-ing the things of Christ to me.
3 Hear-ing His voice in ev-ery line, Mak-ing each faith-ful say-ing mine.
4 More of His king-dom's sure in-crease; More of His com-ing, Prince of Peace.

多多認識耶穌，多多認識耶穌；
More, more, a-bout Je-sus, More, more, a-bout Je-sus;
多多見主救恩豐富，多多認識愛我的主。
More of His sav-ing full-ness see, More of His love who died for me.

求主指示祢的道路
Teach Me Your Way, O Lord

Show me Thy way O Lord; teach me Thy way.
— Psalm 25:4, 5

B. Mansell Ramsey

CAMACHA
B. Mansell Ramsey

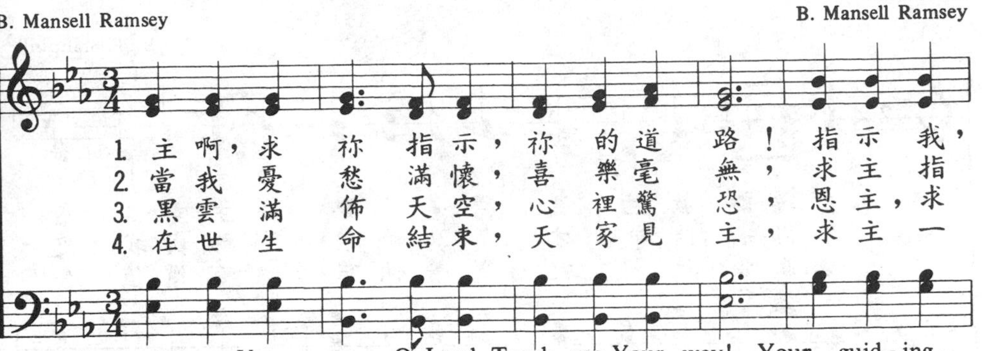

1. 主啊，求 祢 指示，祢 的道 路！指示 我，
2. 當我 憂 愁 滿懷，喜 樂毫 無，求主 指
3. 黑雲 滿 佈 天空，心 裡驚 恐，恩主，求
4. 在世 生 命 結束，天 家見 主，求主 一

1 Teach me Your way, O Lord, Teach me Your way! Your guid-ing
2 *When I am sad at heart, Teach me Your way! When earth-ly*
3 When doubts and fears a-rise, Teach me Your way! When storm-clouds
4 *Long as my life shall last, Teach me Your way! Wher-e'er my*

1. 帶領我，走祢 道 路！使我行 在正路，憑信仰
2. 示我走一祢的 道 路！當我寂 寞困苦，不知未
3. 祢指示，祢的 道 路！不論風 雨陰晴，前路是
4. 路指引，祢的 道 路！跑完世 上路程，冠冕為

1 grace af-ford—Teach me Your way! Help me to walk a-right, More by faith,
2 *joys de-part, Teach me Your way! In hours of lone-li-ness, In times of*
3 fill the skies, Teach me Your way! Shine thru the wind and rain, Thru sor-row,
4 *lot be cast, Teach me Your way! Un-til the race is run, Un-til the*

1. 望我主，恩光引 導 指示一祢的道 路！
2. 來前途，求主向 我 指示一祢的道 路！
3. 突或平，求主指 示 我走一祢的道 路！
4. 我永存，仍求主 指 示我一祢的道 路！阿們。

1 less by sight; Lead me with heaven-ly light— Teach me Your way!
2 *dire dis-tress, In fail-ure or suc-cess, Teach me Your way!*
3 grief and pain; Make now my path-way plain—Teach me Your way!
4 *jour-ney's done, Un-til the crown is won, Teach me Your way!* A-men.

認識主真快樂
Happiness Is The Lord

Therefore God hath anointed thee with the oil of gladness . . . .
— Hebrews 1:9

Ira F. Stanphill

[Ira F. Stanphill]

1. 認識救主就得着快樂，在主愛裡過
2. 得新生命才是真快樂，耶穌與我更
3. 罪蒙赦免就得着快樂，過有價值有
1. Hap - pi - ness is to know the Sav - ior, Liv - ing a life with-
2. Hap - pi - ness is a new cre - a - tion, "Je - sus and me" in
3. Hap - pi - ness is to be for - giv - en, Liv - ing a life that's
1. 甜美生活，行為改變遠離衆罪惡，
2. 親密諧和，祂的救恩今已賜給我，
3. 意義生活，奔走窄路往榮美天國，
1. in His fa - vor, Hav - ing a change in my be - hav - ior—
2. close re - la - tion, Hav - ing a part in His sal - va - tion—
3. worth the liv - in', Tak - ing a trip that leads to heav - en—
1 to vs. 2
2
1. 認識主真快樂。
2. 認識主真快樂。
3. 認識主真快樂。
樂。我有快樂，雖有眼
Lord. Real joy is mine, no mat-ter
1. Hap - pi - ness is the Lord,
2. Hap - pi - ness is the
3. Hap - pi - ness is the

D.C. to vs.3
涙 仍 快 樂；耶 穌 在 我 心，我 有 真 正 快 樂
if tear-drops start; I've found the se-cret—it's Je-sus in my heart!
3
樂！ 認 識 主 真 快 樂， 認 識 主 真 快 樂！
Lord, Hap-pi-ness is the Lord, Hap-pi-ness is the Lord!

曾有人説：

「世間無上的快樂，卽令一個住在茅屋裏的愚夫愚婦也能享受得到的，就是心中的平安，內心的純潔，忠實的勇氣，對於一切卑濁低下事物的制勝，有忍耐、和善、謙卑，和充足的指望。」

這種快樂惟有在耶穌基督裏面，方能充分的享受得到。

349

因祢的慈愛比生命更好

Thy Loving-Kindness Is Better Than Life

Hugh Mitchell and Jon Drevits

Because Thy lovingkindness is better than life, my lips shall praise Thee. — Psalm 63:3

Hugh Mitchell
Arr. by Jon Drevits

1. 因祢的慈愛，比生命更好，因祢的慈愛，比生命更好：
2. 我要奉祢名，舉手稱頌祢，我要奉祢名，舉手稱頌祢：
3. 我要記念祢，使我心滿足，我要記念祢，使我心滿足：
4. 在祢蔭庇下，我高聲歡呼，在祢蔭庇下，我高聲歡呼：

我口讚美祢，我心稱頌祢奉祢的名我舉手稱頌祢。

1. Thy lov-ing-kind-ness is bet-ter than life, Thy lov-ing kind-ness is bet-ter than life:
2. *I lift my hands, Lord, un-to Thy name, I lift my hands, Lord, un-to Thy name:*
3. Re-mem-b'ring Thee, Lord, I'm sat-is-fied, Re-mem-b'ring Thee, Lord, I'm sat-is-fied:
4. *Safe in Thy shad-ow I will re-joice, Safe in Thy shad-ow I will re-joice:*

My lips shall praise Thee, thus will I bless Thee— I will lift up my hands un-to Thy name.

350

最美好的事

The Greatest Thing

We love Him because He first loved us.
— I John 4:19

Mark Pendergrass

Unison

1 我 生命中 最美的事 是讚美祢。
1. The great - est thing in all my life is prais - ing you.

我 生命中 最美的事 是
The great - est thing in all my life is

讚 美祢。
prais - ing you.

我願讚美 祢，
I want to praise you

主，我願讚美 祢，主，我
Lord; I want to praise you Lord. The

生命中 最美的事 是讚 美 祢。
great - est thing in all my life is prais - ing you.

2. 敬愛祢。
3. 事奉祢。

2. loving you .
3. serving you .

351

渴慕耶穌

Longing For Jesus

R. D. Baker *Ho, everyone that thirsteth, come ye to the waters . . . .*— Isaiah 55:1 R. D. Baker

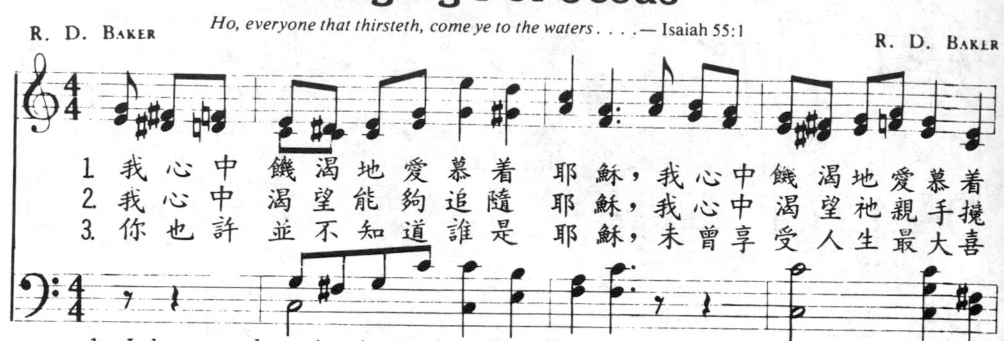
1. 我心中 饑渴地愛慕着 耶穌，我心中饑渴地愛慕着
2. 我心中 渴望能夠追隨 耶穌，我心中渴望祂親手攙
3. 你也許 並不知道誰是 耶穌，未曾享受人生最大喜

1. I have a long-ing in my heart for Je-sus, I have a long-ing in my heart for
2. *I have a long-ing just to walk with Je-sus, I have a long-ing just to hold His*
3. To you who do not know this man named Je-sus, you've never lived or found life's greatest

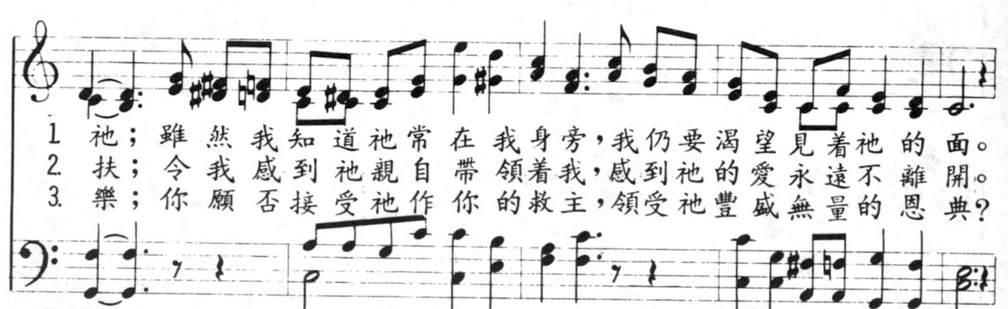
1. 祂；雖然我知道祂常在我身旁，我仍要渴望見着祂的面。
2. 扶；令我感到祂親自帶領着我，感到祂的愛永遠不離開。
3. 樂；你願否接受祂作你的救主，領受祂豐盛無量的恩典？

Him; Al-though I know His presence lingers near me, I have a long-ing just to see His face.
hand; To know He's there for-e-ver near to guide me, To know His love will never let me go.
joy; Oh, won't you now take Him as Lord and Sa-viour, And know the fullness of His matchless love

心中渴慕着 耶穌，我心中 饑渴地愛慕耶 穌；
Long - ing, long-ing for Je-sus, I have a longing in my heart for Him;

但求接 近祂，常與祂同在，我心中饑渴地愛慕耶穌。
Just to be near Him, to feel His pre-sence, I have a long-ing in my heart for Him.

想起難捨

Lord Jesus, When I Think Of Thee

Source unknown
Eng. Tr. by Marshall Huang

My tongue shall speak . . . praise all the day long. — Psalm 35:28

Unknown

1. 主耶穌啊！想起了祢，心中便覺甜蜜；
2. 世上沒有一個聲音，把祢恩典唱盡；
3. 雖然有時流淚傷心，情感不能自禁；
4. 祢愛多麼闊長深高，沒有人能知曉；
1. Lord Je-sus Christ, My heart is thrilled, When e're I think of Thee;
2. No voice can tell, no song des-cribe, The full-ness of Thy grace;
3. Tho' trials may come, tho' tears o'er flow, And sad-ness fills my heart;
4. Thy Love, how deep, how broad, how high, No man can ful-ly know;
1. 巴不得今天就被提，與祢同在一起。
2. 世上也沒有一顆心，受完祢的愛情。
3. 可是想起祢的同情，憂愁化為高興。
4. 蒙愛的人只能說道：哦祢的愛奇妙！
1. And long that to Thy pre-sence near, We soon might rap-ture be.
2. No sin can bind no guilt re-mind, That Thy Love can't e-rase.
3. Yet when I think, that Thou art with me, Joy will my soul im-part.
4. But the re-deemed can on-ly say, "To Thee, our all, we owe."
哦！祢是園中的鳳仙花，祢是沙崙的玫瑰花，
More pre-cious than fine gold or sil - ver, Yes, sweet-er than ho-ney by jar,
祢是谷中的百合花，使我不能捨下。
Thou art the Li - ly of the val - ley, The Bright and Morn-ing Star.

353

親近，更親近
Nearer, Still Nearer

Order my steps in Thy word and let not any iniquity have dominion over me. — Psalm 119:133

Lelia N. Morris

MORRIS
Lelia N. Morris

1. 親 近，更 親 近，親 近 主 心， 親 愛 救
2. 親 近，更 親 近，親 近 我 主， 我 一 無
3. 親 近，更 親 近，終 生 親 近， 直 到 進
1 Near - er, still near - er, close to Thy heart, Draw me, my
2 Near - er, still near - er, noth - ing I bring, Naught as an
3 Near - er, still near - er, while life shall last, 'Til safe in
1. 主 吸 引 我 更 親 近； 願 在 主 懷 中
2. 所 有 獻 給 主 耶 穌； 今 獻 我 憂 傷
3. 入 榮 耀 裡 享 安 息； 一 直 到 永 遠
1 Sav - ior, so pre - cious Thou art; Fold me, O fold me
2 of - fering to Je - sus my King; On - ly my sin - ful,
3 glo - ry my an - chor is cast; Through end-less a - ges,
1. 與 主 相 親， 在 主 慈 愛 保 護 中 享 安
2. 痛 悔 心 靈， 求 主 用 寶 血 將 我 罪 洗
3. 永 無 止 盡， 親 近 我 救 主 與 主 更 親
1 close to Thy breast, Shel - ter me safe in that "Ha - ven of
2 now con-trite heart, Grant me the cleans - ing Thy blood doth im -
3 ev - er to be, Near - er, my Sav - ior, still near - er to
1. 寧， 在 主 慈 愛 保 護 中 享 安 寧。
2. 淨， 求 主 用 寶 血 將 我 罪 洗 淨。
3. 近， 親 近 我 救 主 與 主 更 親 近。 阿 們。
1 Rest," Shel - ter me safe in that "Ha - ven of Rest."
2 part, Grant me the cleans - ing Thy blood doth im - part.
3 Thee, Near - er, my Sav - ior, still near - er to Thee. A-men.

開我的眼，使我看見

Open My Eyes That I May See

Many prophets and kings have desired to see those things which ye see.

Luke 10:23-24

Clara H. Scott
Jeff Redd, alt.

OPEN MY EYES
Clara H. Scott

1. 開我的眼，使我看見 神的真理為我彰顯；
2. 開我耳朵，使我聽見 恩主所賜真理之言；
3. 開我的口，使我宣揚 真理福音傳到各方；

1 O-pen my eyes, that I may see Glimp-ses of truth You have for me;
2 *O-pen my ears, that I may hear Voic-es of truth so sharp and clear;*
3 O-pen my mouth, let me de-clare Words of as-sur-ance ev-ery-where;

1. 求主賜我那奇妙祕鑰，使我自由解我捆鎖
2. 當賜佳音蕩漾我耳中，一切虛假頓失影踪。
3. 開啓我心充滿主的恩，將主大愛分給世人。
1 Place in my hands the won-der-ful key That shall un-lock and set me free.
2 And while the mes-sage sounds in my ear, Ev-ery-thing else will dis-ap-pear.
3 O-pen my heart, and let me pre-pare Your lov-ing kind-ness-es to share.

我今默然專心等候，惟願我主旨意成就；
Si-lent-ly now I wait for You, Read-y, my God, Your will to do;
1. 懇求聖靈，開我的眼，光照引領！
2. 懇求聖靈，開我耳朵，光照引領！
3. 懇求聖靈，開我的心，光照引領！阿門。
1 O-pen my eyes, il-lu-mine me, Spir-it di-vine!
2 O-pen my ears, il-lu-mine me, Spir-it di-vine!
3 O-pen my heart, il-lu-mine me, Spir-it di-vine! A-men.

355

祢必保守他十分平安

Thou Wilt Keep Him in Perfect Peace

. . . because he trusteth in Thee.

— Isaiah 26:3

Isaiah 26:3
Vivian Kretz
PERFECT PEACE
Vivian Kretz
"堅 心倚賴祢的，祢 必保守 他十分平 安。"
"Thou wilt keep him in per - fect peace whose mind is stayed on Thee."
當黑暗來臨，陰影籠罩，祂 必賜你平 安。惟有
When the sha-dows come and dark-ness falls, He giv - eth in-ward peace. O He
救 主能使你真 正 安息，賜 你十分平 安！
is the on-ly per-fect rest-ing place, He giv - eth per-fect peace!
"堅 心倚賴 的，祢 必保守 他 十分 平 安。"
"Thou wilt keep him in per - fect peace whose mind is stayed on Thee."

安居主愛

In Heavenly Love Abiding

Abide in Me, and I in you, as the branch cannot bear fruit unless it abide in the vine . . . — John 15:4

SEASONS

Anna L. Waring — Felix Mendelssohn

1. 居至高者隱密處，心中毫無憂驚；
2. 任主旨意引導我，遇難也不退卻；
3. 前路美境可遠望，好似滿園繁花；
1 In heaven-ly love a-bid-ing, No change my heart shall fear;
2 Wher-ev-er He may guide me, No fear shall turn me back;
3 Green pas-tures are be-fore me, Which yet I have not seen;
1. 住全能者蔭庇所，危險都成安寧。
2. 良牧在旁真穩妥，我心一無所缺。
3. 黑雲密霧化明亮，看到華美天家。
1 And safe is such con-fid-ing, For noth-ing chan-ges here.
2 My Shep-herd is be-side me, And noth-ing shall I lack.
3 Bright skies will soon be o'er me, Where dark-est clouds have been.
1. 雖有風雷聲怒吼，四周波浪顛狂；
2. 主用大智常照顧，對我時刻留意；
3. 我今所望求天父，生命之路指明；
1 The storm may roar with-out me, My heart may low be laid,
2 His wis-dom ev-er wak-eth, His sight is nev-er dim;
3 My hope I can-not meas-ure, My path to life is free;
1. 有主常在我左右，我心何須驚惶？
2. 主用大能開道路，我心何須憂疑？
3. 將我所有交救主，主必與我同行。
1 But God is round a-bout me, And can I be dis-mayed?
2 He knows the way He tak-eth, And I will walk with Him.
3 My Sav-ior is my treas-ure, And He will walk with me.

357

奇妙平安
Wonderful Peace

And the peace of God, which passeth all understanding shall keep your hearts and minds.
- Philippians 4:7

W. D. Cornell

WONDERFUL PEACE
W. G. Cooper

1. 在我心靈的最深處有一泉源，不斷
2. 何等寶貴我有這奇妙的平安，深藏
3. 我今安隱的享受這奇妙平安，有耶
4. 我深信将來我必到那平安城，我與
5. 請問你心靈是否困倦與煩惱？是否
1 Far a - way in the depths of my spir - it to - night Rolls a
2 What a treas - ure I have in this won - der - ful peace, Bur - ied
3 I am rest - ing to - night in this won - der - ful peace, Rest - ing
4 And I think when I rise to that cit - y of peace, Where the
5 O my soul, are you here with - out com - fort or rest, March - ing

1. 湧出美妙的音樂；比那甜美的詩歌曲
2. 在我心靈的深處；雖有惡勢力亦無法
3. 穌在掌管我生命；一切災害危險救主
4. 賜平安的主見面；在榮耀的天上與衆
5. 覺人生道路難走？當黑雲滿佈快來就
1 mel - o - dy sweet - er than psalm; In ce - les - tial-like strains it un -
2 deep in the heart of my soul; So se - cure that no pow - er can
3 sweet-ly in Je - sus' con - trol; For I'm kept from all dan - ger by
4 au - thor of peace I shall see, That one strain of the song which the
5 down the rough path-way of time? Make the Sav - ior your friend when the

1. 調更甘甜，使我靈得平安和喜悦。
2. 将它奪去，因救主永遠與我同住。
3. 晝夜保護，主的榮光充滿我心靈。
4. 聖徒同唱，奇妙平安歌直到永遠。
5. 近主耶穌，祂必賜平安作你良友。
1 ceas - ing - ly falls O'er my soul like an in - fi - nite calm.
2 mine it a - way While the years of e - ter - ni - ty roll;
3 night and by day, And His glo - ry is flood - ing my soul.
4 ran-somed will sing, In that heav - en - ly king - dom shall be:
5 shad-ows grow dark; O ac - cept this sweet peace so sub - lime.

平安，奇妙平安，這是天父所賜的平安；求
Peace! Peace! won-der-ful peace, Coming down from the Fa-ther a - bove; Sweep
主的大慈愛充滿我的心，使我永遠有奇妙平安。
o-ver my spir-it for - ev- er, I pray, In fath-om-less bil-lows of love.

我的平安 357-1

My Peace

My peace I give you . . . not . . . as the world gives. John 14:27

Keith Routledge Keith Routledge

Unison

我將平安賜給你，這平安非世界所能給，這平安非世界所能夠瞭解，藉它知，靠它活，我將平安賜給你。

My peace I give un-to you. It's a peace that the world can not give. It's a peace that the world can not un - der - stand. peace to know, peace to live, my peace I give un - to you.

358

有平安在我心

Constantly Abiding

Now the Lord of hope fill you with all joy and peace . . .

— Romans 15:13

Mrs. C. H. Morris

[Mrs. Will L. Murphy]

1. 有平安在我心，非世界所能賜，這平安無
2. 當這甜美平安，充滿在我心中，普世似向
3. 主賜我這珍寶，藏在我心殿中，在世寄居
1. There's a peace in my heart that the world nev-er gave, A peace it can
2. All the world seemed to sing of a Sav-ior and King, When peace sweetly
3. This treas - ure I have in a tem-ple of clay, While here on His

1. 人能奪去；雖試煉與艱難，如雲四面環繞，
2. 我主歌頌；黑暗頓成光明，愁苦全失影踪，
3. 平安融融；將來榮耀大日，主必再來接我，
1. not take a - way; Tho' the tri-als of life may surround like a cloud,
2. came to my heart; Troubles all fled a - way and my night turned to day,
3. foot-stool I roam; But He's coming to take me some glo - ri - ous day,

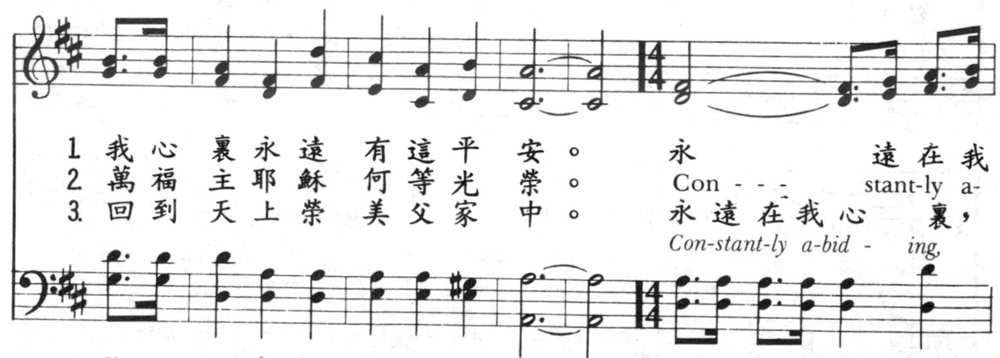

1. 我心裏永遠有這平安。永遠在我
2. 萬福主耶穌何等光榮。Con - - - stant-ly a-
3. 回到天上榮美父家中。永遠在我心裏，
Con-stant-ly a-bid - ing,
1. I've a peace that has come there to stay!
2. Bless-ed Je - sus, how glorious Thou art!
3. O - ver there to my heav - en - ly home!

心 裏， 耶 穌屬我；
bid - - - - ing, Je - - - sus is mine;
永遠在我心裏，是，耶穌屬我，耶穌屬我。
con- stant- ly a- bid- ing, Je- sus is mine, yes, Je - sus is mine;
永 遠在我心 裏， 無 限快
Con - - - stant-ly a - bid - - - ing, rap - - ture di-
永遠在我心裏，永遠在我心裏，無限快樂。啊！
Con-stant-ly a-bid - ing, con-stant-ly a-bid-ing, rap - ture di-vine, O
樂； 主 總不把我 撇 棄，慈聲
vine; He nev-er leaves me lone - - - ly, whis-pers,
無限快樂。主總不把 我 撇棄，總不撇棄，慈聲
rap - ture di-vine; He nev - er leaves me, nev - er leaves me lone-ly, whis-pers,
對我說：“我總不離開你，”耶穌屬我。
O so kind:— "I will nev-er leave thee," Je - sus is mine.
慈聲對我說：“我總不離，總不離你，”耶穌，耶穌屬我。
whis - pers, O so kind:— I will nev-er, nev-er leave thee, Je-sus, Je - sus is mine.

359

我心靈得安寧

It Is Well with My Soul

But God will redeem my soul from the power of death, for He will receive me. –Psalm 49:15

Horatio G. Spafford

VILLE DU HAVRE
Philip P. Bliss

1. 有時享平安，如江河平又穩，有時遇悲
2. 撒但雖來侵；衆試煉雖來臨，但我有確
3. 求主快再來，使信心得實現，雲彩要捲
1 When peace, like a river, attendeth my way, When sorrows like
2 My sin– O the joy of this glorious thought–My sin, not in
3 And, Lord, haste the day when my faith shall be sight, The clouds be rolled
1. 傷似浪滾；不論何環境，我已蒙主引領，
2. 據在我心；基督已清楚，我景況無人助，
3. 起在主前；號筒聲響應，我救主再降臨，
1 sea billows roll– Whatever my lot, Thou hast taught me to say,
2 part, but the whole, Is nailed to the cross, and I bear it no more:
3 back as a scroll: The trump shall resound and the Lord shall descend,
1. 我心靈得安寧，得安寧。我心靈
2. 就為我流寶血，救贖我。It is well 我心靈
3. 願主來我心靈，得安寧。It is well
1 It is well, it is well with my soul.
2 Praise the Lord, praise the Lord, O my soul!
3 "Even so"– it is well with my soul.
得安寧，我心靈得安寧，得安寧。
with my soul, It is well, it is well with my soul.
得安寧，
with my soul,

360

安樂無休

Like a River Glorious

Then had Thy peace been like a river and Thy righteousness as the waves . . . .
— Isaiah 48:18

Frances Ridley Havergal
Jeff Redd, alt., stanza 3

WYE VALLEY
James Mountain

1. 主所賜的平安，彷彿江河流，使我心覺
2. 藏主膀臂之下，災禍不能臨，仇敵我不
3. 各樣歡樂憂傷，皆是主安排，就是遇見

1 Like a riv - er glo - rious Is God's per-fect peace, O - ver all vic-
2 *Hid - den in the hol - low Of His bless - ed hand, Nev - er foe can*
3 Ev - ery joy or test - ing Comes from God a - bove, Giv - en to His

1. 歡欣，永無盡無休；主的恩典完全，越受
2. 懼怕，因它不能侵；實在一無罣慮，心中
3. 災難，主也不離開；我要依靠救主，萬事

1 to - rious In its bright in - crease; Per - fect, yet it flow - eth Full - er
2 *fol - low, Nev - er trai - tor stand; Not a surge of wor - ry, Not a*
3 chil - dren As an act of love; We may trust Him ful - ly All for

1. 越豐滿，主的安樂長存，永世不間斷。
2. 甚穩固，沒有一點煩惱，因有主保護。
3. 交托主，只要信心堅固，主必定幫助。

1 ev - ery day, Per - fect, yet it grow - eth Deep - er all the way.
2 *shade of care, Not a blast of hur - ry Touch the spir - it there.*
3 us to do— Those who trust Him whol - ly Find Him whol - ly true.

我依靠耶和華，滿心得安樂，

Trust - ing in Je - ho - vah, Hearts are ful - ly blest—

照着主的應許，句句都不錯。

Find - ing, as He prom - ised, Per - fect peace and rest.

361

主賜我平安

Jesus Gives Me Peace

Pastor Hsi, d. 1896
Tr. by M. Geraldine Taylor

. . My peace I give unto you; not as the world giveth . . . .
— John 14:27

Chinese folk-hymn
Arr. by Johann Y. Yang

In moderate time
1. 為信主 家貧窮！
2. 為學道 遇逼迫！
3. 為福音 經試練！
4. 為教會 遭磨難！
我心似難安；
1.Through the faith, Grown so poor! How can I but be sad?
2. For the truth, Treat - ed ill; How can I but be sad?
3 For "Good News," Pass through pain; How can I but be sad?
4. For the Church, In sore straits; How can I but be sad?
想念主
1. 在客店！
2. 受捆綁！
3. 被鞭打！
4. 釘苦架！
我心便喜歡。
1. Think of Christ Born so low! And then my heart is glad.
2. Think of Christ Crowned with thorns! And then my heart is glad.
3. Think of Christ Scourged and torn! And then my heart is glad.
4. Think of Christ On the Cross! And then my heart is glad.
主賜我平安，主賜我平安， 主所賜的平安，
Je - sus gives me peace, Je - sus gives me peace. The peace that Je - sus gives
與世福無干，人不能奪去，平安乃在天。
Un - like the joys of this world, None can take a - way. It is the peace of Heaven

English translation used by permission of China Inland Mission, London.

362

神未曾應許
God Hath Not Promised

And if I go to prepare a place for you, I will come again,
. . . that where I am there ye may be also. John 14:3

Annie Johnson Flint

William M. Runyan

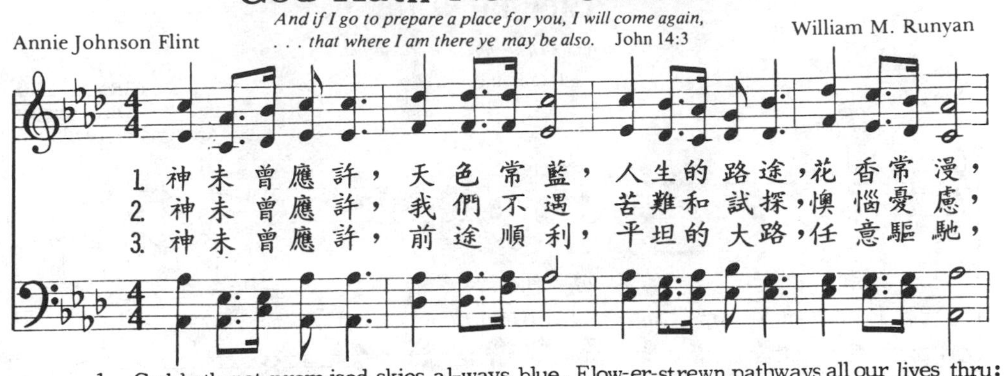

1. 神未曾應許，天色常藍，人生的路途，花香常漫，
2. 神未曾應許，我們不遇 苦難和試探，懊惱憂慮，
3. 神未曾應許，前途順利，平坦的大路，任意驅馳，

1. God hath not prom-ised skies al-ways blue, Flow-er-strewn pathways all our lives thru;
2. *God hath not prom-ised we shall not know Toil and temp-ta-tion, trou-ble and woe;*
3. God hath not prom-ised smooth roads and wide, Swift, eas-y trav-el, need-ing no guide;

1. 神未曾應許，常晴無雨，常樂無痛苦，常安無虞。
2. 神未曾應許，我們不負 許多的重擔，許多事務。
3. 沒有深水拒 汪洋一片，沒有大山阻 高薄雲天。

1. God hath not prom-ised sun with-out rain, Joy with-out sor-row, peace with-out pain.
2. *He hath not told us we shall not bear Man-y a bur-den, man-y a care.*
3. Nev-er a moun-tain rock-y and steep, Nev-er a riv-er tur-bid and deep.

神 卻曾應許，生活有力，行路有亮光，作工得息，
But God hath prom-ised strength for the day, Rest for the la-bor, light for the way,
試煉得恩助，危難有賴，無限的體 諒，不朽的愛。
Grace for the tri-als, help from a-bove, Un-fail-ing sym-pa-thy, un-dy-ing love.

363

永遠生命
Eternal Life

The things which are not seen are eternal.

— II Corinthians 4:18

St. Francis of Assisi

ETERNAL LIFE
Olive Dungan
Arranged by Fred Bock

求主使我成為祢的器皿：
Lord, make me an in-stru-ment of Thy peace:

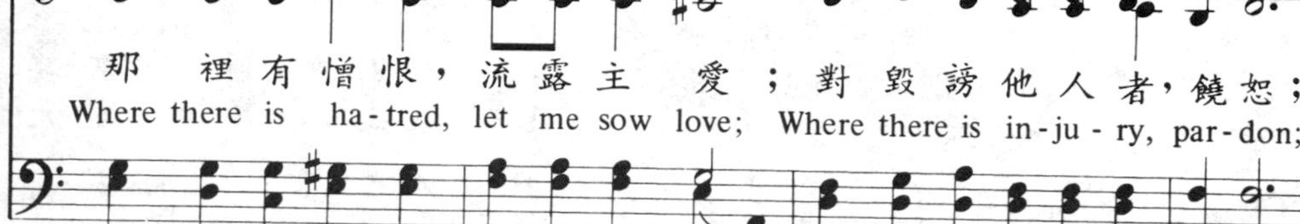

那裡有憎恨，流露主愛；對毀謗他人者，饒恕；
Where there is ha-tred, let me sow love; Where there is in-ju-ry, par-don;

疑惑時，相信；給失望者，盼望；
Where there is doubt, faith; Where there is de-spair, hope;

黑暗中，像明燈；使憂傷者，喜樂。
Where there is dark-ness, light; Where there is sad-ness, joy.

哦，至聖救主，使我不求自己益處，
O Divine Master, grant that I may not so much seek
使我成為安慰使者，使我多瞭解他人的苦楚，
To be consoled as to console, To be understood as to understand,
多付出我的愛；因為施與別人比受有
To be loved as to love; For it is in giving that we re-
福，若饒恕別人，我們得饒恕；若
ceive; It is in pardoning that we are pardoned; It
付出生命，我們才能得永遠生命！
is in dying that we are born to eternal life!

364

信徒們都當向主委身

Come, All Christians, Be Committed

No man having put his hand to the plow, and looking back is fit . . . .
— Luke 9:62

BEACH SPRING
"The Sacred Harp"
Harmonized by James H. Wood

Eva B. Lloyd

Unison
1. 信徒都當到主面前，委身事奉做主工，
2. 所有時間知識才能，都是神所賜的恩，
3. 信徒應當彼此相愛，主所吩咐當遵行，
4. 信徒都當到主面前，讚美歌頌主大愛，

1 Come, all Chris - tians, be com - mit - ted To the ser - vice of the Lord;
2 *Of your time and tal - ents give ye, They are gifts from God a - bove;*
3 God's com - mand to love each oth - er Is re - quired of ev - ery man;
4 *Come in praise and ad - o - ra - tion, All who on Christ's name be - lieve;*

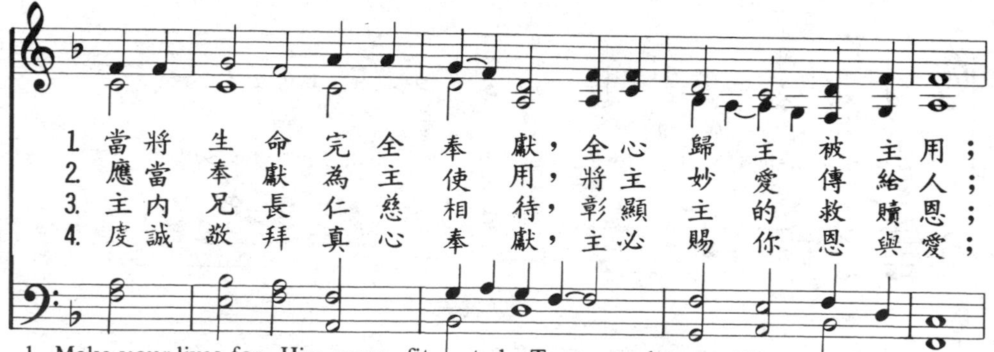
1. 當將生命完全奉獻，全心歸主被主用；
2. 應當奉獻為主使用，將主妙愛傳給人；
3. 主內兄長仁慈相待，彰顯主的救贖恩；
4. 虔誠敬拜真心奉獻，主必賜你恩與愛；

1 Make your lives for Him more fit - ted, Tune your hearts with one ac - cord.
2 *To be used by Chris - tians free - ly To pro - claim His won - drous love.*
3 Show - ing mer - cy to a broth - er Mir - rors His re - demp - tive plan.
4 *Wor - ship Him with con - se - cra - tion, Grace and love will you re - ceive.*

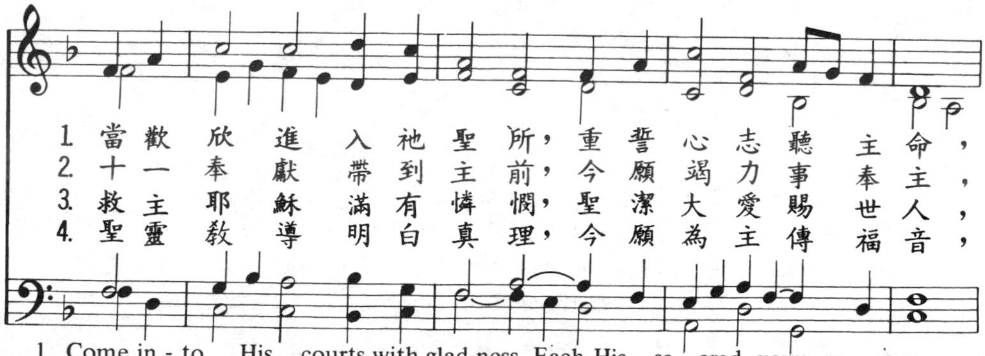
1. 當歡欣進入祂聖所，重誓心志聽主命，
2. 十一奉獻帶到主前，今願竭力事奉主，
3. 救主耶穌滿有憐憫，聖潔大愛賜世人，
4. 聖靈教導明白真理，今願為主傳福音，

1 Come in - to His courts with glad - ness, Each His sa - cred vows re - new,
2 *Come a - gain to serve the Sav - ior, Tithes and of - f'rings with you bring.*
3 In com - pas - sion He has giv - en Of His love that is di - vine;
4 *For His grace give Him the glo - ry, For the Spir - it and the Word,*

1. 除去憂愁遠離罪惡，心意更新與主親。
2. 為主而活討主喜歡，心中樂意讚美主。
3. 十字架上為我被釘，賜我平安赦罪恩。
4. 直到福音傳到地極，榮耀都歸主聖名。

1 Turn a - way from sin and sad - ness, Be trans-formed with life a - new.
2 *In your work, with Him find fa - vor, And with joy His prais-es sing.*
3 On the cross sins were for - giv - en; Joy and peace are ful - ly thine.
4 *And re - peat the gos - pel sto - ry 'Til all men His name have heard.*

365

何處若有聖靈同在

Where the Spirit of the Lord Is

Where the spirit of the Lord is there is liberty.
— II Corinthians 3:17

THERE IS PEACE
Stephen R. Adams

Stephen R. Adams

何處若有聖靈同在—有平安；
Where the Spir - it of the Lord is, there is peace;

何處若有聖靈同在—有愛心。
Where the Spir - it of the Lord is, there is love.

黑暗籠罩主賜你亮光，生命有希望，聖靈
There is com-fort in life's dark - est hour, There is light and life, there is

同在有安慰與力量，聖靈同在—有平安。
help and pow-er In the Spir - it, in the Spir - it of the Lord.

366

凡敬愛主的人到主前來
Come, We that Love the Lord

Ye are come unto Mount Zion, and unto the city of the living God. . . . — Hebrews 12:22

Isaac Watts
Robert Lowry
MARCHING TO ZION
Robert Lowry
1. 凡 敬 愛 主 的 人，到 主 前 來 歡 樂；同
2. 不 認 識 神 的 人，任 他 默 然 無 聲；但
3. 衆 信 徒 當 歡 欣，將 眼 淚 都 擦 淨；同
1 Come, we that love the Lord, And let our joys be known; Join
2 Let those re - fuse to sing Who nev - er knew our God; But
3 Then let our songs a-bound And ev - ery tear be dry; We're
1. 心 同 聲 頌 揚 主 恩，同 心 同 聲 頌 揚 主 恩，
2. 屬 天 父 的 兒 女 們，但 屬 天 父 的 兒 女 們，
3. 走 以 馬 內 利 路 程，同 走 以 馬 內 利 路 程，
1 in a song with sweet ac-cord, Join in a song with sweet ac - cord
2 chil - dren of the heaven - ly King, But chil - dren of the heaven - ly King
3 march-ing thru Em-man-uel's ground, We're march-ing thru Em-man-uel's ground
1. 來 環 繞 主 寶 座，來 環 繞 主 寶 座。
2. 總 要 稱 頌 主 恩，總 要 稱 頌 主 恩。
3. 直 到 美 麗 天 庭，直 到 美 麗 天 庭。
1 And thus sur - round the throne, And thus sur - round the throne.
2 May speak their joys a - broad, May speak their joys a - broad.
3 To fair - er worlds on high, To fair - er worlds on high.
今 同 心 往 聖 山，美 麗 的，美 麗 的 錫 安，大
We're march - ing to Zi - on, Beau - ti - ful, beau - ti - ful Zi - on; We're

家 同 心 齊 往 錫 安，那 美 麗 的 錫 安 聖 城。
march - ing up - ward to Zi - on, The beau - ti - ful cit - y of God.

367

彼此連合

Blest Be the Tie That Binds

Ye are the body of Christ and members in particular . . . . — I Corinthians 12:27

DENNIS
Johann G. Naegeli
Arranged by Lowell Mason

John Fawcett

1. 兄 弟 相 愛 相 親，須 要 心 誠 意 真；
2. 在 父 寶 座 之 前，盡 心 盡 力 祈 求；
3. 我 也 將 你 體 諒，你 也 代 我 擔 當；
4. 在 天 永 無 愁 苦，罪 孽 毫 無 存 留；
1 Blest be the tie that binds Our hearts in Chris - tian love;
2 Be - fore our Fa - ther's throne We pour our ar - dent prayers;
3 We share each oth - er's woes, Each oth - er's bur - dens bear;
4 From sor - row, toil, and pain, And sin we shall be free;

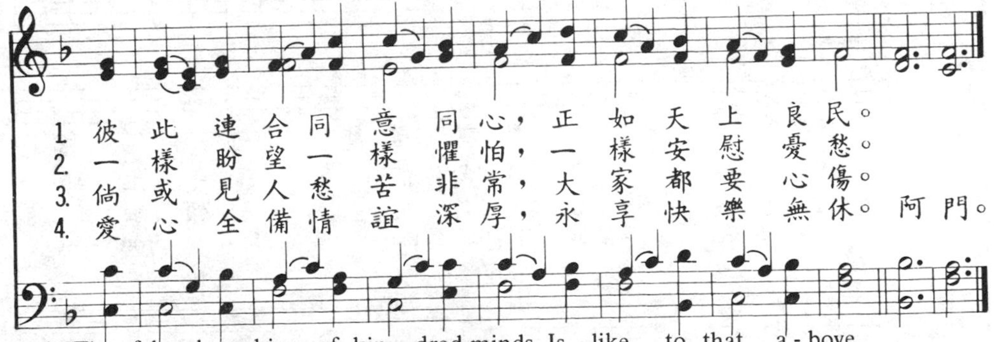
1. 彼 此 連 合 同 意 同 心，正 如 天 上 良 民。
2. 一 樣 盼 望 一 樣 懼 怕，一 樣 安 慰 憂 愁。
3. 倘 或 見 人 愁 苦 非 常，大 家 都 要 心 傷。
4. 愛 心 全 備 情 誼 深 厚，永 享 快 樂 無 休。阿 門。
1 The fel - low-ship of kin - dred minds Is like to that a - bove.
2 Our fears, our hopes, our aims are one, Our com - forts and our cares.
3 And oft - en for each oth - er flows The sym - pa - thiz - ing tear.
4 And per - fect love and joy shall reign Through all e - ter - ni - ty. A-men.

368

默契

There's a Quiet Understanding

I will pray with the understanding, . . . also, I will sing with the understanding . . . . — I Corinthians 14:15

Tedd Smith

QUIET UNDERSTANDING
Tedd Smith

1. 當 我 們 聚 集 在 一 起， 聖 靈 使 我
2. 主 與 我 們 同 在 一 起， 彼 此 分 享
1 There's a qui - et un - der-stand - ing When we're gath-ered
2 *And we know when we're to - geth - er, shar - ing love and*

1. 們 有 默 契， 這 是 主 耶 穌 的 應 許，
2. 靈 裡 默 契， 兄 弟 姐 妹 在 主 愛 裡，
1 in the Spir - it, It's a prom - ise that He gives us,
2 *un - der-stand - ing, That our broth - ers and our sis - ters*

1. 奉 祂 名 聚 在 一 起。 祂 的 慈 愛 充 滿 我 們，
2. 情 同 手 足 心 合 一。 感 謝 耶 穌 感 謝 耶 穌，
1 When we gath - er in His name. There's a love we feel in Je - sus,
2 *Feel the one-ness that He brings. Thank You, thank You, thank You, Je-sus,*

1. 天 上 嗎 哪 餵 養 我 們， 這 是 主 耶
2. 祢 使 我 們 心 靈 滿 足， 引 領 我 們
1 There's a man - na that He feeds us, It's a prom - ise
2 *For the way You love and feed us, For the man - y*

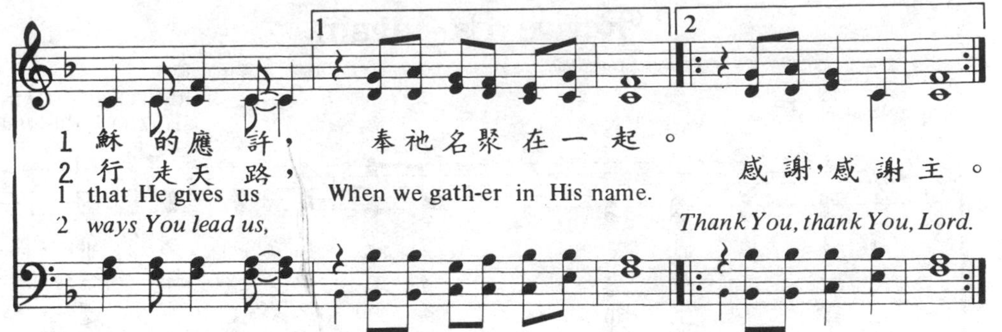
1
2
1. 穌的應許，奉祂名聚在一起。
2. 行走天路，感謝，感謝主。
1 that He gives us When we gath-er in His name.
2 ways You lead us, Thank You, thank You, Lord.

萬方團契

In Christ There Is No East or West

369

. . . In every nation he that feareth Him, and worketh righteousness, is accepted with Him. — Acts 10:35

John Oxenham

ST. PETER
Alexander R. Reinagle

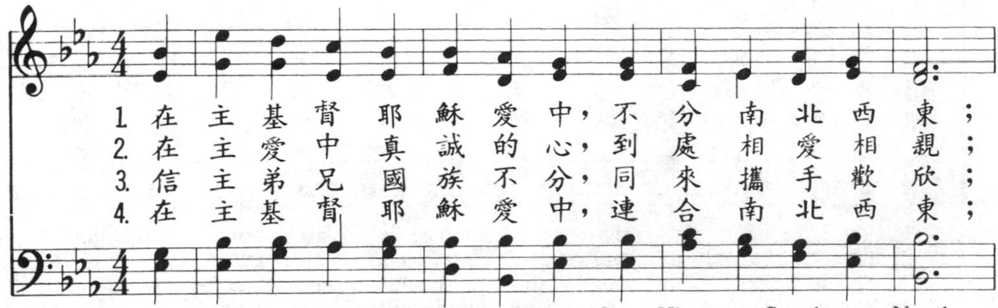
1. 在主基督耶穌愛中，不分南北西東；
2. 在主愛中真誠的心，到處相愛相親；
3. 信主弟兄國族不分，同來攜手歡欣；
4. 在主基督耶穌愛中，連合南北西東；
1 In Christ there is no East or West, In Him no South or North;
2 In Him shall true hearts ev-ery-where Their high com-mu-nion find;
3 Join hands then, broth-ers of the faith, What-e'er your race may be;
4 In Christ now meet both East and West; In Him meet South and North.

1. 整個廣大無邊世界，契合在主愛中。
2. 基督精神如環如帶，契合萬族萬民。
3. 同為天父孝順兒女，契合如敍天倫。
4. 信主之靈結成一體，契合在主愛中。
1 But one great fel-low-ship of love Through-out the whole wide earth.
2 His serv-ice is the gold-en cord Close bind-ing all man-kind.
3 Who serves my Fa-ther as a son Is sure-ly kin to me.
4 All Christ-ly souls are one in Him Through-out the whole wide earth.

370

使我復興

Revive Us Again

Wilt Thou not revive us again; that Thy people may rejoice in Thee? — Psalm 85:6

William P. Mackay
REVIVE US AGAIN
John J. Husband
1. 讚 美 我 天 父， 因 祂 如 此 愛 世，
2. 讚 美 保 惠 師， 奉 主 差 遣 降 臨，
3. 讚 美 主 耶 穌， 今 坐 天 父 右 邊，
4. 求 主 來 復 興， 慈 愛 充 滿 我 心，
1 We praise Thee, O God, for the Son of Thy love,
2 We praise Thee, O God, for Thy Spir - it of light,
3 All glo - ry and praise to the Lamb that was slain,
4 Re - vive us a - gain— fill each heart with Thy love;
1. 願 意 差 遣 獨 生 子 為 罪 人 受 死；
2. 特 為 開 導 並 照 亮 又 感 化 我 心；
3. 我 今 靠 主 的 功 勞 罪 愆 得 赦 免；
3. 聖 靈 火 重 燃 我 靈 使 我 得 復 興；
1 For Je - sus who died and is now gone a - bove.
2 Who has shown us our Sav - ior and ban - ished our night.
3 Who has tak - en our sins and has cleansed ev - ery stain.
4 May each soul be re - kin - dled with fire from a - bove.
哈 利 路 亞，榮 耀 歸 主！哈 利 路 亞，阿 門！哈 利
Hal-le - lu - jah, Thine the glo - ry! Hal-le - lu - jah, a - men! Hal-le -
路 亞， 榮 耀 歸 主！使 我 得 復 興。 阿 門 。
lu - jah, Thine the glo - ry! Re - vive us a - gain. A - men.

先賢之信
Faith of Our Fathers

. . . You should earnestly contend for the faith which was once delivered unto the saints.
— Jude 1:3

Frederick W. Faber

ST. CATHERINE
Henri F. Hemy

1. 先賢之信，萬世永存，火中不滅，刀下猶生；我衆思念，先賢聖蹟，心中亦覺，踴躍奮興！先賢之信，聖潔堅貞，我願至死堅守此信。
2. 我願宣講，先賢所信，善及列邦，吸引萬民；自由真理，本出於神，世人若信，自由永存。先賢之信，聖潔堅貞，我願至死堅守此信。
3. 我願傳揚，先賢所信，愛敵與存，不避危困；行為可親，言語溫馴，善用愛心，廣傳此信。先賢之信，聖潔堅貞，我願至死堅守此信。阿門。

1 Faith of our fathers, living still In spite of dungeon, fire, and sword, O how our hearts beat high with joy When-e'er we hear that glorious word! Faith of our fathers, holy faith, We will be true to thee 'til death.

2 *Faith of our fathers, God's great power Shall win all nations unto thee, And through the truth that comes from God Mankind shall then indeed be free. Faith of our fathers, holy faith, We will be true to thee 'til death.*

3 Faith of our fathers, we will love Both friend and foe in all our strife, And preach thee too as love knows how, By kindly words and virtuous life. Faith of our fathers, holy faith, We will be true to thee 'til death. A-men.

372

聚會將畢

Savior, Again to Thy Dear Name We Raise

And when they had sung a hymn they went out . . . .
— Matthew 26:30

John Ellerton

ELLERS
Edward J. Hopkins

1. 仁 慈 的 救 主， 聚 會 將 完 畢，
2. 求 主 賜 平 安， 歸 程 家 引 領，
3. 求 主 賜 平 安， 長 夜 不 驚 慌，
4. 求 主 眷 顧 我， 一 生 賜 平 安，
1 Sav - ior, a - gain to Thy dear name we raise
2 Grant us Thy peace up - on our home-ward way;
3 Grant us Thy peace, Lord, through the com - ing night;
4 Grant us Thy peace through - out our earth - ly life,
1. 容 我 們 再 次， 唱 詩 讚 美 祢；
2. 使 我 從 今 起， 隨 祢 脚 步 行；
3. 有 救 主 保 護， 隨 處 享 安 康：
4. 憂 傷 賜 安 慰， 苦 難 賜 恩 典；
1 With one ac - cord our part - ing hymn of praise:
2 With Thee be - gan, with Thee shall end the day;
3 Turn Thou for us its dark - ness in - to light:
4 Our joy in sor - row, and our strength in strife;
1. 未 離 聖 堂 前， 同 頌 主 恩 義；
2. 口 不 出 惡 言， 心 裡 常 潔 清；
3. 白 晝 和 黑 夜， 主 看 是 一 樣；
4. 直 到 爭 戰 畢， 聽 從 主 呼 喚；
1 Once more we pray be - fore our wor - ship cease;
2 Guard Thou the lips from sin, the hearts from shame,
3 From harm and dan - ger keep Thy chil - dren free,
4 Then, when Thy voice shall bid our con - flict cease,

1. 低 頭 同 禱 告，求 主 賜 安 息。
2. 遵 主 旨 意 行，披 戴 主 聖 名。
3. 有 主 指 引 我，凡 事 都 順 暢。
4. 與 主 在 天 上，永 遠 享 平 安。阿 門。
1 That Thou wilt grant to us Thy word of peace.
2 *That in this house have called up - on Thy name.*
3 For dark and light are both a - like to Thee.
4 *Call us, O Lord, to Thine e - ter - nal peace.* A-men.

373

晚禱

All Praise to Thee, My God

TALLIS' CANON
Thomas Tallis

Thomas Ken

My praise shall be of Thee in the great congregation; — Psalm 22:25

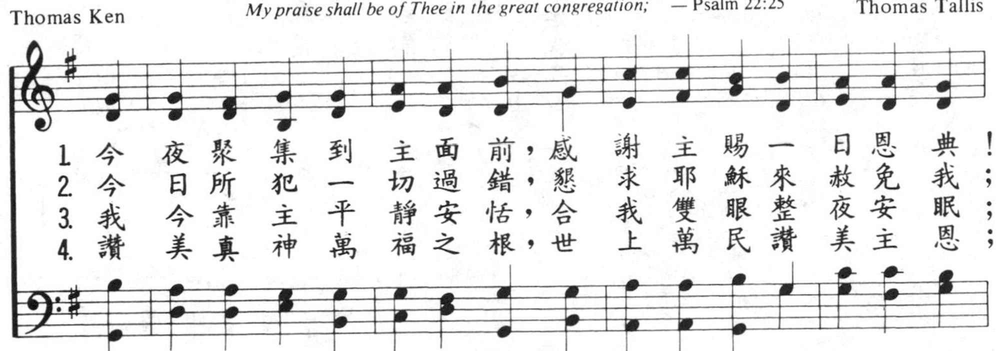
1. 今 夜 聚 集 到 主 面 前，感 謝 主 賜 一 日 恩 典！
2. 今 日 所 犯 一 切 過 錯，懇 求 耶 穌 來 赦 免 我；
3. 我 今 靠 主 平 靜 安 恬，合 我 雙 眼 整 夜 安 眠；
4. 讚 美 真 神 萬 福 之 根，世 上 萬 民 讚 美 主 恩；

1 All praise to Thee, my God, this night, For all the bless-ings of the light!
2 *For - give me, Lord, for Thy dear Son, The ill that I this day have done,*
3 O may my soul on Thee re - pose, And with sweet sleep mine eye-lids close,
4 *Praise God, from whom all bless- ings flow; Praise Him, all crea- tures here be - low;*

1. 萬 王 之 王 求 祢 看 顧，在 祢 翼 下 得 蒙 保 護。
2. 除 我 心 中 一 切 煩 惱，與 神 與 人 彼 此 和 好。
3. 清 晨 醒 來 賜 我 活 力，能 事 奉 主 更 加 竭 力。
4. 天 使 天 軍 讚 美 主 名，讚 美 聖 父 聖 子 聖 靈。阿 門。

1 Keep me, O keep me, King of kings, Be-neath Thine own al-might-y wings.
2 *That with the world, my-self, and Thee, I, when I sleep, at peace may be.*
3 Sleep that may me more vig-orous make To serve my God when I a-wake.
4 *Praise Him a-bove, ye heaven-ly host; Praise Fa-ther, Son, and Ho-ly Ghost.* A-men.

374

今将散去，求主賜福

Lord, Dismiss Us with Your Blessing

Salvation belongeth to the Lord; Thy blessing is upon Thy people.

— Psalm 3:8

John Fawcett

SICILIAN MARINERS
Tattersall's *Psalmody*

1. 今 将 散 去 求 主 賜 福，平 安 歡 樂
2. 感 謝 敬 愛 獻 於 恩 主，因 主 福 音
1 Lord, dis - miss us with Your bless - ing, Fill our hearts with
2 Thanks we give and ad - o - ra - tion For Your gos - pel's
1. 滿 心 靈； 求 主 賜 我 純 真 愛 心，
2. 歡 樂 聲； 願 我 心 思 意 念 言 行，
1 joy and peace; Let us each, Your love pos - sess - ing,
2 joy - ful sound; May the fruits of Your sal - va - tion
1. 日 日 靠 主 恩 得 勝 。 更 添 新 力，
2. 為 主 結 果 極 豐 盛 。 願 主 同 行，
1 Tri - umph in re - deem - ing grace. O re - fresh us,
2 In our hearts and lives a - bound. Ev - er faith - ful,
1. 更 添 心 力，領 我 安 然 曠 野 行 。
2. 願 主 同 行，常 活 在 我 生 命 中 。阿 門 。
1 O re - fresh us, Trav - eling through this wil - der - ness.
2 ev - er faith - ful To the truth may we be found. A - men.

375

天上父神，何等聖潔

Glorious Is Thy Name, Most Holy

We love Him because He first loved us . . . — I John 4:19

Ruth Elliot

HOLY MANNA
William Moore

1. 天上父神何等聖潔，尊貴榮耀是祢名；
2. 我今向主仰望祈求，一切需要主供應；
3. 漫長人生崎嶇路中，每日所需主賜下；

1 Glo - rious is Thy name, Most Ho - ly, God and Fa - ther of us all;
2 *For our world of need and an - guish We would lift to Thee our prayer.*
3 In the midst of time we jour - ney, From Thy hand comes each new day;

1. 我衆僕人主前跪拜，虔誠祈求主應允。
2. 得蒙救贖釋放自由，全靠救主耶穌名。
3. 我當謹慎支配運用，免使主恩被糟踏。

1 We Thy ser - vants bow be - fore Thee, Strive to an - swer ev - ery call.
2 *Faith-ful stew - ards of Thy boun - ty, May we with our broth-ers share.*
3 We would use it in Thy ser - vice, Hum - bly, wise - ly, while we may.

1. 主已賜我生命至寶，長遠關懷情最深；
2. 願做恩主忠心管家，將主恩與人分享；
3. 全能的神宇宙主宰，尊貴頌讚歸與祢；

1 Thou with life's great good hast blest us, Cared for us from ear - liest years;
2 *In the name of Christ our Sav - ior, Who re - deems and sets us free,*
3 So to Thee, Lord and Cre - a - tor, Praise and hon - or we ac - cord,

1. 主愛深厚除我憂驚，願獻身心報主恩。
2. 甘心奉獻身心財寶，為主活必得報償。
3. 天上地下都來敬拜，直到永久不止息。

1 Un - to Thee our thanks we ren - der; Thy deep love o'er-comes all fears.
2 *Gifts we bring of heart and trea - sure, That our lives may wor-thier be.*
3 Thine the earth and Thine the heav - ens, Through all the E - ter - nal Word.

376

榮耀真神恩惠之主

God of Grace and God of Glory

Put on the whole armour of God that ye may be able to stand. — Ephesians 6:11

Harry Emerson Fosdick

CWM RHONDDA
John Hughes

1. 榮耀真神恩惠之主，求将能力
2. 惡魔勢力将我圍住，侮辱基督
3. 除我無知敵對態度，使我謙卑
4. 引我脚踪步向高處，願我生命

1 God of grace and God of glory, On Thy people
2 *Lo! the hosts of evil round us Scorn Thy Christ, as-*
3 Cure Thy children's warring madness; Bend our pride to
4 *Set our feet on lofty places, Gird our lives that*

1. 傾我身；昔日教會為主受苦，榮耀花開
2. 攻擊主；疑慮憂驚長期束縛，今釋我心
3. 倚靠主；不再放縱求己益處，豐盛生命
4. 像恩主；全副軍裝爭戰為主，使人脫離

1 pour Thy power; Crown Thine ancient church's story, Bring her bud to
2 *sail His ways! From the fears that long have bound us, Free our hearts to*
3 Thy control; Shame our wanton, selfish gladness, Rich in things and
4 *they may be Armored with all Christ-like graces In the fight to*

1. 今得勝。求主賜我，智慧勇氣，
2. 讚美主。求主賜我，智慧勇氣，
3. 榮耀主。求主賜我，智慧勇氣，
4. 罪束縛。求主賜我，智慧勇氣，
1 glorious flower. Grant us wisdom, Grant us courage,
2 faith and praise. Grant us wisdom, Grant us courage,
3 poor in soul. Grant us wisdom, Grant us courage,
4 set men free. Grant us wisdom, Grant us courage,

1. 使我面對這時辰，使我面對這時辰。
2. 使我活着能為主，使我活着能為主。
3. 向着標竿跑前路，向着標竿跑前路。
4. 永不辜負我恩主，永不辜負我恩主。

1 For the fac-ing of this hour, For the fac - ing of this hour.
2 *For the liv-ing of these days, For the liv - ing of these days.*
3 Lest we miss Thy kingdom's goal, Lest we miss Thy king-dom's goal.
4 *That we fail not man nor Thee, That we fail not man nor Thee.* A-men.

376-1

懇求聖靈聽我求
Spirit Divine, Hear Our Prayer

Live by the Spirit, and you will not gratify the desires of the sinful nature. Gal. 5:16

Andrew Reed — Bill Wolaver

懇求聖靈，聽我求，求祢來住我心；賜下恩典充能力，求聖靈今降臨。阿門。

Spir - it Di - vine, hear our prayer, And make our hearts Your home; De-scend with all Your gra - cious pow'r, Come, Ho - ly Spir - it, come. A - men.

377

完全的愛
O Perfect Love

A man shall cleave unto his wife; and they shall be one flesh. — Genesis 2:24

Dorothy Gurney

O PERFECT LOVE
Joseph Barnby

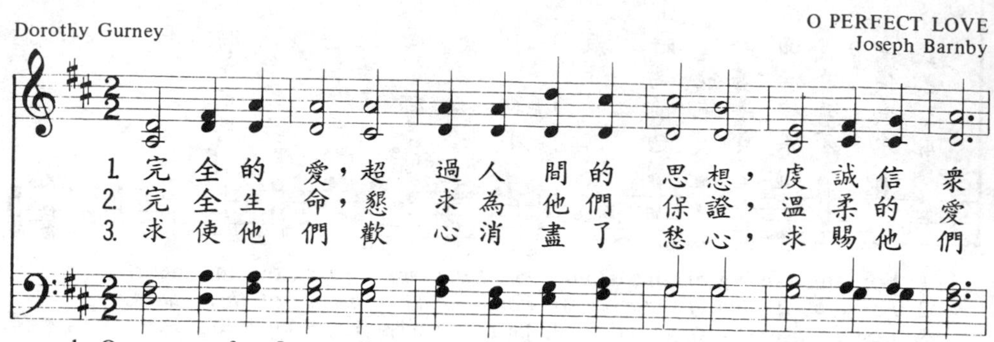
1. 完 全 的 愛，超 過 人 間 的 思 想，虔 誠 信 衆
2. 完 全 生 命，懇 求 為 他 們 保 證，溫 柔 的 愛
3. 求 使 他 們 歡 心 消 盡 了 愁 心，求 賜 他 們

1 O per-fect Love, all hu-man thought tran-scend-ing, Low - ly we kneel
2 *O per-fect Life, be Thou their full as - sur-ance Of ten-der char-*
3 Grant them the joy which bright-ens earth - ly sor - row, Grant them the peace

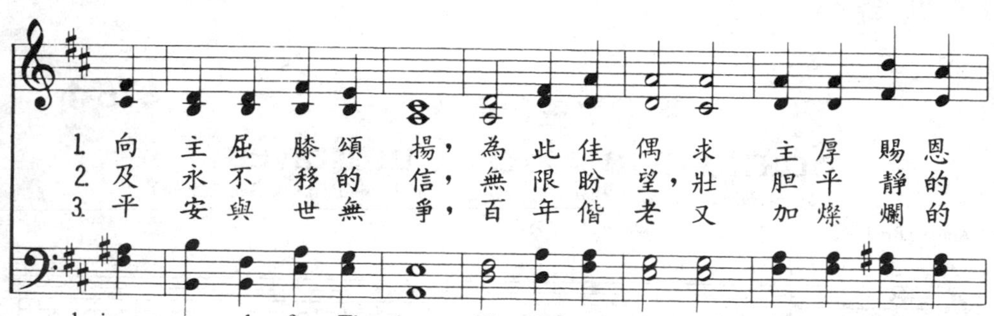
1. 向 主 屈 膝 頌 揚，為 此 佳 偶 求 主 厚 賜 恩
2. 及 永 不 移 的 信，無 限 盼 望，壯 胆 平 靜 的
3. 平 安 與 世 無 爭，百 年 偕 老 又 加 燦 爛 的

1 in prayer be-fore Thy throne, That theirs may be the love which knows no
2 *i - ty and stead-fast faith, Of pa-tient hope, and qui - et, brave en -*
3 which calms all earth - ly strife, And to life's day the glo-rious un-known

1. 無 量，主 作 之 合，恩 愛 地 久 天 長。
2. 堅 忍，純 潔 天 真，艱 難 痛 苦 不 驚。
3. 前 程，重 見 黎 明，恩 愛 生 命 永 恒。阿 門。

1 end - ing, Whom Thou for ev - er - more dost join in one.
2 *dur - ance, With child-like trust that fears nor pain nor death.*
3 mor-row That dawns up - on e - ter - nal love and life. A - men.

将這孩童奉獻

This Child We Dedicate to Thee

And Hannah prayed . . . and the child Samuel grew on, and was in favor with God . . . and man.
— I Samuel 2:1 & 26

From the German
Tr. by Samuel Gilman

FEDERAL STREET
Henry K. Oliver

1. 将這孩童奉獻給祢，恩惠之主聖潔無比！在祢愛中求祢庇護，生命道中免走錯路。
2. 求主聖靈溫柔降下，使他一生守主律法；謹守教訓篤信真理，自幼到老永不偏離。阿門。
1 This child we ded - i - cate to Thee, O God of grace and pu - ri - ty! In Thy great love its life pro - long, Shield it, we pray, from sin and wrong.
2 O may Thy Spir - it gen - tly draw Its will - ing soul to keep Thy law; May vir - tue, pi - e - ty, and truth Dawn e - ven with its dawn - ing youth. A - men.

379

奉獻聖殿
We Dedicate This Temple

I have built a house of habitation for thee. — II Chronicles 6:2a

Ernest K. Emurian — AURELIA, Samuel S. Wesley

1. 虔誠奉獻這聖殿，哦神我的天父，
2. 虔誠奉獻這聖殿，基督耶穌我主，
3. 虔誠奉獻這聖殿，哦至善的聖靈，
4. 虔誠奉獻這聖殿，身心全獻恩主，

1 We ded-i-cate this tem-ple, O Fa-ther, un-to Thee,
2 *We ded-i-cate this tem-ple To Christ, the Lord of love,*
3 We ded-i-cate this tem-ple, O Spir-it from on high,
4 *We ded-i-cate this tem-ple, This la-bor of our hands,*

1. 昔在今在的真神，到永久仍賜福，
2. 帶來父神的啓示，建立主的國度，
3. 惟願時常住我心，接受我的感恩，
4. 惟願三一之真神，聖殿永遠長住，
1 The God of an-cient a-ges And a-ges yet to be:
2 Who brought God's rev-e-la-tion, The king-dom from a-bove:
3 To Thee, in our thanks-giv-ing That Thou art al-ways nigh
4 To Fa-ther, Son and Spir-it, Whose tem-ple ev-er stands

1. 眾信徒誠心敬拜，歌聲直達天庭，
2. 我眾學習主樣式，聖潔仁慈善良，
3. 憂傷來臨常安慰，軟弱時賜力量，
4. 盡心盡意的愛祢，照祢的旨意行，
1 That here our hearts may wor-ship And here our songs as-cend
2 That we may learn His good-ness, His god-li-ness and grace,
3 To com-fort us in sor-row, To strength-en in dis-tress:
4 In hearts that learn to love Thee And minds that com-pre-hend,

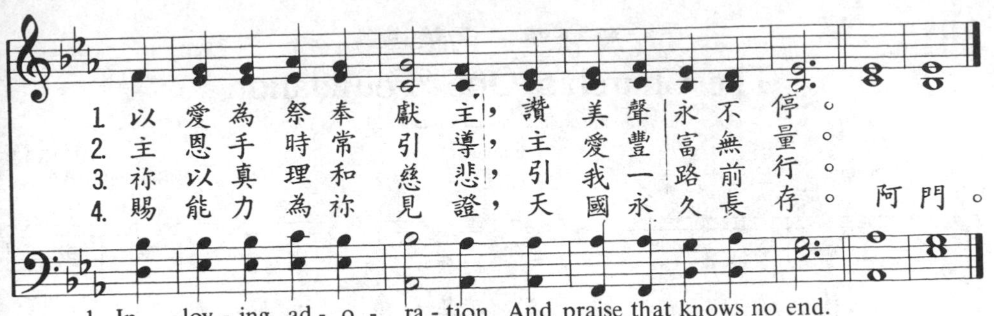
1. 以愛為祭奉獻主，讚美聲永不停。
2. 主恩手時常引導，主愛豐富無量。
3. 祢以真理和慈悲，引我一路前行。
4. 賜能力為祢見證，天國永久長存。阿門。

1 In lov-ing ad-o-ra-tion And praise that knows no end.
2 *Who holds all men and na-tions With-in His love's em-brace.*
3 That we, through truth and mer-cy, May walk in ho-li-ness.
4 *In wills em-powered to wit-ness Thy king-dom with-out end!* A-men.

380

願主耶穌的榮美藉我彰顯

Let The Beauty of Jesus Be Seen In Me

Albert Orsborn

Tom Jones

願主耶穌的榮美藉我彰顯，表彰主奇妙同情純潔美善！懇求聖靈潔淨，使我心靈更新，直到耶穌的榮美藉我彰顯。

Let the beau-ty of Je-sus be seen in me— All His won-der-ful pas-sion and pu-ri-ty! O Thou Spir-it di-vine, All my na-ture re-fine, Till the beau-ty of Je-sus be seen in me.

381

教會唯一的根基
The Church's One Foundation

Other foundation can no man lay than is laid . . . Jesus Christ.
— I Corinthians 3:11

Samuel J. Stone

AURELIA
Samuel S. Wesley

1. 教會惟一的根基，是主耶穌基督，
2. 雖從萬邦選出來，信徒都成一體，
3. 雖她歷盡了艱辛，受人譏笑毀謗，
4. 她雖在地却聯合，真神三位一體，
1 The Church-'s one foun - da - tion Is Je - sus Christ her Lord,
2 E - lect from ev - ery na - tion, Yet one o'er all the earth,
3 'Mid toil and trib - u - la - tion, And tu - mult of her war,
4 Yet she on earth hath un - ion With God, the Three in One,

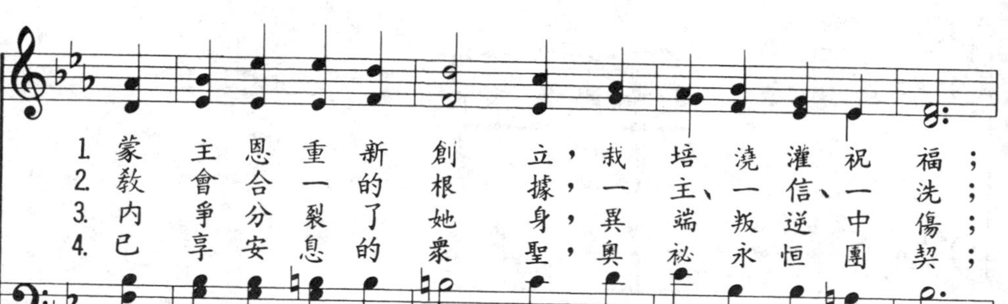
1. 蒙主恩重新創立，栽培澆灌祝福；
2. 教會合一的根據，一主、一信、一洗；
3. 內爭分裂了她身，異端叛逆中傷；
4. 已享安息的衆聖，奧祕永恒團契；
1 She is His new cre - a - tion By wa - ter and the word;
2 Her char - ter of sal - va - tion, One Lord, one faith, one birth;
3 She waits the con - sum - ma - tion Of peace for ev - er - more;
4 And mys - tic sweet com - mun - ion With those whose rest is won;

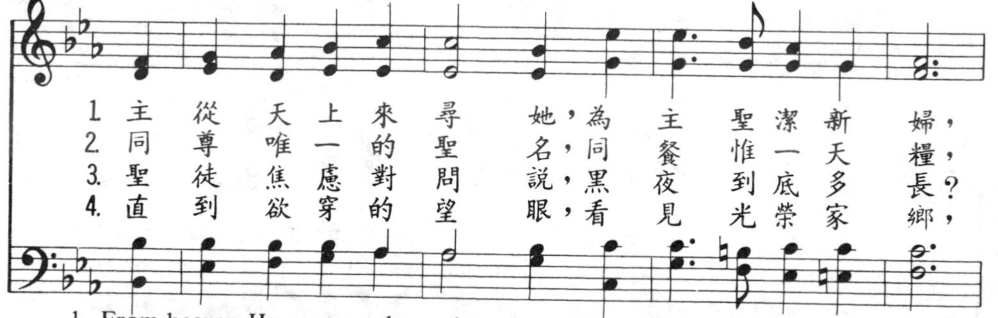
1. 主從天上來尋她，為主聖潔新婦，
2. 同尊唯一的聖名，同餐惟一天糧，
3. 聖徒焦慮對問説，黑夜到底多長？
4. 直到欲穿的望眼，看見光榮家鄉，
1 From heaven He came and sought her To be His ho - ly bride;
2 One ho - ly name she bless - es, Par - takes one ho - ly food,
3 Till with the vi - sion glo - rious, Her long - ing eyes are blest,
4 O hap - py ones and ho - ly! Lord, give us grace that we

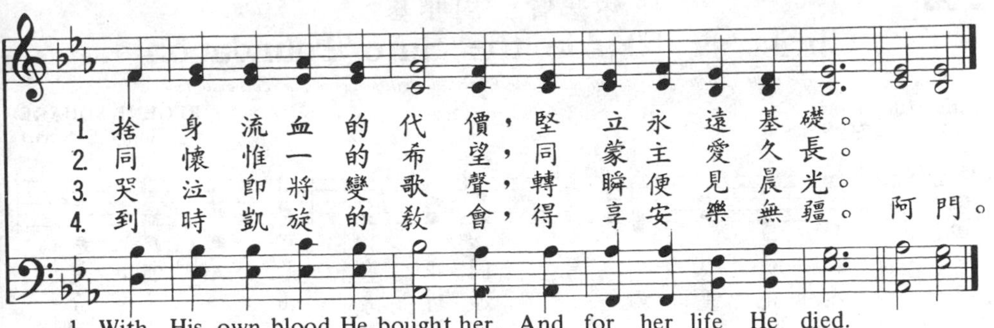
1. 捨身流血的代價，堅立永遠基礎。
2. 同懷惟一的希望，同蒙主愛久長。
3. 哭泣卽將變歌聲，轉瞬便見晨光。
4. 到時凱旋的教會，得享安樂無疆。阿門。
1 With His own blood He bought her, And for her life He died.
2 And to one hope she press - es, With ev - ery grace en - dued.
3 And the great Church vic - to - rious Shall be the Church at rest.
4 Like them, the meek and low - ly, On high may dwell with Thee. A-men.

382

快樂家庭

Happy the Home When God Is There

When I call to remembrance the . . . faith that is in thee, which dwelt first in thy grandmother, . . . and thy mother. — II Timothy 1:5

Henry Ware, Jr.
Bryan Jeffery Leech, alt.

ST. AGNES
John B. Dykes

1. 快樂家庭有神同在，充滿主的慈愛，
2. 快樂家庭顯出主愛，常常彼此關懷，
3. 快樂家庭常常禱告，讚美歌聲不息，
4. 敬求天父恩典日增，教我一家無爭，
1 Hap - py the home when God is there And love fills ev - ery - one,
2 Hap - py the home where God's strong love Is start - ing to ap - pear,
3 Hap - py the home where prayer is heard And praise is ev - ery - where,
4 Lord, let us in our homes a - gree This bless - ed peace to gain;

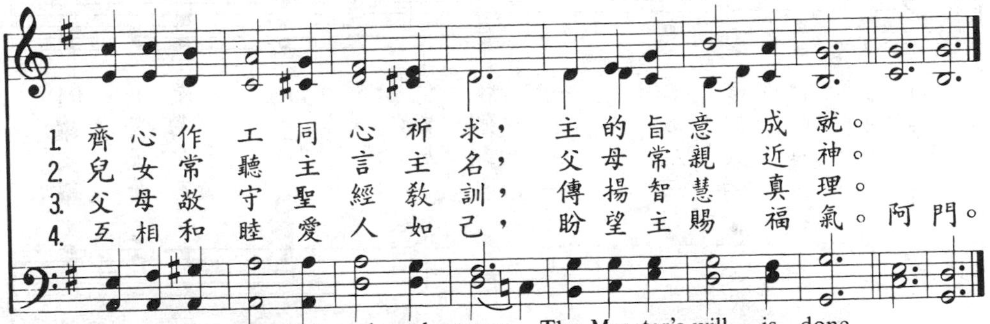
1. 齊心作工同心祈求，主的旨意成就。
2. 兒女常聽主言主名，父母常親近神。
3. 父母敬守聖經教訓，傳揚智慧真理。
4. 互相和睦愛人如己，盼望主賜福氣。阿門。
1 When with u - ni - ted work and prayer The Mas - ter's will is done.
2 Where all the chil - dren hear His fame And par - ents hold Him dear.
3 Where par - ents love the sa - cred Word And its true wis - dom share.
4 U - nite our hearts in love to Thee, And love to all will reign. A-men.

383

耶穌基督堅固根基

Christ Is Made the Sure Foundation

And built upon the foundation . . . Jesus Christ himself being the chief cornerstone.

—Ephesians 2:20

Latin: 7th Century
Tr. by John M. Neale

REGENT SQUARE
Henry T. Smart

1. 耶 穌 基 督 堅 固 根 基，是 元 首，是
2. 在 此 聖 殿 虔 誠 祈 禱，惟 願 主 今
3. 衆 聖 僕 人 在 此 聚 集，求 恩 主 賜
4. 信 徒 聚 集 主 聖 殿 中，齊 向 神 高
1 Christ is made the sure foun - da - tion, Christ the head and
2 To this tem - ple, where we call Thee, Come, O Lord of
3 Here vouch - safe to all Thy serv - ants What they ask of
4 Laud and hon - or to the Fa - ther, Laud and hon - or
1. 房 角 石； 神 所 揀 選 神 所 寶 貴，
2. 日 來 到； 滿 有 憐 憫 慈 愛 救 主，
3. 下 福 氣； 主 所 賜 的 各 樣 福 氣，
4. 聲 稱 頌； 讚 美 聖 父 聖 子 聖 靈，
1 cor - ner - stone, Chos - en of the Lord and prec - ious,
2 hosts, to - day; With ac - cus - tomed lov - ing - kind - ness
3 Thee to gain, What they gain from Thee for - ev - er
4 to the Son, Laud and hon - or to the Spir - it,
1. 被 建 造 合 一 教 會； 祂 是 我 們
2. 求 聆 聽 我 心 傾 訴； 主 的 榮 耀
3. 能 使 人 保 守 到 底； 將 來 天 家
4. 尊 貴 的 三 一 真 神； 滿 有 榮 耀
1 Bind - ing all the Church in one, Ho - ly Zi - on's
2 Hear Thy peo - ple as they pray, And Thy full - est
3 With the bless - ed to re - tain, And here - aft - er
4 Ev - er three and ev - er one, One in might and

1. 幫助源頭，信靠祂直到永久。
2. 豐富恩典，今日來充滿這殿。
3. 在榮耀裡，我與主永遠相依。
4. 滿有能力，千萬年永不止息。阿門。
1 help for-ev-er, And her con-fi-dence a-lone.
2 ben-e-dic-tion Shed with-in its walls al-way.
3 in Thy glo-ry Ev-er-more with Thee to reign.
4 one in glo-ry, While un-end-ing a-ges run. A-men.

383-1 Thanksgiving Day

Father, we around this table thank Thee:

for Thy great gift of life,

that Thy love for us is not dependent upon any unworthiness of ours,

for good health,

that we know neither hunger nor want,

for warm clothes to wear,

for those who love us best,

for friends whose words of encouragement have often chased away dark clouds,

for the zest of living,

for many an answered prayer,

for kindly providences that have preserved us from danger and harm.

We thank Thee that still we live in a land bountifully able to supply all our needs, a land which still by Thy Providence knows peace, whose skies are not darkened by the machines of the enemy, whose fields and woodlands are still unblasted by the flames of war, a land with peaceful valleys and smiling meadows still serene.

O help us to appreciate all that we have, to be content with it, to be grateful for it, to be proud of it–not in an arrogant pride that boasts, but in a grateful pride that strives to be more worthy.

In Thy name, to whose bounty we owe these blessings spread before us, to Thee we give our gratitude. Amen.

–Peter Marshall

384

神的家庭
The Family of God

Gloria Gaither
William J. Gaither
And God said, I will dwell in them . . . and they shall be My people;
. . . and ye shall be My sons and daughters. — II Corinthians 6:16, 18
FAMILY OF GOD
William J. Gaither
真 快樂，我已經 加入神的家庭，主寶
I'm so glad I'm a part of the fam - ily of God— I've been
血洗淨我靈，除我罪刑。有主的生命奔走
washed in the foun-tain, cleansed by His blood! Joint heirs with Je-sus as we
世上路程，因為我已經成為神家中的
trav - el this sod, For I'm part of the fam - ily, the fam - ily of
人。
God.
Fine
1 神的家裡兄弟姐妹有手足之
2 我不再流浪門外主已接我進
1 You will no-tice we say "broth-er and sis-ter" 'round
2 From the door of an or-phanage to the house of the

1. 情，神的愛 充滿我們，使我們更相親；
2. 來，口 唱讚美新歌，因主與我同在；
1 here— It's be-cause we're a fam-ily and these folks are so near;
2 King— No long - er an out-cast, a new song I sing;
1. 憂傷痛苦來臨，我們一同傷心，
2. 生命何等豐盛，主剛強我心靈，
1 When one has a heart-ache we all share the tears,
2 From rags un-to rich-es, from the weak to the strong,
D.C.
1. 當喜樂充滿我們，我們一同歡欣。
2. 我不配屬這家庭，但主賜我宏恩！
1 And re-joice in each vic-tory In this fam-ily so dear.
2 I'm not wor-thy to be here, But, praise God, I be-long!

“看哪，弟兄和睦同居，是何等的善，何等的美！”

詩篇一百三十三篇

385

我今已屬這神的家庭

Getting Used to the Family of God

"But you are . . . a people set apart to sing the praises of God."

— I Peter 2:9

Gloria Gaither
William J. Gaither
TOGETHER
William J. Gaither
1. 一同登高山，一同跨越平原，涉水而過河，苦難彼此分擔；有時有所失，有時有所得，
2. 熱忱的歡迎，新的朋友加入，以愛心相待，使他們認識主；學主的樣式，常與主同行，我今已屬這神的家庭。
1 Climb-ing the moun-tains, cross-ing the plains, Ford-ing the riv-ers, shar-ing the pains; Some-times the loss-es and some-times the gain,
2 Reach-ing our hands to a broth-er that's new, Learn-ing to say that I real-ly love you; Learn-ing to walk as the Mas-ter would do,
Get-ting used to the fam-'ly of God.
我們一同赴歡樂的旅途，我今屬於這
Go-ing to-geth-er, en-joy-ing the trip, Get-ting used to the

家庭，将來要 永遠 同 住；彼 此 要 相愛，常
fam-'ly I'll spend e - ter - ni - ty with; Learn-ing to love you, how
學習 關 懷，我今 已 屬這 神的 家 庭。
eas - y it is, Get-ting used to the fam-'ly of God.

所以在基督裏若有甚麼勸勉，愛心有甚麼安慰，聖靈有甚麼交通，心中有甚麼慈悲憐憫，你們就要意念相同，愛心相同，有一樣的心思，有一樣的意念，使我的喜樂可以滿足。凡事不可結黨，不可貪圖虛浮的榮耀，只要存心謙卑，各人看別人比自己強。各人不要單顧自己的事，也要顧別人的事。你們當以基督耶穌的心為心。

腓立比書第二章
1 — 5 節

386

在每一個家庭中
In the Circle of Each Home

And all thy children shall be taught of the Lord; and great shall be the peace of thy children.
— Isaiah 54:13

Bryan Jeffery Leech

BEL AIR
Bryan Jeffery Leech

1. 在每一個家庭中，需要主的大愛；
2. 在每一個家庭中，主是堅固基礎；
3. 在每一個家庭中，需要主的大愛；
4. 在每一個家庭中，愛心日日增多；
1 In the cir - cle of each home, Lord, Your love is need - ed;
2 In the cir - cle of each home, Be our strong foun - da - tion;
3 In the cir - cle of each home, Lord, Your love is want - ed
4 In the cir - cle of each home, Is af - fec - tion grow - ing?
1. 若將主放在一邊，家庭必受損害。
2. 不論在任何環境，時刻需要恩主。
3. 多多感謝主恩典，常念主的關懷。
4. 務使家中每一個，為主結生命果。
1 For that fra - gile cir - cle bends When You are un - heed - ed.
2 Lord, we need Your wis - dom there In each sit - u - a - tion.
3 So that we'll not take Your grace And our life for grant - ed.
4 Are there fruits of char - ac - ter From a care - ful sow - ing?
1. 若常爭吵不和睦，親蜜關係必中斷，
2. 學習主耶穌榜樣，彼此相愛相扶助，
3. 若不教孩童信主，若我不能見證主，
4. 愛中彼此互稱讚，錯失彼此要饒恕，
1 For that hu - man cir - cle breaks With our pro - longed de - fi - ance,
2 If we have Your sur - er pace, We'll march as to a drum - mer.
3 Should our chil - dren fail to see The proofs of what we've taught them,
4 Do we praise the good we see, And par - don oth - ers' sin - ning?

1. 猶 如 嚴 冬 枯 樹 幹，孤 立 自 恃 抵 嚴 寒。
2. 生 命 必 如 夏 日 樹，能 結 滿 果 子 為 主。
3. 生 命 有 如 落 秋 葉，一 瞬 間 卽 将 全 無。
4. 生 命 如 春 天 來 臨，新 葉 緣 芽 長 滿 樹。
1 And we stand like win - ter trees Made bare by self re - li - ance.
2 Then our lives will fruit - ful be, Like trees we see in sum - mer.
3 Then we'll lack au - thor - i - ty, And fade like trees in au - tumn.
4 Are our branch - es blos - som - filled Like trees at spring's be - gin - ning?

386-1 The Parents' Creed

I believe that my children are a gift of God—the hope of a new tomorrow.

I believe that immeasurable possibilities lie slumbering in each son and daughter.

I believe that God has planned a perfect plan for their future, and that His love shall always surround them; and so

I believe that they shall grow up!—first creeping, then toddling, then standing, stretching skyward for a decade and a half—until they reach full stature—a man and a woman!

I believe that they can and will be molded and shaped between infancy and adulthood—as a tree is shaped by the gardener, and the clay vessel in the potter's hand, or the shoreline of the sea under the watery hand of the mighty waves; by home and church; by school and street, through sights and sounds and the touch of my hand on their hand and Christ's spirit on their heart! So,

I believe that they shall mature as only people can—through laughter and tears, through trial and error, by reward and punishment, through affection and discipline, until they stretch their wings and leave their nest to fly!

O God – I believe in my children. Help me so to live that they may always believe in me—and so in Thee.

—Robert H. Schuller

387

有智慧的獻知識

The Wise May Bring Their Learning

Then Peter said, "Silver and gold have I none, but such as I have, I give unto you.
— Acts 3:6
FOREST GREEN
Anonymous, in The Book of Praise for Children
Arranged by Ralph Vaughan Williams
1. 有智慧的獻知識，富足的獻財富，
2. 今願獻我愛主心，向主讚美歌唱，
3. 不論工作或玩樂，或在家中休息，
1 The wise may bring their learn - ing, The rich may bring their wealth,
2 We'll bring Him hearts that love Him; We'll bring Him thank-ful praise,
3 We'll come and show the Sav - ior The things we do each day;
1. 不論健康或才智，將至好獻於主；
2. 教我謙卑和聖潔，學習主的榜樣；
3. 我願盡我的本份，每日討主歡喜；
1 And some may bring their bril - liance, And some bring strength and health;
2 And young souls hum-bly striv - ing To walk in ho - ly ways:
3 We'll try our best to please Him At home, at school or play:
1. 主的孩童亦願意，將幼小心獻上，
2. 雖然我年紀幼小，愛主心都一樣，
3. 這是最好的禮物，今願恭敬獻上，
1 We too, would bring our trea - sures To of - fer to the King;
2 And these shall be our trea - sures We of - fer to the King,
3 And bet - ter are these trea - sures To of - fer to our King
1. 帶來所有的珍寶：獻給永生君王。
2. 今願將我的珍寶，獻給永生君王。
3. 孩童都有這珍寶：獻給永生君王。阿們。
1 We have no gifts de - serv - ing: What shall we chil - dren bring?
2 And these are gifts that ev - en The young-est child may bring.
3 Than rich - est gifts with - out them: Yet these a child may bring. A-men.

齊來感謝主

Now Thank We All Our God

Our God, we thank Thee and praise Thy glorious name.
I Chronicles 29:13

Martin Rinkart
Tr. by Catherine Winkworth

NUN DANKET
Johann Crüger
Harmonized by Felix Mendelssohn

1. 齊來向主感謝，以心以手以聲音，
2. 但願慈愛真神，一生常與我親近，
3. 感謝讚美真神，聖父聖子與聖靈，

1 Now thank we all our God With hearts and hands and voic - es,
2 *O may this boun-teous God Through all our life be near us,*
3 All praise and thanks to God The Fa - ther now be giv - en,

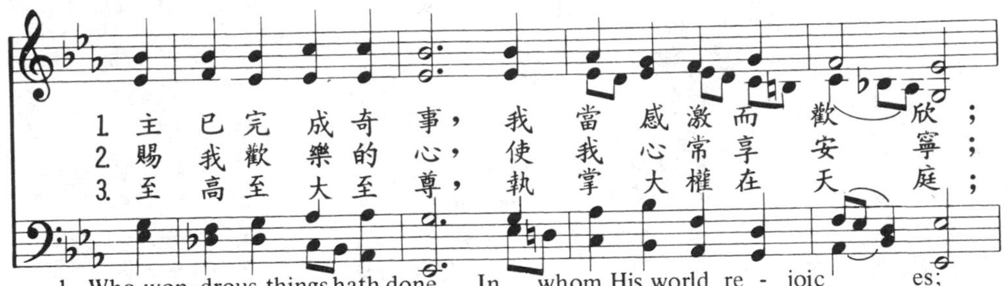
1. 主已完成奇事，我當感激而歡欣；
2. 賜我歡樂的心，使我心常享安寧；
3. 至高至大至尊，執掌大權在天庭；

1 Who won-drous things hath done, In whom His world re - joic es;
2 *With ev - er joy-ful hearts And bless - ed peace to cheer us;*
3 The Son, and Him who reigns With them in high - est heav - en,

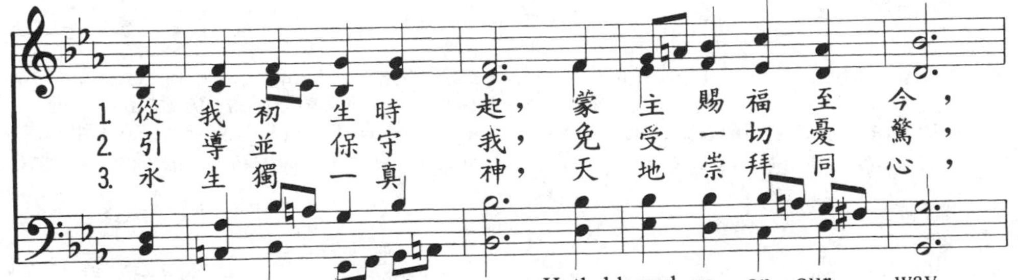
1. 從我初生時起，蒙主賜福至今，
2. 引導並保守我，免受一切憂驚，
3. 永生獨一真神，天地崇拜同心，

1 Who, from our moth-ers' arms, Hath blessed us on our way
2 *And keep us in His grace, And guide us when per - plexed,*
3 The one e - ter - nal God, Whom earth and heaven a - dore;

1. 主豐富的慈愛，賜我無窮無盡。
2. 無論今生來世，使我常蒙主恩。
3. 昔在今在永在，到永遠無窮盡。阿門。

1 With count-less gifts of love, And still is ours to - day.
2 *And free us from all ills In this world and the next.*
3 For thus it was, is now, And shall be ev - er more. A-men.

求主擘開生命之餅

Break Thou the Bread of Life

Based on Matthew 14:19
Mary A. Lathbury, stanzas 1,2
Alexander Groves, stanzas 3, 4

For the bread of God is He which cometh down from Heaven, and giveth life unto the world. — John 6:33

BREAD OF LIFE
William F. Sherwin

1. 求主為我擘開生命之餅，正如當
2. 求主祝福真理，生命的餅，如昔祝
3. 哦主是生命餅，擘開賜我，使我將
4. 求主賜我聖靈，在我心中，照我心
1 Break Thou the bread of life, Dear Lord, to me, As Thou didst
2 Bless Thou the truth, dear Lord, To me, to me, As Thou didst
3 Thou art the bread of life, O Lord, to me; Thy ho - ly
4 O send Thy Spir - it, Lord, Now un - to me, That He may

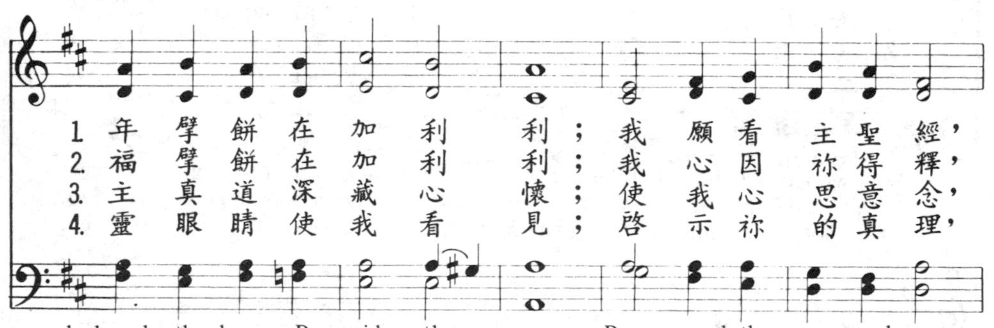
1. 年擘餅在加利利；我願看主聖經，
2. 福擘餅在加利利；我心因祢得釋，
3. 主真道深藏心懷；使我心思意念，
4. 靈眼睛使我看見；啓示祢的真理，
1 break the loaves Be - side the sea; Be - yond the sa - cred page
2 bless the bread By Gal - i - lee; Then shall all bond-age cease,
3 Word the truth That sav - eth me; Give me to eat and live
4 touch my eyes And make me see; Show me the truth con-cealed

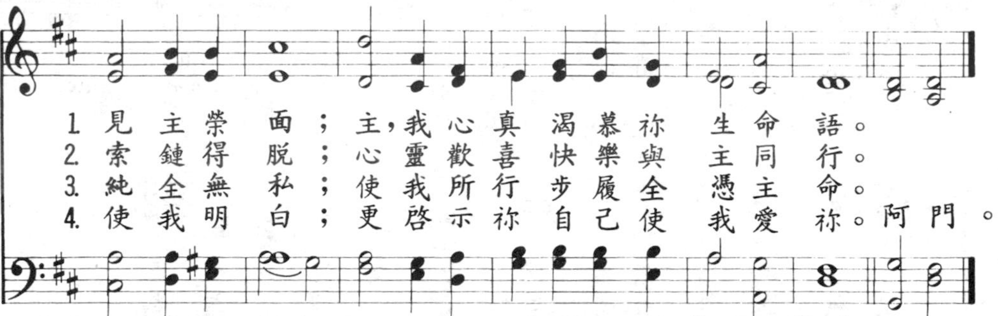
1. 見主榮面；主，我心真渴慕祢生命語。
2. 索鏈得脫；心靈歡喜快樂與主同行。
3. 純全無私；使我所行步履全憑主命。
4. 使我明白；更啓示祢自己使我愛祢。阿門。
1 I seek Thee, Lord; My spir - it pants for Thee, O liv - ing Word.
2 All fet - ters fall; And I shall find my peace, My all in all.
3 With Thee a - bove; Teach me to love Thy truth, For Thou art love.
4 With - in Thy word, For in Thy book re-vealed I see Thee, Lord. A-men.

同來擘餅

Let Us Break Bread Together

He took bread and blessed it, and brake, and gave to them.
— Luke 24:30

American Folk Hymn

LET US BREAK BREAD
American Folk Melody

1. 讓我們同來擘餅紀念主；
2. 讓我們同飲主杯紀念主；
3. 讓我們齊聲讚美紀念主；
1 Let us break bread to - geth-er on our knees;
2 *Let us drink wine to - geth-er on our knees;*
3 Let us praise God to - geth-er on our knees;
1. 讓我們同來擘餅紀念主；
2. 讓我們同飲主杯紀念主；
3. 讓我們齊聲讚美紀念主；
1 Let us break bread to - geth-er on our knees;
2 *Let us drink wine to - geth-er on our knees;*
3 Let us praise God to - geth-er on our knees;
當我們同屈膝，面向朝陽敬拜我主，
When I fall on my knees, With my face to the ris - ing sun,
哦，主，我求祢憐憫。
O Lord, have mer-cy on me.

391

主，我們在此面對面

Here, O My Lord,
I See Thee Face to Face

Horatius Bonar

Thy Face, Lord, will I seek. —Psalm 27:8

PENITENTIA
Edward Dearle

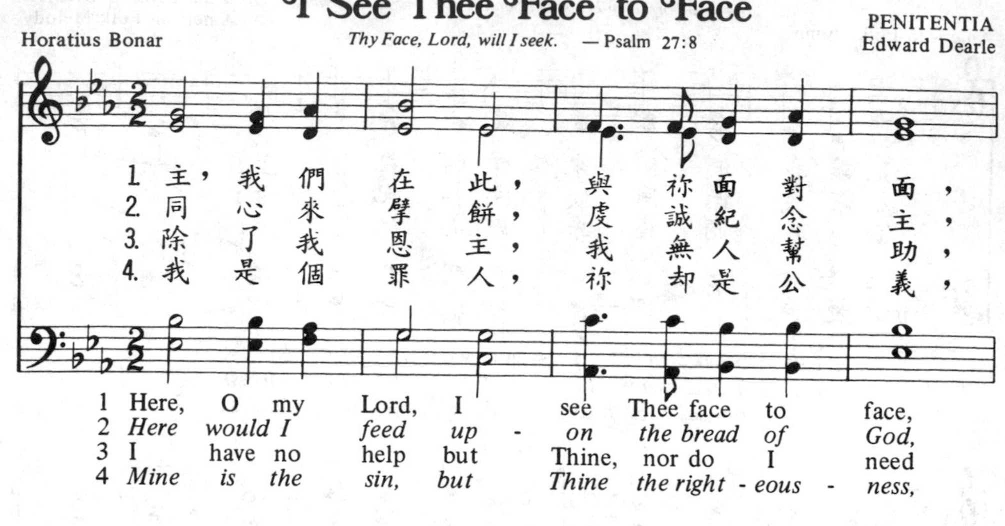
1. 主，我 們 在 此，與 祢 面 對 面，
2. 同 心 來 擘 餅，虔 誠 紀 念 主，
3. 除 了 我 恩 主，我 無 人 幫 助，
4. 我 是 個 罪 人，祢 却 是 公 義，
1 Here, O my Lord, I see Thee face to face,
2 Here would I feed up - on the bread of God,
3 I have no help but Thine, nor do I need
4 Mine is the sin, but Thine the right - eous - ness,

1. 以 信 心 仰 望，求 恩 主 顯 現；
2. 共 飲 主 福 杯，立 約 愛 我 主；
3. 唯 有 主 膀 臂，將 我 常 攙 扶；
4. 我 雖 然 污 穢，祢 用 寶 血 洗；
1 Here would I touch and han - dle things un - seen;
2 Here drink with Thee the roy - al wine of heaven;
3 An - oth - er arm save Thine to lean up - on;
4 Mine is the guilt, but Thine the cleans - ing blood;

1. 願 我 手 緊 握 永 恒 的 恩 典，
2. 今 撇 下 世 上 一 切 的 重 擔，
3. 有 祢 的 慈 愛，我 心 滿 意 足，
4. 主 是 我 義 袍，是 我 的 蔭 庇，
1 Here grasp with firm - er hand e - ter - nal grace,
2 Here would I lay a - side each earth - ly load,
3 It is e - nough, my Lord, e - nough in - deed—
4 Here is my robe, my ref - uge, and my peace—

1. 将一切困苦放在祢脚前。
2. 願再次嚐受主赦罪平安。
3. 主是我力量，我永不孤獨。
4. 靠主的寶血，使我能稱義。阿門。
1 And all my wea-ri-ness up-on Thee lean.
2 Here taste a-fresh the calm of sin for-giv'n.
3 My strength is in Thy might, Thy might a-lone.
4 Thy blood, Thy right-eous-ness, O Lord, my God. A-men.

392

歡欣向主稱頌

A Hymn of Joy We Sing

. . . I went with them to the house of God with . . . joy and praise. — Psalm 42:4

SCHUMANN

Based on Matthew 26:30
Aaron R. Wolfe

Mason and Webb's *Cantica Laudis*

1. 圍坐主的桌前，歡欣向主稱頌；
2. 主在我們中間，今得見祢容顏；
3. 我們同領聖餐，應當彼此相愛；

1 A hymn of joy we sing A-round Thy ta-ble, Lord;
2 *Here have we seen Thy face And felt Thy pres-ence near;*
3 In self-for-get-ting love Be our com-mun-ion shown,

1. 感恩之心向主呈獻，愛主自始至終。
2. 藉主話語生命彰顯，使我得祢恩典。
3. 直到那日在主面前，與主永遠同在。阿門。

1 A-gain our grate-ful trib-ute bring, Our sol-emn vows re-cord.
2 *So may the sa-vor of Thy grace In word and life ap-pear.*
3 Un-til we join the Church a-bove And know as we are known. A-men.

393

我的子民，若向我禱告

If My People Will Pray

If My people . . . pray and seek My face . . . I will forgive . . . — II Chronicles 7:14

CHRONICLES
Jimmy Owens

Based on II Chronicles 7:14

我的子民，稱為我名下的，若向我禱告，向我存自卑的心；
If My people which are called by My name, Shall humble themselves, shall humble themselves and pray;

我的子民，稱為我名下的，若尋求我，轉離他們的惡行；
If My people who are called by My name, Shall seek my face and turn from their wicked ways;

我必從天上垂聽，我必從天上垂聽，
Then will I hear from heaven, Then will I hear from heaven,

我必赦免他們的罪，醫治那地。
Then will I hear and will for - give, for - give their sin.
我的子民，稱為我名下的，若
If my peo - ple which are called by My name, Shall
向我禱告，向我存自卑的心；
hum - ble them-selves, shall hum - ble them-selves and pray;
我必赦免他們，我必赦免他們，
I will for - give their sin, I will for - give their sin,
赦免他們的罪，醫治那地。
I will for - give their sin, And heal their land.

394

生命靈氣

O Breath of Life

. . . He breathed on them and saith unto them: Receive Ye the Holy Ghost. — John 20:22

Bessie Porter Head

BLOMQVIST
Joel Blomqvist

1. 生 命 靈 氣， 吹 透 我 身 心，
2. 真 神 之 靈， 如 風 吹 散 我，
3. 愛 的 靈 氣， 吹 入 我 的 心，
4. 基 督 的 心， 曾 為 我 破 碎，
5. 求 主 復 興， 賜 我 火 熱 心，
1 O Breath of Life, come sweep-ing through us,
2 *O Wind of God, come bend us, break us,*
3 O Breath of Love, come breathe with-in us,
4 *O Heart of Christ, once bro-ken for us,*
5 Re-vive us, Lord! Is zeal a-bat-ing
1. 藉 主 大 能 復 興 敎 會；
2. 使 我 粉 碎 謙 卑 降 服；
3. 為 我 重 造 正 直 心 靈；
4. 使 我 得 着 能 力 安 息；
5. 莊 稼 已 熟 等 待 收 成；
1 Re-vive Your Church with life and power;
2 *'Til hum-bly we con-fess our need;*
3 Re-new-ing thought and will and heart;
4 *In You we find our strength and rest;*
5 While har-vest fields are vast and white?
1. 生 命 靈 氣， 使 我 們 更 新，
2. 在 祢 愛 中， 重 新 建 造 我，
3. 基 督 的 愛， 使 我 們 奮 興，
4. 憂 傷 痛 悔， 今 已 得 安 慰，
5. 求 主 復 興， 裝 備 衆 敎 會！
1 O Breath of Life, come, cleanse, re-new us,
2 *Then in Your ten-der-ness re-make us,*
3 Come, love of Christ, a-fresh to win us,
4 *Our bro-ken con-trite hearts now sol-ace,*
5 Re-vive us, Lord— the world is wait-ing!

1. 使 教 會 與 時 代 相 配。
2. 復 興 我 靈 願 聽 主 命。
3. 願 衆 教 會 都 得 復 興。
4. 願 衆 教 會 蒙 主 恩 惠。
5. 為 主 發 光 拯 救 世 人。 阿 門。
1 And fit Your Church to meet this hour.
2 Re - vive, re - store— for this we plead.
3 Re - vive Your Church in ev - ery part.
4 And let Your wait - ing Church be blest.
5 E - quip Your Church to spread the light. A - men.

Answered Prayer

I asked God for strength,
that I might achieve,
I was made weak,
that I might learn humbly to obey . . .

I asked for health,
that I might do greater things,
I was given infirmity,
that I might do better things . . .

I asked for riches,
that I might be happy,
I was given poverty,
that I might be wise . . .

I asked for power,
that I might have the praise of men,
I was given weakness,
that I might feel the need of God . . .

I asked for all things,
that I might enjoy life,
I was given life,
that I might enjoy all things . . .

I got nothing that I asked for—
but everything I had hoped for;
Almost despite myself,
my unspoken prayers were answered.
I am among all men most richly blessed.

—Unknown Confederate Soldier

395

恩雨大降
There Shall Be Showers of Blessing

Who hath blessed us with all spiritual blessings. — Ezekiel 34:26

Daniel W. Whittle

SHOWERS OF BLESSING
James McGranahan

1. 主必賜恩如降大雨：聖靈帶來大復興；
2. 主必賜恩如降大雨：聖靈已經大降臨；
3. 主必賜恩如降大雨：願主成就祢應許；
4. 主必賜恩如降大雨：求聖靈今日降臨；
1 There shall be show-ers of bless-ing: This is the prom-ise of love;
2 There shall be show-ers of bless-ing— Pre-cious re-viv-ing a-gain;
3 There shall be show-ers of bless-ing: Send them up-on us, O Lord;
4 There shall be show-ers of bless-ing: O, that to-day they might fall,

1. 是救主慈愛的應許，滋潤你枯乾心靈。
2. 高山低谷都得恩雨，教會再得大復興。
3. 心地乾渴心靈疲倦，切求聖靈來復興。
4. 今願悔改向主呼籲，求主接納我身心！
1 There shall be sea-sons re-fresh-ing, Sent from the Sav-ior a-bove.
2 O-ver the hills and the val-leys, Sound of a-bun-dance of rain.
3 Grant to us now a re-fresh-ing, Come, and now hon-or Thy Word.
4 Now as to God we're con-fess-ing, Now, as on Je-sus we call!

恩雨降恩雨，求主賜下大恩雨：
Show-ers of bless-ing, Show-ers of bless-ing we need:

我們雖已略蒙主恩，還渴望大賜恩雨。
Mer-cy-drops 'round us are fall - ing, But for the show-ers we plead.

396

主，我願更親近祢

Just a Closer Walk with Thee

For we also are weak in Him, but we shall live with Him by the power of God.
— II Corinthians 13:4

Unknown

CLOSER WALK
Traditional Folk Song

1. 我本軟弱主剛強，求主保守離罪網；
2. 經勞苦罪網世界，若我跌倒誰關懷？
3. 當我脆弱的生命，不久卽消逝離去；

1 I am weak but Thou art strong; Je - sus, keep me from all wrong;
2 *Through this world of toil and snares, If I fal - ter, Lord, who cares?*
3 When my fee-ble life is o'er, Time for me will be no more;

副歌 主，我願更親近祢，與主相親樂無比，
Refrain: Just a clos - er walk with Thee, Grant it, Je - sus, is my plea,

D.C. for Refrain

1. 心靈滿足無憂傷，當我走，求領我近祢旁。
2. 若有重擔誰分負？親愛主，惟有祢，我救主。
3. 恩主求祢來引領，到天家，永遠與主同居。

1 I'll be sat - is-fied as long As I walk, let me walk close to Thee.
2 *Who with me my bur-den shares? None but Thee, dear Lord, none but Thee.*
3 Guide me gent - ly, safe - ly o'er To Thy king-dom shore, to Thy shore.

每日同行更親密，親愛主，求祢，懇求祢。
Refrain: Dai-ly walk-ing close to Thee, Let it be, dear Lord, let it be.

397 在花園裡

In the Garden

And they heard the voice of the Lord walking in the garden. . .

— Genesis 3:8

C. Austin Miles

GARDEN
C. Austin Miles

1. 獨步徘徊在花園裡，玫瑰花尚有晶瑩
2. 我主慈聲何等甜蜜，小雀鳥停歌屏息
3. 天色將暗夜幕漸垂，我甚願與主留在
1 I come to the gar - den a - lone, While the dew is still on the
2 He speaks, and the sound of His voice Is so sweet the birds hush their
3 I'd stay in the gar - den with Him Though the night a-round me be

1. 朝露，忽有溫柔聲，傳入我耳中，乃
2. 傾聽，主使我聽見，天上美妙音，叫
3. 園中，但主命我去，懇切呼召我，要
1 ros - es; And the voice I hear, fall - ing on my ear, The
2 sing - ing, And the mel - o - dy that He gave to me With -
3 fall - ing, But He bids me go; through the voice of woe, His

1. 是神子主耶穌。
2. 我心快樂甦醒。
3. 我心向祂順從。
祂與我同行又與
And He walks with me, and He
1 Son of God dis - clos - es.
2 in my heart is ring - ing.
3 voice to me is call - ing.

我 共話，對我 說 我單屬於 祂； 與主
talks with me, And He tells me I am His own; And the
在 園 中心靈 真 快樂，前 無人曾經歷 過。
joy we share as we tar - ry there, None oth-er has ev - er known.

感謝

能為小事而感激的人才是真會享受的人。
因為我們時刻都在接受恩惠，
所以我們應習慣性地感謝上帝。
為你所有的感謝上帝；
為你所需的依賴上帝。

He who enjoys much is thankful for little.
Since we receive mercies constantly, gratitude to God should be habitual.
Bless God for what you have and trust Him for what you need.

主我相屬
I Am His and He Is Mine

. . . Yea, I have loved you with an everlasting love;
with loving kindness have I drawn thee.
— Jeremiah 31:3

George Robinson

EVERLASTING LOVE
James Mountain

1. 從亙古主已愛我，蒙恩後我才領悟，
2. 仰視天空色清藍，青翠綠草舖大地，
3. 前有罪使我心驚，今在主裡享安息，
4. 我屬主，永遠屬主，誰能使我離開主？
1 Loved with ev - er - last - ing love, Led by grace that love to know—
2 *Heaven a - bove is soft - er blue, Earth a - round is sweet - er green;*
3 Things that once were wild a - larms Can - not now dis - turb my rest;
4 *His for - ev - er, on - ly His— Who the Lord and me shall part?*

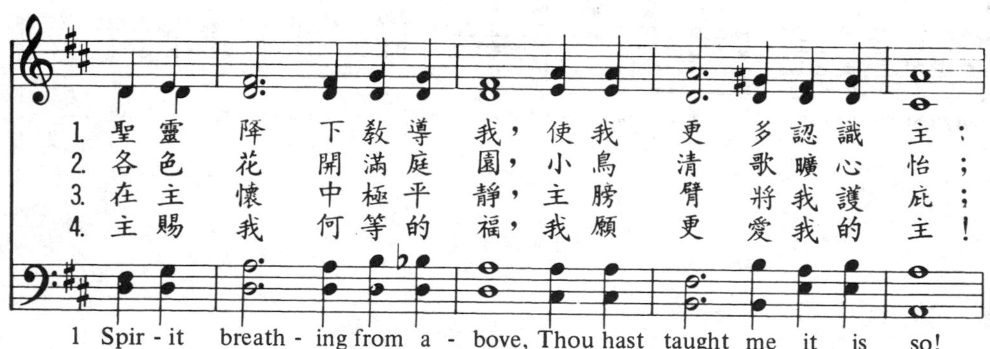

1. 聖靈降下教導我，使我更多認識主；
2. 各色花開滿庭園，小鳥清歌曠心怡；
3. 在主懷中極平靜，主膀臂將我護庇；
4. 主賜我何等的福，我願更愛我的主！
1 Spir - it breath - ing from a - bove, Thou hast taught me it is so!
2 *Some-thing lives in ev - ery hue Christ-less eyes have nev - er seen!*
3 Closed in ev - er - last - ing arms, Pil - lowed on the lov - ing breast!
4 *Ah, with what a rest of bliss Christ can fill the lov - ing heart!*

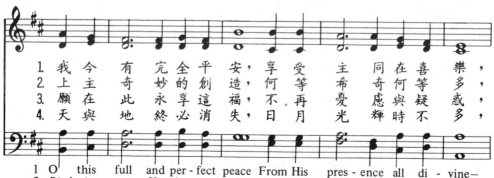

1. 我今有完全平安，享受主同在喜樂，
2. 上主奇妙的創造，何等希奇何等多，
3. 願在此永享這福，不再憂慮與疑惑，
4. 天與地終必消失，日月光輝時不多，

1 O this full and per - fect peace From His pres - ence all di - vine—
2 *Birds in song His glo - ries show, Flow'rs with deep - er beau - ties shine,*
3 O to lie for - ev - er here, Doubt and care and self re - sign,
4 *Heav'n and earth may fade and flee, First-born light in gloom de - cline,*

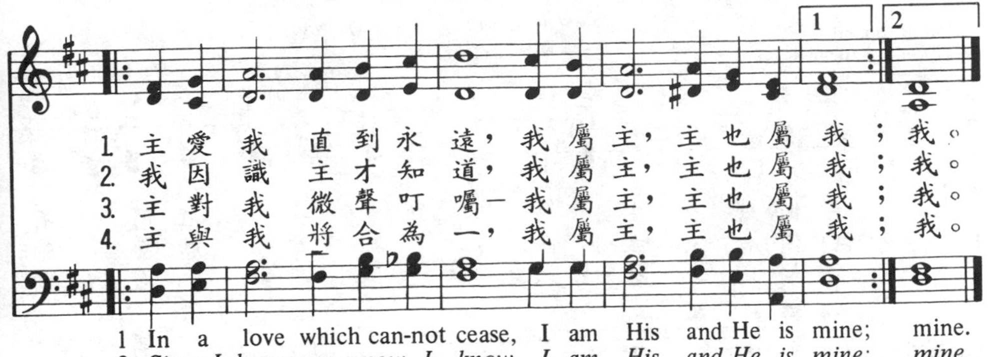
1 2
1. 主愛我 直到永遠，我屬主，主也屬我；我。
2. 我因識主才知道，我屬主，主也屬我；我。
3. 主對我微聲叮囑—我屬主，主也屬我；我。
4. 主與我將合為一，我屬主，主也屬我；我。
1 In a love which can-not cease, I am His and He is mine; mine.
2 Since I know, as now I know, I am His and He is mine; mine.
3 While He whis-pers in my ear— I am His and He is mine; mine.
4 But while God and I shall be, I am His and He is mine; mine.

神在你心裡作工

God Is at Work Within You

399

For it is God who worketh in you . . . — Philippians 2:13

TOPEKA
Fred Bock

Philippians 2:13

Unison
神在你心裡作工，深願你能向祂順從，尊祂
God is at work with-in you, help-ing you want to o-bey Him, And then
旨意行，討祂喜悅，尊祂旨意行，討祂的喜悅。
help-ing you do what He wants, help-ing you do what He wants you to do.

400

任何地有主同行

Anywhere with Jesus

Jessie B. Pounds
Adapted by Helen C. Dixon
. . . He led them. . . by a cloudy pillar; . . . and by a pillar of fire . . .
— Nehemiah 9:12
SECURITY
Daniel B. Towner
1. 任何地有主同行我願意去，任何方有主引領我不畏懼；若無救主同在喜樂會失去，任何地有主同在無需憂慮。
2. 任何地有主同在我不孤單，朋友或離棄我，主是我良伴；雖經曠野路救主親手扶攙，任何地有主同在充滿頌讚。
3. 不論海洋陸地只求主同在，向人傳講救恩領他們悔改；不論去或留願聽救主呼召，任何地惟靠救主親自引導。
1 Anywhere with Jesus I can safely go, Anywhere He leads me in this world below; Anywhere without Him dearest joys would fade, Anywhere with Jesus I am not afraid.
2 Anywhere with Jesus I am not alone, Other friends may fail me, He is still my own; Though His hand may lead me over dreary ways, Anywhere with Jesus is a house of praise.
3 Anywhere with Jesus over land and sea, Telling souls in darkness of salvation free; Ready as He summons me to go or stay, Anywhere with Jesus when He points the way.

任 何地！任 何方！我 心不 畏懼；
An - y-where! an - y-where! Fear I can - not know;
任 何地 有 主 同行，我 願 意 去。
An - y-where with Je - sus I can safe - ly go.

沒有登過高山的人，不會知道在征服了那山時的快慰，也難以了解在攀登時的艱辛；同樣，沒有站過屬靈高原的人，不會知道在那上面的甜美，也難以了解，走在那窄路上的人不多，但跟着主走，十字架路，並不坎坷。

401

永恒君王

Lead On, O King Eternal

Ernest W. Shurtleff

If the Lord be God, follow Him. . . . — I Kings 18:21

LANCASHIRE
Henry T. Smart

1. 永恒君王求前導，出征之時已到，
2. 永恒君王求前導，直到戰爭終了，
3. 永恒君王求前導，我願勇敢跟從，
1 Lead on, O King e - ter - nal, The day of march has come;
2 *Lead on, O King e - ter - nal, Till sin's fierce war shall cease,*
3 Lead on, O King e - ter - nal, We fol - low not with fears,
1. 戰地營幕為我家，惟祢是我倚靠；
2. 聖善之靈低聲唱，阿門平安臨到；
3. 喜樂湧出如晨光，因見我主聖容；
1 Hence-forth in fields of con - quest Thy tents shall be our home.
2 *And ho - li - ness shall whis - per The sweet a - men of peace.*
3 For glad - ness breaks like morn - ing Wher - e'er Thy face ap - pears.
1. 準備時日已久長，靠恩我成剛強，永
2. 陣前不聞戰鼓聲，攻擊不用鎗刀，仁
3. 十架高舉光照耀，指引艱險路程，冠
1 Through days of prep - a - ra - tion Thy grace has made us strong, And
2 *For not with swords' loud clash - ing, Nor roll of stir - ring drums—With*
3 Thy cross is lift - ed o'er us, We jour - ney in its light; The
1. 恒君王在前導，歡唱戰歌聲高。
2. 義兵器勝仇敵，天國榮光普照。
3. 冕留給得勝者，哦，主導我前行。阿門。
1 now, O King e - ter - nal, We lift our bat - tle song.
2 *deeds of love and mer - cy The heaven - ly king - dom comes.*
3 crown a - waits the con - quest: Lead on, O God of might. A - men.

耶穌是萬有之主
Jesus Is Lord of All

No man can serve two masters; . . . he will hold to one . . . .
— Matthew 6:24

Gloria Gaither
William J. Gaither

LORD OF ALL
William J. Gaither

1. 昨日和今日到永久，耶穌是萬有之主。
2. 主為我爭戰永得勝，耶穌是萬有之主。
3. 我一切理想主知道，耶穌是萬有之主。
1 All my to - mor - rows, all my past, Je - sus is Lord of all.
2 All of my con - flicts, all my thoughts, Je - sus is Lord of all.
3 All of my long - ings, all my dreams, Je - sus is Lord of all.
1. 我不再為自己的前途擔憂，耶穌是萬有之主。
2. 不再懷疑主愛專心靠主恩，耶穌是萬有之主。
3. 一切失敗軟弱主能力可靠，耶穌是萬有之主。
1 I've quit my strug - gles, con - tent - ment at last, Je - sus is Lord of all.
2 His love wins the bat - tles I could not have fought, Je - sus is Lord of all.
3 All of my fail - ures His pow - er re - deems, Je - sus is Lord of all.
萬王之王，萬主之主，耶穌是萬有之主，我生命所有全獻給主，耶穌是萬有之主。
King of kings, Lord of lords, Je - sus is Lord of all; All my pos - sess - ions and all my life, Je - sus is Lord of all.

403

慈愛牧者
Gentle Shepherd

I am the good Shepherd and know My sheep . . . .
— John 10:14
Gloria Gaither
William J. Gaither
GENTLE SHEPHERD
William J. Gaither
慈愛牧者，求來引導，因我們需要
Gen-tle Shep-herd, come and lead us, For we need You to
祢指引前路。慈愛牧者，求來餵養，
help us find our way. Gen-tle Shep-herd, come and feed us,
賜力量作隨時的幫助。除祢以外，
For we need Your strength from day to day. There's no oth-er
無人能助，面對明天惟祢能看顧；慈愛
we can turn to Who can help us face an-oth-er day; Gen-tle
牧者，求來引導，因我們需要祢指引前路。
Shep-herd, come and lead us, For we need You to help us find our way.

我是主羊

His Sheep Am I

We are His people, and the sheep of His pastures.
— Psalm 100:3

Orien Johnson　　　　Orien Johnson

Unison
主領　我到青草地，安歇在溪水旁；
In God's green pastures feeding, by His cool waters lie;
黃昏時主與我一路同行，牧場上凡是屬於主的
Soft, in the eve-ning walk my Lord and I, All the sheep of His pastures fare so
羊都強壯　我是主的羊，
wondrously fine, His sheep am I.
Fine
青草地，溪水旁，黃昏時，有主與
Wa-ters cool, pas-tures green, In the eve - ning walk my
死蔭幽谷，高山峻嶺，黃昏時有主與
In the val-ley, On the mountain, In the eve-ning walk my
D.C. al Fine
我同行。黑暗夜，路崎嶇，一步一步隨主行。
Lord and I. Dark the night, Rough the way, Step by step my Lord and I.
我同行。死蔭幽谷，高山峻嶺，一步一步隨主行。
Lord and I. In the val-ley, On the mountain. Step by step my Lord and I.

405

必有恩惠慈愛
Surely Goodness and Mercy
Based on Psalm 23
John W, Peterson
and Alfred B. Smith
We all like sheep have gone astray . . .
and the Lord hath laid on Him the iniquity of us all
- Isaiah 53:6
John W. Peterson
and Alfred B. Smith
1. 我 是客旅 我是流 浪者， 在 黑暗罪
2. 我 疲倦時 祂使我 甦醒， 每 日祂賜
3. 當 我走過 寂寞的 幽谷， 救 主必與
1. A pil - grim was I, and a - wan-d'ring— In the cold night of
2. He re - stor - eth my soul when I'm wea - ry, He giv - eth me
3. When I walk thru the dark lone-some val - ley, My Sav - ior will
1. 惡中徘 徊， 那時慈牧 耶穌找 到我—
2. 力量給 我； 祂領我到 安靜的 水邊，
3. 我行一 路， 祂大能手 保護引 領我，
1. sin I did roam When Je - sus the kind Shepherd found me—
2. strength day by day; He leads me be - side the still wa - ters,
3. walk with me there; And safe - ly His great hand will lead me
1. 我 今正向 父家歸 回。
2. 保 守我每 一步穩 妥。 一生 一世
3. 到 為我預 備的居 處。 Sure - ly good - ness
1. And now I am on my way home.
2. He guards me each step of the way.
3. To the man - sions He's gone to pre - pare.
我 必 有恩 惠 慈 愛隨 着 我，直到
and mer - cy shall fol - low me All the days, all the

永永遠遠；一生一世我必有恩
days of my life; Sure-ly good-ness and mer-cy shall
惠慈愛隨着我，直到永永遠遠。
fol-low me All the days, all the days of my life.
Last verse only
我要住在耶和華的殿中到永遠，敵人面
And I shall dwell in the house of the Lord for-ev-er, And I shall
前祢為我擺設筵席，一生一世
feast at the ta-ble spread for me; Sure-ly good-nesss
我必有恩惠慈愛隨着我，直到永永
and mer-cy shall fol-low me All the days, all the days of
遠遠，隨着我，直到永永遠遠。
my life, all the days of my life.
3
3
3

406

救世主凡事引導我
All the Way My Savior Leads Me

I have glorified Thee; . . . I have finished the work which thou gavest me.

— John 17:4

Fanny J. Crosby

ALL THE WAY
Robert Lowry

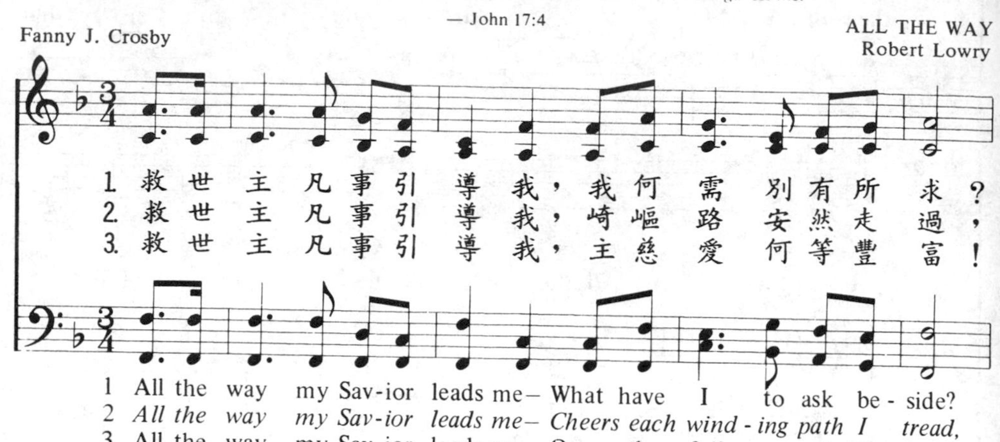

1. 救世主凡事引導我，我何需别有所求？
2. 救世主凡事引導我，崎嶇路安然走過，
3. 救世主凡事引導我，主慈愛何等豐富！
1 All the way my Sav-ior leads me– What have I to ask be - side?
2 All the way my Sav-ior leads me– Cheers each wind - ing path I tread,
3 All the way my Sav-ior leads me– O the full - ness of His love!

1. 主愛憐我何用多疑，我一生蒙主眷佑。
2. 遇試煉主賜恩相助，生命糧日日賜我。
3. 主應許在天父家裡，為我備安樂住處。
1 Can I doubt His ten - der mer - cy, Who through life has been my guide?
2 Gives me grace for ev - ery tri - al, Feeds me with the liv - ing bread.
3 Per - fect rest to me is prom - ised In my Fa - ther's house a - bove.

1. 今因信，享天上平安，蒙安慰何等喜樂！
2. 我步履雖困倦無力，我心靈雖渴難名，
3. 到那日我復活變化，如展翼飛光明所，
1 Heaven-ly peace, di - vin - est com - fort, Here by faith in Him to dwell!
2 Though my wea - ry steps may fal - ter And my soul a-thirst may be,
3 When my spir - it, clothed im - mor - tal, Wings its flight to realms of day,

1. 我深知，無論遇何事，主必為我安排妥；
2. 但我見靈磐現我前，快樂泉源湧不停；
3. 千萬年我仍要歌唱：耶穌凡事引導我；
1 For I know, what-e'er be-fall me, Je-sus do-eth all things well;
2 Gush-ing from the Rock be-fore me, Lo! a spring of joy I see;
3 This my song through end-less a-ges: Je-sus led me all the way;

1. 我深知，無論遇何事，主必為我安排妥。
2. 但我見靈磐現我前，快樂泉源湧不停。
3. 千萬年我仍要歌唱：耶穌凡事引導我。
1 For I know, what-e'er be-fall me, Je-sus do-eth all things well.
2 Gush-ing from the Rock be-fore me, Lo! a spring of joy I see.
3 This my song through end-less a-ges: Je-sus led me all the way.

406-1 The Tangle of the Mind

To seek the meaning of things and God's will does not spare us either from error or from doubt; nor does it solve all the mysteries of our destiny, all the insoluble problems which are set us by any event of Nature or in our lives; nevertheless, it does give a new meaning to our lives.

—Paul Tournier

407

衆聖徒之歌
For All the Saints

God is not ashamed to be called their God; for He hath prepared for them a city.
— Hebrews 11:16

William W. How | SINE NOMINE | Ralph Vaughan Williams

Unison
1. 昔日聖徒，如今完工休息，曾
2. 主是磐石，是聖徒的力量，親
3. 願主精兵，剛強忠誠勇敢，如
4. 何等甜美，信徒團契相交！我
5. 仰看天上，瞬間卽將破曉，極
6. 到那時日，從地極至海濱，衆
1 For all the saints who from their la - bors rest, Who
2 Thou wast their rock, their for - tress, and their might, Thou,
3 O may Thy sol - diers, faith - ful, true, and bold,
4 O blest com - mu - nion, fel - low - ship di - vine!
5 But lo! there breaks a yet more glo - rious day; The
6 From earth's wide bounds, from o - cean's far - thest coast, Through
1. 在人世間，到處宣傳聖績；哦，
2. 自來率領，為聖徒打勝仗；在
3. 昔日聖徒，為主竭力爭戰；與
4. 在世苦戰，先賢已得榮耀；天
5. 光明燦爛，萬千聖徒應召；隨
6. 信徒聚集，經珠門入天庭；高
1 Thee by faith be - fore the world con - fessed, Thy
2 Lord, their cap - tain in the well - fought fight;
3 Fight as the saints who no - bly fought of old, And
4 We fee - bly strug - gle, they in glo - ry shine; Yet
5 saints tri - um - phant rise in bright ar - ray; The
6 gates of pearl streams in the count - less host,

1. 耶 穌 聖 名， 當 讚 美 不 止 息：
2. 黑 暗 當 中， 作 信 徒 的 真 光：
3. 他 們 同 得， 榮 耀 的 金 冠 冕：
4. 上 和 人 間， 愛 裡 合 一 相 交：
5. 榮 耀 君 王， 走 上 凱 旋 之 道：
6. 聲 的 頌 讚， 聖 父 聖 子 聖 靈：
1 name, O Je - sus, be for - ev - er blest:
2 Thou, in the dark - ness drear, their one true light:
3 win with them the vic - tor's crown of gold:
4 all are one in Thee, for all are Thine:
5 King of glo - ry pass - es on His way:
6 Sing - ing to Fa - ther, Son, and Ho - ly Ghost:
哈 利 路 亞！ 哈 利 路 亞！ 阿門。
Al - le - lu - ia! Al - le - lu - ia! A-men.

Music from "The English Hymnal" by permission of Oxford University Press.

哦！我真愛耶穌

O, How I Love Jesus

He that loveth not knoweth not God; for He is love. — I John 4:8

O, HOW I LOVE JESUS
American Melody
Descant by Ralph H. Good Pasteur

Frederick Whitfield

1. 我最喜愛聽一美名，配得稱頌尊敬；
2. 此名使我能知主愛，捨命償我罪債；
3. 此名示我主愛深長，深知我心痛苦；
1 There is a name I love to hear, I love to sing its worth;
2 It tells me of a Sav-ior's love, Who died to set me free;
3 It tells of One whose lov-ing heart Can feel my deep-est woe,

Descant: To
1. 聲音優美悅耳動聽，全地最美之名。耶
2. 救主為我流血受害，罪人惟此倚賴。
3. 為我分擔憂愁悲傷，世間無人像主。
1 It sounds like mu-sic in my ear, The sweet-est name on earth.
2 It tells me of His pre-cious blood, The sin-ner's per-fect plea.
3 Who in each sor-row bears a part That none can bear be-low.

穌，何等奇妙，耶穌，何等奇妙！耶
me, it's won-der-ful, To me, it's won-der-ful! To
哦，我真愛耶穌，哦，我真愛耶穌，
O, how I love Je-sus, O, how I love Je-sus,

穌，何等奇妙，我深知道耶穌屬我！
me, it's won-der-ful To know that Je-sus is mine!
哦，我真愛耶穌—因為祂先愛我！
O, how I love Je - sus– Be-cause He first loved me!

哦，主，我愛祢 408-1

I Love You, Lord
(And I'll follow You)

The Son of God . . . loved me and gave Himself for me. Gal. 2:20

Jack Hayford Jack Hayford

Unison

哦，主，我愛祢，高舉祢名稱頌祢，因祢先愛

Oh, I love You, Lord, and I rise to praise Your name, For You first loved

我，祢的愛永不改變。爲愛我祢釘十架，我亦

me, and Your love has nev - er changed. Your love took a cross, and my

(♭)

願愛祢到底；我願愛祢，主，我願跟隨祢。

love will do the same; For I love You, Lord, and I'll fol - low You.

409

十架有空處為你
There's Room at the Cross

Ira F. Stanphill . . . *While we were yet sinners, Christ died for us.* — Romans 5:8

STANPHILL
Ira F. Stanphill

1. 救 主 釘 死 的 十 架 下， 有 一 蔭 庇 處
2. 千 萬 人 已 得 此 良 友， 離 棄 罪 惡 蒙
3. 救 主 雙 臂 有 力 強 壯， 祂 的 慈 愛 亦
1 The cross up-on which Je-sus died Is a shel-ter in
2 Though mil-lions have found Him a friend And have turned from the
3 The hand of my Sav-ior is strong, And the love of my
1. 我 能 躲 藏； 白 白 的 恩 典 足 夠
2. 恩 主 拯 救； 但 救 主 仍 等 待 祂 已
3. 無 限 無 量； 不 論 晴 或 雨 或 得
1 which we can hide; And its grace so free is suf-
2 sins they have sinned, The Sav-ior still waits to
3 Sav-ior is long; Through sun-shine or rain, through
1. 我 一 生 用，深 海 似 的 泉 源 永 遠 為 我 湧。
2. 將 門 大 開，伸 出 祂 雙 手 歡 迎 罪 人 進 來。
3. 着 或 失 去，加 略 山 的 寶 血 能 洗 淨 罪 污。
1 fi-cient for me, And deep is its foun-tain—as wide as the sea.
2 o-pen the gates And wel-come a sin-ner be-fore it's too late.
3 loss or in gain, The blood flows from Cal-vary to cleanse ev-ery stain.
十 架 有 空 處 為 你， 十 架 有 空 處 為 你； 千
There's room at the cross for you, There's room at the cross for you; Though

萬人前來，但 仍有空 處一有空 處 是為你預 備。
millions have come, There's still room for one—Yes, there's room at the cross for you.
410
愛主更深
More Love to Thee, O Christ
And this I pray, that your love may abound more and more . . . .
Philippians 1:9
Elizabeth P. Prentiss
MORE LOVE TO THEE
William H. Doane
1. 我 願 深 切 愛 主，比 前 更 深！我 今 誠
2. 從 前 貪 愛 世 俗，單 顧 己 身，今 日 所
3. 即 或 死 亡 將 臨，一 息 尚 存，我 仍 呻
1 More love to Thee, O Christ, More love to Thee! Hear Thou the
2 Once earth-ly joy I craved, Sought peace and rest; Now Thee a-
3 Then shall my ev-ery breath Sing out Your praise; This be the
1. 心 屈 膝，求 主 垂 聽；低 頭 祈 禱 深 誓：
2. 愛 惟 祢，如 愛 奇 珍；為 此 懇 求 天 父：
3. 吟 求 告，望 主 賜 恩；使 我 進 入 天 府：
1 prayer I make On bend-ed knee; This is my ear-nest plea:
2 lone I seek, Give what is best; This all my prayer shall be:
3 on-ly song My heart shall raise; This still my prayer shall be:
1. 從 此 更 愛 我 主，
2. 使 我 深 愛 我 主，愛 主 更 深，愛 主 更 深！阿門。
3. 永 遠 深 愛 我 主，
More love, O Christ, to Thee, More love to Thee, More love to Thee! A-men.

我寧願有耶穌

I'd Rather Have Jesus

. . . but as for me and my house, we will serve the Lord. — Joshua 24:15b

Rhea F. Miller

I'D RATHER HAVE JESUS
George Beverly Shea

1. 我寧願有耶穌勝於金錢，我寧屬耶
2. 我寧願有耶穌勝於稱揚，我寧忠於
3. 恩主比百合花美麗鮮艷，祂比蜂房
1 I'd rath-er have Je-sus than sil-ver or gold, I'd rath-er be
2 *I'd rath-er have Je-sus than men's ap - plause, I'd rath-er be*
3 He's fair-er than lil-ies of rar-est bloom, He's sweet-er than

1. 穌勝過財富無邊；我寧願有耶穌勝
2. 主滿足主的心腸；我寧願有耶穌勝
3. 下滴的蜜更甘甜；我帶飢渴心靈來
1 His than have rich-es un-told; I'd rath-er have Je-sus than
2 *faith-ful to His dear cause; I'd rath-er have Je-sus than*
3 hon-ey from out the comb; He's all that my hun-ger-ing

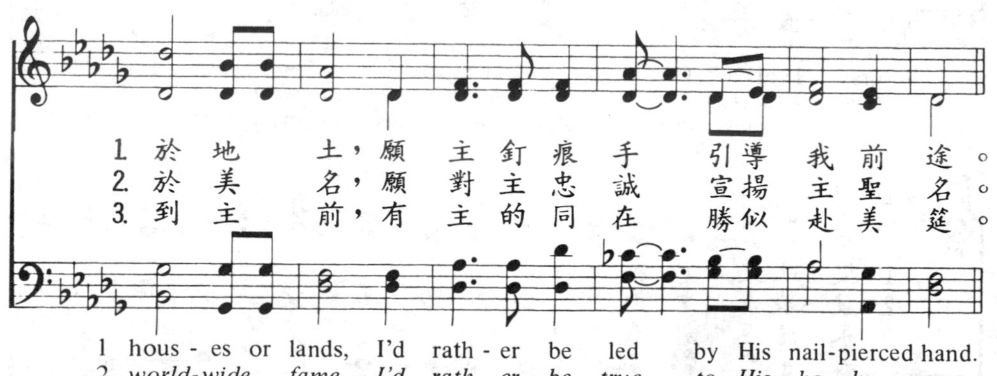
1. 於地土，願主釘痕手引導我前途。
2. 於美名，願對主忠誠宣揚主聖名。
3. 到主前，有主的同在勝似赴美筵。
1 hous-es or lands, I'd rath-er be led by His nail-pierced hand.
2 *world-wide fame, I'd rath-er be true to His ho-ly name.*
3 spir-it needs, I'd rath-er have Je-sus and let Him lead.

勝過做君王，雖統治萬方，却仍受罪惡捆綁；
Than to be the king of a vast do-main Or be held in sin's dread sway;

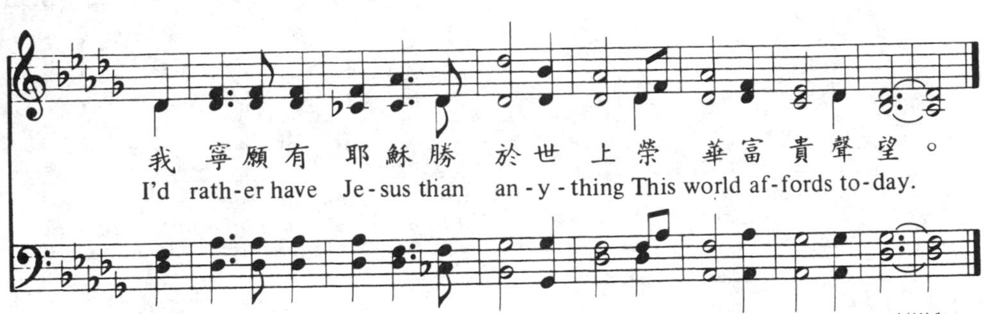
我寧願有耶穌勝於世上榮華富貴聲望。
I'd rath-er have Je-sus than an-y-thing This world af-fords to-day.

靈命的長進在乎肯接受神的造就。

神有時可能藉着驕傲的人，教導我們學習謙卑，

藉粗暴的人，教我們學習溫柔。

藉好佔便宜的人，教我們學習“情願吃虧”，

藉別人譏諷怨言，教我們學習忍耐，

藉着物質的缺乏，教我們學習信心。

藉收入的豐富，教我們顧念別人，

藉着別人得着榮譽地位，教我們學習向主忠誠的心志；

靈命是否長進全在我們能否在這些事上，

從神那裡學習到屬靈的功課。

412

當轉眼仰望耶穌
Turn Your Eyes upon Jesus

I am come that they might have life, and that they might have it more abundantly.
— John 10:10
Helen H. Lemmel
LEMMEL
Helen H. Lemmel
1. 請問你是否困倦煩惱？全無光明
2. 主已從死亡進入永生，我們當跟
3. 救主的應許永不變更，全心信靠
1 O soul, are you wea-ry and trou-bled? No light in the
2 Through death in-to life ev-er-last-ing He passed, and we
3 His word shall not fail you—He prom-ised; Be-lieve Him, and
1. 黑暗滿佈？祗一仰望主就得光明，生
2. 隨主走去；罪的權勢不能再轄制，我
3. 萬事安穩；快去傳揚祂全備救恩，使
1 dark-ness you see? There's light for a look at the Sav-ior, And
2 fol-low Him there; O-ver us sin no more hath do-min-ion— For
3 all will be well: Then go to a world that is dy-ing, His
1. 命更自由豐富！
2. 們已得勝有餘！
3. 凡信的人免沉淪！
當轉眼仰望耶穌，
1 life more a-bun-dant and free!
2 more than con-querors we are!
3 per-fect sal-va-tion to tell!
Turn your eyes up-on Je-sus,
定睛在祂奇妙慈容，在救主榮
Look full in His won-der-ful face. And the things of
耀恩典大光中，世上事必然顯為虛空。
earth will grow strange-ly dim In the light of His glo-ry and grace.

靠近主
Close to Thee

He that sayeth he abideth in Him ought himself also to walk even as He walked.
I John 2:6

Fanny J. Crosby

CLOSE TO THEE
Silas J. Vail

1. 主是我永遠的福份，勝過朋友與生命，
2. 我不求世界的歡樂，也不求世界美名，
3. 帶領我經黑暗幽谷，安然渡苦海危程；

1 Thou, my ev - er-last-ing por - tion, More than friend or life to me,
2 *Not for ease or world-ly pleas - ure Nor for fame my prayer shall be;*
3 Lead me through the vale of shad - ows, Bear me o'er life's fit - ful sea;

1. 在人生孤單旅程中，懇求主與我同行。
2. 我願受任何的勞苦，祗求主與我同行。
3. 當天上永生門大開，願與主同進天庭。

1 All a - long my pil-grim jour - ney, Sav - ior, let me walk with Thee.
2 *Glad-ly will I toil and suf - fer, On - ly let me walk with Thee.*
3 Then the gate of life e - ter - nal May I en - ter, Lord, with Thee.

1. 靠近主，靠近主，靠近主，靠近主；在人
2. 靠近主，靠近主，靠近主，靠近主；我願
3. 靠近主，靠近主，靠近主，靠近主；當天

1 Close to Thee, close to Thee, Close to Thee, close to Thee; All a -
2 *Close to Thee, close to Thee, Close to Thee, close to Thee; Glad - ly*
3 Close to Thee, close to Thee, Close to Thee, close to Thee; Then the

1. 生孤單旅程中，懇求主與我同行。
2. 受任何的勞苦，祗求主與我同行。
3. 上永生門大開，願與主同進天庭。阿門。

1 long my pil - grim jour - ney, Sav - ior, let me walk with Thee.
2 *will I toil and suf - fer, On - ly let me walk with Thee.*
3 gate of life e - ter - nal May I en - ter, Lord, with Thee. A - men.

414

我要唱耶和華的大慈愛

I Will Sing Of The Mercies Of The Lord

Psalm 89:1

. . . They that were scattered abroad went everywhere preaching the word. — Acts 8:4

J. H. Fillmore
Arr. by John W. Peterson

我要唱耶和華的大慈愛到永遠，我要
I will sing of the mer-cies of the Lord for-ev-er, I will
唱，(我要唱，)我要唱，(我要唱，)我要唱耶和華的
sing, (I will sing,) I will sing, (I will sing,) I will sing of the mer-cies
Fine
大慈愛到永遠，我要唱耶和華的大慈愛。
of the Lord for-ev-er, I will sing of the mer-cies of the Lord.
用我口，(我口，)叫人知道，(知道，)祢
With my mouth (my mouth) will I make known (make known) Thy
的信實，祢的信實，用我口，(我口)叫人知
faith-ful-ness, Thy faith-ful-ness, With my mouth (my mouth) will I make

D.C. al Fine
道，(知 道) 祢 的信 實 直 到 永遠 萬 代。
known (make known) thy faith-ful-ness to all gen - er - a - tions.

415

我要來讚美我主
I Just Came To Praise The Lord

Great is the Lord and greatly to be praised.
— Psalm 145:3

Wayne Romero

Wayne Romero

1. 我 要 來 讚 美 我 主，我 要 來 讚 美 我 主；
2. 我 要 來 感 謝 我 主，我 要 來 感 謝 我 主；
3. 我 要 全 心 愛 我 主，我 要 全 心 愛 我 主；
1. I just came to praise the Lord, I just came to praise the Lord;
2. I just came to thank the Lord, I just came to thank the Lord;
3. I just came to love the Lord, I just came to love the Lord;

1. 我 要 來 讚 美 我 主 聖 名，我 要 來 讚 美 我 主。
2. 我 要 來 讚 美 我 主 聖 名，我 要 來 感 謝 我 主。
3. 我 要 來 讚 美 我 主 聖 名，我 要 全 心 愛 我 主。
1. I just came to praise His ho - ly name, I just came to praise the Lord.
2. I just came to praise His ho - ly name, I just came to thank the Lord.
3. I just came to praise His ho - ly name, I just came to love the Lord.

耶穌是我親愛牧人

Savior, Like a Shepherd Lead Us

. . That great shepherd of the sheep . . . make you perfect in every good work.
Hebrews 13:20-21
Attributed to Dorothy A. Thrupp
BRADBURY
William B. Bradbury
1. 耶穌是我親愛牧人，親手引領我前程，
2. 耶穌是我最好朋友，導我天路慰我愁，
3. 讓我趁早討祢歡喜，樂意遵照祢旨意，
1 Sav - ior, like a Shep-herd lead us, Much we need Thy ten-der care;
2 We are Thine; do Thou be - friend us; Be the guard-ian of our way;
3 Ear - ly let us seek Thy fa - vor; Ear - ly let us do Thy will;
1. 領我到祢歡樂草場，領我靠近祢身旁。
2. 我縱迷路祂來尋我，引導羊群免走錯。
3. 願主恩愛滿我心中，我願獻身歸主用。
1 In Thy pleas-ant pas-tures feed us; For our use Thy folds pre-pare.
2 Keep Thy flock; from sin de - fend us; Seek us when we go a - stray.
3 Bless-ed Lord and on - ly Sav - ior, With Thy love our bos-oms fill.
1. 慈愛救主，慈愛救主，領我靠近祢身旁；
2. 慈愛救主，慈愛救主，願祢常聽我祈求；
3. 慈愛救主，慈愛救主，愛我們直到永久
1 Bless-ed Je - sus, Bless-ed Je - sus, Thou hast bought us, Thine we are;
2 Bless-ed Je - sus, Bless-ed Je - sus, Hear Thy chil - dren when they pray;
3 Bless-ed Je - sus, Bless-ed Je - sus, Thou hast loved us, love us still;
1. 慈愛救主，慈愛救主領我靠近祢身旁。
2. 慈愛救主，慈愛救主願祢常聽我祈求。
3. 慈愛救主，慈愛救主，愛我們直到永久。阿門。
1 Bless-ed Je - sus, Bless-ed Je - sus, Thou hast bought us, Thine we are.
2 Bless-ed Je - sus, Bless-ed Je - sus, Hear Thy chil-dren when they pray.
3 Bless-ed Je - sus, Bless-ed Je - sus, Thou hast loved us, love us still. A-men.

祂何等愛你，愛我
O How He Loves You and Me

As the Father hath loved Me, so I have loved you;
— John 15:9

HE LOVES YOU AND ME

Kurt Kaiser — Kurt Kaiser

1. 主 耶 穌 何 等 愛 你，
2. 耶 穌 曾 到 髑 髏 地，
1 O how He loves you and me.
2 *Je - sus to Cal - vary did go,*

1. 祂 也 何 等 的 愛 我；
2. 為 愛 世 人 捨 自 己；
1 O how He loves you and me;
2 *His love for man - kind to show:*

1. 祂 將 生 命 完 全 的 給 你。
2. 帶 給 罪 人 盼 望 與 生 命。
1 He gave His life, what more could He give:
2 *What He did there brought hope from de - spair:*

1. 祂 何 等 愛 你，祂 何 等 愛 我，
2. 祂 何 等 愛 你，祂 何 等 愛 我，
1 O how He loves you, O, how He loves me,
2 *O how He loves you, O, how He loves me,*

1. 祂 何 等 愛 你，愛 我。
2. 祂 何 等 愛 你，愛 我。
1 O how He loves you and me.
2 *O how He loves you and me.*

418

耶穌領我

He Leadeth Me, O Blessed Thought

He leadeth me in the paths of righteousness. — Psalm 23:3

Joseph H. Gilmore

HE LEADETH ME
William B. Bradbury

1. 耶 穌 領 我，我 真 喜 歡！蒙 主 引 導 心 中 平 安；
2. 我 願 緊 握 恩 主 聖 手，甘 心 樂 意 隨 主 行 走；
3. 到 時 行 完 一 世 路 程，內 外 仇 敵 靠 主 全 勝；

1 He lead - eth me, O blessed thought! O words with heav'nly comfort fraught!
2 Lord, *I would clasp Thy hand in mine, Nor ev - er mur-mur nor re-pine;*
3 And when my task on earth is done, When by Thy grace the vic-t'ry's won,

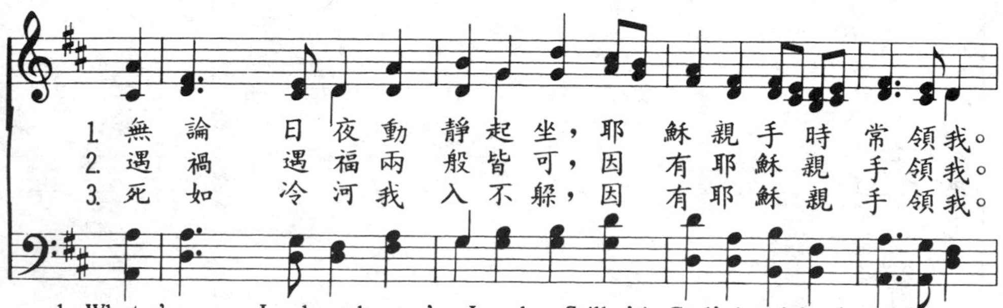
1. 無 論 日 夜 動 靜 起 坐，耶 穌 親 手 時 常 領 我。
2. 遇 禍 遇 福 兩 般 皆 可，因 有 耶 穌 親 手 領 我。
3. 死 如 冷 河 我 入 不 躲，因 有 耶 穌 親 手 領 我。
1 What-e'er I do, where-e'er I be, Still 'tis God's hand that lead-eth me.
2 Con-tent what-ev-er lot I see, Since 'tis my God that lead-eth me.
3 E'en death's cold wave I will not flee, Still God through Jor-dan lead-eth me.

耶 穌 領 我，耶 穌 領 我，耶 穌 天 天 親 手 領 我；
He lead-eth me, He lead - eth me, By His own hand He lead-eth me;
我 願 終 身 跟 主 脚 步，因 蒙 恩 主 親 手 領 我。
His faith-ful fol-lower I would be, For by His hand He lead-eth me.

主耶和華，求祢引領
Guide Me, O Thou Great Jehovah

William Williams
Tr. by Peter Williams

He will guide us even unto death. — Psalm 48:14

CWM RHONDDA
John Hughes

1. 主耶和華，求祢引領，走過今世曠野路；我本軟弱，主有全能，願主聖手常保護；天上嗎哪，天上嗎哪，求主時常賜給我，求主時常賜給我。
2. 求主開通永生泉源，使我路中不乾渴；求主做我雲柱火柱，引導我路不走錯；全能救主，全能救主，做我盾牌保護我，做我盾牌保護我。
3. 當我走到約旦河畔，除我憂懼賜平安；帶領我渡洶湧波瀾，使我歡然進迦南；讚美歌聲，讚美歌聲，永遠歸救主我神，永遠歸救主我神。阿們。
1 Guide me, O Thou great Jehovah, Pilgrim through this barren land; I am weak, but Thou art mighty— Hold me with Thy powerful hand: Bread of heaven, Bread of heaven, Feed me 'til I want no more, Feed me 'til I want no more.
2 Open now the crystal fountain, Whence the healing stream doth flow; Let the fire and cloudy pillar Lead me all my journey through: Strong Deliverer, strong Deliverer, Be Thou still my strength and shield, Be Thou still my strength and shield.
3 When I reach the river Jordan, Bid my anxious fears subside; Bear me through the swelling current, Land me safe on Canaan's side: Songs of praises, songs of praises I will ever give to Thee, I will ever give to Thee. A-men.

興起為耶穌

Stand Up, Stand Up for Jesus

Watch ye, stand fast in the faith. — I Corinthians 16:13

WEBB

George Duffield

George J. Webb

1. 興起，興起為耶穌，作十字架精兵！
2. 興起，興起為耶穌，號令必須服從，
3. 興起，興起為耶穌，一心靠主能力，
4. 興起，興起為耶穌，交戰時日無多，

1 Stand up, stand up for Je - sus, Ye sol - diers of the cross;
2 *Stand up, stand up for Je - sus, The trum - pet call o - bey;*
3 Stand up, stand up for Je - sus, Stand in His strength a - lone;
4 *Stand up, stand up for Je - sus, The strife will not be long;*

1. 各執王旗高高舉，切莫使之倒傾；
2. 今日是主榮耀日，勇敢前赴戰場；
3. 血氣之勇不足恃，自恃一定敗績；
4. 今日雖聞干戈聲，明日即奏凱歌；

1 Lift high His roy - al ban - ner, It must not suf - fer loss.
2 *Forth to the might - y con - flict, In this His glo - rious day.*
3 The arm of flesh will fail you, Ye dare not trust your own.
4 *This day the noise of bat - tle, The next the vic - tor's song.*

1. 主要領你戰諸敵，必定連連得勝，
2. 基督之兵隨主行，敵衆何必驚恐，
3. 速披福音之甲冑，也當儆醒禱祈，
4. 忠心受難得勝者，必得生命冠冕，

1 From vic - t'ry un - to vic - t'ry His ar - my shall He lead,
2 *Ye that are men now serve Him A - gainst un - num-bered foes;*
3 Put on the gos - pel ar - mor, Each piece put on with prayer;
4 *To him that o - ver - com - eth A crown of life shall be:*

1. 直到諸敵盡降服，惟主大奏凱功。
2. 戰場愈險膽愈壯，敵勇更當奮勇。
3. 雖遇危險莫退縮，我要盡忠到底。
4. 與主同死同復活，永遠同操王權。
1 'Til ev - ery foe is con - quered And Christ is Lord in - deed.
2 Let cour - age rise with dan - ger And strength to strength op - pose.
3 Where du - ty calls, or dan - ger Be nev - er want - ing there.
4 He with the King of glo - ry Shall reign e - ter - nal - ly.

421

豈能讓主獨背十字架？

Must Jesus Bear the Cross Alone

If any man come after Me let him . . .
take up his cross and follow . . . — Matthew 16:24

Thomas Shepherd

MAITLAND
George N. Allen

1. 豈能讓主獨背十架，世人竟得安祥？
2. 我願獻身背我十架，一生總不捨下，
3. 榮耀寶架榮耀冠冕！榮耀的復活日！

1 Must Je - sus bear the cross a - lone, And all the world go free?
2 *The con - se - crat - ed cross I'll bear, 'Til death shall set me free,*
3 O pre - cious cross! O glo - rious crown! O res - ur - rec - tion day!

1. 信徒都當背負十架，當以主為榜樣。
2. 忠心到底直到天家，主必親自接納。
3. 天使前來接我升天，在彼永享安息。阿們。

1 No; there's a cross for ev - ery one, And there's a cross for me.
2 *And then go home my crown to wear, For there's a crown for me.*
3 Ye an - gels, from the stars come down, And take my soul a - way. A - men.

基督精兵
Onward, Christian Soldiers

Thou therefore endure hardness as a good soldier . . . — II Timothy 2:3

Sabine Baring-Gould

ST. GERTRUDE
Arthur S. Sullivan

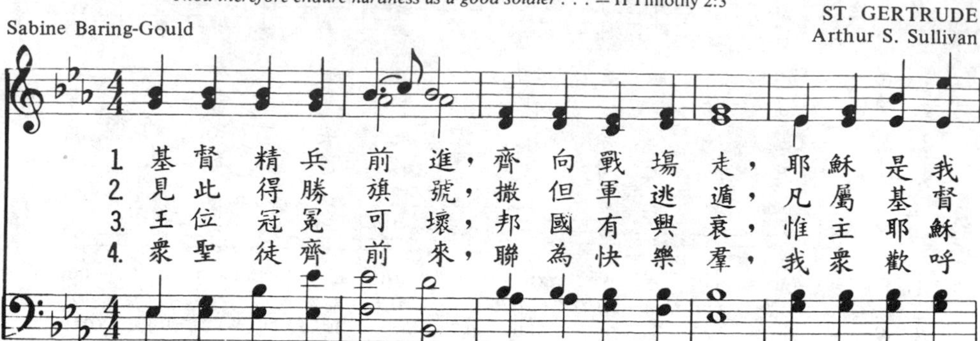
1. 基督精兵前進，齊向戰場走，耶穌是我
2. 見此得勝旗號，撒但軍逃遁，凡屬基督
3. 王位冠冕可壞，邦國有興衰，惟主耶穌
4. 衆聖徒齊前來，聯為快樂羣，我衆歡呼

1 On - ward, Chris-tian sol - diers, march-ing as to war. With the cross of
2 *Like a might - y ar - my moves the Church of God; Broth-ers, we are*
3 Crowns and thrones may per - ish, king - doms rise and wane, But the Church of
4 *On - ward, then, ye peo - ple, join our hap - py throng; Blend with ours your*

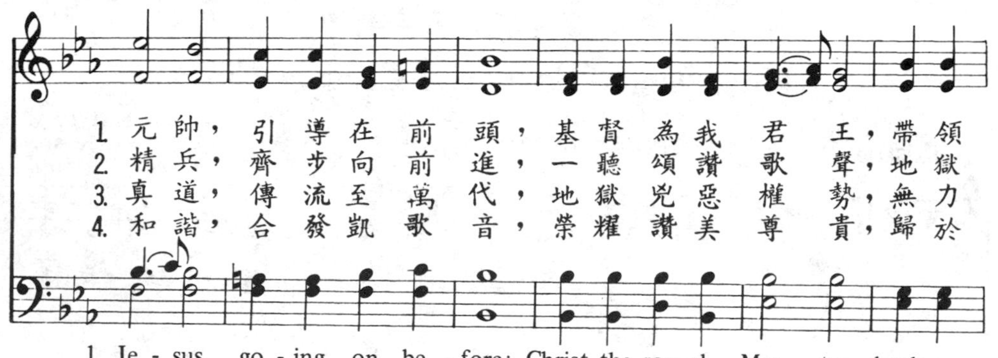
1. 元帥，引導在前頭，基督為我君王，帶領
2. 精兵，齊步向前進，一聽頌讚歌聲，地獄
3. 真道，傳流至萬代，地獄兇惡權勢，無力
4. 和諧，合發凱歌音，榮耀讚美尊貴，歸於

1 Je - sus go - ing on be - fore: Christ, the roy - al Mas - ter, leads a -
2 *tread-ing where the saints have trod, We are not di - vid - ed, all one*
3 Je - sus con - stant will re - main, Gates of hell can nev - er 'gainst that
4 *voic - es in the tri - umph song, Glo - ry, laud, and hon - or un - to*

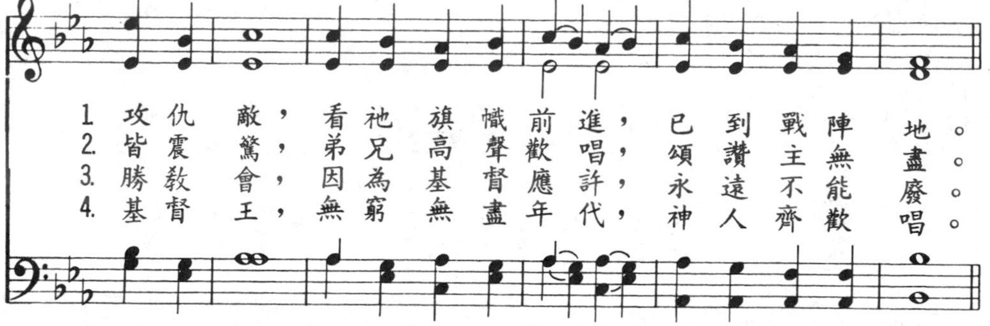
1. 攻仇敵，看祂旗幟前進，已到戰陣地。
2. 皆震驚，弟兄高聲歡唱，頌讚主無盡。
3. 勝教會，因為基督應許，永遠不能廢。
4. 基督王，無窮無盡年代，神人齊歡唱。

1 gainst the foe; For - ward in - to bat - tle, see His ban - ners go.
2 *bod - y we: One in hope and doc - trine, one in char - i - ty.*
3 Church pre - vail; We have Christ's own prom - ise, and that can - not fail.
4 *Christ the King: This through countless a - ges men and an - gels sing.*

基督精兵前進，齊向戰場走，
On-ward, Chris-tian sol - diers, march-ing as to war,
耶穌是我元帥，引導在前頭。
With the cross of Je - sus go - ing on be - fore.

422-1 *Prayer for Unity*

Our Father, we thank You for the privilege of being together at this time and in this place.

As Your people, we pray that Your love will unite us into a fellowship of discovery.

Cleanse us of everything that would sap our strength for togetherness.

Unravel the knots in our spirits.
Cleanse the error of our minds.
Free us from the bondage of our negative imaginations.
Break down the barriers that sometimes keep us apart and cause us to drift along without a dream.

As we go from here–
Explode in us new possibilities for service.
Kindle within us the fires of Your compassion so that we may not wait too long to learn to love.

May we be a people with loving purposes–
Reaching out . . .
Breaking walls . . .
Building bridges . . .
Let us be Your alleluia in a joyless, fragmented world.

In the name of our Lord, we pray.

Amen.

–Champ Traylor

耶穌，我要跟隨祢

Follow, I Will Follow Thee

He that loseth his life for My sake shall find it. — Matthew 10:39

Howard L. Brown
Margaret W. Brown

Howard L. Brown
Arr. by Herbert G. Tovey

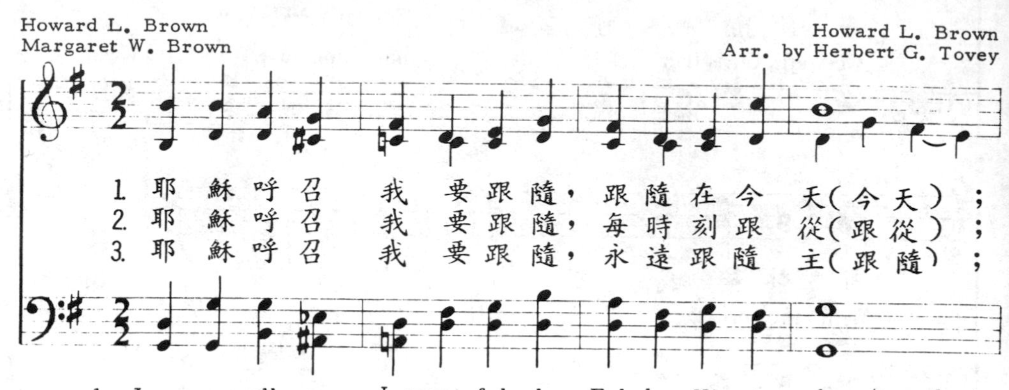

1. 耶 穌 呼 召 我 要 跟 隨，跟 隨 在 今 天（今 天）；
2. 耶 穌 呼 召 我 要 跟 隨，每 時 刻 跟 從（跟 從）；
3. 耶 穌 呼 召 我 要 跟 隨，永 遠 跟 隨 主（跟 隨）；
1. Je - sus calls me. I must fol - low, Fol - low Him to - day (to - day);
2. *Je - sus calls me. I must fol - low, Fol - low ev - ery hour (every hour),*
3. Je - sus calls me. I must fol - low, Fol - low Him al - way (al - way);

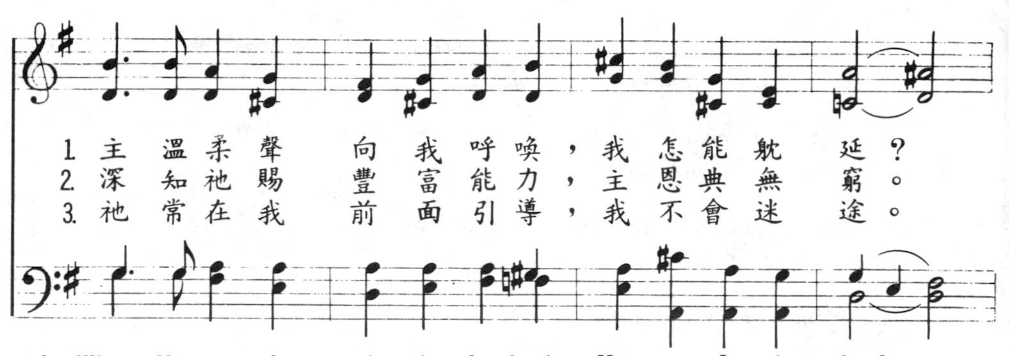

1. 主 溫 柔 聲 向 我 呼 喚，我 怎 能 躭 延？
2. 深 知 祂 賜 豐 富 能 力，主 恩 典 無 窮。
3. 祂 常 在 我 前 面 引 導，我 不 會 迷 途。
1. When His ten - der voice is plead - ing How can I de - lay?
2. *Know the bless - ing of His pres - ence, Full - ness of His power.*
3. When my Sav - iour goes be - fore me I can nev - er stray.

跟 隨，我 要 跟 隨 祢， 我 主， 跟 隨
Fol - low, I will fol - low Thee, my Lord, Fol - - low
跟 隨，跟 隨，我 要 跟 隨，跟 隨 祢，我 主，我 主， 跟 隨，跟 隨
Fol - low, fol - low, I will fol - low, Fol - low thee, my Lord, my Lord, Fol - low, fol - low

每天跟隨 主。 我 的 前途主完
ev-ery pass-ing day. My to-mor-rows are all
每天跟隨，每天跟隨主。跟隨主
ev-ery pass-ing, Fol-low ev-ery day. ev-ery day.
全 知 道， 主 必引領我道 路。
known to Thee, Thou wilt lead me all the way.
完全 知道 主引領，
are known to Thee, Thou wilt lead,

從那時候耶穌就傳起道來，說，天國近了，你們應當悔改。耶穌在加利利海邊行走，看見弟兄二人，就是那稱呼彼得的西門，和他兄弟安得烈，在海裏撒網，他們本是打魚的。耶穌對他們說，來跟從我，我要叫你們得人如得魚一樣。他們就立刻捨了網，跟從了他。從那裏往前走，又看見弟兄二人，就是西庇太的兒子雅各，和他兄弟約翰，同他們的父親西庇太在船上補網，耶穌就招呼他們。他們立刻捨了船別了父親，跟從了耶穌。

馬太福音第四章
17 — 22節

耶穌的脚踪

Footprints Of Jesus

. . . Yea, I have loved you with an everlasting love; with loving kindness have I drawn thee.

— Jeremiah 31:3

Mary B C. Slade

Asa B. Everett

1. 我們聽見主慈聲呼召，來跟從 我；我們看見救
2. 雖然要走過寒冷山岡，尋找迷 羊；或要在西羅
3. 當我們走完世上路程，見主榮 面，安息在主的

1. Sweet-ly, Lord, have we heard Thee call-ing, Come, fol-low Me! And we see where Thy
2. *Tho' they lead o'er the cold, dark mountains, Seek-ing His sheep; Or a-long by Si-*
3. Then at last, when on high He sees us, Our jour-ney done, We will rest where the

1. 主的脚蹤，領 到主 前。
2. 亞的池旁，幫 助病 傷。 耶 穌的 脚 蹤，使
3. 最後脚踪，父 寶座 前。
Foot-prints of Je - sus, that
1. footprints fall-ing Lead us to Thee.
2. lo-am's foun-tains, Help-ing the weak:
3. steps of Je-sus End at His throne.

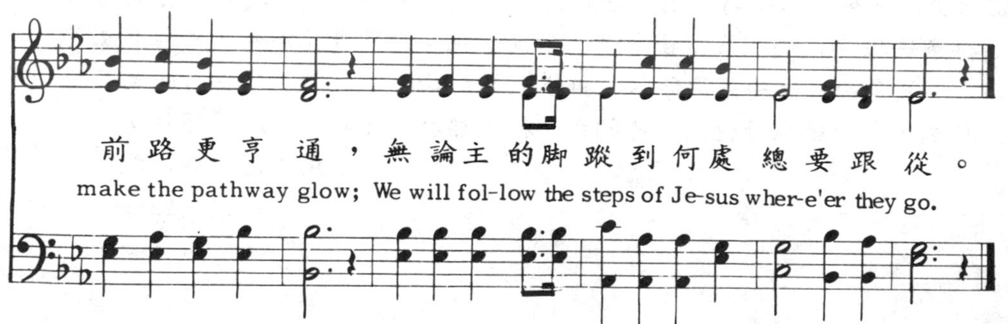
前路更亨 通，無論主的脚蹤到何處 總要跟 從。
make the pathway glow; We will fol-low the steps of Je-sus wher-e'er they go.

求主領我

Lead Me, Savior

But where shall wisdom be found? — Job 28:12

Frank M Davis | Frank M. Davis

1. 求主領我免走錯 體恤引導我全路；
2. 世上風濤浪滾滾， 主是我靈避難所；
3. 求主至終引領我， 直到今世風暴過；
1. Sav-iour, lead me, lest I stray, Gent-ly lead me all the way;
2. Thou the ref-uge of my soul, When life's stormy billows roll,
3. Sav-iour, lead me, then at last, When the storm of life is past,
1. 主在身邊極安全， 願在主愛中居住。
2. 一切希望惟靠主， 主臨近我便穩妥。
3. 使我安抵光明所， 再無眼淚與苦楚。
1. I am safe when by Thy side, I would in Thy love a-bide.
2. I am safe when Thou art nigh, All my hopes on Thee re-ly.
3. To the land of end-less day, Where all tears are wiped away.
領我 領我，求主領我免走錯；
Lead me, lead me, Sav-iour, lead me, lest I stray:
恩領我安渡歲月， 直到享受天家樂。
Gent-ly down the stream of time. Lead me, Sav-iour, all the way.

426

神一路引領
God Leads Us Along

. . . And the sheep hear His voice; and He calls His own sheep by name, and He leadeth them out. — John 10:3

G. A. Young

GOD LEADS US
G. A. Young

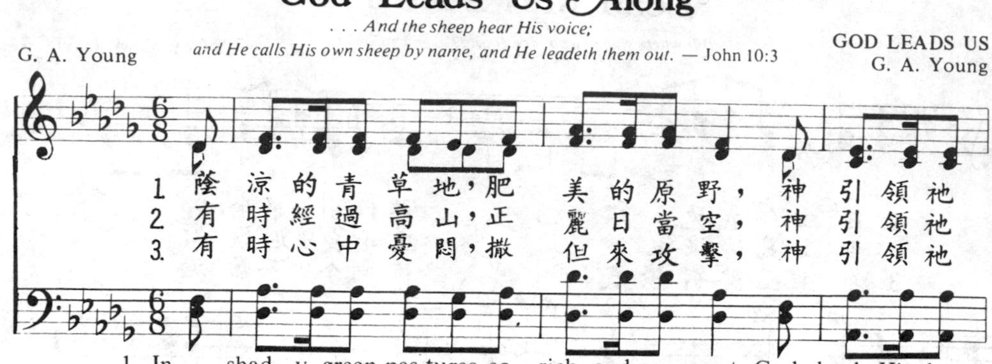

1. 蔭 涼 的 青 草 地，肥 美 的 原 野， 神 引 領 祂
2. 有 時 經 過 高 山，正 麗 日 當 空， 神 引 領 祂
3. 有 時 心 中 憂 悶，撒 但 來 攻 擊， 神 引 領 祂
1 In shad - y, green pas-tures, so rich and so sweet, God leads His dear
2 *Some - times on the mount where the sun shines so bright, God leads His dear*
3 Though sor-rows be - fall us and e - vils op - pose, God leads His dear

1. 兒 女 前 行；清 涼 的 溪 水 旁，供 人 能 安 歇，
2. 兒 女 前 行；有 時 經 過 幽 谷，黑 夜 籠 罩 中，
3. 兒 女 前 行；靠 主 恩 典 得 勝，能 戰 敗 仇 敵，
1 chil-dren a - long; Where the wa - ter's cool flow bathes the wea-ry one's feet,
2 *chil-dren a - long; Some - times in the val - ley, in dark - est of night,*
3 chil-dren a - long; Thru grace we can con-quer, de - feat all our foes,

神 引 領 祂 兒 女 前 行。 或 經 過 狂 波 ，或 經 深
God leads His dear children a - long. Some thru the wa-ters, some thru the
淵，或 經 烈 火，全 靠 主 恩 典； 或 憂 傷 痛 苦，主
flood, Some thru the fire, but all thru the blood; Some thru great sor-row, but

安慰我心，不論是晝夜，神一路引領。
God gives a song, In the night sea-son and all the day long.

427

親愛主，牽我手

Precious Lord, Take My Hand

Thou wilt show me the path of life:
at Thy right hand there are pleasures for evermore.
— Psalm 6:11

PRECIOUS LORD

Thomas A. Dorsey

Arranged by Thomas A. Dorsey

1. 親愛主，牽我手，建立我，領我走；我疲
2. 我道路雖淒涼，主臨近，慰憂傷；我在

1 Pre-cious Lord, take my hand, Lead me on, help me stand; I am
2 *When my way grows drear, Pre-cious Lord, lin-ger near; When my*

1. 倦，我軟弱，我苦愁；經風暴，過黑夜，求領
2. 世快打完美好仗；聽我求，聽我禱，攙我

1 tired, I am weak, I am worn; Thru the storm, thru the night, Lead me
2 *life is al-most gone, Hear my cry, hear my call, Hold my*

1. 我進光明；親愛主，牽我手，到天庭。
2. 手防跌倒；親愛主，牽我手，常引導。

1 on to the light, Take my hand, pre-cious Lord, lead me home.
2 *hand lest I fall; Take my hand, pre-cious Lord, lead me home.*

428

耶穌與我同行
Jesus Will Walk with Me

But if we walk in the light as He is in the light . . . .

— John 1: 7

Haldor Lillenas
JESUS WILL WALK WITH ME
Haldor Lillenas
1. 經過山谷有耶穌與我同行，或經平原主仍
2. 試探來臨有耶穌與我同行，賜我力量使我
3. 若遇風暴有耶穌與我同行，時常保護引我
4. 晨曦之時有耶穌與我同行，黃昏黑夜主仍
1 Je - sus will walk with me down thru the val - ley, Je - sus will walk with me
2 Je - sus will walk with me when I am tempt-ed, Giv-ing me strength as my
3 Je - sus will walk with me, guarding me ev - er, Giv-ing me vic-tory thru
4 Je - sus will walk with me in life's fair morn-ing, And when the shadows of
1. 與我同行；不論前途是幽暗或是光明，
2. 完全得勝；憂傷來臨主親自安慰同在，
3. 到平安地；祂是策士又是我的安慰者，
4. 與我同行；不論生死祂總不把我丟棄，
1 o - ver the plain; When in the shad-ow or when in the sun-shine,
2 need may de - mand; When in af - flic - tion His pres - ence is near me,
3 storm and thru strife; He is my Com-fort-er, Coun - sel - or, Lead - er,
4 eve - ning must come; Liv - ing or dy - ing, He will not for - sake me.
1. 我無怨言若主與我同行。
2. 主大能手將我扶持安穩。
3. 領我一生直到天家安息。
4. 直到永遠耶穌與我同行。
耶 穌與
1 If He goes with me I shall not com-plain.
2 I am up - held by His al - might - y hand.
3 O - ver the un - e - ven jour - ney of life.
4 Je - sus will walk with me all the way home.
Je - sus will

我 同 行，祂 與 我 交 談，祂 與 我 同 行；或 喜 樂 或
walk with me, He will talk with me; He will walk with me; In joy or in
憂 傷，或 今 日 或 明 日，我 知 主 與 我 同 行。
sor - row, to - day and to - mor - row, I know He will walk with me.

你眷顧地，降下透雨，使地大得肥美，上帝的河滿了水，你這樣澆灌了地，好為人豫備五穀。

你澆透地的犁溝，潤平犁脊，降甘霖，使地軟和，其中發長的，蒙你賜福。

你以恩典為年歲的冠冕，你的路徑都滴下脂油。

滴在曠野的草場上，小山以歡樂束腰。

草場以羊羣為衣，谷中也長滿了五穀，這一切都歡呼歌唱

詩篇六十五篇

9 —13

You care for the land and water it;
you enrich it abundantly.
The streams of God are filled with water
to provide the people with grain,
for so you have ordained it.
You drench its furrows
and level its ridges;
you soften it with showers
and bless its crops.
You crown the year with your bounty,
and your carts overflow with abundance.
The grasslands of the desert overflow;
the hills are clothed with gladness.
The meadows are covered with flocks
and the valleys are mantled with grain;
they shout for joy and sing.

— Psalm 65:9-13. NIV

429

慈光導引

Lead Kindly Light

Lead me to the Rock that is higher than I. . . .

— Psalm 61:2

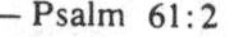

John H. Newman

John B. Dyker

1. 懇求慈光，導引脫離黑蔭，導我前行！
2. 向來未曾如此虛心求主，導我前行；
3. 久蒙引導，如今定能繼續，導我前行，

1. Lead, kind-ly Light, a-mid th'en-cir-cling gloom, Lead thou me on;
2. I was not ev-er thus, nor prayed that Thou Shouldst lead me on;
3. So long Thy power hath blest me, sure it still Will lead me on,

1. 黑夜漫漫我又遠離家庭，導我前行！
2. 我好自專隨意自定程途，直到如今！
3. 經過洪濤經過荒山空谷，夜盡天明；

1. The night is dark, and I am far from home; Lead Thou me on:
2. I loved to choose and see my path; but now Lead Thou me on.
3. O'er moor and fen, o'er crag and tor-rent till The night is gone;

1. 我不求主指引遙遠路程，
2. 從前我愛沉迷繁華夢裏，
3. 夜盡天明晨曦光裏重逢，

1. Keep Thou my feet; I do not ask to see
2. I loved the gar - ish day, and, spite of fears,
3. And with the morn those an - gel fac - es smile,

1. 我只懇求，一步一步導引。
2. 驕癡無忌，舊事乞莫重提！
3. 多年契濶，我心所愛笑容。阿們

1. The dis - tant scene -- one step e - nough for me.
2. *Pride ruled my will: re - mem - ber not past years.*
3. Which I have loved long since, and lost a - while. A - MEN.

430

救主為我預備道路

I Know The Lord Will Make A Way For Me

Show me Thy way O Lord; teach me Thy way.
— Psalm 25:4, 5

Source unknown

Arr. by Haldor Lillenas

我知救主為我預備道路，我知救
I know the Lord will make a way for me, I know the

主為我預備道路，仰望主懇切祈求，雖黑
Lord will make a way for me, If I look to Him and pray, Dark-est

夜也變白晝，我知救主為我預備道路。
night will turn to day, I know the Lord will make a way for me.

跟隨
Follow On

William O. Cushing

A man shall be . . . like the shadow of a great rock in a weary land.
— Isaiah 32:2

Robert Lowry

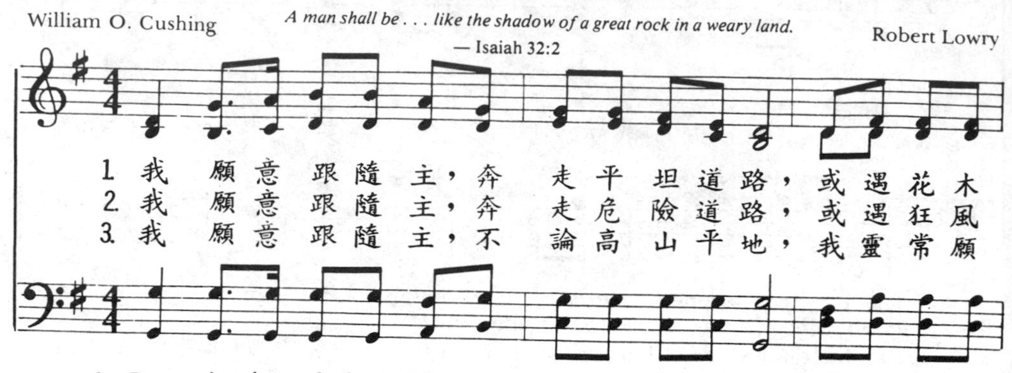
1. 我 願 意 跟 隨 主，奔 走 平 坦 道 路，或 遇 花 木
2. 我 願 意 跟 隨 主，奔 走 危 險 道 路，或 遇 狂 風
3. 我 願 意 跟 隨 主，不 論 高 山 平 地，我 靈 常 願

1. Down in the val - ley with my Sav - ior I would go, Where the flow'rs are
2. Down in the val - ley with my Sav - ior I would go, Where the storms are
3. Down in the val - ley or up - on the moun-tain steep, Close be-side my

1. 茂 盛 清 水 常 流 之 處；既 有 救 主 引 導 我 心
2. 暴 雨 黑 雲 阻 我 前 途；既 有 救 主 引 導 我 心
3. 與 主 親 近 永 不 分 離；祂 必 安 然 領 我 跟 隨

1. bloom-ing and the sweet wa-ters flow; Ev - 'ry - where He leads me I would
2. sweep-ing and the dark wa-ters flow; With His hand to lead me I will
3. Sav - ior would my soul ev - er keep; He will lead me safe - ly in the

1. 歡 然 跟 隨 主， 一 路 走 到 天 上，我 必 跟 從 主。
2. 永 遠 不 受 驚， 總 不 懼 怕 危 險，因 有 主 同 行。
3. 祂 的 脚 踪 行； 我 願 與 主 同 行，一 直 到 天 庭。

1. fol - low, fol - low on, Walk-ing in His foot-steps till the crown be won.
2. nev - er, nev - er fear, Dan - ger can - not fright me if my Lord is near.
3. path that He has trod, Up to where they gath - er on the hills of God.

跟　隨！跟　隨！我願　跟隨　耶穌！不論往何地方，
Fol - low! fol - low! I would fol-low Je - sus! An-y-where, ev-'ry-where,
我要跟隨主！　跟　隨！跟　隨！我願　跟隨
I would fol - low on! Fol - low! fol - low! I would fol - low
耶　穌！只　望　耶　穌引導　我必　跟隨主！
Je - sus! Ev - 'ry-where He leads me I would fol - low on!

路得說，不要催我回去不跟隨你，你往那裏去，我也往那裏去。你在那裏住宿，我也在那裏住宿。你的國就是我的國，你的　神就是我的　神。你在那裏死，我也在那裏死，也葬在那裏。除非死能使你我相離，不然，願耶和華重重的降罰與我。

路得記第一章
16—17節

432

我知道我往何處
I Know Where I Am Going

For I am persuaded that none of these things are hidden . . .
for this thing was not done in a corner. — Acts 26:26

Traditional

Scottish folk melody

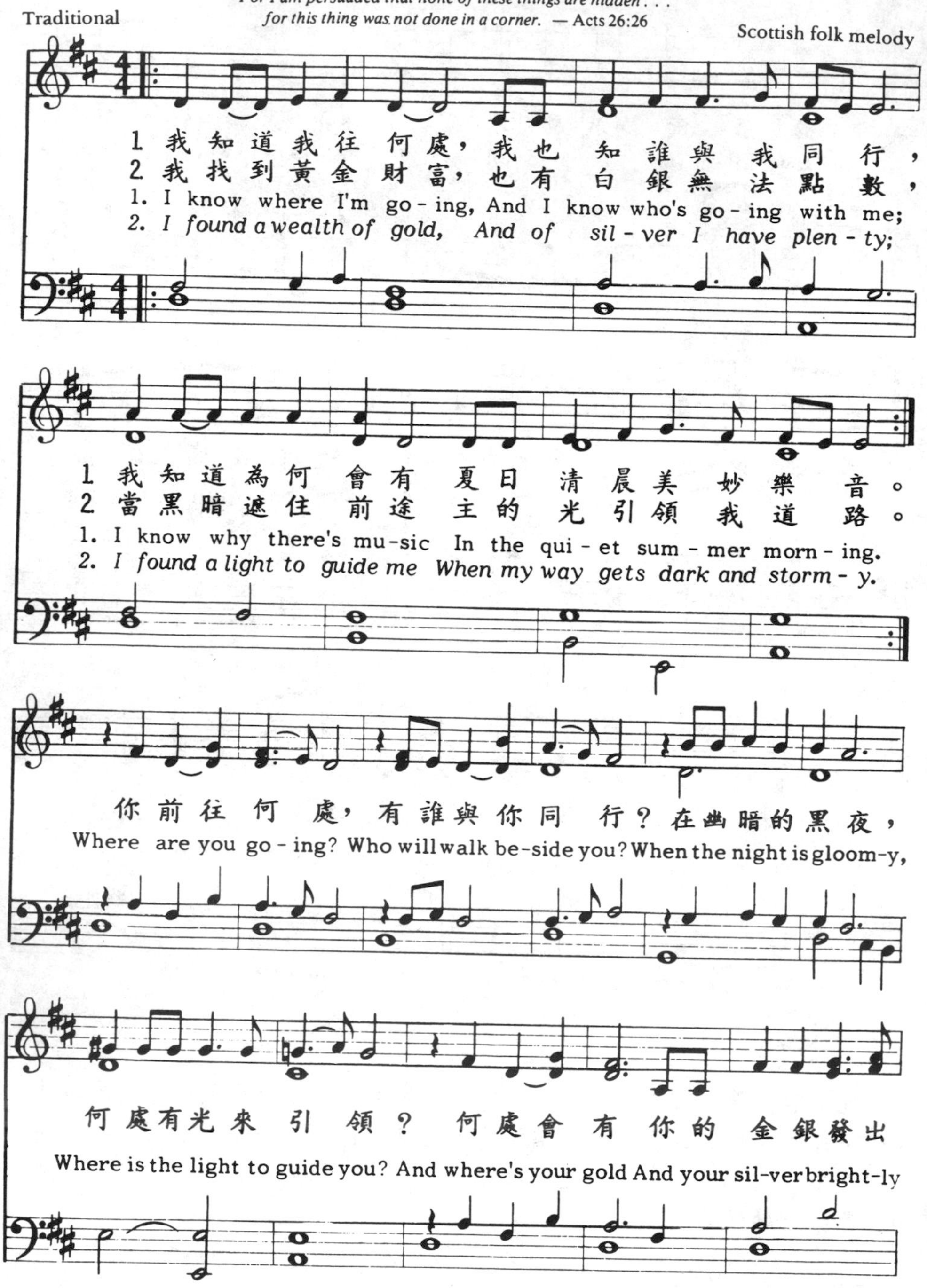

1. 我知道我往何處，我也知道誰與我同行，
2. 我找到黃金財富，也有白銀無法點數，
1. I know where I'm go - ing, And I know who's go - ing with me;
2. I found a wealth of gold, And of sil - ver I have plen - ty;
1. 我知道為何會有夏日清晨美妙樂音。
2. 當黑暗遮住前途主的光引領我道路。
1. I know why there's mu-sic In the qui - et sum - mer morn - ing.
2. I found a light to guide me When my way gets dark and storm - y.
你前往何處，有誰與你同行？在幽暗的黑夜，
Where are you go - ing? Who will walk be-side you? When the night is gloom-y,
何處有光來引領？何處會有你的金銀發出
Where is the light to guide you? And where's your gold And your sil-ver bright-ly

閃 光？ 誰作這 樂章 在這夏日清晨 播 放？
shin - ing? Who writes the mu-sic In the qui - et sum-mer morn-ing?
我要跟主前 往，祂 必常在我 身 旁，為 罪人祂受
I'm go-ing where He goes, And He'll be there be-side me — The love for which He
死，是 我嚮導與 保 障； 是我財 富，是我
died Is all I need to guide me; And He's my gold And my
金銀發的 閃 光， 是祂作 樂章，在這夏日清晨
sil-ver bright-ly shin-ing — He writes the mu-sic In the qui-et sum-mer
播 放！我知我往 何處，但 請問你 何 往？
morn-ing! I know where I'm go-ing — but where are you go - ing? ——

433

事奉祂愈久愈甘甜
The Longer I Serve Him

. . . He that loseth his life for My sake shall find it.
— Matthew 10:39

William J. Gaither

THE SWEETER HE GROWS
William J. Gaither

1 自我進入主的國度，生命由祂掌
2 祂賜我一切的需要，祂有豐富恩
1 Since I start - ed for the King-dom, Since my life He con-
2 Ev - ery need He is sup - ply - ing, Plen - teous grace He be -
1 管，自我獻身心給耶穌，我感到事
2 典，每日賜我新的希望，我感到事
1 trols, Since I gave my heart to Je-sus, The long - er I
2 stows; Ev - ery day my way gets bright-er, The long - er I
1 奉祂，愈久愈甘甜。我感到事奉祂愈久愈
2 奉祂，愈久愈甘甜。
1 serve Him, the sweet-er He grows. The long - er I serve Him the sweet-er
2 serve Him, the sweet-er He grows.
甘甜，我願更愛祂，因祂愛永不變；心中充滿
He grows, The more that I love Him, more love He be-stows; Each day is like
喜樂，在地如在天，我感到事奉祂愈久愈甘甜
heav-en, my heart o-ver-flows, The long-er I serve Him the sweet-er He grows.

求主對我述說

Lord, Speak to Me

434

And He that searcheth the hearts knoweth what is in the mind of the Spirit.
— Romans 8:27

Frances Ridley Havergal

CANONBURY
Robert Schumann

1. 求主對我述說真理，使
2. 求主領我行走義路，使
3. 求主教我真理聖言，我
4. 求主賜我豐富生命，願
5. 求主用我不将我棄，我
1 Lord, speak to me, that I may speak In
2 O lead me, Lord, that I may lead The
3 O teach me, Lord, that I may teach The
4 O fill me with Thy full - ness, Lord, Un -
5 O use me, Lord, use e - ven me, Just
1. 我做祢回聲傳遞；我願尋找迷
2. 我亦能引人脚步；天上靈糧将
3. 好去向世人宣傳；使我言辭帶
4. 主豐盛充滿我心；我的言行全
5. 願順從到任何地；直到在天見
1 liv - ing ech - oes of Thy tone; As Thou hast sought, so
2 wan - dering and the wa - vering feet; O feed me, Lord, that
3 pre - cious things Thou dost im - part; And wing my words, that
4 til my ver - y heart o'er - flow In kin - dling thought and
5 as Thou wilt, and when, and where, Un - til Thy bless - ed
1. 羊像祢，引領迷失罪人歸祢。
2. 我餵養，使我常與他人分享。
3. 祢能力，能使人心回轉向祢。
4. 聽主命，時時讚揚主愛恩情。
5. 主聖容，同享安息快樂光榮。阿門。
1 let me seek Thy err - ing chil - dren lost and lone.
2 I may feed Thy hun - gering ones with man - na sweet.
3 they may reach The hid - den depths of man - y a heart.
4 glow - ing word, Thy love to tell, Thy praise to show.
5 face I see— Thy rest, Thy joy, Thy glo - ry share. A - men.

事奉耶穌真是快樂

Joy in Serving Jesus

Let this mind be in you which is also in Christ Jesus.

— Philippians 2:5

Oxwald J. Smith, Bentley D. Ackisy,

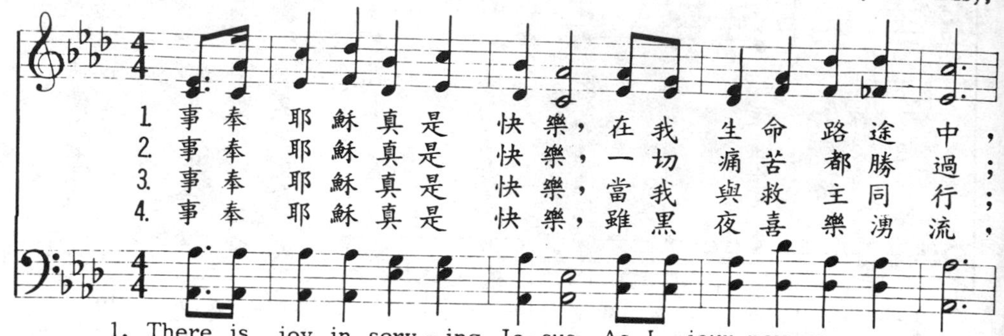

1. 事奉耶穌真是快樂，在我生命路途中，
2. 事奉耶穌真是快樂，一切痛苦都勝過；
3. 事奉耶穌真是快樂，當我與救主同行；
4. 事奉耶穌真是快樂，雖黑夜喜樂湧流，
1. There is joy in serv-ing Je-sus, As I jour-ney on my way,
2. There is joy in serv-ing Je-sus, Joy that tri-umphs o-ver pain;
3. There is joy in serv-ing Je-sus, As I walk a-lone with God;
4. There is joy in serv-ing Je-sus, Joy a-mid the dark-est night,

1. 心中充滿快樂讚美，每時每刻在歌頌。
2. 天上音樂充滿我靈，直到在天同唱和。
3. 主曾為我經歷痛苦，賜下喜樂在我心。
4. 因我已得奇妙祕訣，光明中與主同走。
1. Joy that fills the heart with prais-es, Ev-ery hour and ev-ery day.
2. Fills my soul with heav-en's mu-sic, Till I join the glad re-frain.
3. "Tis the joy of Christ, my Sav-iour, Who the path of suf-fering trod.
4. For I've learned the won-drous se-cret, And I'm walk-ing in the light.

事奉耶穌快樂真是無窮，喜樂心弦
There is joy, joy, Joy in serv-ing Je-sus, Joy that throbs with-

在振動，每時每刻在事奉，支取主能
in my heart: Ev-ery mo-ment ev-ery hour. As I draw un-

力恩崇，真是快樂，快樂永在我心中。
to His power, there is joy, joy, Joy that nev-er shall de-part.

主的僕人

435-1

Make Me A Servant

Kelly Willard

It is the Lord Christ you are serving. Col. 3:24

Kelly Willard

Unison
我願事奉主，柔和謙卑，扶持軟弱的，
Make me a ser-vant, hum-ble and meek, Lord, let me lift up

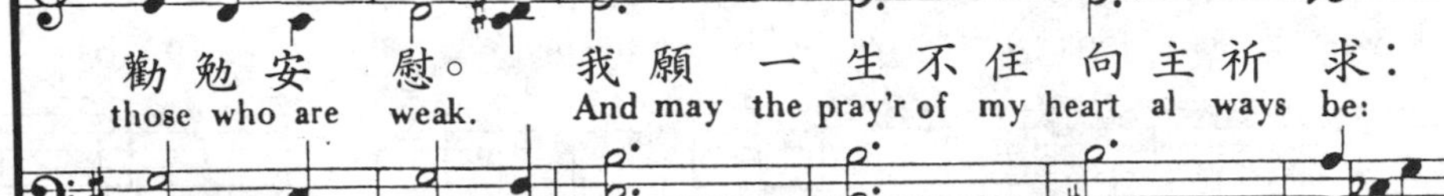
勸勉安慰。我願一生不住向主祈求：
those who are weak. And may the pray'r of my heart al-ways be:

使我事奉祢，做主的僕人，我今是主的僕人。
Make me a ser-vant, make me a ser-vant, make me a ser-vant to-day.

436
救主在等待
The Savior Is Waiting
Ralph Carmichael
Today if ye hear His voice harden not your heart. — Hebrews 3:7,8
CARMICHAEL
Ralph Carmichael
1. 主耶穌正等待進入你心門，為何你
2. 哦，朋友，你若願意接近耶穌，祂會伸
1 The Sav-ior is wait-ing to en-ter your heart, Why don't you
2 If you'll take one step toward the Sav-ior, my friend, You'll find His
1. 不接受祂？這世界無法將你與主分
2. 慈手歡迎；脫離黑暗接受祂做你救
1 let Him come in? There's noth-ing in this world to keep you a-
2 arms o-pen wide; Re-ceive Him, and all of your dark-ness will
1. 開，你要如何回答祂？
2. 主，祂必永住在你心。
1 part, What is your an-swer to Him?
2 end, With-in your heart He'll a-bide.
祂耐心地在你
Time af-ter time He has
心外等待，現在祂仍然在等待，等待
wait-ed be-fore, And now He is wait-ing a-gain To see
盼望你願意打開心門，祂渴望進入你心。
if you're will-ing to o-pen the door: O how He wants to come in.

你心有空處為主嗎？
Have You Any Room For Jesus?

Behold, I stand at the door and knock . . . — Revelation 3:20

ANY ROOM
C. C. Williams

Unknown

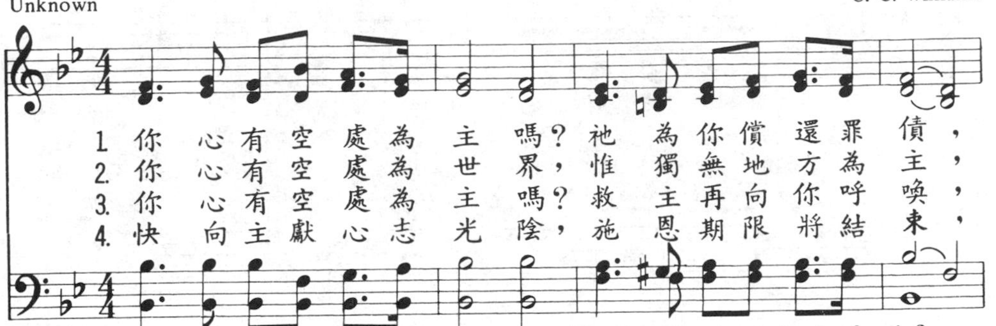
1. 你 心有空處為 主 嗎？祂 為你償還罪 債，
2. 你 心有空處為 世 界，惟 獨無地方為 主，
3. 你 心有空處為 主 嗎？救 主再向你呼 喚，
4. 快 向主獻心志 光 陰，施 恩期限將結 束，
1 Have you an - y room for Je - sus, He who bore your load of sin?
2 Room for pleas-ure, room for busi-ness–But, for Christ the cru - ci - fied,
3 Have you an - y room for Je - sus, As in grace He calls a - gain?
4 Room and time now give to Je - sus, Soon will pass God's day of grace;

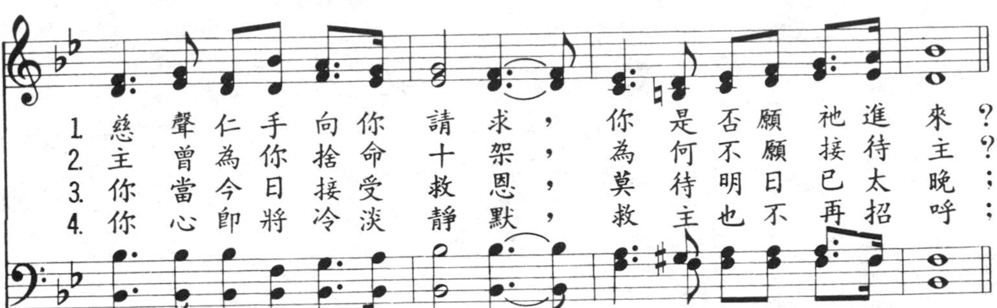
1. 慈 聲仁手向你 請 求， 你 是否願 祂進 來？
2. 主 曾為你捨命 十 架， 為 何不願 接待 主？
3. 你 當今日接受 救 恩， 莫 待明日 已太 晚；
4. 你 心卽將冷淡 靜 默， 救 主也不 再招 呼；
1 As He knocks and asks ad - mis-sion, Will you ev - er let Him in?
2 Not a place that He can en - ter, In the heart for which He died?
3 Here to - day is time ac - cept - ed, To - mor - row you may call in vain.
4 Soon thy heart left cold and si - lent, And thy Sav-ior's plead-ing cease.

讓 榮耀王，耶穌 進 來！切 莫讓祂立門 外；
Room for Je - sus, King of glo - ry! Has - ten now, His word o - bey;
速，開心門 請祂 進 來，機 會過去不 再 來。
Swing your heart's door wide - ly o - pen, Bid Him en - ter while you may.

438

救主是我一切
He's Everything to Me

Ralph Carmichael
. . . What is man that Thou art mindful of him?
Psalm 8:4
WOODLAND HILLS
Ralph Carmichael
1. 羣星閃耀述説主奇工，微風吹動見證主尊榮；陸地海洋在祂掌管中，對我有何意？
2. 救主降生要慶祝歌頌，因這事已記載歷史中；祂來世界使人得自由，
1 In the stars His handiwork I see, On the wind He speaks with majesty; Though He ruleth over land and sea, What is that to me?
2 I will celebrate nativity. For it has a place in history; Sure, He came to set His people free,
1
2
對我有何意？
What is that to me?
直到憑信見主面對面，領會救主奇妙大恩典，
'Til by faith I met Him face to face And I felt the wonder of His grace,

我才深知真神愛無邊，祂時刻關懷
Then I knew that He was more than just a God who did - n't
我，並非遠住在高天，每日與我同行
care, who lived a-way out there. And now He walks be - side me
肩並肩，常常看顧我免遭危險，
day by day, Ev - er watch - ing o'er me lest I stray,
助我走窄路勇往直前，救主是我一
Help-ing me to find that nar - row way, He's ev-ery-thing to
1
切，救主是我一切。
me. He's ev - ery - thing to me.
2

439

在我心裡常吟讚美歌
In My Heart There Rings A Melody

Serve the Lord with gladness: come before His presence with singing.
— Psalm 100:2
Elton M. Roth
HEART MELODY
Elton M. Roth
1. 主耶穌賜我一首詩歌，這詩由天
2. 我愛耶穌因祂為我死，赦罪恩白
3. 耶穌再來掌權的時候，我與天使
1 I have a song that Je - sus gave me, It was sent from
2 I love the Christ who died on Cal - vary, For He washed my
3 'Twill be my end - less theme in glo - ry, With the an - gels
1. 賜給我；從未有此美妙絕倫音樂，真是
2. 白賜我；我真快樂因祂在我心裡，今後
3. 同唱和；這時確有美妙音樂伴奏，同在
1 heaven a - bove; There nev - er was a sweet - er mel - o - dy, 'Tis a
2 sins a - way: He put with - in my heart a mel - o - dy, And I
3 I will sing; 'Twill be a song with glo - rious har - mo - ny, When the
1. 奇妙恩愛歌。
2. 要唱凱旋歌。
3. 寶座前唱歌。
在我心裡常吟讚美歌，時
In my heart there rings a mel - o - dy, There
1 mel - o - dy of love.
2 know it's there to stay.
3 courts of heav - en ring.
常吟奇妙歌，有天使同唱和；在我心裡
rings a mel - o - dy with heav - en's har - mo - ny; In my heart there

常吟讚美歌，時 常吟奇妙恩愛 歌。
rings a mel-o-dy, There rings a mel-o-dy of love.

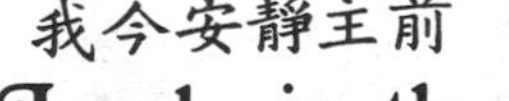

我今安靜主前

Speak, Lord, in the Stillness

440

And the Lord came, and stood, and called. . . . Then Samuel answered, Speak Lord, for thy servant heareth. — I Samuel 3:10

E. May Grimes

QUIETUDE
Harold Green

1. 我今安靜主前，等候主發言；求使我心安靜，使我靈甦醒。
2. 我在主前靜默，主請對我説；使我見祢聖容，得能力恩寵。
3. 主祢話是生命，使我得供應；賜我天上靈糧，我靈得滋養！
4. 一切完全屬祢，不再屬自己；欣然奉獻降服，我單屬我主。
5. 求主賜我智慧，常聽祢訓誨；使我行祢旨意，討祢的歡喜。阿門。

1 Speak, Lord, in the stillness, While I wait on Thee;
Hushed my heart to listen In expectancy.

2 *Speak, O blessed Master, In this quiet hour,*
Let me see Thy face, Lord, Feel Thy touch of power.

3 For the words Thou speakest, "They are life" indeed;
Living Bread from heaven, Now my spirit feed!

4 *All to Thee is yielded, I am not my own;*
Blissful, glad surrender, I am Thine alone.

5 Fill me with the knowledge Of Thy glorious will;
All Thine own good pleasure In my life fulfill. Amen.

441

為何我要歌頌耶穌

Why Do I Sing About Jesus?

I live by the faith of the Son of God who loved me and gave Himself for me. — Galatians 2:21

KETCHUM

Albert A. Ketchum | Albert A. Ketchum

1. 我心靈中充滿快樂，因耶穌已拯救
2. 只要一見主的良善，心靈滿足到永
3. 在萬人中祂最美好，祂是玫瑰百合
1 Deep in my heart there's a glad - ness — Je - sus has saved me from
2 On - ly a glimpse of His good - ness, That was suf - fi - cient for
3 He is the fair - est of fair ones, He is the Lil - y, the
1. 我；讚美救主奇妙恩惠！潔淨我
2. 久；只要一見我的救主，我靈即
3. 花；祂是豐盛恩惠源頭，恩典慈
1 sin! Praise to His name, what a Sav - ior! Cleans - ing with-
2 me; On - ly one look at the Sav - ior, Then was my
3 Rose; Riv - ers of mer - cy sur - round Him, Grace, love, and
1. 裡外罪過。
2. 得真自由。
3. 愛祂賜下。
為何我要歌頌耶穌？
Why do I sing a - bout Je - sus?
1 out and with - in!
2 spir - it set free.
3 pit - y He shows.
為何祂對我寶貴？祂是我主，我的
Why is He pre - cious to me? He is my Lord and my

救 主：祂死，叫我 轉 回!
Sav - ior: Dy - ing, He set me free!

442

愛使我們合一
The Bond of Love

By this shall all men know that ye are My disciples — if ye love one another.
— John 13:35

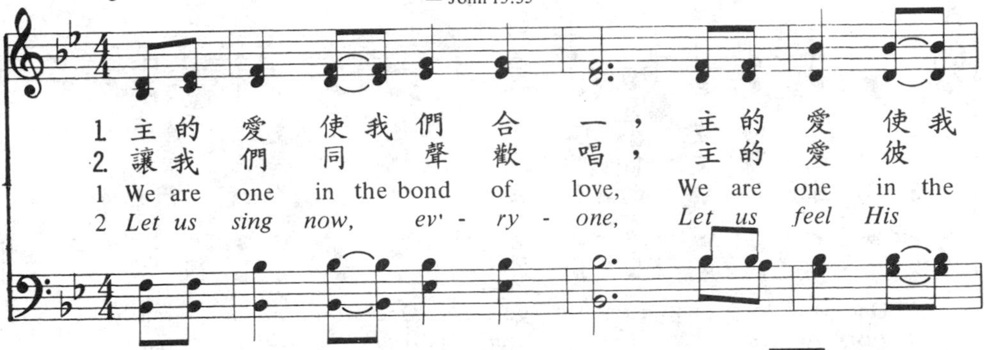

BOND OF LOVE

Otis Skillings

Otis Skillings

1. 主的 愛 使我 們 合 一， 主的 愛 使我 們 合 一； 主的 聖 靈 充滿 在我 們 的心 裡，主的 愛 使我 們 合 一。
2. 讓我 們 同 聲 歡 唱， 主的 愛 彼 此 分 享； 讓我 們 攜 手同 心向 世 人證 明，主的 愛 使我 們 合 一。

1 We are one in the bond of love, We are one in the bond of love; We have joined our spir - it with the Spir - it of God, We are one in the bond of love.

2 *Let us sing now, ev' - ry - one, Let us feel His love be - gun; Let us join our hands that the world will know We are one in the bond of love.*

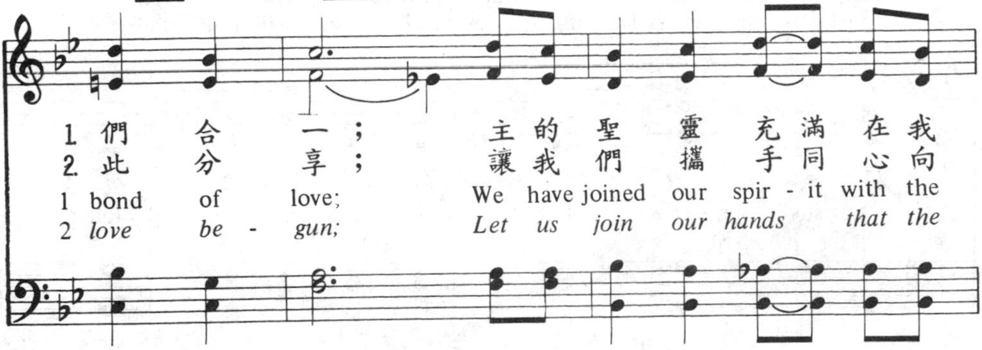

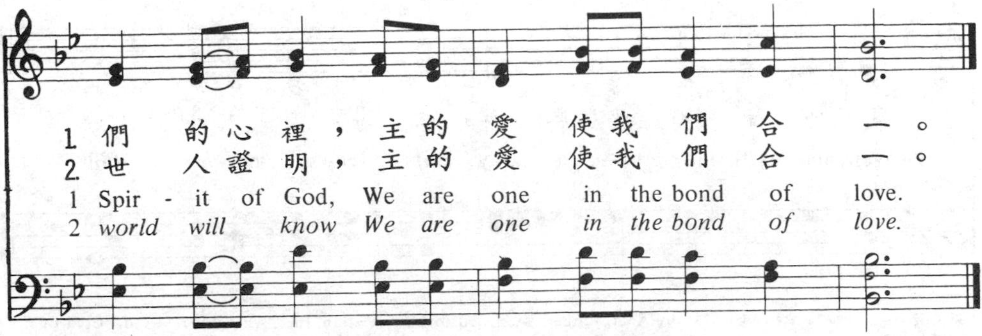

443

耶穌不改變
Jesus Never Fails

Heaven and earth will pass away
but My words shall not . . . . — Matthew 24:35

Arthur A. Luther

JESUS NEVER FAILS
Arthur A. Luther

1. 世間朋友會改變，常疑惑煩擾；
2. 雖有時黑暗滿佈，攻擊如風暴；
3. 生命有時有痛苦，愛情亦轉變；
1 Earth - ly friends may prove un - true, Doubts and fears as - sail;
2 Though the sky be dark and drear, Fierce and strong the gale,
3 In life's dark and bit - ter hour Love will still pre - vail;
1. 耶穌的愛不改變，祂永遠可靠。
2. 切記那愛你的主，祂永遠可靠。
3. 信靠大能的恩主，祂永不改變。
1 One still loves and cares for you, One who will not fail.
2 Just re - mem - ber He is near, And He will not fail.
3 Trust His ev - er - last - ing power— Je - sus will not fail.
耶穌不改變，耶穌不改變；
Je - sus nev - er fails, Je - sus nev - er fails;
天地萬物要廢去，耶穌永不改變。
Heaven and earth may pass a - way, But Je - sus nev - er fails.

天上真光，今照耀我心
There Is Sunshine in My Soul Today

For God who commanded light to shine out of darkness hath shined in our hearts.
— II Corinthians 4:6
SUNSHINE
Eliza E. Hewitt
John R. Sweney
1. 天上真光今照耀我心，無限燦爛輝煌，
2. 美妙音樂今充滿我心，稱頌基督我王，
3. 春之希望跳躍我心間，因主在我身邊，
4. 頌讚歡欣今洋溢我心，充滿盼望仁慈，
1 There is sun-shine in my soul to-day, More glo-ri-ous and bright
2 There is mu-sic in my soul to-day, A car-ol to my King,
3 There is spring-time in my soul to-day, For when the Lord is near
4 There is glad-ness in my soul to-day, And hope and praise and love,
1. 榮耀美麗遠超乎天地，耶穌是我真光。
2. 口雖無聲但耶穌能聽—我心中的歡唱。
3. 主賜聖靈使我心平安，又賜豐富恩典。
4. 因主賜我各樣的福氣，使我喜樂滿溢。
1 Than glows in an-y earth-ly sky, For Je-sus is my light.
2 And Je-sus, lis-ten-ing can hear The songs I can-not sing.
3 The dove of peace sings in my heart, The flowers of grace ap-pear.
4 For bless-ings which He gives me now, For joys laid up a-bove.
何等榮耀，美麗光明，平安喜樂，時刻滿心
O there's sun-shine, bless-ed sun-shine, When the peace-ful, hap-py mo-ments
靈；自我看見耶穌笑容，便有光明在我心。
roll; When Je-sus shows His smil-ing face, There is sun-shine in my soul.

445

祂使我歡樂歌不停
He Keeps Me Singing

Luther B. Bridgers

Speaking . . . in psalms, and hymns, and . . . songs, making melody in your hearts . . . — Ephesians 5:19

SWEETEST NAME
Luther B. Bridgers

1. 我有優美曲調在心中—乃主溫柔叮嚀聲：
2. 昔日多經罪惡與禍患，滿心痛苦與愁煩；
3. 主賜無窮恩福我享用，在祂翼下有安寧；
4. 有時主領我涉過深水，試煉滿佈在前途；
5. 不久主要降自星空外，那時主向我歡迎；
1 There's with-in my heart a mel - o - dy— Je - sus whis - pers sweet and low,
2 All my life was wrecked by sin and strife; Dis - cord filled my heart with pain;
3 Feast-ing on the rich - es of His grace, Rest - ing 'neath His shelt'ring wing,
4 Tho sometimes He leads thru wa - ters deep, Tri - als fall a - cross the way,
5 Soon He's com-ing back to wel-come me, Far be - yond the star - ry sky;

"有我同行心靈當平靜，莫畏世路昇與沉。"
救主理我心琴拂我絃，悠然清韻滿心間。
時刻仰見救主的笑容，使我心高聲歌頌。
有時經崎嶇危險道路，仍願跟隨主腳步。
與主飛向那遙遠美境，同主掌權到永恒。
1 "Fear not, I am with Thee—peace be still," In all of life's ebb and flow.
2 Je - sus swept a - cross the bro-ken strings, Stirred the slumb'ring chords again.
3 Al - ways look - ing on His smil - ing face— That is why I shout and sing.
4 Tho sometimes the path seems rough and steep, See His foot-prints all the way.
5 I shall wing my flight to worlds un-known, I shall reign with Him on high.

耶穌，耶穌，耶穌—最甘美之名，
Je - sus, Je - sus, Je - sus— Sweet-est name I know,
慰我渴切心靈，使我歡樂歌不停。
Fills my ev - ery long - ing, Keeps me sing - ing as I go.

我要唱奇妙的故事
I Will Sing the Wondrous Story

WONDROUS STORY
Francis H. Rowley
Peter P. Bilhorn

1. 我要唱奇妙的故事，主耶穌為我受死，
2. 我從前曾遠離恩主，如迷羊走入歧途，
3. 我身心曾歷盡創傷，主親自為我裹傷，
4. 當黑暗四面環繞我，愁雲密佈我前途，
1 I will sing the won-drous sto-ry Of the Christ who died for me,
2 I was lost but Je-sus found me, Found the sheep that went a-stray,
3 I was bruised but Je-sus healed me, Faint was I from man-y a fall;
4 Days of dark-ness still come o'er me, Sor-row's paths I oft-en tread,
1. 祂離開天上的榮華，被釘死在各各他。
2. 救主以慈愛尋找我，領我歸回走正路。
3. 四圍籠罩懼怕驚慌，救主使我得釋放。
4. 但救主慈愛手牽我，與我同在走前路。
1 How He left His home in glo-ry For the cross of Cal-va-ry.
2 Threw His lov-ing arms a-round me, Drew me back in-to His way.
3 Sight was gone, and fears pos-sessed me, But He freed me from them all.
4 But the Sav-ior still is with me, By His hand I'm safe-ly led.
我要唱奇妙的故事，主耶穌為我受
Yes, I'll sing the won-drous sto-ry Of the Christ who died for
死，與衆聖徒在榮耀裡高聲唱，快樂無比。
me, Sing it with the saints in glo-ry Gath-ered by the crys-tal sea.

447

神蹟
It Took a Miracle

If any man be in Christ he is a new creature . . . — II Corinthians 5:17

John W. Peterson

MONTROSE
John W. Peterson

1. 我天父是無所不能，這是無可否認；
2. 我們無法完全見到，神所顯的榮耀，
3. 聖經講明神的大能，與祂奇妙智慧，
1 My Father is omnipotent, And that you can't deny;
2 Though here His glory has been shown, We still can't fully see
3 The Bible tells us of His power And wisdom all way through,
1. 這大能行奇事的神，穹蒼為祂明證。
2. 直到永恒才能知道，祂權能的奇妙。
3. 野地的花天空飛鳥，都見證神恩惠。
1 A God of might and miracles– 'Tis written in the sky.
2 The wonders of His might, His throne– 'Twill take eternity.
3 And every little bird and flower Are testimonies too.
将星安放在天，已證明是神蹟，地球懸
It took a miracle to put the stars in place, It took a
掛空中，也證明是神蹟；當祂救我靈魂，
miracle to hang the world in space; But when He saved my soul,
使我得潔淨，更證明神的慈愛和奇蹟！
Cleansed and made me whole, It took a miracle of love and grace!

深知所信
I Know Whom I Have Believed

. . . He is able to keep that which I have committed unto Him . . .
— II Timothy 1:12

Based on II Timothy 1:12
Daniel W. Whittle

EL NATHAN
James McGranahan

1. 我真不知神的奇恩，為何臨到我身，
2. 我真不知救我的信，如何進入我心，
3. 我真不知聖靈如何，引人知道已過，
4. 我真不知何時主來，那時我在何處，
1 I know not why God's won-drous grace To me He hath made known,
2 I know not how this sav-ing faith To me He did im-part,
3 I know not how the Spir-it moves, Con-vinc-ing men of sin,
4 I know not when my Lord may come, At night or noon-day fair,

1. 我也不知不堪如我，竟蒙救贖之恩。
2. 我也不知何以一信，便得一個新心。
3. 並由聖經顯明耶穌，使人接祂為主。
4. 到底我當經過死谷，或將空中遇主。
1 Nor why, un-wor-thy, Christ in love Re-deemed me for His own.
2 Nor how be-liev-ing in His word Wrought peace with-in my heart.
3 Re-veal-ing Je-sus through the word, Cre-at-ing faith in Him.
4 Nor if I walk the vale with Him, Or meet Him in the air.

"惟我深知，所信的是誰，並且也深信，祂實在
But "I know whom I have be-liev-ed, and am per-suad-ed that He is
是能，保守我所信託祂的，都全備直到那日。
a-ble To keep that which I've com-mit-ted Un-to Him a-gainst that day."

我是個罪人
Only A Sinner

. . . And I will pardon all their iniquities . .
— Jeremiah 33:8

James M. Gray

Daniel B. Towner

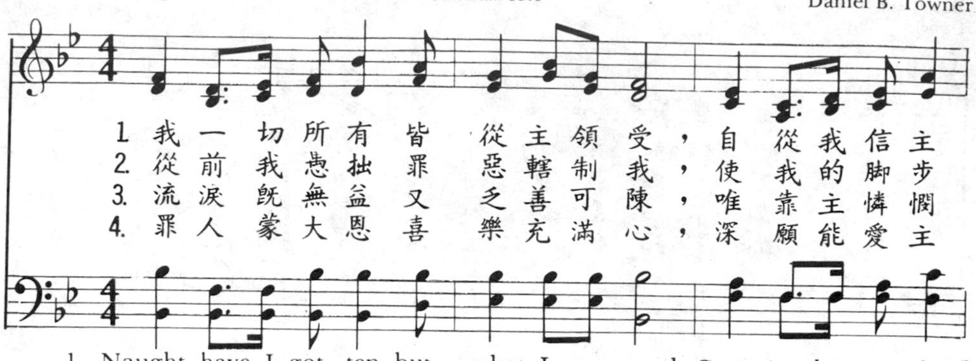
1. 我一切所有皆從主領受，自從我信主
2. 從前我愚拙罪惡轄制我，使我的腳步
3. 流淚既無益又乏善可陳，唯靠主憐憫
4. 罪人蒙大恩喜樂充滿心，深願能愛主

1. Naught have I got-ten but what I re-ceived, Grace has be-stowed it
2. Once I was fool-ish and sin ruled my heart, Caus-ing my foot-steps
3. Tears un-a-vail-ing, no mer-it had I, Mer-cy had saved me
4. Suf-fer a sin-ner whose heart o-ver-flows, Lov-ing His Sav-ior

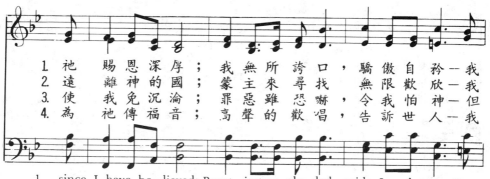

1. 祂賜恩深厚；我無所誇口，驕傲自矜—我
2. 遠離神的國；蒙主來尋找 無限歡欣—我
3. 使我免沉淪；罪惡雖恐嚇，令我怕神—但
4. 為祂傳福音；高聲的歡唱，告訴世人—我

1. since I have be-lieved; Boast-ing ex-clu-ded, pride I a-base— I'm
2. from God to de-part; Je-sus has found me, hap-py my case— I
3. or else I must die; Sin had a-larmed me, fear-ing God's face—But
4. to tell what he knows; Once more to tell it would I em-brace— I'm

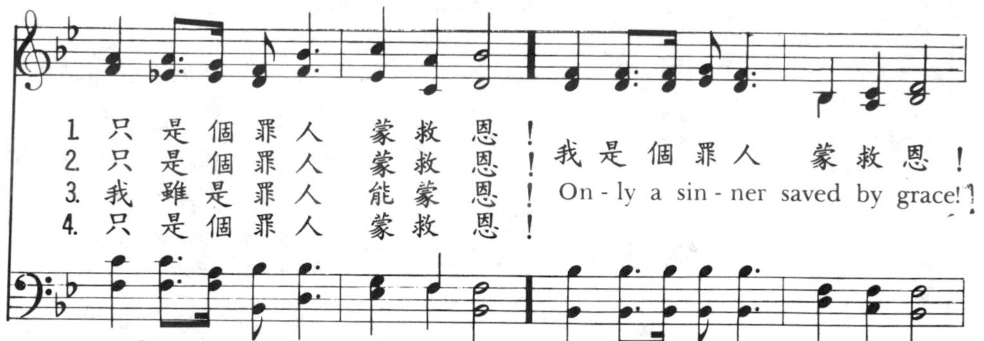
1. 只是個罪人蒙救恩！
2. 只是個罪人蒙救恩！
3. 我雖是罪人能蒙恩！
4. 只是個罪人蒙救恩！
我是個罪人蒙救恩！
On-ly a sin-ner saved by grace!

1. on-ly a sin-ner saved by grace!
2. now am a sin-ner saved by grace!
3. now I'm a sin-ner saved by grace!
4. on-ly a sin-ner saved by grace!

蒙主的恩典 得 重 生！讚 美主耶穌，榮
On - ly a sin - ner saved by grace! This is my sto - ry, To
耀 都歸天父，我 只 是個罪人 蒙救恩！
God be the glo - ry— I'm on - ly a sin - ner saved by grace!

Ephesians 3:14-4:6

For this reason I kneel before the Father, from whom the whole family of believers in heaven and on earth derives its name. I pray that out of His glorious riches He may strengthen you with power through His Spirit in your inner being, so that Christ may dwell in your hearts through faith. And I pray that you, being rooted and established in love, may have power, together with all the saints, to grasp how wide and long and high and deep is the love of Christ, and to know this love that surpasses knowledge—that you may be filled to the measure of all the fullness of God.

Now to Him who is able to do immeasurably more than all we ask or imagine, according to His power that is at work within us, to Him be glory in the church and in Christ Jesus throughout all generations, for ever and ever!

As a prisoner for the Lord, then, I urge you to live a life worthy of the calling you have received. Be completely humble and gentle; be patient, bearing with one another in love. Make every effort to keep the unity of the Spirit through the bond of peace. There is one body and one Spirit—just as you were called to one hope when you were called—one Lord, one faith, one baptism; one God and Father of all, who is over all and through all and in all.

—(NIV)

450

主啊！我今來

I Am Coming, Lord

So Christ was once offered to bear the sins of many. . . . Hebrews 9:28

Lewis Hartsough, 1828-1919 Lewis Hartsough, 1828-1919

1. 我 心何等歡 喜，因 聽救主説 道；我 為你罪流
2. 我 本軟弱可 憐，行 善毫無能 力；惟 主能顯救
3. 求 主賜我聖 靈，充 滿在我的 心；更 求我主恩

1. I hear Thy welcome voice, That calls me, Lord, to thee For cleans-ing in Thy
2. *Though coming weak and vile, Thou do my strength assure; Thou do my vile-ness*
3. 'Tis Je-sus calls me on To per-fect faith and love, To per-fect hope, and

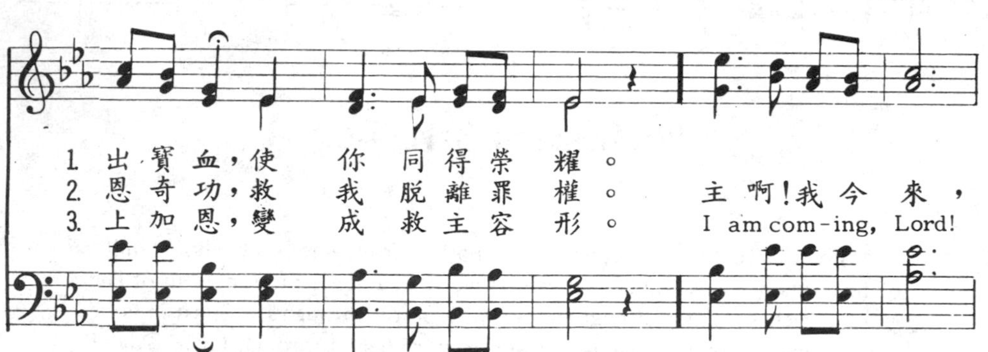

1. 出 寶 血，使 你 同 得 榮 耀 。
2. 恩 奇 功，救 我 脱 離 罪 權 。 主 啊！我 今 來 ，
3. 上 加 恩，變 成 救 主 容 形 。 I am com-ing, Lord!

1. pre-cious blood That flowed on Cal - va -ry.
2. *ful-ly cleanse, Till spot - less all and pure.*
3. peace, and trust, For earth and heaven a-bove.

我今來就祢，求主洗淨 我罪愆，洗 淨在寶血裏 。
Com-ing now to thee! Wash me, cleanse me in the blood That flowed on Cal-va-ry.

耶穌同在就是天堂

Where Jesus Is, 'Tis Heaven

And the Word became flesh and dwelt among us . . . . — John 1:14

C. F. Butler J. M. Black

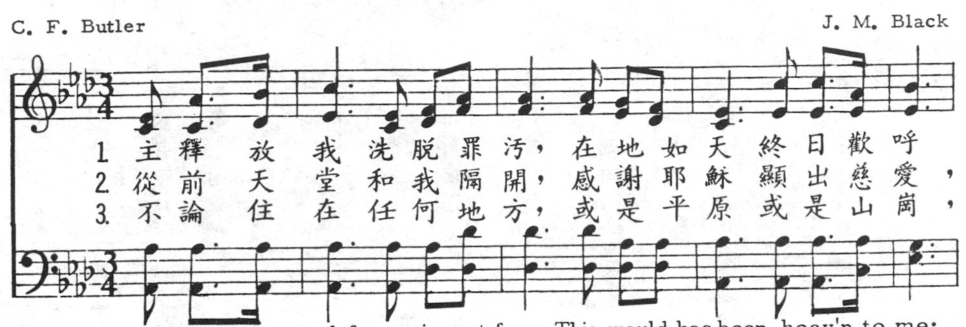
1. 主釋放我洗脱罪污，在地如天終日歡呼
2. 從前天堂和我隔開，感謝耶穌顯出慈愛，
3. 不論住在任何地方，或是平原或是山崗，
1. Since Christ my soul from sin set free, This world has been heav'n to me;
2. Once heav-en seemed a far-off place, Till Je-sus showed His smiling face.
3. What mat-ters where on earth we dwell? On moun-tain-top or in the dell,

1. 世上難免憂愁困苦，認識耶穌得享天福。
2. 如今天堂在我心懷，永永遠遠不會更改。
3. 或是大厦或是帳蓬，耶穌同在就是天堂。
1. And mid earth's sor-rows and its woe 'Tis heav'n my Je-sus here to know.
2. Now it's be-gun with-in my soul; 'Twill last while end-less a-ges roll.
3. In cot-tage or a man-sion fair, Where Je-sus is, 'tis heav-en there.

哈利路亞，真是天堂，罪得赦免，就是天堂，
Oh, hal-le-lu-jah, yes, 'tis heav'n, 'Tis heav'n to know my sins forgiv'n!
無論岸上無論海洋，耶穌同在就是天堂。
On land or sea, what mat-ters where? Where Je-sus is, 'tis heav-en there.

452

祂救我
He Touched Me

William J. Gaither

And Jesus put forth His hand and touched him, saying, I will; be thou clean. — Matthew 8:3

HE TOUCHED ME
William J. Gaither

1. 罪的重擔將我捆住，滿心羞愧與憂愁—幸有耶穌向我伸手，祂釋放我，使我得拯救。
2. 自從我認識主耶穌，祂洗我一切罪污，我願永遠讚美救主—高聲稱頌，到天家見主。
1 Shack-led by a heav-y bur-den, 'Neath a load of guilt and shame— Then the hand of Je-sus touched me, And now I am no long-er the same.
2 Since I met this bless-ed Sav-ior, Since He cleansed and made me whole, I will nev-er cease to praise Him— I'll shout it while e-ter-ni-ty rolls.
祂救我，祂拯救我，天上喜樂今充滿我；救主使我生命改變，祂救我，使我得完全。
He touched me, O He touched me, And O the joy that floods my soul; Some-thing hap-pened, and now I know, He touched me and made me whole.

453

祂拯救我
He Lifted Me

He brought me up out of a horrible pit . . . — Psalm 40:2

HE LIFTED ME
Charles H. Gabriel

Charles H. Gabriel

1. 救主耶穌由天而來，為要使我蒙祂慈愛；
2. 恩主呼聲為時已久，但我硬心不肯回頭；
3. 主為我戴荊棘冠冕，兩手被釘滴下血點；
4. 現在我靈快樂平安，因我住處安全無險；

1 In lov-ing-kind-ness Je-sus came My soul in mer-cy to re-claim,
2 *He called me long be-fore I heard, Be-fore my sin-ful heart was stirred,*
3 His brow was pierced with man-y a thorn, His hands by cru-el nails were torn,
4 *Now on a high-er plane I dwell, And with my soul I know 'tis well;*

1. 祂經羞辱罪惡壓害，伸張恩手救我。
2. 我今醒悟懊悔前非，蒙主赦免拯救。
3. 因我陷在罪中可憐，主伸愛手救我。
4. 我真難以用口說盡，耶穌如何救我。

1 And from the depths of sin and shame Through grace He lift-ed me.
2 *But when I took Him at His word, For-given He lift-ed me.*
3 When from my guilt and grief, for-lorn, In love He lift-ed me.
4 *Yet how or why, I can-not tell, He should have lift-ed me.*

從污泥中祂拯救我，用慈愛手祂拯救我；
From sink-ing sand He lift-ed me, With ten-der hand He lift-ed me;
從黑暗中大顯亮光，讚美主名，祂拯救我！
From shades of night to plains of light, O praise His name, He lift-ed me!

454

主愛救我

Love Lifted Me

To this end was I born, and for this cause came I into the world.
— John 18:37

James Rowe

Howard E. Smith

1. 我曾陷溺罪海中，遠離了安全港，被罪惡壓
2. 我今願獻身心靈，跟隨救主到底，我願讚美
3. 當你遇危險災害，應當仰望救主，祂有恩典

1. I was sink-ing deep in sin, far from the peace-ful shore, Ver - y deep-ly
2. All my heart to Him I give, Ev - er to Him I'll cling, In His bless-ed
3. Souls in dan-ger, look a-bove, Je - sus com-plete-ly saves; He will lift you

1. 身深重，心中痛苦失望；幸蒙萬有大主宰，
2. 主聖名，在祂懷中安息；主的愛廣大真誠，
3. 與大愛，必定拯救幫助；祂是海洋大主宰，

1. stained with-in, Sink-ing to rise no more; But the Mas-ter of the sea
2. pres - ence live, Ev - er His prais - es sing. Love so might-y and so true
3. by His love Out of the an - gry waves. He's the Mas-ter of the sea,

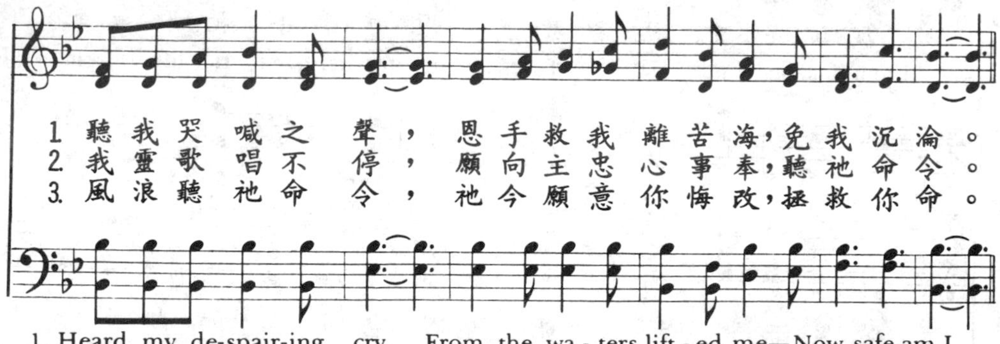
1. 聽我哭喊之聲，恩手救我離苦海，免我沉淪。
2. 我靈歌唱不停，願向主忠心事奉，聽祂命令。
3. 風浪聽祂命令，祂今願意你悔改，拯救你命。

1. Heard my de-spair-ing cry, From the wa - ters lift - ed me—Now safe am I.
2. Mer - its my soul's best songs; Faith-ful, lov - ing serv - ice too To Him be-longs.
3. Bil - lows His will o - bey; He your Sav - ior wants to be— Be saved to-day.

主愛救我，主愛救我，當我灰
Love lift - ed me, Love lift - ed me; When noth - ing
心絕望，主愛救我。主愛救我，
else could help, Love lift - ed me. Love lift - ed me,
主愛救我；當我灰心絕望，主愛救我。
Love lift - ed me; When noth-ing else could help, Love lift-ed me.

The Lord appeared to us in the past, saying:
"I have loved you with an everlasting love;
I have drawn you with lovingkindness."

— Jeremiah 31:3. NIV

455

天上榮耀，将我心靈充滿

Heaven Came Down and Glory Filled My Soul

John W. Peterson

And suddenly there shone round about Him a light from Heaven; Acts 9:3

HEAVEN CAME DOWN

John W. Peterson

1. 何 等的 奇 妙，奇 妙 的 日 子， 那 日 子 不 能 忘
2. 屬 天的 生 命 由 聖 靈 而 生， 進 入 神 聖 的 家
3. 我 已 經 得 着 確 實 的 盼 望， 當 我 生 命 将 結
1 O what a won-der-ful, won-der-ful day— Day I will nev-er for-
2 Born of the Spir-it with life from a-bove In-to God's fam-ily di-
3 Now I've a hope that will sure-ly en-dure Aft-er the pass-ing of

1. 記 ； 當 我 在 黑 暗 道 路 中 流 離 ， 我 與 主
2. 中 ； 因 加 略 山 的 愛 我 得 稱 義 ， 何 等 福
3. 束 ； 在 天 家 主 為 我 預 備 住 處 ， 榮 耀 中
1 get; Aft-er I'd wan-dered in dark-ness a-way, Je-sus my
2 vine, Jus-ti-fied ful-ly through Cal-va-ry's love, O what a
3 time; I have a fu-ture in heav-en for sure, There in those

1. 耶 穌 相 遇 。 何 等的 溫 柔，祂 是 我 良 友，
2. 氣 與 光 榮 ！ 我 是 個 罪 人 來 到 主 面 前，
3. 與 主 同 住 。 都 因 那 奇 妙 難 忘 的 日 子，
1 Sav-ior I met. O what a ten-der, com-pas-sion-ate friend—
2 stand-ing is mine! And the trans-ac-tion so quick-ly was made
3 man-sions sub-lime. And it's be-cause of that won-der-ful day

1. 滿 足 我 心 靈 需 求 ； 黑 雲 已 消 散，我
2. 主 賜 我 赦 罪 恩 典 ； 祂 已 拯 救 我，讚
3. 十 架 下 我 的 祈 求 ； 永 遠 的 福 氣，極
1 He met the need of my heart; Shad-ows dis-pel-ling, With
2 When as a sin-ner I came, Took of the of-fer Of
3 When at the cross I be-lieved; Rich-es e-ter-nal And

1. 欣喜的去傳，祂使黑夜變為白晝！
2. 美祂的聖名，我今接受這大恩典！
3. 豐富的賞賜，全從祂恩手中接受。
1 joy I am tell-ing, He made all the dark-ness de-part!
2 grace He did prof-fer– He saved me, O praise His dear name!
3 bless-ings su-per-nal From His pre-cious hand I re-ceived.
天上榮耀將我心靈充滿，
Heav-en came down and glo-ry filled my soul,
十架恩典今使我得完全；我
When at the cross the Sav-ior made me whole; My
罪已經洗清，黑夜已轉為光明；
sins were washed a-way And my night was turned to day–
天上榮耀將我心靈充滿！
Heav-en came down and glo-ry filled my soul!

456
自耶穌來住在我心
Since Jesus Came Into My Heart
But the fruit of the spirit is love, joy, peace, ... — Galatians 5:22
Rufus H. McDaniel
McDANIEL
Charles H. Gabriel
1. 我生命已有了真奇妙的改變，自耶穌來
2. 我已停止流蕩不再入那迷途，自耶穌來
3. 我深知與救主將永住那美城，自耶穌來
1 What a won-der-ful change in my life has been wrought Since Je-sus came
2 I have ceased from my wan-dering and go-ing a-stray, Since Je-sus came
3 I shall go there to dwell in that Cit-y, I know, Since Je-sus came
1. 住在我心！我久慕的亮光今照耀我魂間，
2. 住在我心！我的罪雖衆多主寶血已塗抹，
3. 住在我心！我心中充滿喜樂勇敢往前行，
1 in-to my heart! I have light in my soul for which long I have sought,
2 in-to my heart! And my sins, which were man-y, are all washed a-way,
3 in-to my heart! And I'm hap-py, so hap-py, as on-ward I go,
自耶穌來住在我心！自耶穌來住在我
Since Je-sus came in-to my heart! Since Je-sus came in-to my
心，自耶穌來住在我心，喜樂潮溢我
heart, Since Je-sus came in-to my heart, Floods of joy o'er my
魂如海濤浪滾滾，自耶穌來住在我心。
soul like the sea bil-lows roll, Since Je-sus came in-to my heart.

我今永遠屬祢

Now I Belong to Jesus

Abide in Me, and I in you. — John 15:4

ELLSWORTH
Norman J. Clayton

Norman J. Clayton

1. 耶 穌 我 主 愛 我 永 不 止 息，無 權 勢 能 叫
2. 從 前 我 在 罪 中 迷 醉 浮 沉，耶 穌 降 世 給
3. 我 心 快 樂 因 我 已 得 拯 救，前 為 罪 奴 今
1 Je - sus my Lord will love me for - ev - er, From Him no power of
2 Once I was lost in sin's deg - ra - da - tion, Je - sus came down to
3 Joy floods my soul for Je - sus has saved me, Freed me from sin that
1. 我 與 主 分 離，祂 救 贖 我 捨 命 於 十 架，
2. 我 帶 來 救 恩，不 再 有 羞 恥 憂 傷 懼 怕，
3. 主 賜 我 自 由，為 救 贖 我 祂 寶 血 流 下，
1 e - vil can sev - er, He gave His life to ran - som my soul,
2 bring me sal - va - tion, Lift - ed me up from sor - row and shame,
3 long had en-slaved me; His pre-cious blood He gave to re - deem,
1. 我 今 永 遠 屬 祂；
2. 我 今 永 遠 屬 祂；
3. 我 今 永 遠 屬 祂；
我 今 屬 於 主
Now I be - long to
1 Now I be - long to Him;
2 Now I be - long to Him;
3 Now I be - long to Him;
耶 穌，主 耶 穌 屬 於 我，並 非 暫
Je - sus, Je - sus be-longs to me, Not for the
時 與 祂 相 連，乃 是 直 到 永 遠。
years of time a - lone, But for e - ter - ni - ty.

458

我已蒙恩得救

Edwin O. Excell

I know that my redeemer liveth . . . . — Job 19:25

OTHELLO
Edwin O. Excell

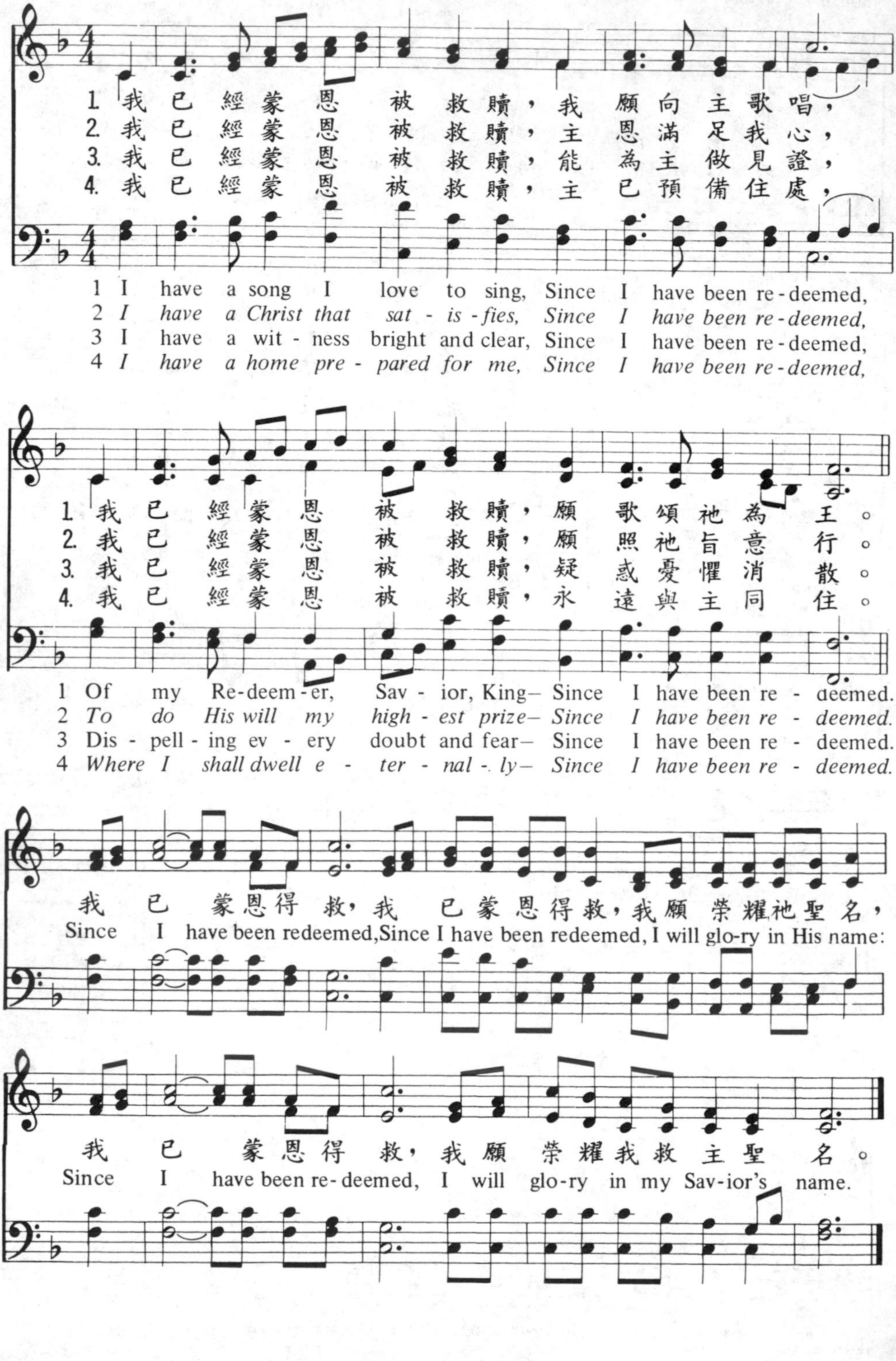

1. 我已經蒙恩被救贖，我願向主歌唱，
2. 我已經蒙恩被救贖，主恩滿足我心，
3. 我已經蒙恩被救贖，能為主做見證，
4. 我已經蒙恩被救贖，主已預備住處，

1 I have a song I love to sing, Since I have been re-deemed,
2 *I have a Christ that sat - is - fies, Since I have been re-deemed,*
3 I have a wit - ness bright and clear, Since I have been re-deemed,
4 *I have a home pre - pared for me, Since I have been re-deemed,*

1. 我已經蒙恩被救贖，願歌頌祂為王。
2. 我已經蒙恩被救贖，願照祂旨意行。
3. 我已經蒙恩被救贖，疑惑憂懼消散。
4. 我已經蒙恩被救贖，永遠與主同住。

1 Of my Re-deem - er, Sav - ior, King– Since I have been re - deemed.
2 *To do His will my high - est prize– Since I have been re - deemed.*
3 Dis - pell - ing ev - ery doubt and fear– Since I have been re - deemed.
4 *Where I shall dwell e - ter - nal - ly– Since I have been re - deemed.*

我已蒙恩得救，我已蒙恩得救，我願榮耀祂聖名，
Since I have been redeemed, Since I have been redeemed, I will glo-ry in His name:

我已蒙恩得救，我願榮耀我救主聖名。
Since I have been re-deemed, I will glo-ry in my Sav-ior's name.

救贖
Redeemed

Let the redeemed of the Lord say so. . . . — Psalm 107:2

REDEEMED

Fanny J. Crosby William J. Kirkpatrick

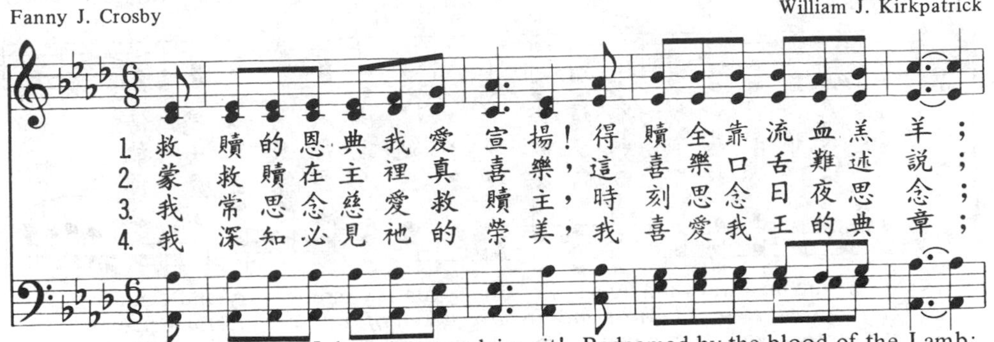
1. 救贖的恩典我愛宣揚！得贖全靠流血羔羊；
2. 蒙救贖在主裡真喜樂，這喜樂口舌難述說；
3. 我常思念慈愛救贖主，時刻思念日夜思念；
4. 我深知必見祂的榮美，我喜愛我王的典章；

1 Redeemed—how I love to pro-claim it! Redeemed by the blood of the Lamb;
2 *Redeemed and so hap-py in Je-sus, No lan-guage my rap-ture can tell;*
3 I think of my bless-ed Re-deem-er, I think of Him all the day long;
4 *I know I shall see in His beau-ty The King in whose law I de-light;*

1. 因神憐憫我已蒙救贖，做神兒女恩福永享。
2. 我深知祂常與我同在，慈愛光輝常引導我。
3. 我禁不住要向祂歌唱，歌唱主的慈愛甘甜。
4. 祂親切的保守我腳步，使我在黑夜中歌唱。

1 Redeemed through His in-fi-nite mer-cy, His child, and for-ev-er, I am.
2 *I know that the light of His pres-ence With me shall con-tin-ual-ly dwell.*
3 I sing, for I can-not be si-lent; His love is the theme of my song.
4 *Who lov-ing-ly guards ev-ery foot-step, And gives me a song in the night.*

救贖，救贖，得贖全靠流血羔羊。
Re-deemed, re-deemed, Re-deemed by the blood of the Lamb.
救贖，救贖，做神兒女恩福永享。
Re-deemed, re-deemed, His child, and for-ev-er, I am.

460

藉我賜恩福

Make Me a Blessing

And I will make them and the places round about my hill a blessing . . .
— Ezekiel 34:26

Ira B. Wilson | SCHULER | George S. Schuler

1. 在塵世生命崎嶇道路中，多少人困倦悲傷；
2. 述說耶穌基督慈愛故事，述說祂赦罪大能；
3. 白白得來故要白白施與，愛人要像主愛你；
1 Out in the high-ways and by-ways of life, Man-y are wea-ry and sad;
2 Tell the sweet sto-ry of Christ and His love, Tell of His power to for-give;
3 Give as 'twas giv-en to you in your need, Love as the Mas-ter loved you;
1. 黑暗滿佈快把真光照亮 使憂傷者變歡暢。
2. 別人信主要藉你去見證，生活時刻像明燈。
3. 對軟弱者務要盡力攙扶，忠於主始終如一。
1 Car-ry the sun-shine where dark-ness is rife, Mak-ing the sor-row-ing glad.
2 Oth-ers will trust Him if on-ly you prove True, ev-ery mo-ment you live.
3 Be to the help-less a help-er in-deed, Un-to your mis-sion be true.
藉我賜恩福，藉我賜恩福，藉我生命榮耀主名；藉我賜恩福，救主，聽我求，藉我賜恩福，使他人得救。
Make me a bless-ing, Make me a bless-ing — Out of my life May Je-sus shine; Make me a bless-ing, O Sav-ior, I pray, Make me a bless-ing to some-one to-day.

趕快去傳福音
Rescue the Perishing

RESCUE
And His disciples came to Him. . . , saying, Lord, save us, we perish.
Matthew 8:25
Fanny J. Crosby
William H. Doane
1. 趕 快 去 傳 福 音，救 失 喪 靈 魂，從 罪 惡 中 及 陰
2. 人 雖 輕 忽 主 愛，主 還 是 等 待，盼 望 他 們 為 罪
3. 世 人 心 靈 深 處，經 試 探 摧 殘，知 覺 麻 木 惟 靠
4. 趕 快 去 傳 福 音，是 信 徒 本 份，主 加 力 量 使 你
1 Res - cue the per - ish - ing, Care for the dy - ing, Snatch them in pit-y from
2 Tho they are slight-ing Him, Still He is wait - ing, Wait - ing the pen-i-tent
3 Down in the hu-man heart, Crushed by the tempt-er, Feel - ings lie bur-ied that
4 Res - cue the per - ish - ing– Du - ty de-mands it! Strength for thy la-bor the
1. 府 救 亡 羊；替 迷 路 人 哀 求，引 他 們 回 頭，
2. 憂 傷 悔 改；當 以 溫 柔 誠 懇，勸 他 們 虛 心，
3. 主 恩 甦 醒；用 愛 心 相 款 待，仁 慈 的 照 應，
4. 能 勝 此 任；當 以 忍 耐 勤 勞，領 他 走 窄 路，
1 sin and the grave; Weep o'er the err - ing one, Lift up the fall - en,
2 child to re - ceive; Plead with them ear-nest-ly, Plead with them gen-tly,
3 grace can re - store; Touched by a lov - ing heart, Wak - ened by kind - ness,
4 Lord will pro-vide; Back to the nar - row way Pa - tient-ly win them,
1. 傳 揚 耶 穌，有 大 權 能 拯 救。
2. 若 肯 相 信，必 蒙 赦 罪 大 恩。
3. 心 弦 雖 斷，仍 能 再 發 聲 音。
4. 主 已 代 死，罪 人 當 信 耶 穌。
趕 快 去 傳 福 音，
Res - cue the per - ish-ing,
1 Tell them of Je - sus, the might - y to save.
2 He will for - give if they on - ly be - lieve.
3 Chords that are bro - ken will vi - brate once more.
4 Tell the poor wan-derer a Sav - ior has died.
救 失 喪 靈 魂；耶 穌 滿 心 慈 悲，拯 救 罪 人。
Care for the dy - ing; Je - sus is mer - ci - ful, Je - sus will save.

462

我願傳講我是基督徒
I'll Tell the World That I'm A Christian

For I am not ashamed of the gospel of Christ . . . — Romans 1:16

Baynard L. Fox
TUCKER
Baynard L. Fox
1. 我願傳講 我是基督徒，靠祂的名 不以為
2. 我願傳講 祂必要再來，或在近處 或在遠
1 I'll tell the world that I'm a Chris-tian— I'm not a-shamed His name to
2 I'll tell the world that He is com-ing— It may be near or far a-
1. 恥；我願傳講 我是基督徒，我與 祂同行
2. 地；應當儆醒 等候祂再來，或許 是明日
1 bear; I'll tell the world that I'm a Chris-tian— I'll take Him with me
2 way; But we must live as if His com-ing Would be to-mor-row
1. 任何地。對世人說—耶穌拯救我，祂又賜
2. 或今日。當祂再來—生命將過去，但信靠
1 an-y-where. I'll tell the world how Je-sus saved me, And how He
2 or to-day. For when He comes and life is o-ver, For those who
1. 給我 新的生命；我深知 你若願信祂，
2. 祂的 必得永生；祂為你 也為我預備，
1 gave me a life brand-new; And I know that if you trust Him
2 love Him there's more to be; Eyes have nev-er seen the won-ders

1. 祂也必賜你 新的生命。對世人說一
2. 眼未曾見的 一切豐盛。快向人說一
1 That all He gave me He'll give to you. I'll tell the world
2 That He's pre - par - ing for you and me. O tell the world
1. 祂是我救主，無人像祂 如此愛我；我的生
2. 你是基督徒，靠祂的名 不以為恥；快向人
1 that He's my Sav-ior, No oth-er one could love me so; My life, my
2 that you're a Chris-tian, Be not a-shamed His name to bear; O tell the
1. 命 已完全屬祂，任祂差遣我，我必去。
2. 說 你是基督徒，祂與你同行，任何地。
1 all is His for - ev - er, And where He leads me I will go.
2 world that you're a Chris-tian, And take Him with you ev - ery - where.

463

我們有一故事傳給萬邦

We've a Story to Tell to the Nations

Go ye, therefore, and teach all nations. . . . — Matthew 28:19

MESSAGE

H. Ernest Nichol — H. Ernest Nichol

1. 我們有一故事傳給萬邦，能使人心
2. 我們有一詩歌唱給萬邦，能使人心
3. 我們有一信息傳給萬邦，主在高天
4. 我們要將救主傳給萬邦，祂曾經歷

1 We've a sto - ry to tell to the na - tions That shall turn their
2 *We've a song to be sung to the na - tions That shall lift their*
3 We've a mes - sage to give to the na - tions—That the Lord who
4 *We've a Sav - ior to show to the na - tions Who the path of*

1. 回轉歸正，這故事真實又美妙，滿
2. 向主歸降，這詩歌能勝過罪惡，能
3. 掌權做王，差遣獨生子救我們，真
4. 人間痛苦，但願世上一切人們，在

1 hearts to the right, A sto - ry of truth and mer - cy, A
2 *hearts to the Lord, A song that shall con - quer e - vil And*
3 reign - eth a - bove Hath sent us His Son to save us And
4 *sor - row hath trod, That all of the world's great peo - ples Might*

1. 有平安與光明，滿有平安與光明。
2. 粉碎利劍矛槍，能粉碎利劍矛槍。
3. 神的慈愛無量，真神的慈愛無量。
4. 真理之下屈服，在真理之下屈服。

1 sto - ry of peace and light, A sto - ry of peace and light.
2 *shat - ter the spear and sword, And shat - ter the spear and sword.*
3 show us that God is love, And show us that God is love.
4 *come to the truth of God, Might come to the truth of God.*

因黑 夜必要轉為 晨 光，到正 午更顯得輝煌 ，
For the dark-ness shall turn to dawn-ing, And the dawn-ing to noon-day bright,
基 督國度就降 臨 地上，全 地充滿愛與 光 。
And Christ's great king-dom shall come on earth, The king-dom of love and light.

這事以後，主又設立七十個人，差遣他們兩個兩個的，在他前面往自己所要到的各城各地方去。就對他們說，要收的莊稼多，作工的人少，所以你們當求莊稼的主，打發工人出去收他的莊稼。你們去吧，我差你們去，如同羊羔進入狼羣。

路加福音十章
1—3

After this the Lord appointed seventy-two others and send them two by two ahead of him to every town and place where he was about to go. He told them, "The harvest is plentiful, but the workers are few. Ask the Lord of the harvest, therefore, to send out workers into his harvest field. Go! I am sending you out like lambs among wolves.

Luke 10 : 1-3. NIV

464

往普天下傳福音

Far, Far Away in Sin and Darkness Dwelling

Based on Matthew 28:18-20
James McGranahan

Then said I, Here am I; send me. — Isaiah 6:8

GO YE
James McGranahan

1. 遥遠地方，罪惡黑暗正籠罩，千萬靈魂，即
2. 世界各處，傳福音門已開放，基督精兵，應
3. "何必死亡?"這是救主的呼聲，"何必死亡?"當
4. 但願不久，普天下萬族萬邦，"榮耀歸神!"得
1 Far, far a-way, in sin and dark-ness dwell-ing, Mil-lions of souls for-
2 See o'er the world wide o-pen doors in-vit-ing, Sol-diers of Christ, a-
3 "Why will ye die?" the voice of God is call-ing, "Why will ye die?" re-
4 God speed the day, when those of ev-ery na-tion "Glo-ry to God!" tri-

1. 将永遠喪亡；有誰願意，為主前往去宣道，
2. 當勇敢前往！信徒興起！集合衆人的力量，
3. 奉主名响應；耶穌受死，救人脱死亡得生，
4. 勝凱歌高唱；蒙恩救贖，充滿了歡欣盼望，
1 ev-er may be lost; Who then will go, sal-va-tion's sto-ry tell-ing,
2 rise and en-ter in! Chris-tians, a-wake! your forc-es all u-nit-ing,
3 ech-o in His name; Je-sus hath died to save from death ap-pall-ing,
4 um-phant-ly shall ring; Ran-somed, re-deemed, re-joic-ing in sal-va-tion,

1. 不怕付代價，将福音傳揚？
"一切權
2. 粉碎罪鎖鏈，将福音傳揚。
3. 快快去傳揚，主救人福音。
"All power is
4. 唱哈利路亞，尊救主為王。
1 Look-ing to Je-sus, mind-ing not the cost?
2 Send forth the gos-pel, break the chains of sin.
3 Life and sal-va-tion there-fore go pro-claim.
4 Shout Hal-le-lu-jah, for the Lord is King.

柄已賜給我，一　切權　柄已賜給我，你們要往
giv-en un-to Me, All power is giv-en un-to Me, Go ye in-to
普天下去　宣傳福音，我　必　與你　永遠　同在，"
all the world and preach the gos-pel, And lo, I am with you al-way."

我又聽見主的聲音，說，我可以差遣誰呢？誰肯為我去呢？我說，我在這裡，請差遣我。

以賽亞書六章
8

Then I heard the voice of the Lord saying,
"Whom shall I send? And who will go for us?"

Isaiah 6:8. NIV

465

我愛傳講主福音
I Love to Tell the Story

. . . They that were scattered abroad went everywhere preaching the word.

— Acts 8:4

HANKEY
Katherine Hankey
William G. Fischer
1. 我愛傳講主福音，傳講天上妙事，
2. 我愛傳講主福音，福音美妙清新，
3. 我愛傳講主福音，越傳越覺甘甜，
4. 我愛傳講主福音，有人雖常聽聞，
1 I love to tell the story Of unseen things above,
2 I love to tell the story– More wonderful it seems
3 I love to tell the story– 'Tis pleasant to repeat
4 I love to tell the story– For those who know it best
1. 傳講耶穌愛罪人，傳講祂為人死；
2. 勝過一切的珍品，勝過所有黃金；
3. 每逢對人來講論，愈講愈覺新鮮；
4. 但仍飢渴願多聽，像那未聽之人；
1 Of Jesus and His glory, Of Jesus and His love;
2 Than all the golden fancies Of all our golden dreams;
3 What seems, each time I tell it, More wonderfully sweet;
4 Seem hungering and thirsting To hear it like the rest;
1. 我愛傳講主福音，福音是神大能，
2. 我愛傳講主福音，向人不斷傳講，
3. 我愛傳講主福音，傳講救恩信息，
4. 一日我必唱新歌，在那榮耀天庭，
1 I love to tell the story– Because I know 'tis true,
2 I love to tell the story– It did so much for me,
3 I love to tell the story– For some have never heard
4 And when in scenes of glory I sing the new, new song,

1. 能救罪人免沉淪，能叫死人得生。
2. 福音使我得生命，使我心靈歡暢。
3. 尚有人從未聽聞，真神救人故事。
4. 新歌仍是我一生所愛—老舊福音。
1 It sat - is - fies my long - ings As noth - ing else can do.
2 And that is just the rea - son I tell it now to Thee.
3 The mes - sage of sal - va - tion From God's own ho - ly word.
4 'Twill be the old, old sto - ry That I have loved so long.
我愛傳講主福音！傳講老舊的福音—
I love to tell the sto - ry! 'Twill be my theme in glo - ry—
傳講耶穌愛罪人，傳講耶穌救恩。
To tell the old, old sto - ry Of Je - sus and His love.

馬其頓呼聲
Macedonia

And the word of the Lord was published throughout all the region. — Acts 13:49

Anne Ortlund

ALL SAINTS, NEW
Henry S. Cutler

1. 世界正在迅速沉淪，人心痛苦呻吟，
2. 荒野蠻人迷信偶像，懼怕黑夜來臨，
3. 現代傳播工具日新，知識迅速加增，
4. 審判鐘聲今正鳴响，基督十架隱現，
1 The vi - sion of a dy - ing world Is vast be - fore our eyes;
2 *The sav - age hugs his god of stone And fears de - scent of night;*
3 To - day, as un - der - stand - ing's bounds Are stretched on ev - ery hand,
4 *The warn - ing bell of judg - ment tolls, A - bove us looms the cross;*

1. 眼見各種預兆象徵，迫切需要救恩；
2. 城市居民孤單惆悵，雖處華美灯林；
3. 用新方法傳主福音，使全地得救恩；
4. 多少靈魂沉淪失喪，何等可惜可憐！
1 We feel the heart - beat of its need, We hear its fee - ble cries:
2 *The cit - y dwell - er cring - es lone A - mid the gar - ish light:*
3 O clothe Thy Word in bright, new sounds, And speed it o'er the land;
4 *A - round are ev - er - dy - ing souls– How great, how great the loss!*

1. 懇求我主，復興教會，現今正是時機！
2. 懇求我主，興起教會，關心世人苦情！
3. 懇求我主，賜下力量，多方傳主救恩！
4. 懇求我主，激勵教會，盡速傳揚佳音！
1 Lord Je - sus Christ, re - vive Thy church In this, her cru - cial hour!
2 *Lord Je - sus Christ, a - rouse Thy church To see their mute dis - tress!*
3 Lord Je - sus Christ, em - pow - er us To preach by ev - ery means!
4 *O Lord, con - strain and move Thy church, The glad news to im - part!*

1. 懇 求 我 主，喚 醒 教 會，充 滿 聖 靈 能 力。
2. 懇 求 我 主，恩 待 教 會，充 滿 憐 憫 愛 心。
3. 懇 求 我 主，剛 強 教 會，遠 近 都 蒙 主 恩。
4. 懇 求 我 主，感 動 教 會，首 先 感 動 我 心。阿門。
1 Lord Je - sus Christ, a - wake Thy church With Spir - it - giv - en power.
2 Lord Je - sus Christ, e - quip Thy church With love and ten - der - ness.
3 Lord Je - sus Christ, em - bold - en us In near and dis - tant scenes.
4 And Lord, as Thou dost stir Thy church, Be - gin with - in my heart. A-men.

耶穌進前來，對他們說，
天上地下所有的權柄，都賜給我了。
所以你們要去，使萬民作我的門徒，
奉父子聖靈的名，給他們施洗。
凡我所吩咐你們的，都教訓他們遵守；
我就常與你們同在，直到世界的末了。

馬太二十八章18—20

And Jesus came up and spoke to them, saying,
"All authority has been given to Me
In Heaven and on earth.
Go therefore and make disciples of all the nations,
Baptizing them in the name of the Father,
And the Son and the Holy Spirit.
Teaching them to observe all that I commanded you;
and lo,
I am with you always, even to the end of the age."

Matthew 28:18-20

任主差派
I'll Go Where You Want Me to Go

Paul, a servant of Jesus Christ . . . separated unto the Gospel of God. — Romans 1:1

Mary Brown, stanza 1
Charles E. Prior, stanzas 2, 3

I'LL GO
Carrie E. Rounsefell

1. 主願用我事奉祂之處，未必是要隔重洋，
2. 如今耶穌有慈愛話語，祂願我去為祂傳，
3. 我知主差我作工之處，是世上廣大禾田，

1 It may not be on the moun-tain's height Or o - ver the storm-y sea,
2 *Per - haps to - day there are lov-ing words Which Je-sus would have me speak,*
3 There's sure-ly some-where a low - ly place In earth's har-vest fields so wide,

1. 未必是在那荒山區路，或艱難危險戰場；
2. 如今有人在行走錯路，耶穌願我去追還；
3. 我一生時日不再虛度，全為榮耀主在天；

1 It may not be at the bat-tle-front My Lord will have need of me;
2 *There may be now, in the paths of sin, Some wan-derer whom I should seek;*
3 Where I may la-bor thru life's short day For Je - sus the Cru - ci - fied;

1. 但聞救主溫柔聲招呼，令我赴陌生之途，
2. 主若願引導光滿前途，雖經過幽暗之中，
3. 今願將所有全交我主，報答主莫大恩情，

1 But if by a still, small voice He calls To paths I do not know,
2 *O Sav - ior, if Thou wilt be my Guide, Tho dark and rug-ged the way,*
3 So, trust - ing my all un - to Thy care – I know Thou lov - est me –

1. 我必 欣然的回答 我主，命我何往我必聽從 。
2. 我聞 主命我願隨 主步，命我何言我必聽從 。
3. 願遵 主旨意甘心 順服，派我做何事我必行 。

1 I'll an-swer, dear Lord, with my hand in Thine, I'll go where You want me to go.
2 *My voice shall ech-o the mes-sage sweet, I'll say what You want me to say.*
3 I'll do Thy will with a heart sin-cere, I'll be what You want me to be.

任 主差我何往我 必前往，或 經高山或隔重 洋；

I'll go where You want me to go, dear Lord, O'er moun-tain or plain or sea;

我 必遵主旨意傳主 言語，樂 意事主忠心到底 。

I'll say what You want me to say, dear Lord, I'll be what You want me to be.

468

信徒奮興
O Zion, Haste, Thy Mission High Fulfilling

Mary A. Thomson — *Go ye therefore, and teach all nations . . . .* — Matthew 28:19 — TIDINGS, James Walch

1. 信徒奮興，快將福音去傳揚，普告天
2. 快去傳講，向萬族萬國萬邦，真神是
3. 差遣子女，去傳榮耀的福音，奉獻金
1 O Zi - on, haste, thy mis-sion high ful - fill - ing, To tell to
2 Pro-claim to ev - ery peo-ple, tongue, and na - tion That God in
3 Give of thy sons to bear the mes-sage glo - rious, Give of thy

1. 下，惟有真神是光；使人知道，真神不
2. 愛，是世人的保障；為救罪人，虛己降
3. 錢，差他們到遠方；恒切代禱，幫助他
1 all the world that God is light; That He who made all na - tions
2 whom they live and move is love; Tell how He stooped to save His
3 wealth to speed them on their way; Pour out thy soul for them in

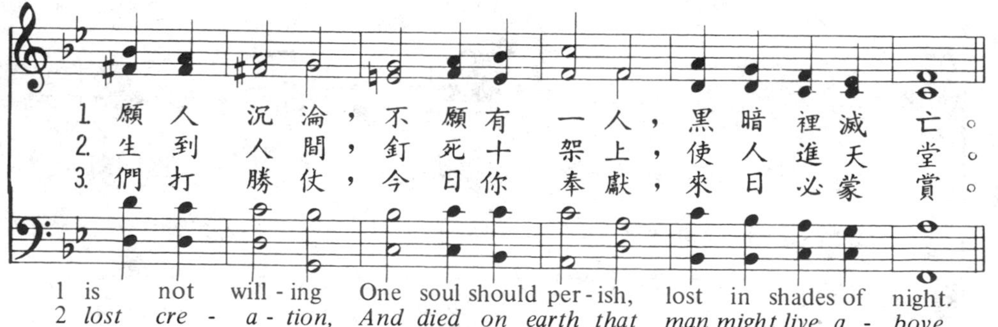
1. 願人沉淪，不願有一人，黑暗裡滅亡。
2. 生到人間，釘死十架上，使人進天堂。
3. 們打勝仗，今日你奉獻，來日必蒙賞。
1 is not will - ing One soul should per - ish, lost in shades of night.
2 lost cre - a - tion, And died on earth that man might live a - bove.
3 prayer vic - to - rious, And haste the com-ing of the glo - rious day.

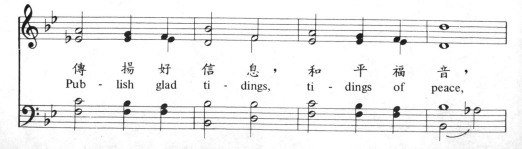

傳揚好信息，和平福音，

Pub - lish glad ti - dings, ti - dings of peace,

傳揚主耶穌已經救贖罪人。阿門。
Ti - dings of Je - sus, re - demp - tion, and re - lease. A - men.

469

等候耶和華的

They that Wait upon the Lord

They that wait upon the Lord . . .
shall mount up with wings as eagles . . . . — Isaiah 40:31

Isaiah 40:31
Stuart Hamblen

TEACH ME LORD
Stuart Hamblen

但那等候耶和華的，必定從新得力，
They that wait up-on the Lord shall re - new their strength;

他們必如鷹展翅上騰；
They shall mount up with wings like ea - gles;

他們奔跑却不困倦，他們行走不疲乏。
They shall run, and not be wea - ry; They shall walk, and not faint.

親愛主，教導我等候。
Teach me, Lord, teach me, Lord, to wait.

470

我差遣你
So Send I You

Peace be unto you; as My Father hath sent me, even also send I you. — John 20:21

Based on John 20:21
E. Margaret Clarkson
SO SEND I YOU
John W. Peterson
1. 我差遣你—靠我恩典能剛強，為我得勝黑暗罪惡權勢，奉我的名，依靠我能力爭戰—我差遣你，為我爭取勝利。
2. 我差遣你—釋放被罪捆綁的，真理話語使他們得永生，罪惡死亡，不能再轄制束縛—我差遣你，尋回失喪的人。
3. 我差遣你—軟弱時我賜力量，憂傷痛苦我賜平安喜樂，我有能力，應許你夠用恩典—我差遣你，為永恒多結果。
4. 我差遣你—忍耐的背起十架，直到天家在我面前卸下，聽我讚賞："你已得榮耀冠冕—忠心僕人，我歡迎你回
1 So send I you— by grace made strong to tri - umph O'er hosts of hell, o'er dark - ness, death and sin, My name to bear, and in that name to con - quer—So send I you, my vic - to - ry to win.
2 So send I you— to take to souls in bond - age The word of truth that sets the cap - tive free, To break the bonds of sin, to loose death's fet - ters—So send I you, to bring the lost to me.
3 So send I you— My strength to know in weak - ness, My joy in grief, My per - fect peace in pain, To prove My power, My grace, My prom-ised pres - ence—So send I you, e - ter - nal fruit to gain.
4 So send I you— to bear My cross with pa - tience, And then one day with joy to lay it down, To hear My voice, "Well done, My faith - ful serv - ant— Come, share My throne, my king-dom and My
Sts. 1,2,3

St. 4
家！" "父神怎樣差遣我，我也差遣你。"
crown!" "As the Fa - ther hath sent Me, So send I you."

471

永生神的靈
Spirit of the Living God

The Holy Spirit fell on us as on them in the beginning.
— Acts 11:15

Daniel Iverson

LIVING GOD
Daniel Iverson

求永生真神的靈，今來復興我，
Spir - it of the Liv - ing God, Fall a - fresh on me,

求永生真神的靈，今來復興我。
Spir - it of the Liv - ing God, Fall a - fresh on me.

碎我，熔我，陶我，用我。
Melt me, mold me, Fill me, use me.

求永生真神的靈，今來復興我。
Spir - it of the Liv - ing God, Fall a - fresh on me.

世界的光是耶穌

The Light of the World Is Jesus

Christ shall give thee light. — Ephesians 5:14

Philip P. Bliss

LIGHT OF THE WORLD
Philip P. Bliss

1. 全世界失喪在黑暗罪惡中，這世界的
2. 凡在耶穌裡面的就無黑暗，這世界的
3. 在天堂裡極光明不需陽光，這世界的
1 The whole world was lost in the dark-ness of sin– The Light of the
2 *No dark-ness have we who in Je-sus a-bide– The Light of the*
3 No need of the sun-light in heav-en, we're told– The Light of that

1. 光是耶穌；主大榮耀如同日光在高空，
2. 光是耶穌；跟主腳步如同行在光明間，
3. 光是耶穌；在金色的城裡羔羊是真光，
1 world is Je-sus; Like sun-shine at noon-day His glo-ry shone in–
2 *world is Je-sus; We walk in the Light when we fol-low our Guide–*
3 world is Je-sus; The Lamb is the Light in the Cit-y of Gold–

1. 這世界的光是耶穌。
2. 這世界的光是耶穌。
3. 這世界的光是耶穌。
快來就光，這
Come to the Light, 'tis
1 The Light of the world is Je-sus.
2 *The Light of the world is Je-sus.*
3 The Light of that world is Je-sus.

光是為你！主的恩光 已照我心裡； 前我瞎
shin - ing for thee! Sweet - ly the Light has dawned up-on me; Once I was
眼，但 今能看見一這 世 界的 光 是 耶 穌。
blind, but now I can see– The Light of the world is Je - sus.

Psalm 89

I feel like singing this morning, O Lord.
I feel like telling everyone about me
how great You are.
If only they could know the depths of Your love
and Your eternal concern for those who
will follow You!
But my songs are so often off-key.
My speech is so inadequate.
I simply cannot express what I feel,
what I know to be true about Your love
for Your creatures upon this world.

But even the songs of the birds
proclaim Your praises.
The heavens and the earth beneath them,
the trees that reach toward You,
the flowers that glow in colorful beauty,
the green hills and soaring mountains,
the valleys and the plains,
the lakes and the rivers,
the great oceans that pound our shores,
they proclaim Your greatness, O God,
and Your love for the sons of men.

How glorious it is to be alive, O Lord!
May every breath of my body,
every beat of my heart,
be dedicated to Your praise and glory.

—Leslie Brandt

473

主耶穌今日在呼召
Hear the Voice of Jesus Calling

They will not believe in Him unless they have heard of Him. — Romans 10:14b

Daniel March
Bryan Jeffery Leech, alt.

RIPLEY
Gregorian Chant
Adapted by Lowell Mason

1. 主耶穌今日在呼召，"誰肯為我去工作？"
2. 你雖不能遠渡重洋，為主到那遙遠地，
3. 你雖不能站在高處，為主作個守望者，
4. 你切勿向救主回答，"我無恩賜事奉主；"

1 Hear the voice of Je-sus call-ing, "Who will go and work to-day?"
2 *If you do not cross the o-cean And a dis-tant land ex-plore,*
3 If you can-not be a watch-man Stand-ing high on Zi-on's wall,
4 *Nev-er find your-self re-peat-ing, "There is noth-ing I can do,"*

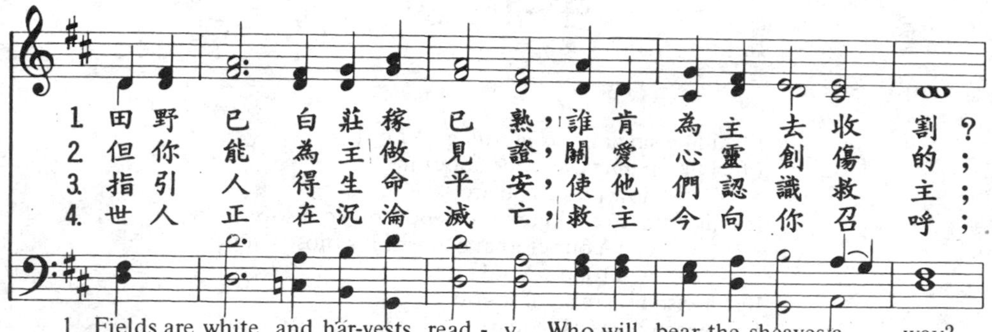
1. 田野已白莊稼已熟，誰肯為主去收割？
2. 但你能為主做見證，關愛心靈創傷的；
3. 指引人得生命平安，使他們認識救主；
4. 世人正在沉淪滅亡，救主今向你召呼；
1 Fields are white and har-vests read-y, Who will bear the sheaves a-way?
2 You can give a lov-ing wit-ness, heal-ing those whose hearts are sore.
3 Point-ing men to find the Sav-ior, Who is life and peace to all,
4 While a world of men is dy-ing, There's a work God calls you to.

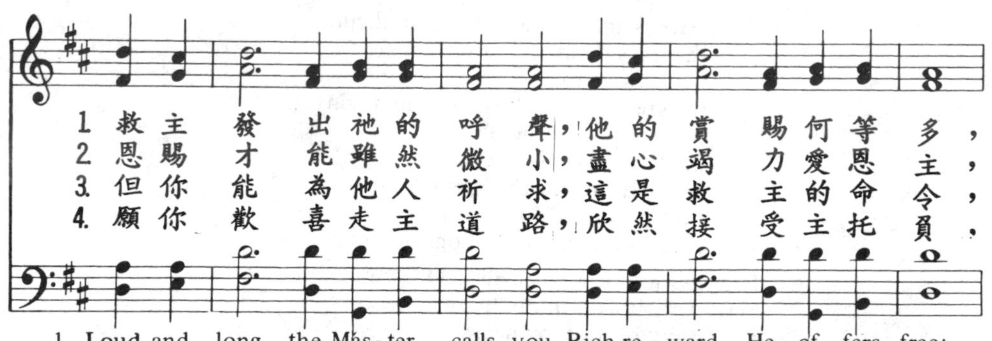
1. 救主發出祂的呼聲，他的賞賜何等多，
2. 恩賜才能雖然微小，盡心竭力愛恩主，
3. 但你能為他人祈求，這是救主的命令，
4. 願你歡喜走主道路，欣然接受主托負，
1 Loud and long the Mas-ter calls you, Rich re-ward He of-fers free;
2 Though your tal-ents may be mea-ger, Of-fer up the things you can,
3 With your gifts and in-ter-ces-sions You can do as He com-mands,
4 Glad-ly take the task He gives you, Let His will your pleas-ure be;

1. 有誰肯欣然的回答，“我在這裡請差我。
2. 奉獻身心為主使用，你所作的都蒙福。
3. 有人為主在遙遠地，你願否與他同心？
4. 當他召你快快回答，“我在這裡請差我。
1 Who will an - swer, glad - ly say - ing, "Here am I, send me, send me."
2 *All that you can do for Je - sus Will be use - ful in His hand.*
3 Join-ing with all faith-ful spokes - men Serv - ing Him in dis - tant lands.
4 *An - swer quick - ly, when He calls you, "Here am I, send me, send me."*

Te Deum

We praise Thee, O God:
We acknowledge Thee to be the Lord.
All the earth doth worship Thee, the Father everlasting.
To Thee all angels cry aloud; the heavens and all the powers therein.
To Thee cherubim and seraphim continually do cry:
Holy, Holy, Holy, Lord God of Sabaoth.
Heaven and earth are full of the majesty of Thy glory.
The glorious company of the apostles praise Thee.
The goodly fellowship of the prophets praise Thee.
The noble army of martyrs praise Thee.
The holy Church, throughout all the world, doth acknowledge Thee,
The Father of an infinite majesty;
Thine adorable, true, and only Son;
Also the Holy Spirit, the Comforter.
Thou art the King of glory, O Christ.
Thou art the everlasting Son of the Father.
When Thou tookest upon Thee to deliver man,
Thou didst humble Thyself to be born of a virgin.
When Thou hadst overcome the sharpness of death,
Thou didst open the kingdom of heaven to all believers.
Thou sittest at the right hand of God, in the glory of the Father.
We believe that Thou shalt come to be our Judge.
We therefore pray Thee, help Thy servants,
Whom Thou hast redeemed with Thy precious blood.
Make them to be numbered with Thy saints in glory everlasting.
O Lord, save Thy people, and bless Thy heritage.
Govern them, and lift them up forever.
Day by day we magnify Thee;
And we worship Thy name ever, world without end.
Vouchsafe, O Lord, to keep us this day without sin.
O Lord, have mercy upon us, have mercy upon us.
O Lord, let Thy mercy be upon us, as our trust is in Thee.
O Lord, in Thee have I trusted;
Let me never be confounded.

Amen.

474

伸手同情

Reach Out and Touch

. . . And as many as touched became perfectly whole. — Matthew 14:36
Charles F. Brown
Unison
REACH OUT
Charles F. Brown
1. 伸手幫助心靈飢渴的人，當同情那心
2. 安慰心中憂傷痛苦的人，當指引那迷
1 Reach out and touch a soul that is hun-gry, Reach out and touch a
2 Reach out and touch a friend who is wea-ry, Reach out and touch a
1. 中失望的人，憐憫體恤生命痛苦
2. 失方向的人，付上代價捨去自己
1 spir-it in de-spair, Reach out and touch a life torn and
2 seek-er un-a-ware, Reach out and touch, though touch-ing means
1. 污穢，孤單可憐的人—你若能！對那恨
2. 生命，伸手幫助別人—你若肯！將你的
1 dirt-y, A man who is lone-ly– If you care! Reach out and
2 los-ing A part of your own self– If you dare! Reach out and
1. 你的鄰舍要愛他，陌生的人，當善意對
2. 愛給那需要愛的，用你的家，接待沒有
1 touch that neigh-bor who hates you, Reach out and touch that stran-ger who
2 give your love to the love-less, Reach out and make a home for the

1. 待 他， 弟 兄 有 需 要 扶 持 幫 助 他，讓 神
2. 家 的， 将 神 的 光 傳 送 到 黑 暗 地，讓 神
1 meets you, Reach out and touch the broth-er who needs you, Reach out
2 home-less, Reach out and shed God's light in the dark-ness, Reach out
1 2
1. 的 笑 容 在 你 臉 上 顯 出 。
2. 的 笑 容 在 你 臉 上 顯 出 。
1 and let the smile of God touch thru you.
2 and let the smile of God touch thru you.

We're Hungry, Lord

We're hungry for something, Lord.
We have so much rich food and cake and candy for ourselves,
but we're hungry.
People around us are so stiff and tight and hard to reach.
And they make us that way.
But we're hungry for something more.
People we know keep talking about great ideas, brilliant questions,
and the problem of God's existence.
But we're hungry for You, not ideas or theories.
We want You to touch us, to reach inside us and turn us on.
There are so many people who will counsel us to death.
But we're hungry for someone who really knows You and has
You, someone who can get so close to us that we can see You
there.
We have so many things, but we're hungry for You.
Deep, deep down inside we're hungry, even if we appear to be
silly, lazy, or unconcerned at times.
We're hungry for Your kind of power and love and joy.
Feed us, Lord, feed us with Your rich food.

– *Anonymous*

475

讓人從你認識耶穌
Let Others See Jesus in You

That they might live . . . unto Him who died for them.
II Corinthians 5:15

B. B. McKinney　　B. B. McKinney

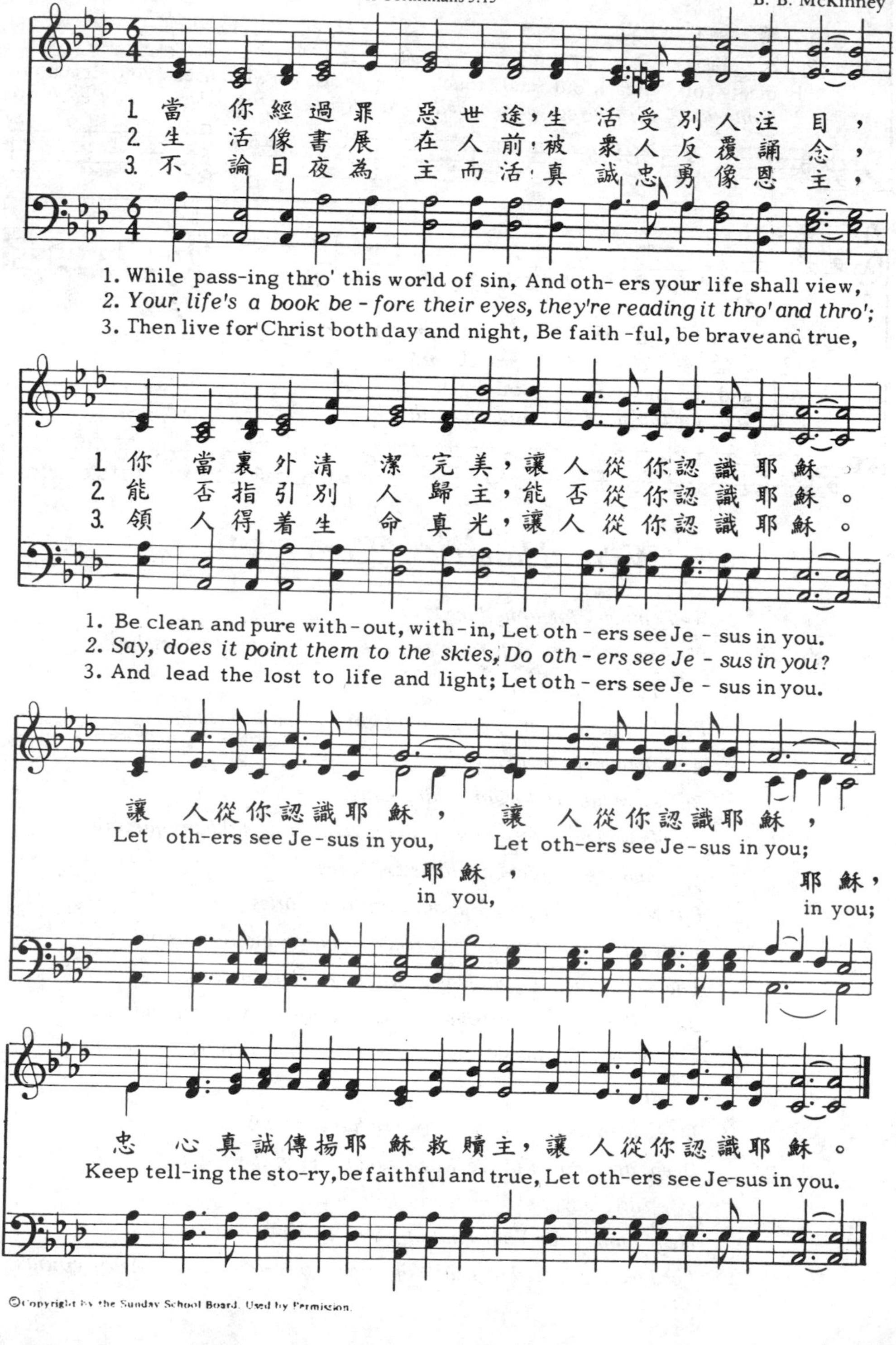

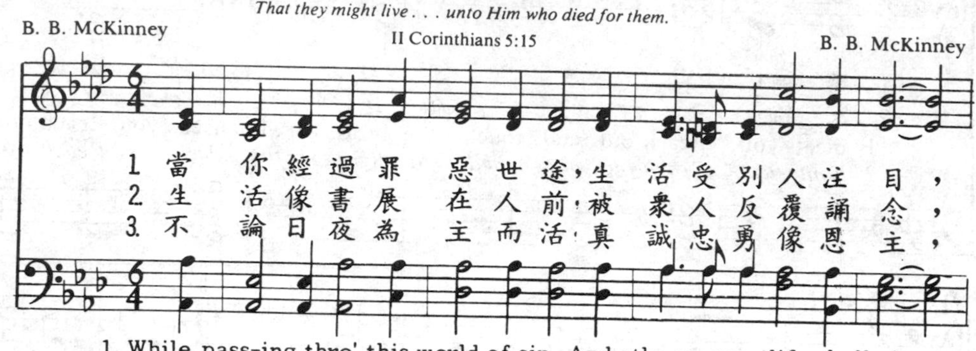

1. 當你經過罪惡世途，生活受別人注目，
2. 生活像書展在人前，被衆人反覆誦念，
3. 不論日夜為主而活，真誠忠勇像恩主，

1. While pass-ing thro' this world of sin, And oth-ers your life shall view,
2. Your life's a book be-fore their eyes, they're reading it thro' and thro';
3. Then live for Christ both day and night, Be faith-ful, be brave and true,

1. 你當裏外清潔完美，讓人從你認識耶穌。
2. 能否指引別人歸主，能否從你認識耶穌。
3. 領人得着生命真光，讓人從你認識耶穌。

1. Be clean and pure with-out, with-in, Let oth-ers see Je-sus in you.
2. Say, does it point them to the skies, Do oth-ers see Je-sus in you?
3. And lead the lost to life and light; Let oth-ers see Je-sus in you.

讓人從你認識耶穌，耶穌，讓人從你認識耶穌，耶穌，
Let oth-ers see Je-sus in you, in you, Let oth-ers see Je-sus in you; in you;

忠心真誠傳揚耶穌救贖主，讓人從你認識耶穌。
Keep tell-ing the sto-ry, be faithful and true, Let oth-ers see Je-sus in you.

我歌頌祢
I Sing Of Thee

Give unto the Lord the glory due His name.
— I Chronicles 16:29

Chas. F. Weigle

Cladys Blanchard Muller

Unison Or Duet
1. 我歌頌　祢，尊貴的　主，藉祢恩　典，把我救　贖；
2. 我歌頌　祢，縱淚滿　襟，憂傷來　臨，仍覺歡　欣；
3. 我歌頌　祢，直到離　世，不論在　家，海洋陸　地；

1. I sing of Thee, O bless-ed Christ, Since Thou hast saved me by Thy grace;
2. *I'll sing of Thee, and smile thro' tears, When sorrow comes to make me sad;*
3. Of Thee I'll sing while life shall last. At home, a-broad, on land or sea;

1. 祢救贖　我代價極　重，我與天　使向祢歌　頌。
2. 因我回　想救主恩　典，使我歌　唱快樂無　邊。
3. 或經死　亡進入永　生，永永遠　遠我歌頌　祢。

1. Re-deemed by Thee at dread-ful price, With an-gels I would sing Thy praise.
2. *For I re-mem-ber thro' the years thy grace, and sing be-cause I'm glad.*

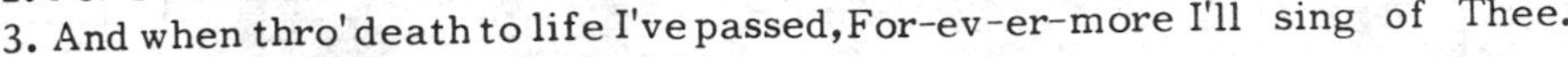

3. And when thro' death to life I've passed, For-ev-er-more I'll sing of Thee.

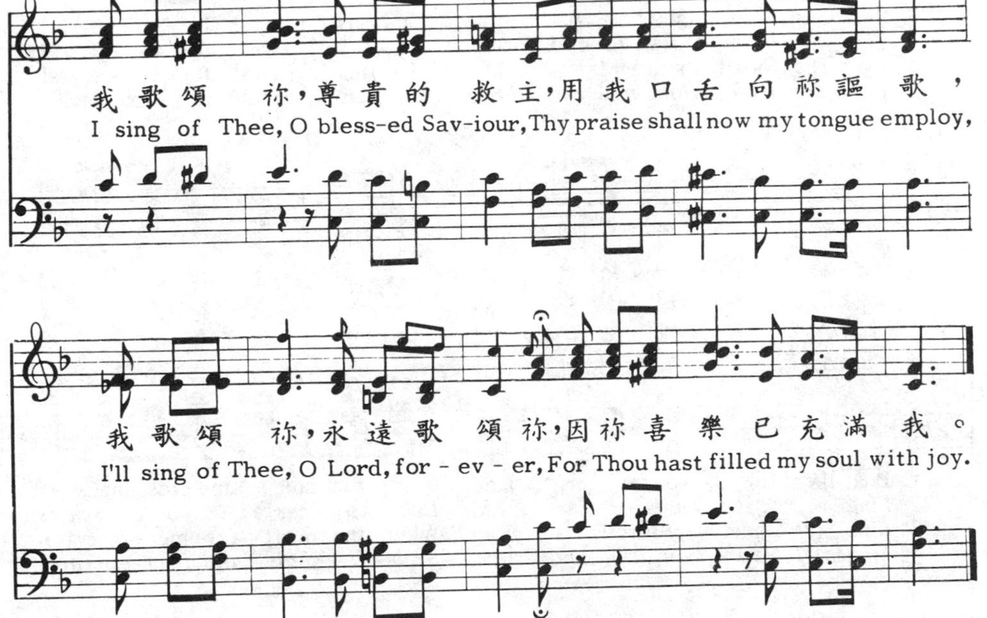

我歌頌　祢，尊貴的　救主，用我口舌向祢謳　歌，
I sing of Thee, O bless-ed Sav-iour, Thy praise shall now my tongue employ,
我歌頌　祢，永遠歌　頌祢，因祢喜樂已充滿　我。
I'll sing of Thee, O Lord, for - ev - er, For Thou hast filled my soul with joy.

477

主耶穌救罪人

Jesus Saves!

. . . Joy shall be in heaven over one sinner that repenteth . . . . — Luke 15:7

Priscilla J. Owens

JESUS SAVES
William J. Kirkpatrick

1. 我聽見歡樂聲音：主耶穌救罪人！
2. 越過大海報喜信：主耶穌救罪人！
3. 爭戰時當高聲唱：主耶穌救罪人！
4. 臨風疾呼傳救恩：主耶穌救罪人！
1 We have heard the joy - ful sound: Je - sus saves! Je - sus saves!
2 Waft it on the roll - ing tide: Je - sus saves! Je - sus saves!
3 Sing a - bove the bat - tle strife: Je - sus saves! Je - sus saves!
4 Give the winds a might - y voice: Je - sus saves! Je - sus saves!
1. 到各處傳此佳音：主耶穌救罪人！
2. 向罪人傳此救恩：主耶穌救罪人！
3. 主已經得勝死亡：主耶穌救罪人！
4. 萬國萬民當歡騰：主耶穌救罪人！
1 Spread the ti - dings all a - round: Je - sus saves! Je - sus saves!
2 Tell to sin - ners far and wide: Je - sus saves! Je - sus saves!
3 By His death and end - less life: Je - sus saves! Je - sus saves!
4 Let the na - tions now re - joice: Je - sus saves! Je - sus saves!
1. 將福音傳給萬民，渡重洋攀山越嶺；
2. 衆島嶼應當歌唱，海上波濤齊响應；
3. 經幽谷輕聲柔唱，心中仰望主救恩；
4. 高聲歡呼同歡樂，主救恩白白賜人；
1 Bear the news to ev - ery land, Climb the steeps and cross the waves;
2 Sing, ye is - lands of the sea; Ech - o back, ye o - cean caves;
3 Sing it soft - ly through the gloom, When the heart for mer - cy craves;
4 Shout sal - va - tion full and free, High - est hills and deep - est caves;

1. 遵主命令向前行；主耶穌救罪人！
2. 普世百姓當宣揚：主耶穌救罪人！
3. 過死河高聲頌揚：主耶穌救罪人！
4. 這是我們得勝歌：主耶穌救罪人！
1 On - ward! 'tis our Lord's com - mand; Je - sus saves! Je - sus saves!
2 Earth shall keep her ju - bi - lee: Je - sus saves! Je - sus saves!
3 Sing in tri - umph o'er the tomb: Je - sus saves! Je - sus saves!
4 This our song of vic - to - ry: Je - sus saves! Je - sus saves!

Luke 4:14-22

And Jesus returned in the power of the Spirit into Galilee: and there went out a fame of Him through all the region round about. And He taught in their synagogues, being glorified of all.

And He came to Nazareth, where He had been brought up: and, as His custom was, He went into the synagogue on the sabbath day, and stood up for to read. And there was delivered unto Him the book of the prophet Esaias. And when He had opened the book, He found the place where it was written, The Spirit of the Lord is upon me, because He hath annointed me to preach the gospel to the poor; He hath sent me to heal the brokenhearted, to preach deliverance to the captives, and recovering of sight to the blind, to set at liberty them that are bruised, to preach the acceptable year of the Lord. And He closed the book, and He gave it again to the minister, and sat down. And the eyes of all them that were in the synagogue were fastened on Him. And He began to say unto them, This day is this Scripture fulfilled in your ears. And all bare Him witness, and wondered at the gracious words which proceeded out of His mouth.

–(KJV)

478

傳給人

Pass It On

Kurt Kaiser

PASS IT ON
Kurt Kaiser

If God so loved us we ought also to love one another. — I John 4:11

1. 一點星星之火，可以將火點燃起，
2. 春天何等美麗，新葉嫩綠滿樹上，
3. 朋友，願你分享我已得到的喜樂，
1 It only takes a spark to get a fire go-ing,
2 *What a won-drous time is spring—when all the trees are bud-ding,*
3 I wish for you, my friend, this hap-pi-ness that I've found—

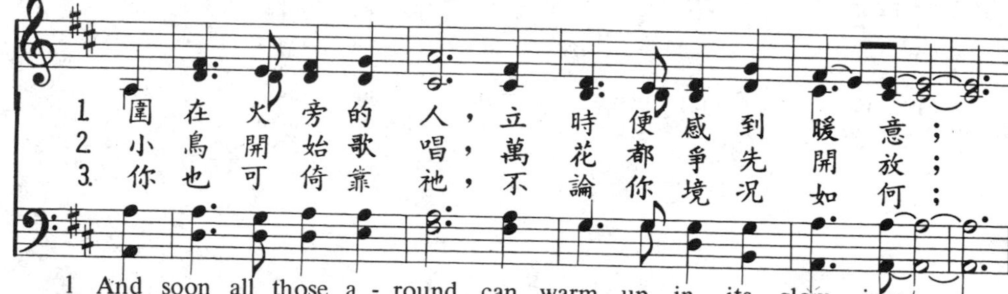
1. 圍在火旁的人，立時便感到暖意；
2. 小鳥開始歌唱，萬花都爭先開放；
3. 你也可倚靠祂，不論你境況如何；
1 And soon all those a-round can warm up in its glow-ing;
2 *The birds be-gin to sing, the flow-ers start their bloom-ing;*
3 You can de-pend on Him, it mat-ters not where you're bound;

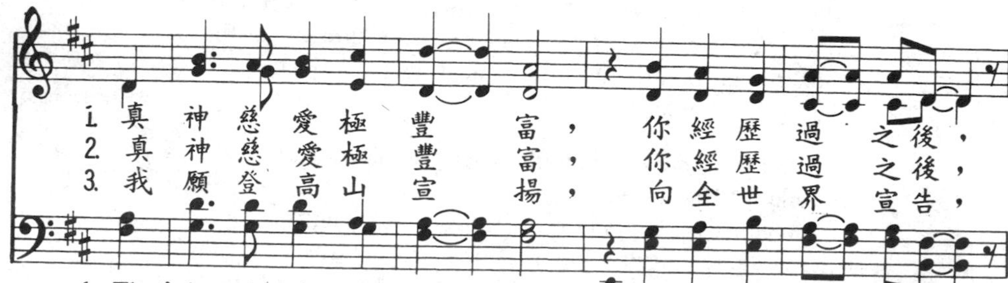
1. 真神慈愛極豐富，你經歷過之後，
2. 真神慈愛極豐富，你經歷過之後，
3. 我願登高山宣揚，向全世界宣告，
1 That's how it is with God's love, once you've ex-per-i-enced it:
2 *That's how it is with God's love, once you've ex-per-i-enced it:*
3 I'll shout it from the moun-tain top, I want my world to know:

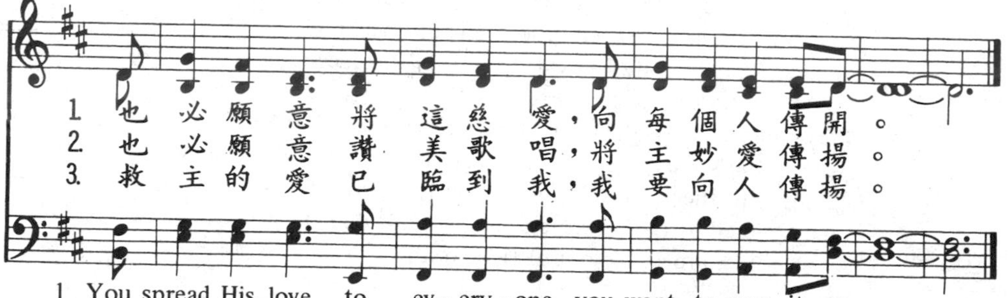
1. 也必願意將這慈愛，向每個人傳開。
2. 也必願意讚美歌唱，將主妙愛傳揚。
3. 救主的愛已臨到我，我要向人傳揚。
1 You spread His love to ev-ery-one, you want to pass it on.
2 *You want to sing, it's fresh like spring, you want to pass it on.*
3 The Lord of love has come to me, I want to pass it on.

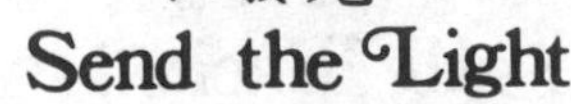
快發光

Send the Light

For God who commanded the light to shine out of darkness, hath shined in our hearts . . . . — II Corinthians 4:6

Charles H. Gabriel

McCABE
Charles H. Gabriel

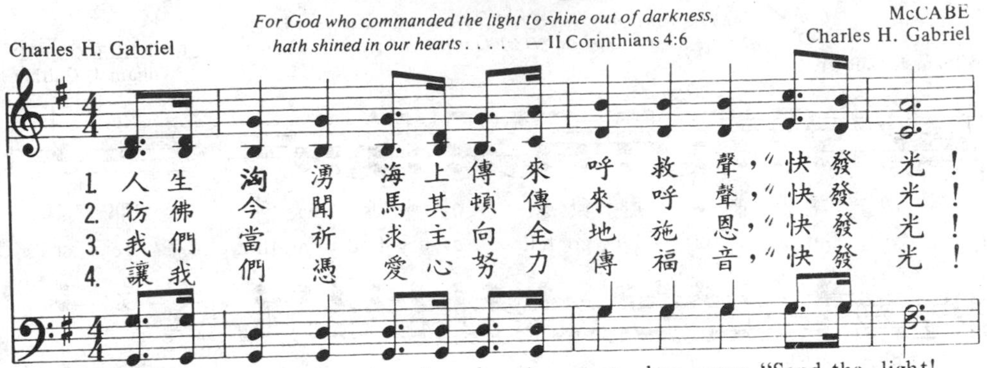
1. 人生洶湧海上傳來呼救聲，"快發光！
2. 彷彿今聞馬其頓傳來呼聲，"快發光！
3. 我們當祈求主向全地施恩，"快發光！
4. 讓我們憑愛心努力傳福音，"快發光！

1 There's a call comes ring - ing o'er the rest - less wave, "Send the light!
2 *We have heard the Mac - e - do - nian call to - day, "Send the light!*
3 Let us pray that grace may ev - ery - where a - bound, Send the light!
4 *Let us not grow wea - ry in the work of love, Send the light!*

1. 快發光！"多少靈魂苦盼耶穌的救恩，
2. 快發光！"到主十架前快來奉獻己身，
3. 快發光！"將基督的慈愛顯示於世人，
4. 快發光！"為要得着冠冕我們不灰心，

1 Send the light!" There are souls to res - cue, there are souls to save,
2 *Send the light!" And a gold - en of - fering at the cross we lay,*
3 Send the light! And a Christ - like spir - it ev - ery - where be found,
4 *Send the light! Let us gath - er jew - els for a crown a - bove,*

快發光！快發光！快發光！發出福音真光；
Send the light! Send the light! Send the light the bless-ed gos - pel light;
1
2
讓真光普照四方！快發光普照四方！
Let it shine from shore to shore! Send the shine from shore to shore!

讓我們一起興奮

Get All Excited

And He hath on His vesture and on His thigh a name written: KING OF KINGS, and LORD OF LORDS. — Revelation 19:16

William J. Gaither

GET ALL EXCITED
William J. Gaither

讓我們一起興奮的告訴大家，耶穌
Get all ex-cit - ed, go tell ev-ery-bod - y that Je - sus

祂是王！讓我們一起興奮的告訴大家，
Christ is King! Get all ex-cit - ed, go tell ev-ery-bod - y that

耶穌祂是王！讓我們一起興奮
Je - sus Christ is King! Get all ex-cit - ed, go tell

的告訴大家，耶穌祂是王，
ev-ery-bod - y that Je - sus Christ is King,

耶穌基督是萬王之王，王之王！
Je-sus Christ is still the King of kings, King of kings!

Fine

你所談論的人，所談論的一切事情實在
You talk a-bout peo-ple, you talk a-bout things that real-ly aren't im-
並不重要，你也談論天氣，你也談論許多在
port-ant at all, You talk a-bout weath-er, you talk a-bout prob-lems we
家或在外的問題；朋友，我真興奮，因
have here at home and a-broad; But, friend, I'm ex-cit-ed a-
世界問題已有解答，我要高聲歡唱，
bout a so-lu-tion for the world—I'm going to shout and sing,
D.C. al Fine
"耶穌基督是萬王之王，王之王！"
"Je-sus Christ is still the King of kings, King of kings!

481

世人知道我們是基督徒是因為愛
They'll Know We Are Christians by Our Love

Based on John 13:35
Peter Scholtes

. . . that they may be one, even as We are one . . . . — John 17:22

ST. BRENDAN'S
Peter Scholtes

Unison
1. 我們在靈裡合一，在主裡合為一，
2. 我們併肩同行走，緊緊地手拉手，
3. 我們齊心作主工，彼此竭力扶助，
4. 我們來讚美天父，因祂厚賜萬物，
1 We are one in the Spir - it, we are one in the Lord,
2 We will walk with each oth - er, we will walk hand in hand,
3 We will work with each oth - er, we will work side by side,
4 All praise to the Fa - ther, from whom all things come,
1. 我們在靈裡合一，在主裡合為一，
2. 我們併肩同行走，緊緊地手拉手，
3. 我們齊心作主工，彼此竭力扶助，
4. 我們來讚美天父，因祂厚賜萬物，
1 We are one in the Spir - it, we are one in the Lord,
2 We will walk with each oth - er, we will walk hand in hand,
3 We will work with each oth - er, we will work side by side,
4 And all praise to Christ Je - sus, His on - ly Son,
1. 同心求聖靈引導，使我們衆人合一。
2. 團結在一起，同把主的福音來傳揚。
3. 我們彼此互相的尊敬，互相的看顧。
4. 感謝祂賜下聖靈，使我們衆人合一。
1 And we pray that all u - ni - ty may one day be re - stored:
2 And to - geth - er we'll spread the news that God is in our land:
3 And we'll guard each man's dig - ni - ty and save each man's pride:
4 And all praise to the Spir - it, who makes us one:

世人知道我們是基督徒，因着愛，
And they'll know we are Christ-ians by our love, by our love,
世人知道基督徒是因着愛。
Yes, they'll know we are Christ-ians by our love.

The People of God

My dear people, let us love one another since love comes from God and everyone who loves is begotten by God and knows God. Anyone who fails to love can never have known God, because God is love. God's love for us was revealed when God sent into the world His only Son so that we could have life through Him; this is the love I mean: not our love for God, but God's love for us when He sent His Son to be the sacrifice that takes our sins away. My dear people, since God has loved us so much, we too should love one another. No one has ever seen God; but as long as we love one another God will live in us and His love will be complete in us. We can know that we are living in Him and He is living in us because He lets us share His Spirit.

We ourselves saw and we testify that the Father sent His Son as Savior of the world. If anyone acknowledges that Jesus is the Son of God, God lives in Him, and He in God. We ourselves have known and put our faith in God's love towards ourselves. God is love and anyone who lives in love lives in God, and God lives in Him. Love will come to its perfection in us when we can face the day of judgement without fear; because even in this world we have become as He is. In love there can be no fear, but fear is driven out by perfect love: because to fear is to expect punishment, and anyone who is afraid is still imperfect in love. We are to love, then because He loved us first. Anyone who says, "I love God", and hates his brother, is a liar, since a man who does not love the brother that he can see cannot love God, whom he has never seen. So this is the commandment that He has given us, that anyone who loves God must also love his brother.

— 1 John 4:7-21 (JB)

482

我若賺得世界
If I Gained the World

For what is a man profited if he gain the whole world and lose his own soul? — Matthew 16:26

Anna Ölander
Tr. composite
TRUE RICHES
Swedish Melody
1. 我若賺得世界失去救主，我如此活
2. 若有千萬家財人間情愛，豐功偉業
3. 若無救主人生.一片虛空，世界充滿
4. 在耶穌裡我已得着喜樂，是醫治破
1 If I gained the world but lost the Sav - ior, Were my life worth
2 Had I wealth and love in full - est meas - ure, And a name re -
3 O what emp - ti - ness with - out the Sav - ior Mid the sins and
4 O the joy of hav - ing all in Je - sus! What a balm the
1. 着有何意義？世上繁華轉眼都將
2. 聲名傳四方，人生於我却無半點
3. 罪惡與愁苦！若無救主永恒充滿
4. 碎心靈良藥！罪惡雖重救主都能
1 liv - ing for a day? Could my yearn-ing heart find rest and
2 vered both far and near, Yet no hope be - yond, no har - bor
3 sor - rows here be - low! And e - ter - ni - ty, how dark with -
4 bro - ken heart to heal! Ne'er a sin so great but He'll for -
1. 消失，空虛心靈何處得安息？若賺
2. 希望，風雨孤舟何處是歸航？若賺
3. 黑暗，無止盡的眼淚與痛苦！若無
4. 赦免，憂傷痛苦祂全都知道！若在
1 com - fort In the things that soon must pass a - way? If I
2 wait - ing Where my storm-tossed ves - sel I could steer— If I
3 out Him— On - ly night and tears and end-less woe! What though
4 give it, Nor a sor - row that He does not feel! If I

1. 得世界但失去救主，我一生奮
2. 得世界但失去救主，誰能捨命
3. 救主雖我仍能生活，但生命盡
4. 世我惟獨只有耶穌，除此以外
1 gained the world, but lost the Sav - ior, Would my gain be
2 gained the world, but lost the Sav - ior, Who en - dured the
3 I might live with - out the Sav - ior, When I come to
4 have but Je - sus, on - ly Je - sus, Noth - ing else in
1. 鬥有何價值？基督充滿我使我得
2. 十架拯救我？苦難來臨何處我能
3. 頭我將何往？若無救主如何面對
4. 我一無所有，但在耶穌裡我已有
1 worth the life - long strife? Are all earth - ly pleas - ures worth com -
2 cross and died for me, Could then all the world af - ford a
3 die, how would it be? O to face the val - ley's gloom with -
4 all the world be - side, O then ev - ery - thing is mine in
1. 喜樂，世上的福樂怎能相比？
2. 藏躲？世上何處是我避難所？
3. 死亡？若無救主將永遠滅亡！
4. 一切——因祂供給我一切需求。
1 par - ing For a mo - ment with a Christ - filled life?
2 ref - uge, Whith - er in my an - guish I might flee?
3 out Him! And with - out Him all e - ter - ni - ty!
4 Je - sus— For my needs and more He will pro - vide.

483

耶穌是全世界於我

Jesus Is All the World to Me

Greater love hath no man than this . . . . — John 15:13

ELIZABETH

Will L. Thompson　　　　Will L. Thompson

1. 耶穌是全世界於我，生命，喜樂，珍寶；
2. 耶穌是全世界於我，急難時的良友；
3. 耶穌是全世界於我，我要忠誠待祂；
4. 耶穌是全世界於我，此外無所愛慕；

1 Je - sus is all the world to me, My life, my joy, my all;
2 *Je - sus is all the world to me, My Friend in tri - als sore;*
3 Je - sus is all the world to me, And true to Him I'll be;
4 *Je - sus is all the world to me, I want no bet - ter friend;*

1. 祂是我的隨時力量，離祂我必跌倒。
2. 恩上加恩難於計算，當我向祂祈求。
3. 祂對於我何等誠實，我豈忍心負祂？
4. 我信靠祂時刻靠祂，無論遇禍遇福。

1 He is my strength from day to day, With - out Him I would fall.
2 *I go to Him for bless - ings, and He gives them o'er and o'er.*
3 O how could I this Friend de - ny, When He's so true to me?
4 *I trust Him now, I'll trust Him when Life's fleet - ing days shall end.*

1. 當我愁苦來就耶穌，無人似祂如此安慰；
2. 祂賜日光又施甘霖，祂使禾田金穀豐盈；
3. 跟祂腳踪我可安心，仰望十架時刻儆醒；
4. 得此良友慰此一生，與祂親近喜樂日增；

1 When I am sad to Him I go, No oth - er one can cheer me so;
2 *He sends the sun - shine and the rain, He sends the har - vest's gold - en grain;*
3 Fol - low - ing Him I know I'm right, He watch - es o'er me day and night;
4 *Beau - ti - ful life with such a Friend; Beau - ti - ful life that has no end;*

1. 使 我 喜 樂 ， 解 我 心 憂 ， 祂 是 我 友 。
2. 日 光 甘 霖 ， 大 好 收 成 ， 祂 是 我 友 。
3. 與 祂 同 行 ， 或 夜 或 明 ， 祂 是 我 友 。
4. 永 生 喜 樂 ， 無 窮 無 盡 ， 祂 是 我 友 。
1 When I am sad He makes me glad, He's my Friend.
2 Sun-shine and rain, har-vest of grain, He's my Friend.
3 Fol-low-ing Him by day and night, He's my Friend.
4 E-ter-nal life, e-ter-nal joy, He's my Friend.

My Symphony

To live content with small means;
To seek elegance rather than luxury,
 and refinement rather than fashion;

To be worthy, not respectable,
 and wealthy, not rich;

To study hard, think quietly, talk
 gently, act frankly;

To listen to stars and birds, to babes
 and sages, with open heart;

To bear all cheerfully, do all bravely,
 await occasions, hurry never.

In a word, to let the spiritual, unbidden
 and unconscious, grow up through the common.

This is to be my symphony.

— William Ellery Channing

484

快樂日

O Happy Day!

Let the wicked forsake his way for He will abundantly pardon. — Isaiah 55:7

Philip Doddridge
Gloria Gaither, stanza 4, alt.

HAPPY DAY
Edward F. Rimbault

1. 前有一日我意立定，信靠耶穌救我靈魂；
2. 基督為我流血捨命，我願奉獻全身全心；
3. 救贖大恩今已完成，救主屬我我亦屬主；
4. 我今脱離邪惡世俗，靈裡平靜心中安息；

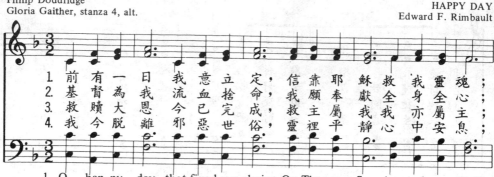

1 O hap-py day that fixed my choice On Thee, my Sav - ior and my God!
2 *O hap-py bond that seals my vows To Him who mer - its all my love!*
3 It's done, the great trans - ac - tion's done—I am my Lord's and He is mine;
4 *At peace, my long - di - vid - ed heart, Can in this calm as - sur - ance rest;*

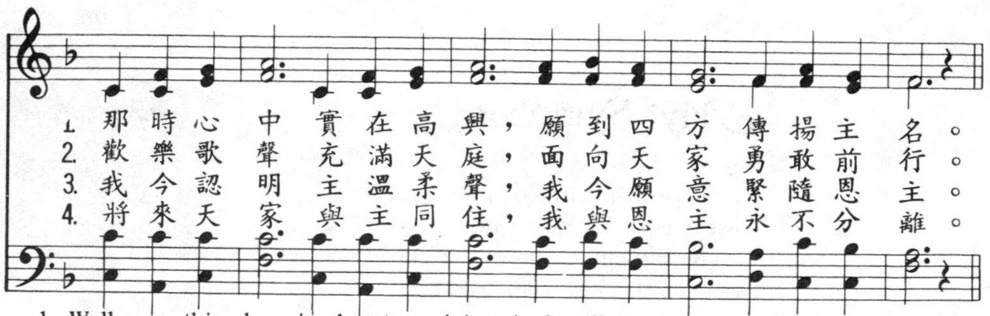

1. 那時心中實在高興，願到四方傳揚主名。
2. 歡樂歌聲充滿天庭，面向天家勇敢前行。
3. 我今認明主溫柔聲，我今願意緊隨恩主。
4. 將來天家與主同住，我與恩主永不分離。

1 Well may this glow - ing heart re - joice And tell its rap - tures all a - broad.
2 *Let cheer - ful an - thems fill His house, While to that sa - cred shrine I move.*
3 He drew me, and I fol - lowed on, Thrilled to con - fess the voice di - vine.
4 *There is no power can make me part From Love by which I've been pos - sessed.*

快樂日，快樂日，救主洗淨我的罪孽！
Hap - py day, hap - py day, When Je - sus washed my sins a - way!

心裡清潔，極大歡喜，這日永遠不能忘記；
He taught me how to watch and pray And live re - joic - ing ev - ery day;

快樂日，快樂日，救主洗淨我的罪孽！
Hap-py day, hap-py day, When Je-sus washed my sins a-way!

485

再相會

God Be with You 'Til We Meet Again

May the Lord watch between me and thee . . . . — Genesis 31:49

GOD BE WITH YOU
William G. Tomer

Jeremiah E. Rankin

1. 願主同在直到再相會，主為良師常指導你，
2. 願主同在直到再相會，主翅膀下將你覆庇，
3. 願主同在直到再相會，若試煉危險臨到你，
4. 願主同在直到再相會，主以愛為旗招引你，

1 God be with you 'til we meet a-gain, By His coun-sels guide, up-hold you,
2 *God be with you 'til we meet a-gain, 'Neath His wings pro-tecting hide you,*
3 God be with you 'til we meet a-gain, If life's tri-als should con-found you,
4 *God be with you 'til we meet a-gain, Keep love's banner floating o'er you,*

1. 主為牧人常看顧你：願主同在直到再相會。
2. 天上嗎哪日日賜你：願主同在直到再相會。
3. 主用大能膀臂護你：願主同在直到再相會。
4. 罪的死亡不能害你：願主同在直到再相會。

1 With His sheep se-cure-ly fold you: God be with you 'til we meet a-gain.
2 *Dai - ly man-na still pro-vide you: God be with you 'til we meet a-gain.*
3 God will put His arms a-round you: God be with you 'til we meet a-gain.
4 *Smite death's threat'ning wave before you: God be with you 'til we meet a-gain.*

當你禱告
When You Pray

Bow down Thine ear, O Lord, and hear me; for I am poor and needy

Psalm 86:1

Audrey Mieir

一日劳碌完畢，你禱告屈膝，願否将
每當黎明晨曦，
At the close of the day, When you kneel to pray, Will you re -
break
我惦記？ 我每日需求主，賜能
mem - ber me? I need help ev - 'ry day, This is
力幫助，願否将我惦記？
why I pray, Will you re - mem - ber me?
當你求，願否為我求，因我需要
我 必定 你 你
When you pray will you pray for me for I need His
I I will you you

主 愛 看 顧；
當 你 求，有否
我 必定
love and His care.
When you pray will you
I I will
為 我 求，是否 微 聲 提 我 名 代 求。
你 必定 你
pray for me, will you whis-per my name in your prayer.
you, I will your my

我勸你第一要為萬人懇求、禱告、代求、祝謝。為君王和一切在位的也該如此，使我們可以敬虔端正，平安無事的度日。這是好的，在　神我們救主面前可蒙悅納。他願意萬人得救，明白真道，因為只有一位　神，在神和人中間，只有一位中保，乃是降世為人的基督耶穌。他捨自己作萬人的贖價，到了時候，這事必證明出來。

提摩太前書第二章
1—6節

487

為你祈求
I Am Praying for You

We give thanks . . . praying always for you. — Colossians 1:3

S. O'Maley Cluff

INTERCESSION
Ira D. Sankey

1. 我 有 一 救 主，在 天 為你 祈 求，祂 是 親 愛
2. 我 有 一 天 父，賜 我 豐富 恩 典，有 永 遠 的
3. 我 有 一 白 衣，光 明 潔白 美 麗，是 主 為 我
4. 主 已 拯 救 你，當 向 別人 傳 述，讓 人 因 你

1 I have a Sav - ior–He's plead - ing in glo - ry, A dear, lov - ing
2 *I have a Fa - ther–to me He has giv - en A hope for e -*
3 I have a robe; 'tis re - splen - dent in white-ness, A - wait - ing in
4 *When He has found you-tell oth - ers the sto - ry, That my lov - ing*

1. 救 主，勝 過 衆 朋 友；祂 時 常 關 心 我，對
2. 盼 望，福 氣 真 無 限；不 久 祂 要 召 我，在
3. 預 備，在 榮 耀 日 裡；那 日 我 必 穿 上，極
4. 認 識—親 愛 的 救 主；常 為 他 們 祈 求，領

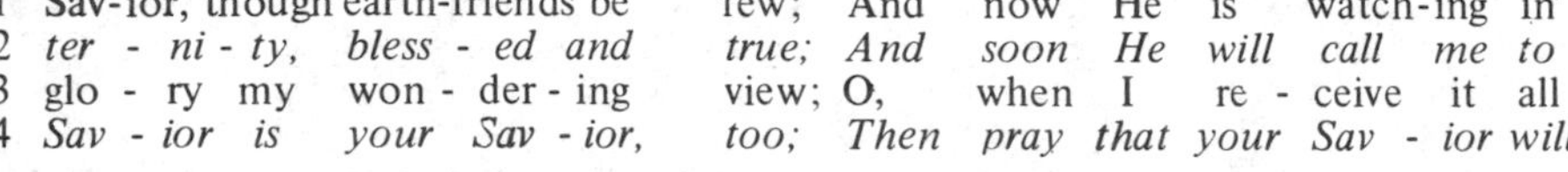

1 Sav-ior, though earth-friends be few; And now He is watch-ing in
2 *ter - ni - ty, bless - ed and true; And soon He will call me to*
3 glo - ry my won - der - ing view; O, when I re - ceive it all
4 *Sav - ior is your Sav - ior, too; Then pray that your Sav - ior will*

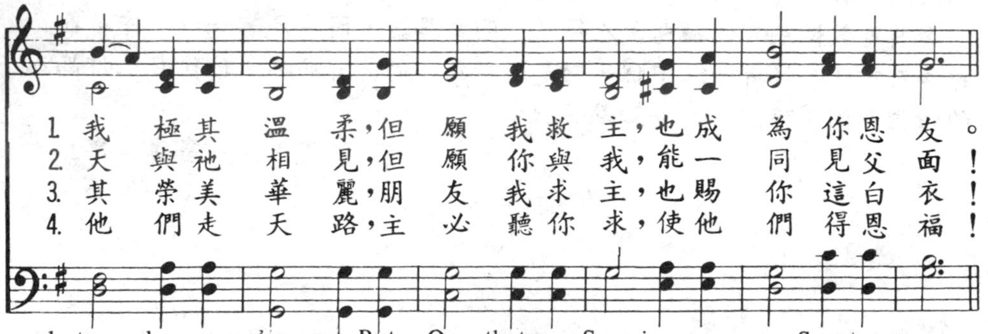

1. 我 極其 溫 柔，但 願 我救 主，也成 為 你恩 友。
2. 天 與祂 相 見，但 願 你與 我，能一 同 見父 面！
3. 其 榮美 華 麗，朋 友 我求 主，也賜 你 這白 衣！
4. 他 們走 天 路，主 必 聽你 求，使他 們 得恩 福！

1 ten - der-ness o'er me, But O that my Sav - ior were your Sav - ior, too.
2 *meet Him in heav - en, But O that He'd let me bring you with me, too!*
3 shin - ing in bright - ness, Dear friend, could I see you re - ceiv - ing one, too!
4 *bring them to glo - ry, And prayer will be an-swered-'twas an-swered for you!*

我今為你祈求，我今為你祈求，我
For you I am pray - ing, For you I am pray - ing, For
今為你祈求，常為你祈求。
you I am pray - ing, I'm pray - ing for you.

神阿，我心堅定，我心堅定，我要唱詩，我要歌頌。
我的靈阿，你當醒起，琴瑟阿，你們當醒起，我自己要極早醒起。
主阿，我要在萬民中稱謝你，在列邦中歌頌你。
因為你的慈愛，高及諸天，你的誠實，達到穹蒼。
神阿，願你崇高，過於諸天，願你的榮耀，高過全地。

詩篇五十七篇
7 —11

My heart is steadfast, O God,
my heart is steadfast;
I will sing and make music.

Awake, my soul!
Awake, harp and lyre!
I will awaken the dawn.

I will praise you, O Lord, among the nations;
I will sing of you among the peoples.
For great is your love, reaching to the heavens;
your faithfulness reaches to the skies.

Be exalted, O God, above the heavens;
let your glory be over all the earth.

Psalm 57 : 7-11. NIV

488

天父我神
God of Our Fathers

The Lord of hosts is with us, the God of Jacob is our refuge. — Psalm 48:7

Daniel C. Roberts

NATIONAL HYMN
George W. Warren

1. 天 父 我 神，用 大 全 能 聖 手，
2. 真 神 慈 愛，自 古 引 導 眷 顧，
3. 願 主 膀 臂，作 我 護 衛 保 障，
4. 前 路 艱 難，求 主 甦 醒 我 靈，
Trumpets before each stanza
1 God of our fa-thers, whose al-might-y hand
2 Thy love di-vine hath led us in the past,
3 From war's a-larms, from dead-ly pes-ti-lence,
4 Re-fresh Thy peo-ple on their toil-some way,

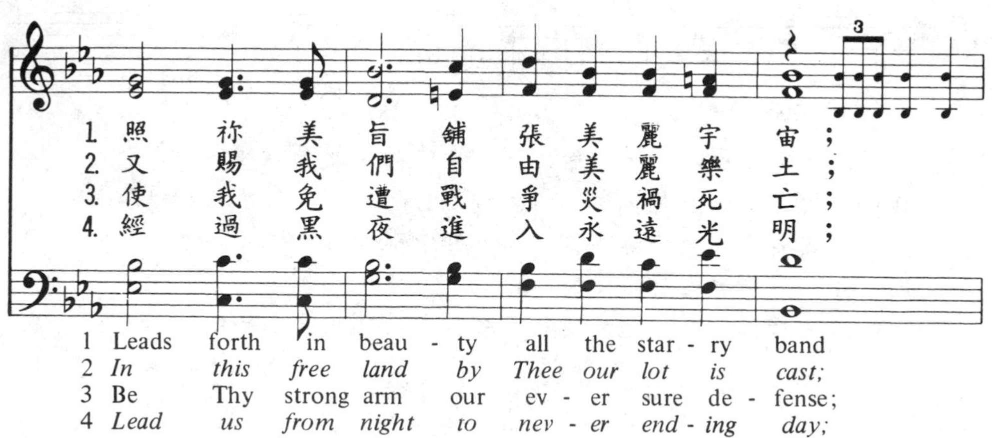
1. 照 祢 美 旨 鋪 張 美 麗 宇 宙；
2. 又 賜 我 們 自 由 美 麗 樂 土；
3. 使 我 免 遭 戰 爭 災 禍 死 亡；
4. 經 過 黑 夜 進 入 永 遠 光 明；
1 Leads forth in beau-ty all the star-ry band
2 In this free land by Thee our lot is cast;
3 Be Thy strong arm our ev-er sure de-fense;
4 Lead us from night to nev-er end-ing day;

1. 榮 耀 光 芒 在 太 空 中 輝 映，
2. 願 我 聖 父 統 領 扶 助 保 護，
3. 願 祢 聖 道 在 我 心 中 增 長，
4. 願 我 生 命 滿 有 愛 與 恩 典，
1 Of shin-ing worlds in splen-dor through the skies,
2 Be Thou our rul-er, guard-ian, guide, and stay,
3 Thy true re-li-gion in our hearts in-crease,
4 Fill all our lives with love and grace di-vine,

1. 敬 向 寶 座 獻 上 感 恩 歌 聲 。
2. 袮 言 袮 道 作 我 律 法 道 路 。
3. 袮 的 良 善 使 我 永 享 安 康 。
4. 榮 耀 頌 讚 歸 神 直 到 永 遠 ！
1 Our grate - ful songs be - fore Thy throne a - rise.
2 Thy word our law, Thy paths our cho - sen way.
3 Thy boun - teous good - ness nour - ish us in peace.
4 And glo - ry, laud, and praise be ev - er Thine! A-men.

獻上感恩的心

Give Thanks

488-1

Give thanks to the Lord for His unfailing love and His wonderful deeds. Ps. 107:8

Henry Smith — Henry Smith

獻 上 感 恩 的 心， 歸 給 聖 潔 眞 神； 因
Give thanks with a grate-ful heart, give thanks to the Ho - ly One; Give

祂 賜 下 獨 生 子 主 耶 穌 基 督。 獻 督 如
thanks be-cause He's giv-en Je - sus Christ, His Son. Give Son. And

1.3 / 2.4

今 軟 弱 者 能 變 剛 强， 貧 窮 者 成 爲 富 足， 都 因 爲
now let the weak say, "I am strong," let the poor say, "I am rich" be-cause of

主 爲 我 成 就 大 事； 如 事。 獻 事。 感 謝。
what the Lord has done for us; And us. Give us. Give thanks.

1.3. / 2. *D.S. al* Coda / ⊕ Coda

489 我的眼睛已經看見
Mine Eyes Have Seen The Glor

If the trumpet give an uncertain sound who shall prepare himself for the battle? — I Corinthians 14: 8

BATTLE HYMN OF THE REPUBLIC
American Melody

Julia Ward Howe

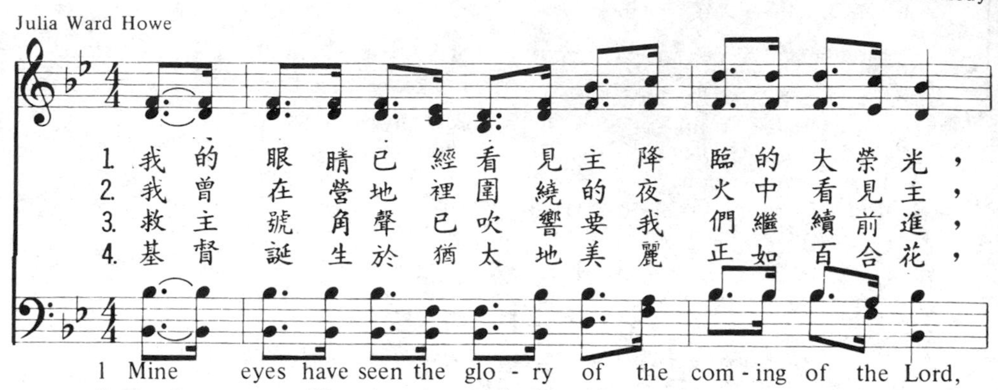

1. 我的眼睛已經看見主降臨的大榮光，
2. 我曾在營地裡圍繞的夜火中看見主，
3. 救主號角聲已吹響要我們繼續前進，
4. 基督誕生於猶太地美麗正如百合花，
1 Mine eyes have seen the glo - ry of the com - ing of the Lord,
2 *I have seen Him in the watch-fires of a hun - dred cir - cling camps,*
3 He has sound - ed forth the trum - pet that shall nev - er call re - treat,
4 *In the beau - ty of the lil - ies Christ was born a - cross the sea,*

1. 祂正踏盡一切不良葡萄使公義顯彰；
2. 夜間露水濕潤中有祭壇是為祂建築；
3. 祂正坐在榮耀寶座上審判世人的心；
4. 在祂心懷滿有榮光使我們改變像祂；
1 He is tram - pling out the vin - tage where the grapes of wrath are stored;
2 *They have build - ed Him an al - tar in the eve - ning dews and damps;*
3 He is sift - ing out the hearts of men be - fore His judg-ment seat;
4 *With a glo - ry in His be - ing that trans - fig - ures you and me;*

1. 祂已抽出祂的怒劍發出閃閃的光芒，
2. 祂公義的字句出現藉微光我能讀出，
3. 我的靈速回答主我心在祂面前歡欣！
4. 祂捨命使世人成聖我也願捨己救人！
1 He hath loosed the fate - ful light - ning of His ter - ri - ble swift sword,
2 *I can read His right-eous sen - tence by the dim and flar - ing lamps,*
3 O be swift, my soul, to an - swer Him, be ju - bi - lant, my feet!
4 *As He died to make men ho - ly let us live to make men free!*

1. 祂 真 理 在 進 行。
2. 祂 日 子 在 進 行。 榮 耀！榮 耀！哈 利
3. 真 神 正 在 進 行。 Glo - ry! glo - ry! Hal - le -
4. 真 神 正 在 進 行。
1 His truth is march - ing on.
2 His day is march - ing on.
3 Our God is march - ing on.
4 While God is march - ing on.
路 亞！ 榮 耀！榮 耀！哈 利 路 亞！
lu - jah! Glo - ry! glo - ry! Hal - le - lu - jah!
榮 耀！榮 耀！哈 利 路 亞！祂 真 理 在 進 行！
Glo - ry! glo - ry! Hal - le - lu - jah! His truth is march-ing on!

願主賜福
The Lord Bless You and Keep You

The Lord bless thee and keep thee, . . . and make His face to shine upon thee . . . .
— Numbers 6:24, 25

Numbers 6:24-26

BENEDICTION
Peter C. Lutkin

願 主 賜 福 與 保 護 你；願 主 常 向 你 仰 臉，向
The Lord bless you and keep you; The Lord lift His coun-te-nance up-
你 仰 臉， 賜 你 平 安， 賜 你 平 安； 願
on you, and give you peace, and give you peace; The Lord
The
賜 你 平 安， 賜 你 平 安，
and give you peace, and give you peace;
Lord make His
主 使 祂 臉 上 榮 光 照 你，賜 恩 給 你，願 主
make His face to shine up - on you, And be gra cious un - to
賜 恩 給 你，
And be gra-cious
賜 恩 給 你， 願 主 常 賜 恩，常 賜 恩 給 你。阿 門。
you, be gra-cious, The Lord be gra-cious, gra-cious un-to you. A - men.
賜 恩 給 你，
and be gra-cious,

榮耀歸神
Glory to God

Now unto God and our Father be glory forever and ever. — Philippians 4:20

Source unknown

Unknown

榮耀歸與最高神！榮耀歸神！榮耀歸神！榮耀歸與最
Glo-ry to God in the high-est! Glo-ry to God! Glo-ry to God! Glo-ry to God in the
高神！讚美讚美不盡。讚美真神慈愛最深，讚
high-est. Praise Him for ev-er more. Praise Him from whom all blessing flow, Praise
美真神恩及萬人，讚美真神聲達天庭，讚美聖父聖
Him all crea-tures here below, Praise Him above ye heavenly host, Praise Father, Son, and
子聖靈，榮耀歸與最高神！榮耀歸與最高神！
Ho-ly Ghost. Glo-ry to God in the highest. Glo-ry to God in the highest.
1. 2.
榮耀，榮耀，榮耀，榮耀，榮耀歸與最高神！神！
Glory! Glory! Glory! Glory! Glory in the high — est. -est.

阿門頌 阿門
492
Amen
Louis Bourgeois
阿 門。
A - - - - men.
二疊阿門
493
Twofold Amen
Dresden
阿 門，阿 門。
A - men, A - - men.
三疊阿門
494
Threefold Amen
Traditional
阿 門，阿 門，阿 門。
A - - men, A - men, A - men.
六疊阿門
495
Sixfold Amen
Paul Sjolund
Moderato
sempre cresc. - - -
p
mf
阿 門，阿 門，
A - men, A - men,
pp
Ped.
f
rit.
ff
阿 門，阿 門，阿 門，阿 門！
A - men, A - men, A - men. A - men!
© Copyright 1976 by Paragon Associates, Inc. All rights reserved.

到主聖殿中

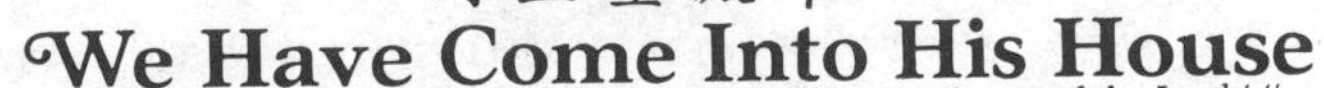

We Have Come Into His House

"I was glad when they said to me, 'Let us go into the house of the Lord.' "
—Psalm 122:1

Bruce Ballinger

WORSHIP HIM
Bruce Ballinger

我們 來到聖殿中，奉 祂的名聚集 一
讓我 們忘記自己，尊 主的名為大 來
1 We have come in-to His house and gath-ered in His name to
2 Let's for - get a-bout our-selves and mag-ni-fy His name and

同 敬拜， 我們 來到聖殿中，奉
敬 拜祂， 讓我 們忘記自己，尊
1 wor - ship Him. We have come in-to His house and
2 wor - ship Him. Let's for - get a-bout our-selves and

祂的 名聚集 一 同 敬拜， 我們
主的 名為大 來 敬 拜祂， 讓我
1 gath-ered in His name to wor - ship Him. We have
2 mag-ni-fy His name and wor - ship Him. Let's for -

來到聖殿中，奉 祂的名聚集 一 同 敬拜 上
們忘記自己，尊 主的名為大 來 敬 拜 主 基
1 come in-to His house and gath-ered in His name to wor-ship Christ the
2 get a-bout our-selves and mag-ni-fy His name and wor-ship Christ the

主， 敬 拜祂， 主 基 督。
督， 敬 拜祂， 主 基 督。
1 Lord. Wor - ship Him, Christ the Lord.
2 Lord. Wor - ship Him, Christ the Lord.

497 尊貴的主
Majesty

"Yours, O Lord; is the greatness, the power, and the glory, the victory, and the majesty;"—I Chronicles 29:11

Jack Hayford | MAJESTY Jack Hayford

敬拜主，敬拜尊貴救主，榮耀尊貴與頌讚都歸耶穌。
Maj - es - ty, wor-ship His maj - es - ty. Un - to Je - sus be all glo - ry, hon - or, and praise.
敬拜主，敬拜全能的主，至高寶座,天國權柄，都屬基督！
Maj - es - ty, king-dom au - thor - i - ty flow from His throne un - to His own; His an-them raise.
當歡呼，應當高舉耶穌的聖名，來讚美，耶穌基督是榮耀君王。
So ex - alt, lift up on high the name of Je - sus. Mag - ni - fy, come glo - ri - fy Christ Je - sus, the King.

3
3
3
敬拜主，敬拜尊貴的主，
Maj - es - ty, wor-ship His maj - es - ty;
3
3
3
3
3
3
*
袘曾捨命，今得榮耀，萬王之王。
Je - sus who died, now glo - ri - fied, King of all kings.
3
3
3
3

498 榮耀主聖名

Glorify Thy Name

"If God is glorified in Him, God will also glorify Him in Himself."—John 13:32

GLORIFY THY NAME
Donna Adkins

Donna Adkins

天父，
耶穌，我愛袮，我讚美袮，敬拜袮。
聖靈，

1 Fa - ther, we love You, we wor - ship and a - dore You,
2 Je - sus, we love You, we wor - ship and a - dore You,
3 Spir - it, we love You, we wor - ship and a - dore You,

榮耀主聖名，全地讚美。榮耀主聖名，
Glo - ri - fy Thy name in all the earth. Glo - ri - fy Thy name,

榮耀主聖名，榮耀主聖名全地讚美！
Glo - ri - fy Thy name, Glo - ri - fy Thy name in all the earth.

499

唯獨祢配

Thou Art Worthy

"Worthy is the Lamb who was slain to receive power and riches and wisdom, and strength and honor and glory and blessing!"—Revelation 5:12

Based on Revelation 4:11, 5:9
Pauline M. Mills
WORTHY LORD
Pauline M. Mills
至高眞神，尊貴救主，唯獨祢配接受，
Thou art worthy, Thou art worthy, Thou art worthy, O Lord,
配接受榮耀，榮耀與尊貴，榮耀與
To receive glory, glory and honor, Glory and
尊貴，權柄。因祢創造萬物，祢創造了
honor and pow'r. For Thou hast created, hast all things cre-
萬物，因祢創造了萬物，照祢的
ated; Thou hast created all things. And for Thy
旨意創造了萬物，哦主，祢配得尊榮。
pleasure they are created; For Thou art worthy, O Lord.

祢名何等美好

How Majestic Is Your Name

"They shall lift up their voice, they shall sing; for the majesty of the Lord."
—Isaiah 24:14

HOW MAJESTIC
Michael W. Smith
Michael W. Smith
哦，主，我神，祢的名在全地是何等美
O Lord, our Lord, how ma - jes - tic is Your name in all the
好。哦，好。哦，主，我讚美祢哦，
earth. O earth. O Lord, we praise Your name. O
主 我尊祢名為大，和平君全能
Lord, we mag - ni - fy Your name: Prince of Peace, might-y
神。哦，主 全能真 神。哦，神。
God; O Lord God Al - might - y. O y.
D.S.

501

至高眞神

Be Exalted, O God

"The Lord lives! Blessed be my Rock! Let the God of my salvation be exalted."—Psalm 18:46

Brent Chambers
Based on Psalm 57:9-11

BE EXALTED
Brent Chambers

我要向祢稱謝，哦，主，在萬民當中。
I will give thanks to Thee, O Lord, a-mong the peo-ple.

我要讚美祢的名在列邦之中。
I will sing prais-es to Thee a-mong the na-tions.

祢的慈愛不改變，慈愛高過諸天，
For Thy stead-fast love is great, is great to the heav-ens;

祢的信實，祢的信實達到穹蒼。
And Thy faith-ful-ness, Thy faith-ful-ness to the clouds.

至高眞神，哦，主，我願尊崇祢。
Be ex-alt-ed, O God, a-bove the heav-ens;

祢的榮耀與崇高高過天地。
Let Thy glo - ry be o - ver all the earth.

至高眞神，哦，主，我願尊崇祢。
Be ex - alt - ed, O God, a - bove the heav - ens;

祢的榮耀與崇高高過天地。
Let Thy glo - ry be o - ver all the earth.

502

聖哉，哦，至高主

Holy, O Lord Most High

Holy, holy, holy is the Lord Almighty;
the whole earth is full of His glory! Isa. 6:3

Mary A. Lathbury; from Isaiah 6:3

CHAUTAUQUA
William F. Sherwin

聖哉，聖哉，聖哉，萬軍之主，天地充滿
Ho - ly, ho - ly, ho - ly, Lord God of Hosts! Heav'n and earth are
主榮光，天地同向主歌唱，哦，至高主！
full of Thee! Heav'n and earth are prais - ing Thee, O Lord most high!

503

榮耀歸萬王之王
We Will Glorify

"'I am the Alpha and the Omega, the Beginning and the End,' says the Lord, who is, who was and who is to come, the Almighty!"—Revelation 1:8

Twila Paris

WE WILL GLORIFY
Twila Paris

1. 一切榮耀歸萬王之王，榮耀歸被殺羔羊，一切榮耀歸萬主之主，祂是偉大的眞神。
2. 主耶和華掌權有威嚴，寶座前我願敬拜，以誠實公義來敬拜祂，單單要向祂敬拜。
3. 祂是天和地的大主宰，祂是世人的救主，祂是至高主超過萬物，配受讚美與尊崇。
4. 哈利路亞歸萬王之王，哈利路亞歸羔羊，哈利路亞歸萬主之主，祂是偉大的眞神。

1 We will glo-ri-fy the King of kings, we will glo-ri-fy the Lamb; We will glo-ri-fy the Lord of lords, who is the great I Am.
2 Lord Je-ho-vah reigns in maj-es-ty, we will bow be-fore His throne; We will wor-ship Him in right-eous-ness, we will wor-ship Him a-lone.
3 He is Lord of heav-en, Lord of earth, He is Lord of all who live; He is Lord a-bove the u-ni-verse, all praise to Him we give.
4 Hal-le-lu-jah to the King of kings, hal-le-lu-jah to the Lamb; Hal-le-lu-jah to the Lord of lords, who is the great I Am.

504

當快樂
Be Joyful

They worshiped Him and returned to Jerusalem with great joy. Luke 24:52

2 Part Canon
I
BE JOYFUL
Kurt Kaiser
當快樂，快樂，因主是活着，
Be joy-ful, joy-ful, the Lord is a-live,
II
我們當快樂，快樂，因主是活着。
Come on be joy-ful, joy-ful, the Lord is a-live!

我們願向主敬拜
We Worship and Adore You

They sang praises with gladness and bowed their heads and worshiped. 2 Chr. 29:30

Traditional

我們願向主敬拜，向主屈膝跪拜，
We wor - ship and a - dore You, Bow - ing down be - fore You,

高聲讚美稱頌，哈利路亞響應。哈利
Songs of prais - es sing - ing, Hal - le - lu - jahs ring - ing. Hal - le -

路亞，哈利路亞，哈利路亞，阿門。
lu - jah, hal - le - lu - jah, hal - le - lu - jah, A - men.

506

主，聽我禱告
Hear Our Prayer, O Lord

George Whelpton

Psalm 143:1

主，聽我禱告，主，聽我禱告，
Hear our prayer, O Lord, Hear our prayer, O Lord;
留心聽我懇求，並賜我平安，阿門。
In - cline Thine ear to us, And grant us Thy peace. A - men.

神 掌 權
Our God Reigns

How beautiful . . . are the feet of those who bring good news . . . "Your God reigns!" Isa. 52:7

Leonard W. Smith
OUR GOD REIGNS
Leonard W. Smith
1. 傳 報 福 音 登 山 報 喜 信 的 脚 踪
2. 祂 無 佳 形 美 容，祂 不 被 人 尊 重
3. 出 離 墳 墓， 祂 帶 能 力 祂 有 恩 典，
1. How love - ly on the moun-tains are the feet of him
2. He had no state - ly form, He had no maj - es - ty,
3. Out from the tomb He came with grace and maj - es - ty,
何 等 佳 美， 佳 美， 傳 報 平
無 人 羨 慕 祂 美 貌， 被 人 藐
祂 已 復 活， 復 活， 請 看 主
who brings good news, good news An - nounc-ing
That we should be drawn to Him. He was de -
He is a - live, He is a - live. God loves us
安， 報 好 信 息 的 向 人 說： 神 已 作
視， 被 人 厭 棄 掩 面 不 看， 祂 已 作
手， 主 脚， 祂 捨 身 爲 愛 我， 我 深 知
peace, pro - claim - ing news of hap - pi - ness. Our God
spised and we took no ac - count of Him, Yet now He
so, see here His hands, His feet, His side. Yes, we
王， 神 掌 權。
王， 掌 王 權。 神 作 王，
道，， 祂 活 着。
reigns, Our God reigns!
reigns with the Most High. Our God reigns!
know, He is a - live.

神 掌 權，神 作 王，神 掌 權！
Our God reigns! Our God reigns! Our God reigns!

以馬内利

Emmanuel

508

They will call Him Immanuel—which means, "God with us." Matt. 1:23

EMMANUEL
Bob McGee

Unison

以馬内利，以馬内利，
Em-man-u-el, Em-man-u-el,

袘名稱爲以馬内利，
His name is called Em-man-u-el;

神同在，袘與我同在，
God with us, re-vealed in us;

袘名稱爲以馬内利。
His name is called Em-man-u-el.

509 主，求祢聽祢兒女禱告

Lord, Listen to Your Children Praying

"Give ear to my prayer, O God, and do not hide Yourself from my supplication."—Psalm 55:1

Ken Medema

CHILDREN PRAYING
Ken Medema

主，求祢聽祢兒女禱告，求聖靈
Lord, lis - ten to Your chil - dren pray - ing, Lord, send Your

與我們同在；主，求祢聽祢兒女禱告，
Spir - it in this place; Lord, lis - ten to Your chil - dren pray - ing,

1 (optional) D.C. Final

賜能力，賜恩惠，賜仁愛。愛
Send us love, send us pow'r, send us grace. grace.

510 先求神的國

Seek Ye First

Seek first His kingdom and His righteousness. Matt. 6:33

based on Matthew 6:33; 7:7

Karen Lafferty

1. 你們要先求祂的國，先求祂的義，
2. 你們祈求就必給你們，尋找，就尋見，
1. Seek ye first the king - dom of God And His righ - teous - ness,
2. Ask and it shall be giv - en un - to you, Seek and ye shall find,

這些東西祂都要加給你們。阿利路，阿利路亞。
叩門的就必給你們開門。
And all these things shall be add-ed un-to you— Al-le-lu, al-le-lu-ia!
Knock and the door shall be o-pened un-to you—
© 1972, arr. © 1986 MARANATHA! MUSIC. All Rights Reserved. International Copyright Secured. Used by Permission.
按祂時候
In His Time
511
He has made everything beautiful in its time. Eccl. 3:11
Diane Ball
IN HIS TIME
Diane Ball
1. 祂做事，有定時，
2. 祢做事，有定時，
1. In His time (in His time), in His time (in His time);
2. In Your time (in Your time), in Your time (in Your time);
按祂時候能成就美好事，
按祢時候能成就美好事，
He makes all things beau-ti-ful in His time (in His time).
You make all things beau-ti-ful in Your time (in Your time).
主，求祢每日指示，教我明白祢心思，
主，我獻身心給祢，我口稱頌讚美祢，
Lord, please show me ev-'ry day As You're teach-ing me Your way,
Lord, my life to You I bring; May each song I have to sing
我願遵行祢旨意，等候祢！
我願令祢心滿意，等候祢！
That You do just what You say in Your time (in Your time).
Be to You a love-ly thing in Your time (in Your time).
© 1978 MARANATHA! MUSIC. All Rights Reserved. International Copyright Secured. Used by Permission.

512

親愛的主
I Love You, Lord

Love the Lord, all His saints! Ps. 31:23

Laurie Klein

I LOVE YOU, LORD
Laurie Klein

親 愛 的 主， 我 願 稱 頌 祢， 我 靈 歡
I love you Lord, and I lift my voice to wor ship

喜 敬 拜 祢， 愛 祢！ 哦， 主， 我 王， 求 祢
you, O My soul, re - joice! Take joy, my King, in

側 耳 聽， 以 我 默 念 爲 甘 甜 滿足祢 心
what you hear, may it be a sweet, sweet sound in your ear.

513

耶穌，我的主
Jesus, Lord to Me

You are my Lord, my goodness is nothing —*Psalm 16:2*

Gary McSpadden
Greg Nelson

JESUS, LORD TO ME
Gary McSpadden
Greg Nelson

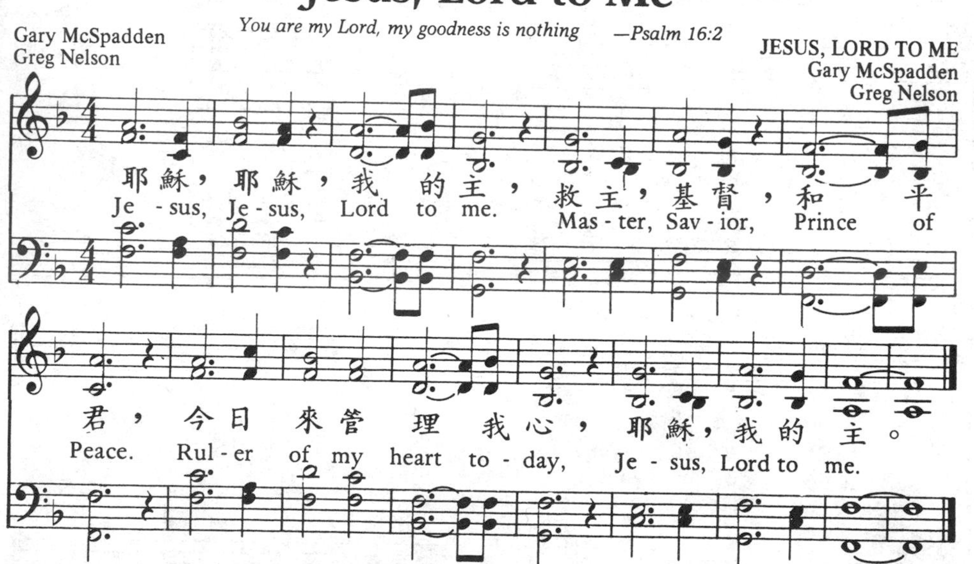
耶穌，耶穌，我 的主， 救主，基督，和 平
Je - sus, Je - sus, Lord to me. Mas - ter, Sav - ior, Prince of
君， 今日 來管 理 我心， 耶穌，我的 主。
Peace. Rul - er of my heart to - day, Je - sus, Lord to me.

514

耶穌在萬名之上

Jesus, Name Above All Names

"So let Your name be magnified forever . . ."—II Samuel 7:26

Naida Hearn

HEARN
Naida Hearn

Unison

耶 穌，在萬名之上，美麗的救主，榮耀之主，以馬内利，神與人同在，賜福的救主，生命之道。

Je - sus, name a-bove all names, beau-ti-ful Sav - ior, glo-ri-ous Lord. Em - man - u - el, God is with us, bless-ed Re - deem - er, Liv - ing Word.

515

來到主面前

Come into His Presence

Come before Him with joyful songs. Ps. 100:2

Source unknown

4 Part Canon

I
II
III
IV

1. 來到主的面前同唱，哈利路亞，哈利路亞，哈利路亞，
2. 來到主的面前同唱，耶穌是主，耶穌是主，耶穌是主，
3. 到主面前齊來讚美，被殺羔羊，配得讚美，配得稱頌，
4. 到主面前齊來讚美，榮耀歸神，榮耀歸神，榮耀歸神。

1. Come in - to His pres-ence sing-ing Al - le-lu-ia, al - le-lu-ia, al - le-lu-ia.
2. Come in - to His pres-ence sing-ing Je - sus is Lord, Je - sus is Lord, Je - sus is Lord.
3. Praise the Lord together singing Worthy the Lamb, worthy the Lamb, worthy the Lamb.
4. Praise the Lord to-geth-er sing-ing Glo - ry to God, glo - ry to God, glo - ry to God.

516

唱哈利路亞

Sing Hallelujah

Shout for joy to the Lord, all the earth. Ps. 100:1

LINDA STASSEN LINDA STASSEN

唱 哈利 路亞讚 美 主，
Sing hal - le - lu - jah to the Lord,
唱 哈利 路亞 讚 美 主，
Sing hal - le -- lu - jah to the Lord,
唱 哈利
sing hal - le
唱 哈利 路 亞， 哈 利 路
sing hal-le -- lu - jah, hal - - le - - lu -
路亞讚美 主。
lu-jah to the Lord.
唱 哈利 路 亞， 唱 哈利
Sing hal - le - lu - jah, sing hal-le
repeat several times
Last ending
亞， 唱 哈 利 路 亞 讚 美 主。
jah, sing hal-le -- lu- jah to the Lord.
路 亞， 唱 哈利 路 亞 讚 美 主。
lu - jah, sing hal- le - lu - jah to the Lord.

美好時辰

In Moments Like These

Praise the Lord. Sing to the Lord a new song. Ps. 149:1

DAVID GRAHAM DAVID GRAHAM

Unison
這美好時辰，我願高聲唱，我願高聲唱我愛耶穌。
In moments like these I sing out a song, I sing out a love song to Jesus.
這美好時辰，我向神舉手，我向神舉手讚美主。
In moments like these I lift up my hand I lift up my hands to the Lord.
高唱我愛祢，主，高唱我愛祢，主，高唱我愛祢，主，我愛祢
Singing I love you, Lord, singing I love you, Lord, singing I love you. Lord, I love you.

我尊崇祢
I Exalt Thee

Thou art exalted far above all gods, Psalm 97:9
Pete Sanchez, Jr.
Words and Music by
Pete Sanchez, Jr.
VERSE
哦，主我神，至高超乎全地，願祢被
For Thou, Oh Lord, art high a-bove all the earth. Thou art ex-
尊崇超乎萬神之上 哦主，我神，至高
alt-ed far a-bove all----- gods: For Thou, Oh Lord, art high
超乎全地， 願祢被尊崇超乎
a-bove all the earth. Thou art ex-alt-ed far a-
萬神之上 我尊崇祢， 我尊
bove all gods. I ex-alt Thee! I ex-
崇祢， 我尊崇祢， 哦，主 我尊
alt Thee! I ex-alt The. Oh Lord! I ex-
2. fine

519

我要稱頌我主
I Will Bless Thee, O Lord

"But if anyone loves God, this one is known by Him."—I Corinthians 8:3

Psalm 103:1
Unknown
我要稱頌我主，我要稱頌我主，
I will bless Thee, O Lord. I will bless Thee, O Lord.
我心充滿了感謝，我要
With a heart of thanks-giv-ing I will
稱頌我主。我手向祂舉起，
bless Thee, O Lord. With my hands lift-ed up,
我口向祂讚美，我心充滿了
and my mouth filled with praise, with a heart to thanks-
感謝，我要稱頌我主。
giv-ing I will bless Thee, O Lord.

520
釋放我的靈
Set My Spirit Free

... that we ... might be for the praise of His glory. Eph. 1:12

UNKNOWN

521
祢是我藏身處
You Are My Hiding Place

MICHAEL LEDNER

You have been ... a shelter from the storm. Isa. 25:4

MICHAEL LEDNER

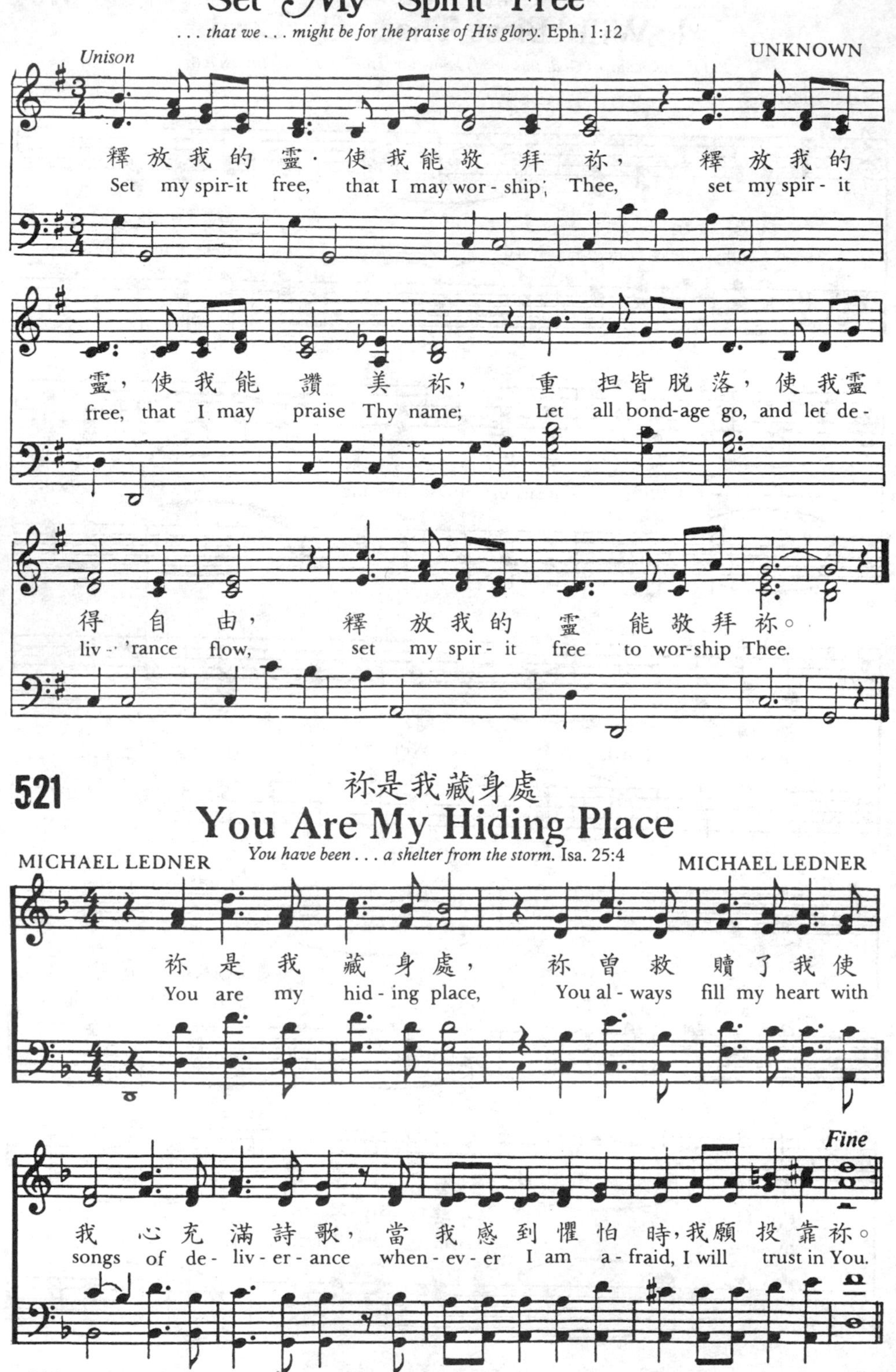

Unison
釋放我的靈·使我能敬拜祢，釋放我的
Set my spir-it free, that I may wor-ship Thee, set my spir-it
靈，使我能讚美祢，重担皆脱落，使我靈
free, that I may praise Thy name; Let all bond-age go, and let de-
得自由，釋放我的靈能敬拜祢。
liv-'rance flow, set my spir-it free to wor-ship Thee.
祢是我藏身處，祢曾救贖了我使
You are my hid-ing place, You al-ways fill my heart with
我心充滿詩歌，當我感到懼怕時，我願投靠祢。
songs of de-liv-er-ance when-ev-er I am a-fraid, I will trust in You.
Fine

D.C. al Fine
我願投靠祢。 倚靠主賜我力量，使軟弱變剛强。
I will trust in You; Let the weak say, "I am strong in the strength of the Lord!"

奇妙的，奇妙的耶穌 522

Wonderful, Wonderful Jesus

We know that this Man really is the Savior of the world. John 4:42

B.A.B. Benjamin A. Baur

奇妙的，奇妙的耶穌，誰能與祢相比？
Won-der-ful, won-der-ful Je - sus, Who can com- pare with Thee!

奇妙的，奇妙的耶穌，祢是我主，何等美麗！
Won-der-ful, won-der-ful Je - sus, Fair-er than all Thou art to me!

奇妙的，奇妙的耶穌，哦，我心真愛祢！
Won-der-ful, won-der-ful Je - sus, O how my soul loves Thee!

美好中祢最美好，耶穌，我心屬祢！
Fair-er than all the fair - est, Je - sus, Thou art to me!

523

聖靈之歌
Spirit Song

Since we live by the Spirit, let us keep in step with the Spirit. Gal. 5:25

JOHN WIMBER JOHN WIMBER

Unison
1. 願神愛子以祂的聖靈，和祂慈愛環繞你，讓祂充滿你使你心靈滿足。哦，聖靈彷彿鴿子降臨，願你順服祂旨意，使你得完全生命，永遠屬主。
2. 哦，願你能歡樂的歌唱，唱出心中的喜悦，舉起你的手稱頌讚美主名。哦，讓祂安慰你的憂傷，抹乾你一切眼淚，使你能靠主的名，得新生命。耶穌，哦，耶穌，來充滿我心。
1. Oh let the Son of God en- fold you, with His Spir - it and His love, let Him fill your heart and sat- is fy your soul. Oh let Him have the things that hold you, and His Spir - it like a dove, will de - scend up - on your life, and make you whole.
2. Oh come and sing this song with glad - ness, as your hearts are filled with joy, lift your hands in sweet sur- ren- der to His name. Oh give Him all your tears and sad - ness, give Him all your years of pain, and you'll en- ter in - to life in Je - sus's name. Je - sus, Oh Je - sus, come and fill your lambs.

耶 穌，哦，耶 穌，來 充 滿 我 心。
Je - sus, Oh Je - sus, come and fill your lambs.
祂名叫耶穌
524
His Name Is Jesus
There is no other name . . . by which we must be saved. Acts 4:12
UNKNOWN
Unison
祂名叫 耶 穌，耶 穌，能
His name is Je - sus, Je - sus,
使 憂 傷 變 歡 暢。祂 能
sad hearts weep no more. He has
醫 治 破 碎 心 靈，使 罪 人 得 着 釋 放，祂 能
healed the bro - ken heart - ed, o - pened wide the pris - on doors, He is
救 你，使 你 得 永 遠 盼 望。
a - ble to de - liv - er ev - er - more.

525 開我的眼，主

Open Our Eyes, Lord

Robert Cull

Blessed are the pure in heart, for they will see God. Matt. 5:8

OPEN OUR EYES
Robert Cull

1. 開我的眼，主，我渴望見耶穌，我願意靠近祂，全心全意愛祂。睛，我渴望見耶穌。
2. 開我的耳，主，我願聽主話語，求主開我眼

1. O-pen our eyes, Lord, we want to see Je-sus, to reach out and touch Him, and say that we love Him. Lord, we want to see Je-sus.
2. O-pen our ears, Lord, and help us to lis-ten, O-pen our eyes,

526 感謝祢，主

We Thank You, Lord

We give thanks to You, O God, we give thanks, for Your Name is near. Ps. 75:1

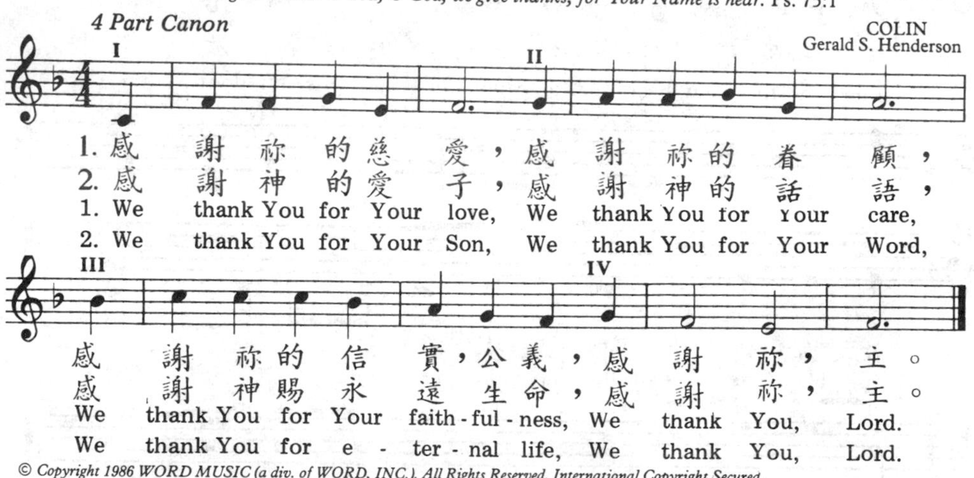

4 Part Canon
COLIN
Gerald S. Henderson
I
II
III
IV
1. 感謝祢的慈愛，感謝祢的眷顧，感謝祢的信實，公義，感謝祢，主。
2. 感謝神的愛子，感謝神的話語，感謝神賜永遠生命，感謝祢，主。
1. We thank You for Your love, We thank You for Your care, We thank You for Your faith-ful-ness, We thank You, Lord.
2. We thank You for Your Son, We thank You for Your Word, We thank You for e-ter-nal life, We thank You, Lord.

527

恩惠、慈愛與感動

Grace, Love and Fellowship

May Your blessing be on Your people. Ps. 3:8
based on 2 Cor. 13:14
CANE PEAK
Tom Fettke
Unison
1
2
rit.
但願 主 基 督 的 恩 惠，與 天 父 上 帝 的
May the grace of Christ, our Sav - ior, and the love of God, our
慈 愛，和 聖 靈 的 感 動 常 與 我 們 同 在，
Fa - ther, and the fel - low - ship of the Spir - it be with us.
但 願 在 從 今 時，到
May the us for - ev - er, and
永 遠，直 到 永 遠，阿 門。
ev - er, for - ev - er - more, A - men.

527-A

阿門
Amen

THREEFOLD
Denmark
阿 門，阿 門，阿 門。
A-men, A-men, A - men.

Indexes
目　錄

目　錄

一劃

二劃

三劃

四劃

五劃

六劃

七劃

八劃

九劃

十劃

十一劃

十二劃

十三劃

十四劃

十五劃

十六劃

十七劃

十八劃

十九劃

二十劃

二十二劃

二十三劃

二十四劃

二十六劃

分 類 目 錄
Topical Index of Hymns

CHILDREN'S HYMNS 孩童詩歌

CHINESE TUNES 中國調

CHOIR RESPONSES 崇拜特用—宣召、祈禱

CHORUSES 短詩

CHRISTMAS 聖誕詩

CHURCH, FAMILY OF BELIEVERS

教會信徒生活

CLOSING HYMNS 聚會結束

COMFORT & ENCOURAGEMENT

安慰與勸勉

NEW YEAR 新年

PEACE — INNER 内心平安

PRAYER AND INTERCESSION 禱告代求

REFUGE 避難所

RENEWAL AND REVIVAL 更新與復興

SPIRITUALS 靈歌

STEWARDSHIP (See also Thanksgiving, Discipleship) 受託、捐獻

TESTIMONY, WITNESS, AND EVANGELISM 見證、福音、佈道

THANKSGIVING 感恩

TRINITY 三位一體

WORSHIP AND ADORATION 崇拜與頌讚

Psalms & Readings

Alphabetical Index
of Hymn Titles and First Lines

A

J

Y

Copyright Acknowledgements

Those marked (JB) are from *The Jerusalem Bible*. Copyright 1966 by Darton, Longman & Todd, Ltd. and Doubleday & Company, Inc. Reprinted by permission of the publisher.

Those marked (J.B. Phillips) are from *The New Testament in Modern English*, revised edition. Reprinted with permission of MacMillan Publishing Co., Inc. © Copyright J. B. Phillips 1958, 1960, 1972.

Those marked (NIV) are Scripture taken from the Holy Bible: New International Version. Copyright © 1973-1978 by the International Bible Society. Used by permission of Zondervan Bible Publishers.

Those marked (RSV) are from *The Revised Standard Version of the Bible*, ● *Copyright 1946, 1952, 1971, 1973. Used by permission.*

Those marked (KJV) are from the Authorized King James Version of the Bible.

SOURCES OF READINGS AND PRAYERS

47-1 From Amazing Love. Copyright material used by permission of the Christian Literature Crusade, Fort Washington, PA 19034.

145-1 Reprinted from *Lord, Make My Life a Miracle*, A Regal Book. Used by permission of G/L Publications - Copyright 1974 by G/L Publications, Glendale, CA 91209.

150-1 © Copyright 1975 by Paragon Associates. From *His Love...Reaching*. Used by permission.

212-1 From *Let God Love You*. © Copyright 1974 by Word, Inc., Waco, Texas. Used by permission.

270-1 From *Folk Psalms of Faith*. © Copyright 1973 by Ray Stedman. Published by Regal Books, a division of G/L Publications, Glendale, CA 91209.

295-1 From *Lord, Be With*. © Copyright 1969 by Concordia Publishing House. All rights reserved. Used by permission.

313-1 From *Letters to Malcolm; Chiefly on Prayer*. Published by Harcourt Brace Jovanovich, Inc. © Copyright 1963, 1964. Used by permission.

314-1 From *The Holy Spirit and You*. © Copyright 1971 by Logos International, Plainfield, New Jersey. Used by permission.

383-1 From *Prayers*. © Copyright 1963 by Sheed & Ward, Inc., New York, N. Y. Used by permission.

386-1 From *Power Ideas for a Happy Family*. Copyright © 1972 by Robert Harold Schuller. A Spire Book published by Pillar Books for Fleming H. Revell Company. Used by permission.

406-1 Excerpt from p. 37, *A Doctor's Casebook*, Harper and Row, Jubilee Edition 1976.

422-1 From *Prayer*, © 1976 John T. Benson Publishing Company, 365 Great Circle Road, Nashville, Tennessee 37228. All rights reserved.

NOTE:

Every effort has been made to locate the owners of copyrighted material used in this publication. Upon notification, the Publisher will make proper correction in subsequent printings.

教會聖詩

編輯：陳王露茜
郭汝容
陳人昌
出版：「教會聖詩」編輯委員會
發行：美國加州羅省基督教會
承印： C & R Printing Co.

一九八五年一月初版
一九八六年九月再版
一九八八年十二月三版
一九九〇年五月四版
一九九二年五月五版

Hymns for God's People

Editors: Lucy Chen
Thomas Kuo
Chris Chen

Publisher: Hymns for God's People Publication Committee

Sponsor: First Evangelical Church of Los Angeles

Printing: Griffin Printing & Lithograph Co., Inc.

1st. Edition: January 1985
2nd. Edition: September 1986
3rd. Edition: December 1988
4th Edition: May 1990
5th Edition: May 1992